TECHNICAL DATA

	PAGE
Index	1-4
Introduction	5-6
Bearing Design	7-20
Bearing Ratings and Life	21-26
Bearing Operating Characteristics	27-34
Determination of Applied Loads	35-42
Bearing Selection	43-59
Mounting of Bearings	61-90
Bearing Analysis and Loading Symbols	91, 92

HT 1972 BY THE TIMKEN COMPANY · PRINTED IN U.S.A.

BEARING ANALYSIS FORMULAE

L10 in Revolutions

$$L_{10} = \left(\frac{C(90)}{P}\right)^{10/3} \times 90 \times 10^6 \text{ Rev}$$

L10 in Hours

$$L_{10} = \left(\frac{C(90) \times SF}{P}\right)^{10/3} \times 3000 \text{ hr}$$

$$L_{10} = (LF)^{10/3} \times 3000 \text{ hr}$$

Required Radial Rating

$$C(90)R = \frac{P \times LF \times AF}{SF}$$

Required Thrust Rating

$$CA(90)R = \frac{F_a \times LF \times AF}{SF}$$

Life Factor

$$LF = \frac{C(90) \times SF}{P \times AF} = \frac{CA(90) \times SF}{F_a \times AF}$$

$$LF = \left(\frac{L_{10}}{3000}\right)^{3/10}$$

Ratios of Bearing Life to Loads, Horsepower and Speeds

Condition	Equation
Variable Load and Variable Speed	$L_2 = L_1 \left(\dfrac{P_1}{P_2}\right)^{10/3} \left(\dfrac{S_1}{S_2}\right)$
Variable Horsepower and Variable Speed	$L_2 = L_1 \left(\dfrac{HP_1}{HP_2}\right)^{10/3} \left(\dfrac{S_2}{S_1}\right)^{7/3}$
Constant Load and Variable Speed	$L_2 = L_1 \left(\dfrac{S_1}{S_2}\right)$
Constant Horsepower and Variable Speed	$L_2 = L_1 \left(\dfrac{S_2}{S_1}\right)^{7/3}$
Variable Load and Constant Speed	$L_2 = L_1 \left(\dfrac{P_1}{P_2}\right)^{10/3}$
Variable Horsepower and Constant Speed	$L_2 = L_1 \left(\dfrac{HP_1}{HP_2}\right)^{10/3}$

Speed Factor

$$SF = \left(\frac{500}{S}\right)^{3/10}$$

Weighted Average Bearing Load, Life and Speed

General Case - Variable Loading — Variable Speed — Variable % Time

$$F_{wt} \text{ @ 500 RPM} = F_{max} \left[T_1\left(\frac{F_1}{F_{max} \cdot SF_1}\right)^{10/3} + T_2\left(\frac{F_2}{F_{max} \cdot SF_2}\right)^{10/3} + \ldots T_n\left(\frac{F_n}{F_{max} \cdot SF_n}\right)^{10/3} \right]^{3/10}$$

Variable Loading — Variable Speed — Variable % Time

$$L_{10} = \frac{1}{\dfrac{T_1}{L_{10_1}} + \dfrac{T_2}{L_{10_2}} + \ldots \dfrac{T_n}{L_{10_n}}}$$

Variable Loading — Constant Speed — Variable % Time

$$F_{wt} = F_{max} \left[T_1\left(\frac{F_1}{F_{max}}\right)^{10/3} + T_2\left(\frac{F_2}{F_{max}}\right)^{10/3} + \ldots T_n\left(\frac{F_n}{F_{max}}\right)^{10/3} \right]^{3/10}$$

Constant Loading — Variable Speed — Variable % Time

$$S_{av} = \frac{S_1 t_1 + S_2 t_2 + \ldots S_n t_n}{t_t}$$

Uniformly Increasing Load — Constant Speed

$$F_{wt} = F_{min} + 0.645 \, (F_{max} - F_{min})$$

Constant Loading — Constant or Average Speed

$$F_{wt} \text{ @ 500RPM} = \frac{F}{SF}$$

Dynamic Equivalent Radial Load Formulae

1. Single-Row Mounting (With External Thrust, T_e, on Bearing A)

Design	Dynamic Equivalent Radial Load Formulae	
	$P_A = 0.4 \, F_r A + K_A \left(\dfrac{0.47 \, F_r B}{K_B} + T_e\right)$	If $P_A < F_r A$, then use $P_A = F_r A$
	$P_B = 0.4 \, F_r B + K_B \left(\dfrac{0.47 \, F_r A}{K_A} - T_e\right)$	If $P_B < F_r B$, then use $P_B = F_r B$

2. Two-Row Mounting (With External Thrust, T_e)

Identical Bearing Series, $K_A = K_B$			Dissimilar Bearing Series, $K_A \neq K_B$		
Design	Condition	Dynamic Equivalent Radial Load Formulae	Design	Condition	Dynamic Equivalent Radial Load Formulae
	$T_e \leq \dfrac{0.6 \, F_r}{K_A}$	$P_A = 0.5 \, F_r + 0.83 \, K_A T_e$ $P_B = 0.5 \, F_r - 0.83 \, K_A T_e$		$T_e \leq \dfrac{0.6 \, F_r}{K_A}$	$P_A = \dfrac{K_A}{K_A + K_B} (F_r + 1.67 \, K_B T_e)$ $P_B = \dfrac{K_B}{K_A + K_B} (F_r - 1.67 \, K_A T_e)$
	$T_e > \dfrac{0.6 \, F_r}{K_A}$	$P_A = 0.4 \, F_r + K_A T_e$ $P_B = 0$		$T_e > \dfrac{0.6 \, F_r}{K_A}$	$P_A = 0.4 \, F_r + K_A T_e$ $P_B = 0$

See Bearing Analysis and Loading Symbols on pages 91 and 92 for terms in equations.

Index

TECHNICAL DATA INDEX

PAGE

— A —

ACRO-SET 70

ADDITIVES TO LUBRICANTS 90

ADJUSTING DEVICES
Cone 71-73
Cup 74, 75

ALUMINUM ALLOYS FITTING PRACTICE (See Reference Tables)

ANALYSIS AND SELECTION OF BEARINGS
Single-Row Bearings
  Combined Radial and Thrust Loads 52
  Radial Load Only 51
  Slow Oscillating Application 54
  Thrust Load Only 53
Two-Row Bearings
  Dissimilar Series at Fixed Position
    Combined Radial and Thrust Loads 57
  Identical Series at Fixed Position
    Combined Radial and Thrust Loads 56
    Radial Load Only 55

ANNULAR GROOVE CLOSURES 76, 78, 80

APEX POINT OF TAPERED ROLLER BEARING 8

APPLICATION ENGINEER 5

APPLICATION FACTORS 48, 91

ASTM GRADE DESIGNATION OF OIL 88

AUTOMATED BEARING SETTING METHODS
Acro-Set 70
Set-Right 70
Torque-Set 70

AXIAL DEFORMATION OF BEARING 34

— B —

BACKING DESIGNS
Housings 65-67
Shafts 63, 64

BASIC DYNAMIC LOAD RATING 22, 91

BASIC PRINCIPLE OF TAPERED ROLLER BEARING ... 8

BASIC DYNAMIC RADIAL LOAD RATING 22, 91

BASIC DYNAMIC THRUST LOAD RATING 22, 91

BEARING

Analysis and Selection
  Single-Row Bearings 50-54
  Two-Row Bearings 55-59

Basic Types
Four-Row
  TQO 18
  TQOE 18
  TQITS 19
  TQITSE 19

Single-Row
  J-Line 10, 14
  TS (Pressed Steel Cage) 10
  TS (Pin Type Cage) 10
  TSF 11
  TSG 11
  TSL 11
  TSU 11

Thrust Bearings
  TTC 20
  TTCS 20
  TTHD 20
  TTSP 20

PAGE

Two-Row
  AP 14
  SR 14
  SS 14
  Square Bore 16
  TDI 12
  TDIT 12
  TDO 13
  TDODC 13
  TNA 15
  TNADC 15
  TNASW 15
  TNASWE 15
  TNASWH 16
  TXR 17

Clearance Effect on Fatigue Life 24, 25

Deformation 34

Design
  Basic 8
  Product Precision 9
  Sound Testing 9
  Steel 9

Effective Spread 44

Heat Dissipation 31, 32

Heat Generation 31

Life Ratios to Loads, Horsepower and Speeds ... 48, 49

Limiting Speeds 32, 33

Loading Symbols 91, 92

Lubrication 32-34, 88-90

Mountings (See Mountings)

Nomenclature 8

Operating Characteristics 27-34

Ratings and Life
  Basic Dynamic 22
  Static 22

Reactions
  Shaft on Two Supports 45
  Shaft on Three or More Supports 45

Reliability 24

Selection 43-59

Setting 5, 68

Setting Devices 68-75
  Cone 71-73
  Cup 74, 75

Spring Rate 34

Steel 9

Thrust Formulae 45, 46

Thrust Reaction 45

Torque
  Running Torque 28
    Calculation Example 30
    Combined Loading 29
    Radial Loads 29
    Thrust Loads 28, 29
  Set-Up Torque 30

BELT DRIVE FACTORS 41

BENCH END PLAY 82

— C —

CAGE 8

CENTRIFUGAL FORCE FORMULA 42

CLOSURE DESIGNS
Annular Groove 76, 78, 80
Combination, Labyrinth and Radial Lip Seal ... 79, 80

PAGE

CLOSURE DESIGNS (cont'd)
Duo-Face Seal 79
Flingers 76-78, 80
Labyrinth 78, 79
Piston Rings 80
Radial Lip Seal 76, 77, 78, 80
Stampings 76-78
Vertical Shaft 80
COMBINED LOADING 20, 52, 56, 57
COMPARISON OF RATINGS WITH COMPETITIVE BEARINGS 23
CONE 8
CONE ADJUSTING DEVICES 71-73
CONE BACKING DESIGNS
Back Face 63
Front Face 64
CONE SEAT SURFACE FINISH (See Reference Tables)
CONE FITTING PRACTICE (See Reference Tables)
CONE RIB SPEED FORMULAE 32
CONE SPACERS 13, 14, 18, 69, 73
CHAIN DRIVE FACTORS 41
CUP 8
CUP ADJUSTING DEVICES 74, 75
CUP BACKING DESIGNS
Back Face 65, 66
Front Face 67
CUP FITTING PRACTICE (See Reference Tables)
CUP SEAT SURFACE FINISH (See Reference Tables)
CUP SPACERS 12, 14, 18, 19, 69, 75

— D —

DEFORMATION OF BEARING
Axial 34
Radial 34
DETERMINATION OF APPLIED LOADS
Belt and Chain Drive Factors 41
Centrifugal Force Formula 42
Gearing Formulae
  Herringbone 36
  Hypoid 36-38
  Single Helical 36
  Spiral Bevel 36-38
  Spur 36
  Straight Bevel 36, 37
  Worm 39, 40
  Zerol 36-38
Power Conversion Units 42
Shock Loads 41
Tractive Effort and Wheel Speed 42
DIRECT MOUNTING 44, 83, 86
DUO-FACE SEAL 11, 79, 82
DYNAMIC EQUIVALENT RADIAL LOAD FORMULAE 46, 47

— E —

EFFECT OF LUBRICATION ON FATIGUE LIFE 26
EFFECT OF MISALIGNMENT ON FATIGUE LIFE 25, 26
EFFECTIVE LOAD CENTER 44, 45
EFFECTIVE SPREAD OF TAPERED ROLLER BEARINGS
Direct 44
Indirect 44

PAGE

EFFECTS OF LOAD AND SPEED ON FATIGUE LIFE 23
ELASTIC DEFORMATION OF BEARING 34
END PLAY 68
ENGINEERING POLICY 5
ENVIRONMENTAL FACTORS
Effect of Load Zone on Fatigue Life 24
Effect of Lubrication on Fatigue Life 26
Effect of Misalignment on Fatigue Life 25, 26
EQUIVALENT RADIAL LOAD, DYNAMIC 46, 47
Single-Row Mounting Formulae 47
Two-Row Mounting Formulae 47
EQUIVALENT RADIAL LOAD FORMULAE, STATIC 22
EXTREME PRESSURE ADDITIVES 34, 89

— F —

FACTORS
Application 48, 91
Environmental 24-26
G 28-30
K 22, 28, 91
Life 48, 91
Load Zone 24, 25
Speed 23, 48, 92
FILTRATION OF LUBRICANTS 89
FITTING PRACTICE (See Reference Tables)
FLINGERS 76-78, 80
FORMULAE
Bearing Thrust Reaction 45, 46
Bearing Torque 28-30
Belt and Chain Drive 41
Centrifugal Force 42
Equivalent Radial Load, Dynamic 46, 47
Equivalent Radial Load, Static 22
Gearing 36-40
Heat Dissipation 31, 32
Heat Generation 31
Horsepower 31, 42
Kilowatt 31, 42
L_{10} 23, 91
Life Calculation 23, 48, 49
Life Factor 48, 92
Rating Comparison of Competitive Bearings 23
Ratios of Bearing Life to Loads, Horsepower
  and Speeds 49
Ratio of Life Factors 49
Required Dynamic Radial Load Rating 50
RPM of Wheel 42
Rib Speed 32
Speed Factor 23, 48, 92
Weighted Average Bearing Load, Life and Speed 48, 49, 58, 59
FUNCTION OF LUBRICANTS 88

— G —

G - FACTOR 28-30
GEAR LOADING FORMULAE
Herringbone 36
Hypoid 36-38
Single Helical 36
Spiral Bevel 36-38
Spur 36

Index

PAGE

GEAR LOADING FORMULAE (cont'd)
Straight Bevel 36, 37
Worm 39, 40
Zerol 36-38
GREASE LUBRICATION 33, 89

— H —

HEAT GENERATION FORMULAE 31
HEAT DISSIPATION 31, 32
HEAVY DUTY FITTING PRACTICE (See Reference Tables)
HELICAL GEARING FORMULAE 36
HERRINGBONE GEARING FORMULAE 36
HYPOID GEARING FORMULAE 38

— I —

INCH SYSTEM BEARING FITTING PRACTICE (See Reference Tables)
INDIRECT MOUNTING 44, 81, 82, 84, 85

— J —

J-LINE BEARINGS 14

— K —

K - FACTOR 22, 28, 91

— L —

L₁₀ FORMULA 23, 91
LABYRINTH CLOSURES 78, 79
LIFE CALCULATION FORMULAE
Constant Horsepower and Variable Speed 49
Constant Load and Variable Speed 49
Variable Horsepower and Constant Speed 49
Variable Horsepower and Variable Speed 49
Variable Load and Constant Speed 49
Variable Load and Variable Speed 49
LIFE FACTOR 48, 91
LIMITING SPEED OF BEARING 32, 33
LOAD RATINGS
Basic Dynamic 22
Static 22
LOAD ZONE EFFECT ON FATIGUE LIFE 24, 25
LOADING SYMBOLS 91, 92
LUBRICANTS 33, 34, 88-90
LUBRICATION
ASTM Chart 28, 89
ASTM Grade Designations 88
Additives 90
Filtration 89
Function 88
Types 88
Grease 89
Oil 88, 89
Solid 88
LUBRICATION EFFECT ON FATIGUE LIFE 26
LUBRICATION SYSTEMS
Forced Feed Oil 33
Grease 33, 89
Static Oil Level 33
Static Oil Level with Splash 33

PAGE

— M —

MACHINED FLINGERS 76, 78
MAGNESIUM ALLOYS FITTING PRACTICE (See Reference Tables)
METAL STAMPING CLOSURES 76-78
METRIC SYSTEM BEARING FITTING PRACTICE (See Reference Tables)
MISALIGNMENT EFFECT ON FATIGUE LIFE 25, 26
MODIFYING FACTORS FOR COMPARING RATINGS WITH COMPETITIVE BEARINGS 23
MOUNTING
Direct 44, 83, 86
Indirect 44, 81, 82, 84, 85
MOUNTING OF BEARINGS
Backing Designs 62
Housings 65-67
Shaft 63, 64
Bearing Setting Devices 68-75
Cones 71-73
Cups 74, 75
Closure Designs 76-80
Cone Fitting Practice (See Reference Tables)
Cup Fitting Practice (See Reference Tables)
Typical Mountings 81-87
MOUNTINGS
Flanged Cup - Type TSF Bearing 81, 82
Indirect Mounting 81
Rotating Cone 81
Rotating Cup 82
Stationary Cone 82
Stationary Cup 81
Single-Row - Type TS Bearings 81-84
Direct Mounting 83
Rotating Cone 83
Rotating Cup 83
Stationary Cone 83
Stationary Cup 83
Indirect Mounting 81, 82
Rotating Cone 81
Rotating Cup 82
Stationary Cone 81
Stationary Cup 82
Thrust Bearings
Types TTC and TTCS Bearings 87
Type TTHD Bearing 87
Type TTSP Bearing 87
Two-Row Arrangements 81, 84-86
Direct Mounting 86
Rotating Cone 86
Stationary Cup 86
Indirect Mounting 81, 82, 84, 85
Rotating Cone 81, 84
Rotating Cup 85
Stationary Cone 85
Stationary Cup 81, 84, 86
Two-Row Bearings - Double Cone - Single Cups 86
Straight Bore 86
Tapered Bore 86
Two-Row Bearings - Double Cup - Single Cones 81, 84, 85
Rotating Cone 81, 84
Types TDO and TDODC Bearings 81, 84
Types TNA and TNADC Bearings 84
Stationary Cone 85
Type TNASW Bearing 85
Type TNASWE Bearing 85

PAGE

— O —

OIL LUBRICATION 33, 88, 89
OIL VISCOSITY CHART 28, 88
OPTIMUM BEARING SELECTION 5
OPTIMUM PRELOAD 68, 69

— P —

PARTS OF A TAPERED ROLLER BEARING 8
PISTON RING CLOSURES 80
POWER CONVERSION UNITS 42
PRECISION CLASS BEARINGS FITTING PRACTICE (See Reference Tables)
PRELOAD 68
PRE-SET BEARING ASSEMBLIES 62
PRODUCT PRECISION 9

— R —

RADIAL DEFORMATION OF BEARING 34
RADIAL LIP SEAL MOUNTINGS 76, 79, 80
RADIAL LIP SEAL SEAT SURFACE FINISH AND HARDNESS 76, 77
RADIAL LIP SEALS 76, 79, 80
RATED LIFE 22
RATING COMPARISON WITH COMPETITIVE BEARINGS .. 23
RATIOS OF BEARING LIFE TO LOADS, HORSEPOWER AND SPEEDS 49
RATIOS OF LIFE FACTORS 49
RELIABILITY
   Bearing 24
   System 24
REQUIRED DYNAMIC RADIAL LOAD RATING FORMULA 50
REQUIRED DYNAMIC THRUST LOAD RATING FORMULA 50
RESEARCH 6
ROLLER-RIB SEATING FORCE 8
ROLLING MILL EQUIPMENT FITTING PRACTICE (See Reference Tables)
ROTATING CONE APPLICATIONS FITTING PRACTICE (See Reference Tables)
ROTATING CUP APPLICATIONS FITTING PRACTICE (See Reference Tables)

— S —

SALES ENGINEER 5
SEAL SURFACE FINISH AND HARDNESS 76, 77
SEALS (See Closure Designs)
SEATING FORCE OF ROLLER-RIB 8
SET-RIGHT 70
SELECTION AND ANALYSIS OF BEARINGS 50-59
SERVICE ENGINEER 5
SHOCK LOADS 41
SINGLE HELICAL GEARING FORMULAE 36
SOLID LUBRICANT 88
SOUND TESTING 9
SPACERS 12-14, 18, 19, 62, 69
   Cone 13, 14, 18, 69, 73
   Cup 12, 14, 18, 19, 69, 75
SPEED CAPABILITIES OF TAPERED ROLLER BEARINGS 32-34
SPEED FACTOR FORMULA 23, 48, 92
SPIRAL BEVEL GEARING FORMULAE 36-38

PAGE

SPRING RATE OF BEARING 34
SPUR GEARING FORMULAE 36
STAMPINGS, METAL CLOSURES 76-78
STANDARD FITTING PRACTICE TABLES (See Reference Tables)
STATIC EQUIVALENT RADIAL LOAD FORMULA 22
STATIC LOAD RATINGS 22
STATIONARY CONE APPLICATIONS FITTING PRACTICE (See Reference Tables)
STATIONARY CUP APPLICATIONS FITTING PRACTICE (See Reference Tables)
STEEL, BEARING 9
STEEL, SPECIAL 9
SURFACE FINISH
   Cone Seat (See Reference Tables)
   Cup Seat (See Reference Tables)
   Seal Lip Seat 77
SYMBOLS, BEARING ANALYSIS AND LOADING 91, 92
SYSTEM RELIABILITY 24

— T —

TAPERED ROLLER 8
TAPERED ROLLER BEARING APEX 8
TAPERED ROLLER BEARING LUBRICATION 32-34, 88-90
TAPERED ROLLER BEARING PARTS 8
TAPERED ROLLER BEARING SPEED CAPABILITIES 32
THRUST BEARING FITTING PRACTICE (See Reference Tables)
THRUST REACTION 45, 46
TORQUE, BEARING 28-31
   Running Torque 28
     Calculation Example 30
     Combined Loading 29
     Radial Loads 29
     Thrust Loads 28
   Set Up Torque 30, 31
TORQUE-SET 70
TRAINING CUSTOMER ASSEMBLY PERSONNEL 6
TYPES OF LUBRICANTS 88
   Grease 89, 90
   Oil 88, 89
   Solid 88
TYPICAL BEARING ANALYSIS AND SELECTION 50-59

— V —

VERTICAL SHAFT CLOSURES 80
VISCOSITY CHART 28, 88

— W —

WEIGHTED AVERAGE BEARING LOAD, LIFE AND SPEED FORMULAE
   Constant Loading - Constant or Average Speed 49, 59
   Constant Loading - Variable Speed - Variable % Time .. 49, 59
   Uniformly Increasing Load - Constant Speed 49, 59
   Variable Loading - Constant Speed - Variable % Time .. 49, 59
   Variable Loading - Variable Speed - Variable % Time .. 49, 58
WHEEL SPEED FORMULA 42
WORM GEARING FORMULAE 39, 40

— Z —

ZEROL GEARING FORMULAE 36-38

Engineering Policy

A completely comprehensive engineering service related to the application of Timken bearings is available to you with no charge or obligation. This not only includes "on-the-spot" calculation of loads, selection of type and size of bearing and suggested mounting arrangements by a Timken Company sales engineer who is as near as your phone, but, when needed, computer calculations of loads, deflections, bearing deformations, bearing life, etc. tailored to satisfy your particular design specifications.

Service engineers are available to assist in the actual installation and maintenance of bearings after selection by our sales engineer. They are strategically located throughout our worldwide organization. Their services are at no charge and used by many leading equipment manufacturers.

All Timken bearings are guaranteed against defects in material and workmanship for a period of one year **from date of delivery**.

When The Timken Company reviews or proposes bearing applications, all percentage loadings are dependent upon the validity of loading data supplied by the customer or his agent. If there is a change in rating or known loading of the application or component where Timken bearings are used, new studies should be requested of The Timken Company.

Sales Engineer

A Timken Company sales engineer, by education, training and experience, is thoroughly qualified to assist machinery designers and builders in all aspects of bearing application engineering. This includes all stages of design, testing, production planning and manufacturing through to the assembled product. Available through him are the knowledge and experience gained from the application of more than 2.5 billion Timken bearings to virtually all types of machinery.

A Timken Company sales engineer goes far beyond supplying you with "price and delivery" information. He takes pride in performing extra creative and constructive services for machinery builders. And he has the capability to accomplish them in your office immediately. His services are available at no cost or obligation to you, and are continually used by leading manufacturers of all types of mechanical equipment.

Service Engineer

A Timken Company service engineer is well equipped through extensive training and wide experience to work with your production, maintenance and service personnel in the care, assembly and maintenance of Timken bearings. And if you are involved in an "on-site" installation, his services are generally available there too, at your request.

Application Engineer

Operating loads, speeds and other environmental factors as well as life requirements vary considerably for different types of machinery. Where variable loads and speeds are involved, Timken Company sales engineers can assist designers in determining whether a maximum load, an average load or a weighted-average load calculation should be used. Where different conditions are many and complex, custom computer calculations can be utilized for obtaining required bearing rating figures.

The sales engineer is backed up by The Timken Company application engineering departments for solution of complex problems that require in-depth study. These departments are staffed with bearing specialists who investigate new applications and new concepts in application engineering.

Optimum Bearing Selection

Timken Company sales engineers can help equipment designers select the type of bearing best suited for an application from the design, economic and manufacturing points of view.

Mounting Arrangements

The versatility of the Timken tapered roller bearing permits many possible application design arrangements such as direct or indirect mountings, single-row, two-row or four-row installations. Timken Company sales engineers, working closely with designers, can assist in determining which mounting arrangement will most fully utilize the numerous advantageous characteristics of the Timken bearing.

Bearing Setting

Timken Company sales engineers and service engineers will assist in determining the bearing setting best suited for a given application—and from a manufacturing point of view, offer a practical and economical method by which it may be achieved.

Assembly and Manufacturing Economics

Timken Company engineers can help you further capitalize on the basic economies of Timken bearing applications. They offer typical designs of tools, gauges, fixtures and devices to facilitate the handling and assembly of Timken bearings into your products. Often they can suggest arrangements permitting wider tolerances and lower machining costs.

Training Customer Assembly Personnel

Timken Company engineers will aid in training your assembly and service personnel in recommended bearing handling and service techniques. When desired, custom group presentations are available.

Testing and Experimental Programs

Continuous testing in The Timken Company laboratories assures that Timken bearings are of consistent high quality. Special testing is conducted to evaluate bearing wear and rolling contact fatigue, the effect of environmental factors on bearing life, lubrication analysis, deflection and misalignment.

Timken Company engineers will help organize and evaluate experimental programs for laboratory or field testing of prototype models to check bearing life and performance.

Research

The Timken Company supports an extensive research program to maintain its leadership as the world's foremost manufacturer of tapered roller bearings. Advanced technology in the area of bearings, manufacturing techniques and metallurgy is applied in constant search of improved quality and performance of tapered roller bearings. Such investigations as the internal operating characteristics of a bearing, lubrication, heat generation, application development, sound and vibration, process metallurgy, X-ray, ultrasonic and eddy current techniques and heat treatment are conducted at Timken Research.

Bearing Design

		PAGE
A.	Basic Design	8
B.	Bearing Steel	9
C.	Product Precision	9
D.	Sound Testing	9
E.	Basic Bearing Types	9-20
	Single-Row Bearings	10, 11, 17
	Two-Row Bearings	12-17
	Four-Row Bearings	18, 19
	Thrust Bearings	20

A. Basic Design

The tapered roller bearing consists of four basic components (see figure 1), the inner race or cone, the outer race or cup, the tapered rollers, and the roller retainer or cage. The design is such that under proper operating conditions all components carry the load with the exception of the cage whose primary function is to space the rollers around the cone.

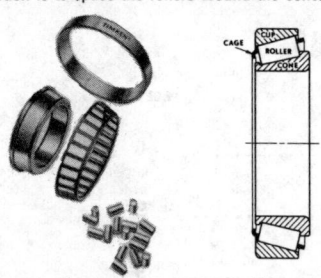

Figure 1. The parts of a Timken bearing. The cup, cone, cage and rollers.

The basic geometry of the cone and cup raceways and rollers of the Timken tapered roller bearing assures positive roller alignment for maximum bearing performance.

The principle of the tapered roller bearing is remarkably simple and is based on these considerations.

1. By constructing the rolling elements as well as the races on the principle of the cone, true rolling motion is obtained. This is brought out clearly in figure 2.

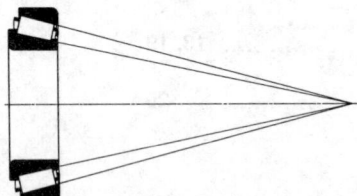

Figure 2. The basic principle of the tapered roller bearing. The apices of the tapered surfaces meet at a common point on the axis of the bearing.

2. Because of the tapered races the bearing will handle any combination of radial and thrust load. Increasing the bearing cup angle will increase the ratio of thrust rating to radial rating.

3. In commercial class bearings the roller bodies are crowned. This optimizes contact between rollers and races under load and assures uniform stress distribution across the entire roller length. Thus, fatigue is minimized and bearing life greatly extended. The nominal contact stress between the roller and race under 100% basic radial rating is approximately 200,000 to 250,000 PSI.

4. A spherical end is ground on the large end of the roller with the radius slightly less than the apex length. Under **no load,** the end of the roller makes a point contact on the cone rib. Under **load,** this contact becomes elliptical, allowing the formation of a lubricant film on the contact area. Fatigue here is not a problem because of the relatively low stress level.

As the rollers in a tapered roller bearing leave the no-load zone and enter the load zone, the radial force or thrust force or a combination of both applied to the bearing will be transmitted to the roller in a resultant force normal to the respective cone and cup race contact surfaces. This results in a roller-rib seating force which is a function of the included angle of the roller thus assuring positive roller alignment and full load-carrying ability.

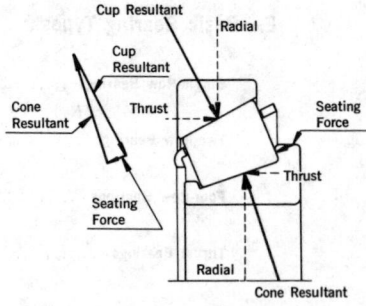

Figure 3. The rib of the tapered roller bearing performs a necessary and useful function. Seating force helps align rollers.

As shown in figure 3, the two resultant forces form two sides of a force diagram. The third side, or seating force of the roller, is shown to complete the force triangle. Since the included angle of the roller is generally very small, the roller end pressure on the rib is correspondingly small.

B. Bearing Steel

All Timken bearing cups and cones are machined from forged steel. Rollers are either cold formed from cold drawn wire or are machined from hot-rolled rods and bars. In the smaller sizes, cups and cones are made from rotary-forged seamless steel tubing. For larger bearing sizes a separate ring is forged for each part. In either case the best steel analysis is chosen at the outset to provide the required load-carrying capacity in the finished bearing.

Timken bearings are manufactured from low carbon carburizing grade, electric furnace, vacuum degassed bearing quality alloy steels. Depending on the size of the bearing to be produced, appropriate quantities of nickel, molybdenum and chromium are added to the steel melt to assure optimum properties in the finished product. After machining, carbon is introduced into the surfaces of the bearing components to a depth adequate to sustain bearing loads. This carbon and the alloy added earlier assure the proper combination of a hard, fatigue-resistant case and a tough, ductile core in the carburized and heat treated part. Additional benefits derived from the carburizing of tapered roller bearings are the residual compressive stresses present in the surface layers which improve the bending fatigue resistance at the large rib undercut and retard the propagation of fatigue cracks that initiate in the bearing surfaces.

Much effort has been expended in studying bearing life and performance in our laboratory—as well as in field applications—to arrive at the best steel composition and heat treatment combinations. The selection of the most satisfactory steel is determined only after extremely careful research. This control, not only of the actual manufacture of the bearing but also of the steel used, assures an unsurpassed product with consistently uniform quality.

Specialty steels for critical bearing applications are available in Timken tapered roller bearings. These specialty steels include consumable electrode vacuum melted steel for extremely high reliability applications and vacuum degassed steels alloyed for high temperature bearing applications.

If environmental conditions indicate a need for bearings made of special steel, a Timken Company sales engineer is readily available for consultation and suggestions toward preparation of proper specifications.

C. Product Precision

Product precision can only be improved by producing parts of better geometry and surface texture. Timken Research personnel have developed and improved finishing methods and machines to produce the extremely fine finish of Timken bearing rollers and raceways.

Surface finish and geometrical accuracy have been so greatly improved that ultra precision bearings with radial and axial runout accuracies within 75 millionths of an inch are being produced in regular production quantities. Bearings are also now available with a maximum runout of 25 millionths of an inch when required.

D. Sound Testing

Special sound testing equipment placed in soundproof booths located in The Timken Company's production lines are used to assure that the bearing noise levels are within specified limits.

Timken bearings can be used successfully in most applications without objectionable noise levels by applying the proper class bearing to meet the requirements. Special class bearings can be ordered for those applications where the noise level is unusually critical.

E. Basic Bearing Types

Timken bearings have the ability to carry both radial and thrust loads in any combination.

The single-row type TS bearing shown on page 10 is the basic tapered roller bearing design.

Some applications require that the type TS bearing design be expanded to include two-row bearings, four-row bearings and thrust bearings. The available types of tapered roller bearings are described on the following pages.

Basic Bearing Types—Continued

Single-Row Bearings

The single-row type TS bearing, which includes the J-Line group, is made with various angles and roller lengths in order to vary the radial and thrust rating to suit application requirements. Variations like flanged cups and "Duo-face" seals have been added to the type TS bearing to make it more versatile.

Multiple-Row Assemblies

Two-row and four-row bearing assemblies are available for those applications where greater bearing rating is needed within limited space. Either a double-inner or double-outer race bearing may be used depending on the design requirements. In some cases, spacers or snap rings can be added to solve mounting problems.

Thrust Bearings

Thrust bearings are made in several different types and they are used on applications where only thrust loads are to be carried.

Bearings Designed To Meet Customers' Special Requirements

Most applications can use one of the previously described bearings to carry the loads. Occasionally the designer cannot locate a bearing in The Timken Company Engineering Journal which meets the specific requirements of the application. In this case it is recommended that The Timken Company be consulted to determine if a special bearing is necessary and feasible.

Single-Row Bearings

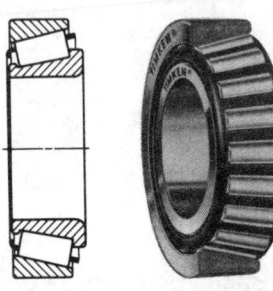

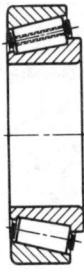

TS (Pressed Steel Cage)

The type TS single-row bearing is the most popular tapered roller bearing and is available in sizes ranging from 0.3125" (7,937 mm) bore to 67.000" (1701,8 mm) bore.

A tabulation of available sizes is shown in the Bearing Tables section of this journal.

TS (Pin Type Cage)

A pin type cage is used on bearings requiring maximum rating. More rollers can be used with a pin type cage than with a pressed steel cage because cage pins pass through a hole in the roller, thereby reducing the required clearance between rollers.

Single-Row Bearings—Continued

TSF

The flanged cup bearing permits through-boring of the housing, assuring accurately aligned cup seats. The cup flange is mounted against the shoulder of the housing and need not normally be clamped in position.

A tabulation showing available sizes is in the Bearing Tables section of this journal.

TSG

The type TSG bearing was designed specifically for steering gear applications and a limited number of sizes are available. The cage and roller assembly and cup, produced by The Timken Company, operate on a cone profile generated on the steering gear worm.

For information on the sizes available, consult your Timken Company sales engineer.

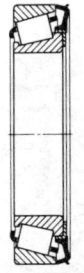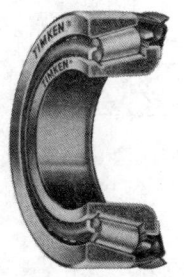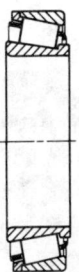

TSL (With "Duo-Face" Seal)

The "Duo-face" seal bearing is an economical selection for grease-lubricated applications operating at moderate speeds where a seal is needed on one side of the bearing. The seal is pressed onto the bearing cone. One lip operates in the housing bore. The other lip seals against the bearing cup – a smooth, hardened, ground, flat surface.

A tabulation of available sizes is shown in the Bearing Tables section of this journal.

TSU (UNIT-BEARING)

The single-row UNIT-BEARING offers unique load carrying characteristics. It was specifically developed for use on the rear axle of automobiles. It is pre-set, takes thrust in either direction, and carries heavy radial loads as well. The UNIT-BEARING is the only single-row tapered roller bearing which offers this versatility and is now finding new applications in transmissions, gear reduction units, and various other types of industrial equipment.

For information on the sizes available, consult your Timken Company sales engineer.

Two-Row Bearings

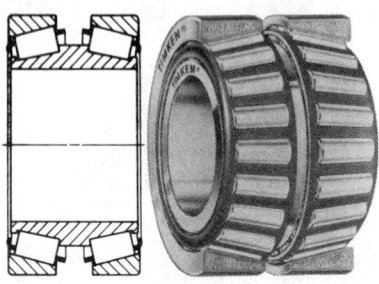

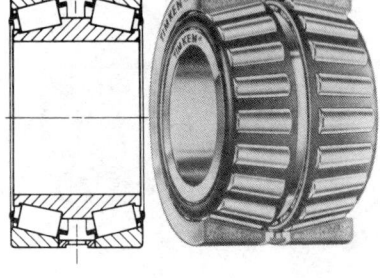

TDI and TDI with cup spacer

The type TDI bearing is made by combining one double cone and two single cups. A cup spacer can be furnished to control the bearing internal clearance. Solid spacers or those having lubrication entrances are available. This bearing type finds application in gear reduction units, cranes, marine drives and many other types of industrial equipment.

A tabulation of available sizes is shown in the Bearing Tables section of this journal.

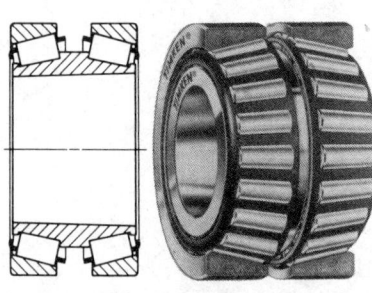

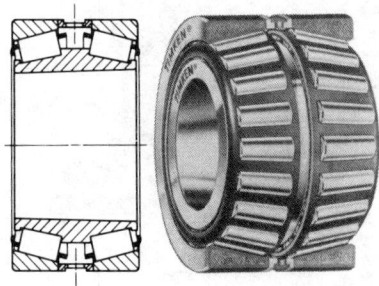

TDIT and TDIT with cup spacer

The type TDIT bearing is identical to the type TDI bearing except that the cone bore is tapered. It is also available with a cup spacer to provide a pre-set assembly.

The tapered bore allows for easy cone removal where interference fits are necessary and frequent removal of the bearing from the shaft is desired. The type TDIT bearing is used on adaptor-type pillow blocks, light and medium duty rolling mill roll necks and on calenders processing rubber, paper and plastic sheeting.

A tabuation of available sizes is shown in the Bearing Tables section of this journal.

Two-Row Bearings—Continued

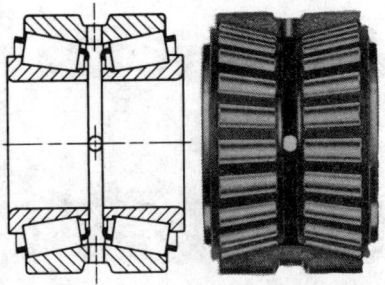
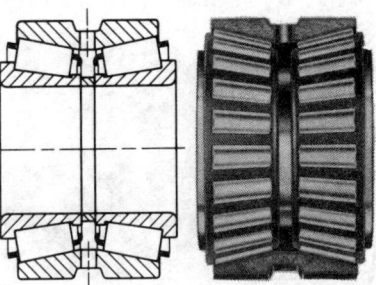

TDO and TDO with cone spacer

The type TDO bearing contains a double cup with two single cones. A groove with oil holes is provided in the cup for lubrication. A cone spacer, either solid or having lubrication entrances, can be supplied to provide a pre-set assembly.

The type TDO bearing can be either fixed or allowed to float in the housing bore to compensate for shaft expansion. Because of the wide effective spread of the type TDO bearing, it is ideal to support loads created by overturning moments. Type TDO bearings find wide usage in gear reduction units, machine tools, cranes and mining and construction equipment.

A tabulation of available sizes is shown in the Bearing Tables section of this journal.

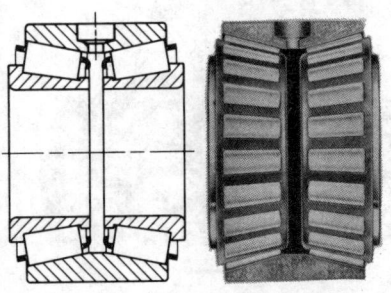
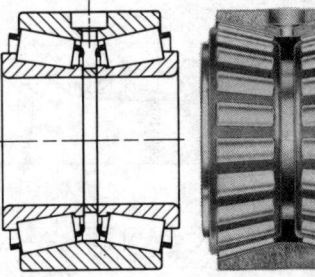

TDODC and TDODC with cone spacer

The type TDODC bearing is the same as the type TDO bearing except that the type TDODC bearing cup contains only **one** counterbored lubrication hole. By inserting a pin, which is slightly smaller in diameter than the counterbored hole, circumferential creeping of a loose-fitted cup is eliminated. The type TDODC bearing is also available with a cone spacer for a pre-set assembly application.

A tabulation of available sizes is shown in the Bearing Tables section of this journal.

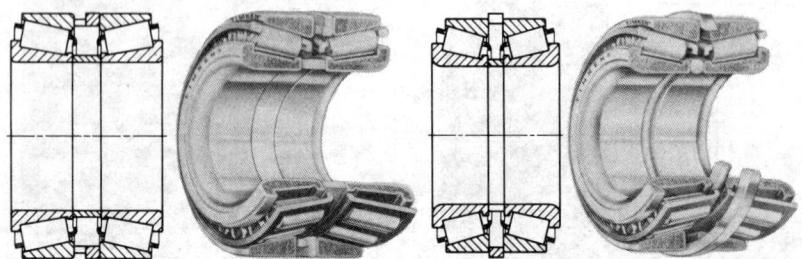

SR

Fixed length cup and cone spacers along with two 'J-Line bearings mounted indirectly make up the "SR" pre-set bearing assembly. The "SR" cup spacer is designed so that a commercial snap ring can be used to locate the bearing axially. It is also slotted for lubrication. The "SR" assembly provides an economical two-row bearing for either floating or fixed positions.

Available sizes are shown in the Bearing Tables section of this journal.

SS

"SS" two-row assemblies are produced using high volume "Green Light" type TS bearings with a snap ring cup spacer and a rolled ring cone spacer. Not only do the rings provide a pre-set assembly but the snap ring allows the cups to be located axially in a through-bored housing. "SS" assemblies can be provided, in some sizes, with "Duo-face" seals on either one or both sides.

A tabulation of available sizes is contained in the Bearing Tables section of this journal.

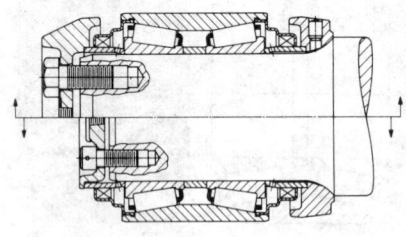

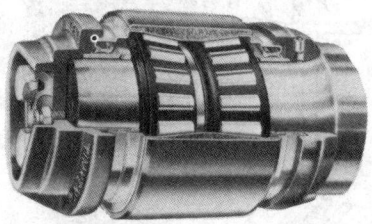

AP (All Purpose)

The "AP" bearing is a self-contained, pre-lubricated, pre-set and sealed assembly consisting of the two-row tapered roller bearing together with a backing ring, seal wear rings, seals, cap screws and an end cap. The standard railway end cap is shown above the centerline, in the line drawing with the recessed end cap shown below. The latter is used in applications where a narrower assembly is required.

This economical package, initially supplied half filled with grease, is used in various industrial applications such as cranes, steel mill rolling stock, table rolls, and sheaves.

Complete data on the "AP" bearing is shown in the supplement on "AP" Bearings in Industrial Equipment.

Two-Row Bearings—Continued

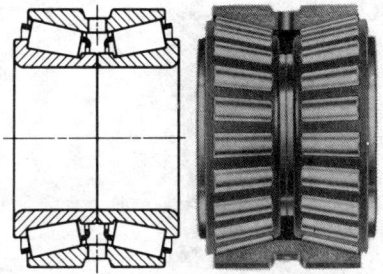
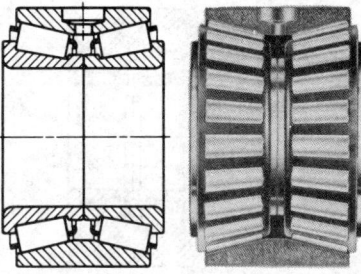

TNA and TNADC

Bearing types TNA and TNADC are similar to types TDO and TDODC with this exception—the internal clearance is controlled by extending the front face of the cones so they contact each other. This eliminates the use of a cone spacer. The internal clearance in types TNA and TNADC bearings is satisfactory for most applications when the recommended fitting practice is used. On those machines requiring closer control of internal clearance, type TDO or TDODC bearings with cone spacers should be used.

A tabulation of available sizes is shown in the Bearing Tables section of this journal.

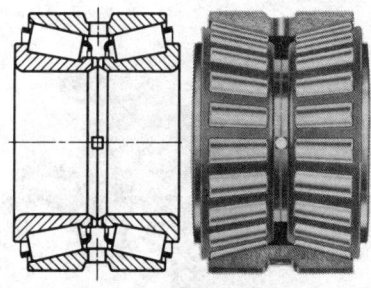
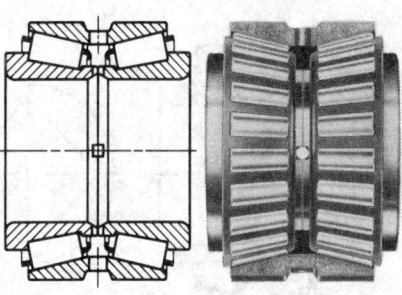

TNASW and TNASWE

The types TNASW and TNASWE bearings are practically the same as the standard type TNA bearing assembly with the exception that the type TNASW bearing provides inside chamfers and slots on the cone faces for lubrication. The type TNASWE bearing is similar to the type TNASW bearing with the exception that the cone back face rib is ground on the O.D. and extended sufficiently to permit the use of a seal or a stamped closure.

A tabulation of available sizes is shown in the Bearing Tables section of this journal.

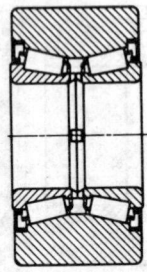
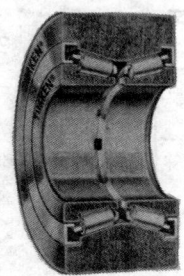

TNASWH

Both cone and roller assemblies in type TNASWH bearings are identical to type TNASWE. The cup is different. It is manufactured with a heavy wall section to permit use as steady rest rollers in machine tools and as backup rollers in Sendzimir mills. Other applications include sheet and strip levellers. This type bearing is also furnished in some sizes with a flanged outer race to make it a complete wheel assembly. In all designs a stamped metal closure is supplied to allow for grease retention. Type TNASWH assemblies are **not** provided with an initial grease supply.

A tabulation of available sizes and types is contained in The Timken Company brochure on type TNASWH bearings.

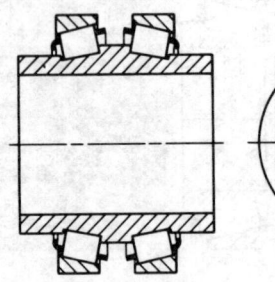
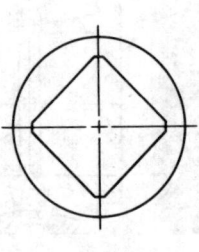

SQUARE BORE

The Square Bore bearing was developed specifically for disc harrow applications in farm machinery. The hardened and ground inner-race extension provides an excellent surface for effective sealing and makes this bearing reliable under severe operating conditions.

A tabulation of available sizes is shown in The Timken Company brochure on Square Bore Bearings.

Two-Row Bearings—Continued

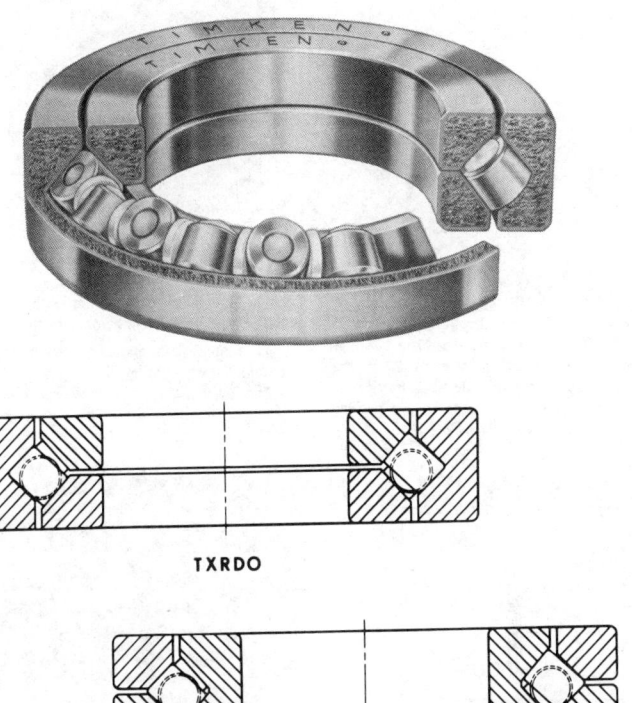

TXRDO

TXRDI

TXR (Crossed Roller Bearing)

The Crossed Roller bearing has been developed to provide the advantages of a two-row bearing in the space of a single-row bearing. This maximum stability bearing has the ability to withstand high overturning moments which makes it ideal for machine tool ap- plications such as vertical boring mills, vertical grinding machines and other applications.

A tabulation of sizes is shown in The Timken Company brochure on Crossed Roller Bearings.

Four-Row Bearings

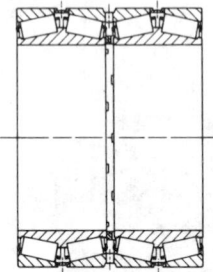

TQO

The heavy duty type TQO bearing is used on roll necks of low and medium speed rolling mills to give maximum rating in a minumum space. The bearings are applied to the necks with a loose fit. When the fillet and filler rings do not already have lubrication slots, they are provided in the faces of the bearing cones. Slots in the cone spacer faces permit lubricant flow from the bearing chamber to the roll neck.

Available sizes and engineering information are contained in the Rolling Mill Equipment Supplement to The Timken Company Engineering Journal.

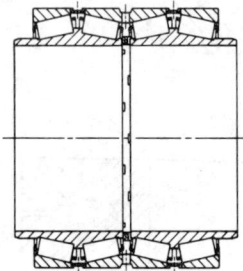
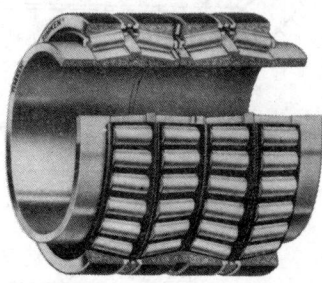

TQOE

The type TQOE bearing is the same as the type TQO bearing except the inner races are extended to provide a hardened, concentric and smooth surface for radial lip seals.

Available sizes and engineering information are contained in the Rolling Mill Equipment Supplement to The Timken Company Engineering Journal.

Four-Row Bearings—Continued

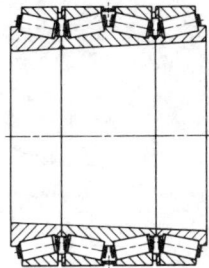

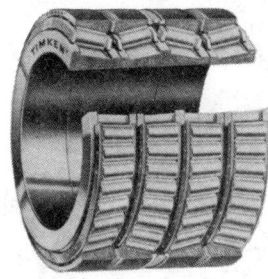

TQITS

The tapered bore cones of this heavy duty roll neck bearing permit an interference fit on the back-up rolls of high speed mills where the loose cone fit of the straight bore type TQO bearing could result in excessive neck wear. Maximum stability and roll rigidity result from the indirect arrangement of the races.

Available sizes and engineering information are contained in the Rolling Mill Equipment Supplement to The Timken Company Engineering Journal.

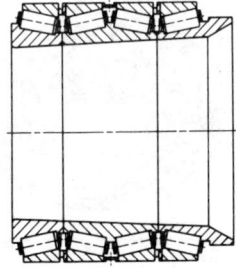

TQITSE

The type TQITSE bearing is the same as the type TQITS bearing except the large I.D. inner race adjacent to the roll body has an extension to provide a hardened, concentric and smooth surface for radial lip seals. Increased roll neck rigidity is realized because of the elimination of a fillet ring between the roll barrel and bearing, allowing the centerline of the bearing to be moved closer to the roll body. Shorter and less costly rolls also result through the use of this "extended cone" tapered bore bearing.

Available sizes and engineering information are contained in the Rolling Mill Equipment Supplement to The Timken Company Engineering Journal.

Thrust Bearings

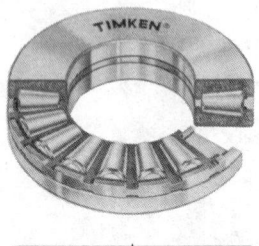

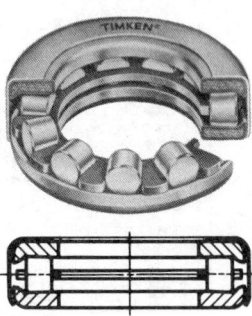

TTHD

The type TTHD heavy duty thrust bearing is designed for moderately high speed applications. Having rollers ground to precision limits and properly spaced by means of a cage, this bearing is extensively used in numerous applications including oil well swivels, extruders and piercing mill thrust blocks.

A tabulation of available sizes is shown in the Bearing Tables section of this journal.

TTSP

The type TTSP thrust bearing is employed extensively in the steering pivot position of automotive and industrial applications.

A tabulation of available sizes is shown in the Bearing Tables section of this journal.

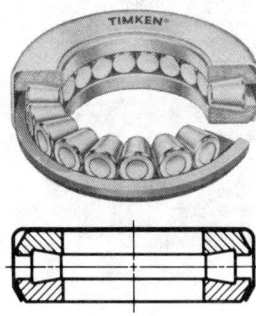

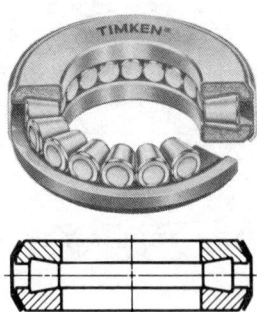

TTC and TTCS

Types TTC and TTCS bearings are thrust bearings specifically designed for oscillating or slow rotation applications. These cageless assemblies with metal retainer are identical with the exception of retainer construction.

A tabulation of available sizes is shown in the Bearing Tables section of this journal.

Bearing Ratings and Life

		PAGE
A.	**Load Ratings**	**22**
	1. Basic Dynamic	22
	2. Static	22
B.	**Rated Life**	**22**
C.	**Effects of Load and Speed**	**23**
D.	**Bearing Reliability**	**24**
E.	**System Reliability**	**24**
F.	**Effects of Environmental Factors**	**24-26**
	1. Load Zone	24, 25
	2. Misalignment	25, 26
	3. Lubrication	26

A. Load Ratings

There are two fundamental load ratings for tapered roller bearings, a **basic dynamic** load rating and a **static** load rating. The basic dynamic load rating is used to establish the life expectancy of a rotating bearing. The static load rating is used to determine the maximum permissable load that could be applied to a bearing when it is not rotating without producing damaging brinell.

1. Basic Dynamic

Since 1915 The Timken Company has developed specific rating methods for its tapered roller bearings. Customers have benefited by periodic bearing rating revisions which have been published only after thorough verification by continuous testing programs. The testing schedule, which is now established as an international "quality audit program", randomly samples bearings as packaged in The Timken Company distribution centers and subjects these standard bearings to rigorous additional measurements and geometry and material evaluations before the final life testing that verifies the mathematical load rating model.

This continuous testing of standard product bearings from all of our manufacturing plants is the basis for periodic revisions of bearing ratings and reappraisal of the rating formula used by The Timken Company. The latest revision of Timken bearing ratings as printed in this journal was adopted in 1967.

In general, the rating of a bearing is a function of internal bearing geometry, which includes cup angle, cone angle, effective contact length between races and rollers and roller diameter. It is also a function of the number of rollers in each row and the number of rows in the bearing. These parameters, together with size effect and a material constant, are formulated in the rating equation.

The ratings as published in this journal are the **basic dynamic radial load rating**, C(90), and the **basic dynamic thrust load rating**, CA(90). Also published is a bearing K-factor which indicates the ratio of basic dynamic radial rating to basic dynamic thrust rating. The following relationship holds:

$$K = C(90)/CA(90)$$
or
$$K = 0.389 \times \cot\alpha$$

Where:

α = 1/2 included cup angle

2. Static

A non-rotating tapered roller bearing can endure static loads that result in the formation of fine visible brinell lines on the bearing raceway. These will have no measurable effect on bearing life when the bearing is subsequently loaded near its rating under rotation.

For the complete line of tapered roller bearings we have established static load ratings for both radial and thrust loading. Actual values for these ratings may be obtained from your Timken Company sales engineer.

For combined loading a static equivalent radial load (P_0) may be calculated from:

$$P_0 = 0.5\ F_r\ + 0.564\ KF_a$$
$$\text{If}\quad F_a \rangle \ \frac{0.6\ F_r}{K}$$

or

$$P_0 = 1.6\ F_r - 1.269\ KF_a$$
$$\text{If}\quad \frac{0.6\ F_r}{K} \rangle F_a \rangle \frac{0.47\ F_r}{K}$$

Where:

F_r = Applied radial load
F_a = Net thrust load (see page 46)
K = Bearing K-factor

B. Rated Life

The life of a tapered roller bearing, properly applied on a shaft, is usually completed after repeated stressing causes pitting or spalling of the contacting surfaces. In The Timken Company laboratories a bearing is considered fatigued when the pitted or spalled area reaches 0.01 square inch, even though prolonged life tests have shown that the useful life of that bearing may extend considerably beyond this point.

Since bearings that appear to be identical exhibit considerable life scatter when tested under the same conditions, a statistical method is used to evaluate the life of tapered roller bearings. An extreme value distribution called the Weibull distribution is generally used to determine the statistical life of bearings at any reliability level. Using this distribution, The Timken Company has established the "rated life" or L10 of all Timken bearings. This L10 is defined as the number of revolutions (or hours at some given speed) that 90% of a group of identical bearings will complete or exceed before fatigue reaches the failure criterion.

C. Effects of Load and Speed

The basic dynamic load ratings shown in this journal are values which are based on a "rated life" of 90 million revolutions or 3000 hours at 500 RPM. The relationship between "rated life" and load is as follows:

$$L_{10} = \left(\frac{C(90)}{P}\right)^{10/3} \times 90 \times 10^6 \text{ Revolutions}$$

Where:

P = Dynamic equivalent radial load as determined by use of formulae on page 47.

To determine "rated life" in hours at a given speed, the above equation can be expressed as follows:

$$L_{10} = \left(\frac{C(90) \times SF}{P}\right)^{10/3} \times 3000 \text{ Hours}$$

Where:

SF = Speed factor at bearing speed "S" in RPM. See table of speed factors in the Reference Tables section. These factors are derived from the formula:

$$SF = \left(\frac{500}{S}\right)^{3/10}$$

In order to visualize the effects of load and speed on bearing life the following rules apply:

(1) Doubling the **load** reduces the life to about one-tenth and reducing the load by one-half increases the life about ten times.

(2) Doubling the **speed** reduces the life by one-half. Reducing the speed by one-half doubles the life. For a listing of specific life ratio formulae for varying loads and speeds, see page 49.

When comparing a Timken bearing with that of a competitive manufacturer whose basis for rating is other than 90 million revolutions or 3000 hours at 500 RPM, **modifying factors** must be used.

These factors are derived from the following expression:

Timken bearing load rating =

$$\text{Competitive bearing rating} \times \left(\frac{S_1}{500}\right)^{1/f} \times \left(\frac{L_1}{3000}\right)^{1/f}$$

Where:

S_1 = RPM at which competitive bearing is rated

L_1 = Hours life at which competitive bearing is rated

f = Competitive bearing fatigue factor

Example:

A spherical roller bearing, whose dynamic load rating is 10,000 pounds based on 33-1/3 RPM, 500 hours and a fatigue factor of 3.33, would have an equivalent Timken bearing load rating of 2600 pounds.

Timken bearing load rating =

$$10,000 \times \left(\frac{33.3}{500}\right)^{1/3.33} \times \left(\frac{500}{3000}\right)^{1/3.33}$$

$$= 10,000 \times 0.26 = 2600 \text{ lb}$$

A simplification of this equation for a manufacturer who rates his bearings at one million revolutions would be as follows:

Timken bearing load rating =

$$\text{Competitive bearing rating} \times \left(\frac{1 \text{ million}}{90 \text{ million}}\right)^{1/f}$$

D. Bearing Reliability

Rated life is an expression of reliability, i.e., 90% reliability that a bearing will equal or exceed a given life. In some bearing applications greater than 90% reliability is required. The following graph (figure 4) can be used to select the appropriate reduced life to give the desired increase in reliability.

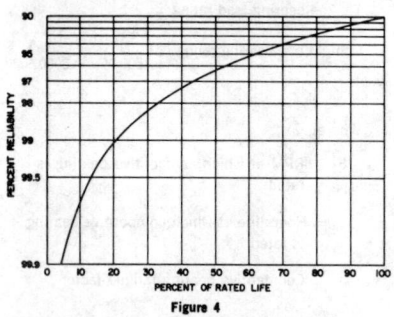

Figure 4

E. System Reliability

System reliability is encountered when one desires to consider the probability that all of several bearings will survive to some given life, that is:

$$\text{Reliability (System)} = (R_1)(R_2)(R_3) \ldots\ldots (R_n)$$

Where:

$R_1, R_2, R_3 \ldots R_n$ represent reliability for each bearing in a system to a required system life.

Example:

What is the reliability of a system which requires 6,000 hours life, when the rated life of the four bearings in the system are 12,000, 10,000, 9,000 and 8,000 hours?

Rated Life	System Life As % of Rated Life	% Reliability Bearing to System Life
12,000	50	96
10,000	60	95
9,000	66.7	94
8,000	75	93

Reliability (System) = (0.96) (0.95) (0.94) (0.93)
= 0.80 or 80%

F. Effects of Environmental Factors

The present methods of selecting bearings for a particular application are not exact sciences. In many cases the criteria for bearing selections are empirical relationships based on past successful experience. Using this approach the calculated life for a given set of conditions may be different than the actual field life. In most cases this empirical method gives satisfactory results and may be conservative.

In the past, in those applications in which the actual life did not agree with the calculated life, experience has provided application factors to account for conditions or factors that, in addition to load and speed, evidently have an effect on bearing life.

Ideally, bearing selections should be made on the basis of absolute loads, speeds and precise operating conditions. Then, catalog ratings would yield a calculated life representative of actual field life. With more accurate knowledge, these goals will more precisely be approached as time goes by and thus eliminate empirical relationships.

More recent efforts of Timken Research have been directed toward defining special facets of these factors and quantitatively evaluating their effects.

1. The Effect of Load Zone on the Fatigue Life of Tapered Roller Bearings

The fatigue life of a bearing is a function of internal load distribution and the number of stress cycles that the various bearing components are subjected to over this distribution in one revolution. The bearing load zone is a measure, in degrees, of the extent of the load distribution within a bearing. It is a direct indication of how many rollers share the applied load. Therefore, life is directly related to the load zone existing within a bearing. Figure 5 is an illustration of some typical load zones that exist in a bearing.

Except for the condition of thrust load only, all loading of a tapered roller bearing is combined loading, i.e., a combination of radial and thrust load. A single tapered roller bearing subjected to any radial load always experiences a thrust reaction which is counteracted by an equal and opposite thrust load external to the bearing. The amount of thrust load in relation to the applied radial load then determines the bearing load zone.

Bearing Ratings and Life

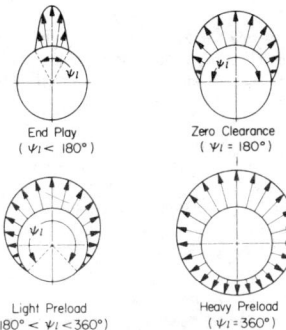

End Play
$(\psi_l < 180°)$

Zero Clearance
$(\psi_l = 180°)$

Light Preload
$(180° < \psi_l < 360°)$

Heavy Preload
$(\psi_l = 360°)$

Figure 5. Typical Load Zones

The load zone is also dependent on the amount of bearing endplay or preload. A bearing operating with endplay has a load zone of less than 180°. Endplay is the relative axial clearance of the cup to its cone on an assembled shaft. On the other hand, when the axial clearance is metal to metal, the condition is known as preload and defines an operating load zone of greater than 180°.

If the bearing setting or loading is such that the load zone is 180°, the bearing is generally referred to as operating under radial load only. For the laboratory fatigue rating program mentioned under "Basic Dynamic Load Ratings", Timken bearings are run with about 0.002″ (0,051 mm) endplay in each bearing. Therefore an allowance for endplay of this magnitude is built into the rating of a Timken tapered roller bearing.

In field applications, the actual load zone in an operating bearing may be difficult to assess because in a practical sense the load zone can be altered by several factors:

a. Bearing Load

The load zone will change with external radial load because the elastic deformation within the bearing is load-dependent.

b. Bearing Geometry

Bearings with different numbers of rollers, different diameters and different internal geometries will exhibit different elastic deformation characteristics which in turn influence the load zones.

c. Clearance

Radial clearance is dependent on endplay; however, because of the varying cup angles possible in different tapered roller bearings, two bearings with the same endplay and different K-factors can have internal radial clearances varying more than 5 to 1.

d. Temperature Gradient

Under operating conditions, endplay will change from the original assembled endplay depending on temperature rise or the temperature gradients developed between cone and cup.

e. Housing Deformation

Under load the housing will deform, altering the bearing load zone.

For these reasons, in those applications in which larger than normal endplay must be used, life adjustment factors may be required. All of the above-mentioned factors must be taken into account so that the effect of the operating endplay on life can be established.

2. The Effect of Misalignment on the Fatigue Life of Tapered Roller Bearings

For optimum performance and life, the races of a tapered roller bearing should be perfectly aligned. However, in every application of a bearing there exists a certain amount of misalignment. The misalignment may be due to shaft deflection, inaccuracies in machining of shaft or housing, press fits, plus a host of other possible factors.

The basic dynamic load rating of a Timken tapered roller bearing is based on laboratory tests during which some of these conditions prevail. Therefore, a certain allowance for misalignment is built into the bearing ratings. As long as this allowance is not exceeded, the bearing will perform to catalog expectations.

The exact effect of misalignment depends on applied load, bearing endplay and internal bearing geometry. It therefore varies for different bearing series and conditions of the application of the bearing. As a general rule a Timken tapered roller bearing may be expected to give catalog life as long as the misalignment angle does not exceed 3 to 4 minutes or approximately 0.001 inch per inch (0,001 mm per mm) slope through the bearing. This is only an approximate misalignment tolerance for the reasons mentioned.

The exact analysis of misalignment effect involves the determination and evaluation of the pressure distribution along the contact lengths between the misaligned races and rollers under a given load. The calculations are rather involved and are best accomplished by computers. Our engineering department can offer you assistance in this area.

Multiple-row bearing mountings involving type TDO bearings may under conditions of misalignment result in unequal load reactions on the individual bearing rows. The load effect and misalignment effect must be combined in such cases to determine bearing life.

3. The Effect of Lubrication on the Fatigue Life of Tapered Roller Bearings

Theories for the determination of the elastohydrodynamic lubricant film that occurs in highly stressed Hertzian contacts have been in existence for some time. Timken Research has conducted extensive testing to evaluate the effect that film thickness and other lubricant properties have on the fatigue life of tapered roller bearings.

This testing has verified that in applications with low values of lubricant film thickness, low speeds, or high temperatures, the reduction in bearing life can be estimated by considering those factors that directly influence the film thickness. As a general rule in an application in which viscosity is below 60 SUS (10cs) at operating temperature, lubricant temperature above 200°F or where a combination of low speeds and high bearing loads prevails, bearing life may be below that calculated using standard life estimating methods.

The film thickness may be improved by increasing lubricant viscosity, lowering the temperature by increasing lubricant flow through the bearing or lowering the inlet oil temperature.

See pages 88 through 90 for a discussion on lubrication specifications for tapered roller bearings.

Analyses involving effect on the fatigue life of tapered roller bearings, load zone, misalignment and lubricant film and viscosity are complicated and best accomplished with the aid of a computer. Critical applications for which such an analysis is required should be given to your Timken Company sales engineer for a solution.

Bearing Operating Characteristics

PAGE

A. **Bearing Torque** **28-31**

    1. Running Torque **28**

      a. Thrust Loads **28, 29**

      b. Radial Loads **29**

      c. Combined Loading **29**

      d. Torque Calculation Example **30**

    2. Set-Up Torque **30, 31**

B. **Heat Generation** **31**

C. **Heat Dissipation** **31, 32**

D. **Speed Capabilities of Tapered Roller Bearings** **32-34**

    1. Lubrication Systems **33**

      a. Grease **33**

      b. Static Oil Level **33**

      c. Static Oil Level with Splash **33**

      d. Forced Feed Oil Systems **33**

    2. Lubricants **33, 34**

E. **Bearing Deformation** **34**

F. **Bearing Spring Rate** **34**

COPYRIGHT 1972 BY THE TIMKEN COMPANY - PRINTED IN U.S.A

A. Bearing Torque

1. Running Torque

The rotational resistance of a tapered roller bearing is dependent upon bearing geometry, load and its distribution among the rollers, speed of rotation, quantity of lubricant in the bearing, and the viscosity of the oil at the operating temperature of the bearing. Since the viscosity of the oil varies significantly with temperature, a good approximation of the bearing operating temperature should be made if a realistic value for running torque is to be obtained.

An estimate of a bearing's running torque for speeds greater than 100 RPM can be determined by using the graph (figure 6) and the discussions below for (a.) Radial Load, (b.) Thrust Load and (c.) Combined Loading. For running torque values at speeds less than 100 RPM, The Timken Company's engineering department should be consulted.

In the following discussion and accompanying graphs the variables are defined as follows:

M = Running torque (lb-in)

S = Bearing speed (RPM)

μ = Viscosity of oil in centipoises at the bearing operating temperature

F_r = Radial load applied to the bearing (lb)

F_a = The total thrust (lb) on the bearing that carries the equivalent load and can be calculated from:

$$F_a = T_e + \frac{0.47 \; F_{r2}}{K_2}$$

Where:

T_e = External applied thrust (lb)

F_{r2} = Radial load on opposing bearing (lb)

K_2 = K-factor of opposing bearing

G = Bearing G-factor obtained from Bearing Selection Index. (The bearing G-factor is a bearing geometry factor that is comprised of those internal bearing dimensions that have an effect on bearing running torque.)

f_t = Torque combined loading factor. For radial load only f_t = 0.108. See also (b) and (c) below.

a. Thrust Loads

An estimate of a bearing's running torque for thrust load only can be determined by using the graph in figure 6. To use this Torque Graph locate the intersection of a speed-viscosity parameter (μS) and a thrust load (F_a).

From this point a horizontal line can be drawn to the vertical scale to obtain a value for a torque bearing geometry ratio (M/G). Since the bearing geometry factors are listed in the Bearing Selection Index, a value for the running torque (M) can be determined for a desired bearing series and specific operating conditions.

THIS GRAPH MAY UNDERESTIMATE BEARING TORQUE AT SPEEDS LESS THAN 100 RPM

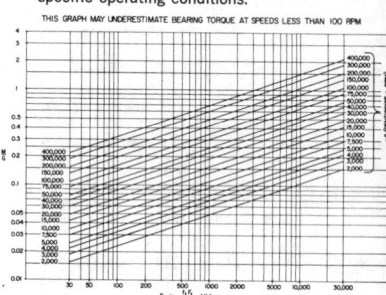

Figure 6

Figure 7 provides a means for determining the viscosity of typical ASTM oils at different operating

ASTM VISCOSITY SYSTEM FOR INDUSTRIAL FLUID LUBRICANTS (ASSUME 90 VI

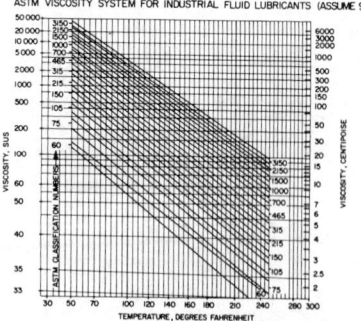

Figure 7

Bearing Operating Characteristics

temperatures. A convenient conversion from SUS to centipoise viscosity units, assuming a constant specific gravity of 0.9, is also given in figure 7.

Under thrust load only, bearing running torque is directly proportional to the G-factors. When two bearings are operating under identical conditions of load, speed, temperature and lubrication, the bearing with the lower G-factor will exhibit lower rotational resistance.

b. Radial Loads

To determine the torque for a radial-load-only condition, calculate the ratio $f_t F_r/K$, using $f_t = 0.108$. Use this value to enter the horizontal axis of the graph in figure 6 and locate the intersection of the applicable speed-viscosity parameter (μS) to obtain the M/G ratio in the same manner as for thrust load only.

Under radial loads only, bearing running torque is directly proportional to the ratio $\dfrac{G}{(K)^{1/3}}$

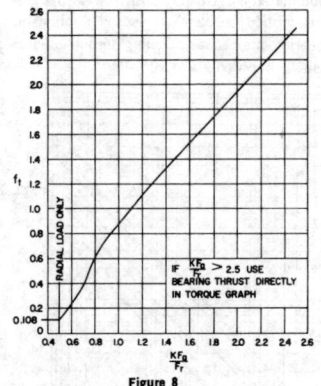

Figure 8

c. Combined Loading

If the torque is required for a bearing that is subjected to a combined radial and thrust load, determine a value for the ratio KF_a/F_r. It is important to realize that for a combined loading situation, F_a is the sum of the external applied

thrust (T_e) plus the induced thrust from the opposite bearing. The value of F_a for any loading condition can be determined from the thrust reaction equations given on page 46. With the ratio KF_a/F_r known, the torque combined loading factor (f_t) can be determined from figure 8. This value of f_t, along with the radial load (F_r) applied to the bearing for the combined loading condition, is used to determine a value for the load parameter $f_t F_r/K$ in the Torque Graph. If the ratio KF_a/F_r is greater than 2.5, the thrust load F_a on the bearing predominates and should be used to enter the horizontal axis of the Torque Graph, figure 6. The intersection of the applicable speed-viscosity parameter (μS) is then located to obtain the M/G ratio.

Under combined loading, bearing running torque is proportional to the G-factors, provided the bearings under consideration have approximately equal K-factors. In all other cases calculate the torque to compare the torque characteristics of the bearings.

The torque obtained using these methods applies for a bearing lubricated with grease or an oil bath system where the oil level covers one half of the bottom dead center roller. The Torque Graph also applies to circulating oil systems assuming nominal flow rates and suitably designed drains. High speed applications often use such a system to more effectively cool the bearing. Research into the oil pumping characteristics of a tapered roller bearing reveals that a portion of the running torque at high speeds is due to the quantity of oil in the bearing. If inadequate drains are provided or excessive flow rates are used, the running torque on high speed applications will be underestimated by the Torque Graph.

The running torque obtained from the graph is a value for a bearing whose torque has stabilized after a period of run-in under operating conditions. Starting torque and the torque of a new bearing varies from this value. Should this information be required, consult The Timken Company's engineering department.

The bearing torque in a shaft is the sum of the torques determined for each of the individual bearings.

If radial lip seals are used, their contribution to the total system torque is significant and must be considered.

d. Torque Calculation Example

A pair of HM88600 series bearings mounted on a shaft are subjected to the following loading conditions (see application analysis example page 52 for loading analysis).

Bearing A and B = HM88600 series

K = 1.07 (from Bearing Selection Index)

G = 18.6 (from Bearing Selection Index)

Estimated operating temperature = 132°F

Lubricant is oil with a viscosity of 700 SUS at 100°F.

Speed = 3500 RPM

Bearing A,

Radial Load, F_r = 800 lb

Thrust Load, $F_a = \dfrac{0.47\ F_rB}{K_B} + T_e$

$= \dfrac{0.47 \times 700}{1.07} + 450 = 757$ lb

Bearing B,

Radial Load only, F_r = 700 lb

Question: What is the bearing torque in the shaft?

Solution: From figure 7, an oil with a viscosity of 700 SUS at 100°F has a viscosity of 280 SUS at 132°F. From figure 7, this viscosity is equal to 55 centipoises. (See vertical scale on right hand side of figure 7). The speed-viscosity parameter (μS) is:

$3500 \times 55 = 192,500$

(1) Torque in bearing B (radial load only).

The load parameter for radial load only is:

$\dfrac{0.108\ F_r}{K} = \dfrac{0.108 \times 700}{1.07} = 70.65$

From the torque graph in figure 6, page 28, $\dfrac{M}{G} = 0.2$

Then torque $M_B = G \times 0.2 = 18.6 \times 0.2 = 3.7$ lb-in

(2) Torque in Bearing A (combined loading).

In figure 8, page 29,

$\dfrac{KF_a}{F_r} = \dfrac{1.07 \times 757}{800} = 1.012$

Therefore the load parameter (f_t) for the combined loading condition is 0.87 (figure 8, page 29),

$\dfrac{0.87 \times F_r}{K} = \dfrac{0.87 \times 800}{1.07} = 650$

From the torque graph in figure 6, page 28,

$\dfrac{M}{G} = 0.42$

Then torque $M_A = G \times 0.42$
$= 18.6 \times 0.42 = 7.8$ lb-in

(3) Torque in the shaft from both bearings is,

$M_A + M_B = 7.8 + 3.7 = 11.5$ lb-in

2. Set-Up Torque

The automated setting technique known as torque-set described on page 70 uses a relationship between bearing preload and rolling torque at slow rotation, usually between 2 and 10 RPM.

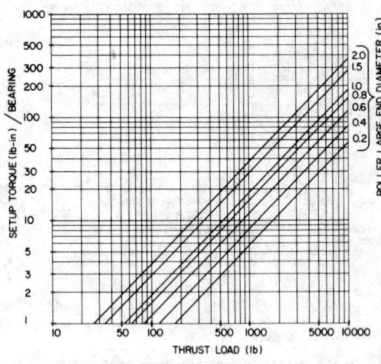

Figure 9

Figure 9 gives this information as a function of the large end roller diameter which can be scaled from the bearing drawings in Section 2 of The Timken Company

Bearing Operating Characteristics

Engineering Journal. The torque determined using this graph is not applicable to most normal operating speeds and therefore should not be used to calculate power losses. This torque is applicable only to new bearings. Bearings that have been in operation for an extended period of time will have a set-up torque approximately 50% that of new bearings.

Additional information on torque and more specific details covering the limitations of the torque relations given above can be obtained from The Timken Company.

B. Heat Generation

Churning of excess lubricant can be the major source of heat developed within a bearing. In a properly lubricated tapered roller bearing, most of the heat is developed between the rollers and raceways; relatively little is developed by the roller-rib contact. But if the lubricant is lost from the roller-rib area, this is where the effects of heat show up first because of the sliding contact.

The heat generated within a bearing is determined from bearing torque and speed using standard energy conversion factors. Heat is a function of all the variables discussed under torque including speed, load, preload, size, internal bearing geometry and lubricant properties.

Once the bearing torque (M) is approximated on the basis of the information discussed above, the heat generated (Q) may be calculated from the following equation:

$$Q = 0.000673 \times S \times M$$

Where:

Q = Heat (BTU/min)

S = Bearing speed (RPM)

M = Torque (lb-in)

The effects of temperature on viscosity and of viscosity on torque are such that when in a given application only the speed is varied, bearing torque may show only minor change. This is because the product of viscosity-speed (μS) in the torque equation tends to stay constant over reasonable speed ranges.

The following energy and power conversion factors may be utilized to convert to other units.

1 lb-in $= 0.1071 \times 10^{-3}$ BTU (British Thermal Units)

1 lb-ft $= 0.001285$ BTU

1 HP $= 2544$ BTU/hr
$= 33000$ lb-ft/min

1 kw-hr $= 3413$ BTU

C. Heat Dissipation

The problem of determining the heat flow from a bearing in a specific application is rather complex. To establish equations that would be applicable in a general sense with any accuracy is not practical.

In general it can be said that factors affecting the rate of heat dissipation include the following:

(1) Temperature gradient from bearing to housing. This is affected by size and configuration of the housing and any external cooling such as fans or water cooling or fan action of rotating parts.

(2) Temperature gradient from bearing to shaft. Any other heat sources such as gears and additional bearings and their proximity to the bearing considered will influence the temperature of the shaft.

(3) The heat carried away by a circulating oil system.

To what extent (1) and (2) can be controlled or varied will depend on the application and will largely be dictated by functional and economic considerations.

The amount of heat removed by the lubricant can be controlled more easily. In a splash lubrication system, cooling coils (with water circulated through the coils) may be used to control the bulk oil temperature. In a circulating oil system the oil may be cooled externally and the quantity of oil can be regulated.

The amount of heat (Q_{out} in BTU/min) carried away in a circulating oil system by the lubricant can be approximated from the following equation:

$$Q_{out} = 0.42 \times f \times (\theta_o - \theta_i)$$

Where:

f = Flow rate of oil (US-pints/min)

θ_i = Oil inlet temperature (°F)

θ_o = Oil temperature as it leaves the bearing (°F)

If the properties of the lubricant are known, the heat may be calculated more accurately from:

$$Q_{out} = 0.0167 \, c_p \times \rho \times f \times (\theta_o - \theta_i)$$

Where:

0.0167 = Factor to convert pints to cubic ft

c_p = Specific heat of lubricant in BTU/lb$_m$/°F

ρ = Density of lubricant in lb_m/cubic ft

lb_m = Pound (mass)

Assuming unrestricted drainage, the rate at which oil can be freely passed through a bearing depends, in addition to bearing size, on direction of flow, speed, internal bearing geometry and lubricant properties. A tapered roller bearing actually will pump oil from the small end to the large end of the bearing rollers. If it is desired to maximize oil flow and heat dissipation, the oil inlet should be provided adjacent the small end of the bearing rollers.

Much work has been performed at Timken Research on the pumping characteristics of a tapered roller bearing. For quantitative evaluations of the pumping ability of a bearing, the speed, oil level, and oil viscosity and density at operating temperature must be known.

D. Speed Capabilities of Tapered Roller Bearings

Tapered roller bearings have been successfully applied to a wide range of speeds. Bearing speed is usually expressed in cone rib circumferential velocity in FPM, rather than RPM, in order to provide a common base for bearings of different sizes. This may be calculated from:

$$\text{Rib speed} = \frac{\text{RPM} \times \pi \times \text{cone rib dia. (in)}}{12}$$

Cone rib diameter is measured at midpoint of roller contact (see figure 10).

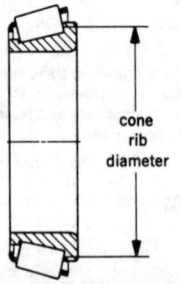

cone rib diameter

Figure 10. Diameter at Midpoint of Roller Contact

Standard off-the-shelf tapered roller bearings with circulating oil and adequate cooling to prevent oil degradation can attain cone rib velocities approaching 10,000 FPM. However, as operating speeds are increased, lubrication becomes critical.

Normally, oil flows through a tapered roller bearing from the small end to the large end of the rollers. A lubricating film is developed between the rollers and the cup and cone and in the sliding roller-rib contact area. Very little lubricant is needed to develop and maintain these films.

As cone speed increases, so does the action of the rollers. Centrifugal force acting on the oil causes it to deflect from the roller-rib contact until that area is completely starved of lubricant. It is this starvation of lubricant at a critical contact area that limits the speed of conventionally lubricated tapered roller bearings.

Such starvation is shown in figure 11 on a 3.500″ bore bearing. At low speeds, some oil leaves the bearing between the cone rib O.D. and cage and some between the cage and I.D. of the cup. With increased speed, the amount of oil leaving the bearing between the cone rib O.D. and cage diminishes until there is almost none at 7,000 RPM cone speed.

The key to overcoming the effects of speed is the technique used to maintain lubrication of the roller-rib contact area. Tests at The Timken Company have shown that by redirecting the lubricant flow through the bearing or by introducing a second source of lubricant directly to the critical contact area, tapered roller bearings can be run at speeds to 20,000 FPM cone velocity. This is equivalent to 16,000 RPM on a 3.500″ bore bearing (over 1.4 million DN, where D = bore in mm and N = speed in RPM).

The limiting speed of a bearing depends on load, bearing design and thermal and lubrication considerations. Bearing limiting speed should therefore be determined based on the application, with special emphasis on the lubricant and the lubrication system. Below are given general guidelines on limiting speeds related to bearing lubrication. In addition to the method of lubrication, the speed capability of a given size of bearing is influenced by its internal details such as cup angle and length and number of rollers. Applications where speed may be critical for the conditions of operation should be referred to The Timken

Bearing Operating Characteristics

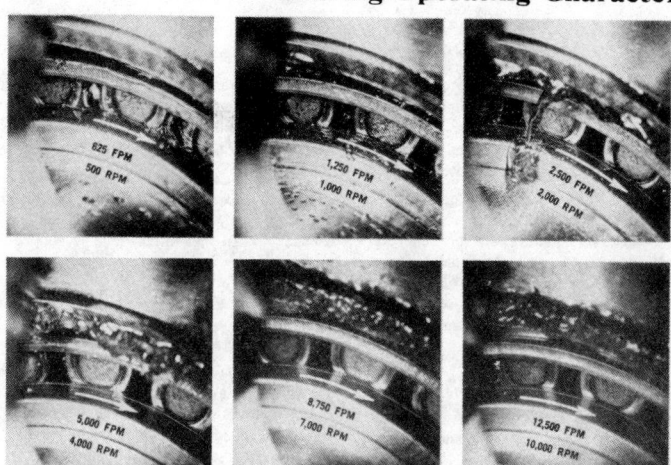

Figure 11. Effect of centrifugal force on lubricant flow.

company engineering department for review and recommendation.

Lubrication Systems

a. Grease

In general, grease lubrication may be used for continuous bearing speeds up to 2500 FPM rib speed. With careful specific lubricant selection, intermittent speed and optimization of other factors, higher speeds may be obtained. Grease lubrication obviously has very limited capacity to dissipate heat. It is also difficult to provide a continuous supply of lubricant to the roller-rib contact at high speed operation.

b. Static Oil Level

This method of lubrication is used successfully for speeds up to 3500 FPM. By providing oil circulation slots around the bearing cups, a continuous supply of lubricant to all vital bearing areas is assured. Increased contact of lubricant with the housing results in an improved means of dissipating heat over grease lubrication.

c. Static Oil Level with Splash

Splash by gears improves the heat transfer over that of an oil level system by distributing the oil over larger areas of the housing or case. Troughs or catch basins may be provided above the bearing to collect splash and direct oil flow into the bearings. Heat exchangers may be provided to maintain a constant oil temperature.

Well designed systems of this type with provisions to control the oil temperature can operate at speeds of up to 5000 FPM rib speed.

d. Forced Feed Oil Systems

Bearing speeds above 5000 FPM generally require a circulating oil system with definite rates of oil flow to each bearing. Heat exchangers for temperature control of the oil may be required.

Because centrifugal forces tend to starve the roller-rib contact area of lubricant, the main problem with running faster is still getting the lubricant to where it is needed. This may require a more sophisticated means to distribute the oil to the roller-cone rib contact to provide a continuous film of oil completely around the cone.

2. Lubricants

Lubricant properties have important effects on bearing performance. For high speed applications, it is preferable to use the lowest viscosity possible without causing a reduction in fatigue life. The elastohydrodynamic (EHD) theory is used to determine the fatigue life/viscosity relationship for particular conditions, but a guideline of 60 SUS minimum at the maximum operating temperature provides a reasonable approximation. It is desirable to utilize the lowest possible viscosity because this has an important effect on minimizing bearing torque which is manifested as heat generation.

Extreme pressure (EP) additives are very beneficial to tapered roller bearings by protecting against roller-end scoring under marginal conditions of lubrication. See pages 88 through 90 for additional discussion on lubrication specifications for tapered roller bearings.

E. Bearing Deformation

Bearing deformation is the relative elastic displacement between the cup and cone and is taken normal to the cup race. It is usually resolved into two components, radial and axial. In addition to the local deformations between the rollers and races, there is cup and housing elastic expansion and cone and shaft elastic contraction. The factors that influence deformation are the bearing, housing, shaft materials and geometry, the load and its distribution among the rollers, and the endplay or preload that is present. Under severe or abnormal loading conditions, plastic yielding or permanent deformation may occur. For these conditions, the static rating of the bearing should be considered.

Computer printouts are available for customers interested in the radial or axial deformations of bearings under radial or thrust load. In these printouts, cup and housing expansion and cone and shaft contraction are neglected for radial loads but are taken into consideration for thrust loads. The radial deformations are given for a range of radial loads while the axial deformations are given for both a range of thrust loads and a range of housing wall sections.

For complex applications such as those involving combined loads, loose fits, endplay or preload, individual analyses can be provided by The Timken Company when appropriate data is supplied by the customer.

F. Bearing Spring Rate

Bearing spring rate can be described as that factor which relates the load and elastic deformation. In the past it was considered to be a constant equal to the load divided by the deformation. However, this is not true because of the non-linearity of the deformation equation and the variability of the load zone in the bearing. In spite of this fact, there are still many applications where the bearing spring rate is not critical and a constant value can be assumed.

In the past few years bearing spring rate has become important in many applications, especially those involving dynamic considerations such as machine tool spindles. The need to know the rigidity of tapered roller bearings in either the radial or axial direction under any combined load has led to the development of more exact bearing spring rate values. These have been derived under the assumptions of zero clearance and rigid shaft and housing. Since, in general, the determination of these values can become very complex, it is recommended that The Timken Company be contacted for individual applications.

Determination of Applied Loads

PAGE

A. Gearing 36-40

    Spur 36

    Single Helical 36

    Straight Bevel 36, 37

    Zerol 36-38

    Spiral Bevel 36-38

    Hypoid 36-38

    Worm 39, 40

B. Belt and Chain Drive Factors 41

C. Shock Loads 41

D. General Formulae......................... 42

    Power Conversion Units 42

    Centrifugal Force 42

    Tractive Effort and Wheel Speed 42

The first step in selecting the correct bearing for an application is the determination of the loads on the bearings. This requires that external forces acting on the bearing be correctly evaluated. The following pages give the formulae for determining the forces that are developed by machine elements commonly encountered in bearing applications.

A. Gearing

Spur Gearing Formulae

Tangential Force, TF $= \dfrac{126{,}000 \times HP}{D_P \times RPM}$

Separating Force, $S_{TF} = TF \times \tan \phi$

Where:
  HP = Input horsepower to pinion or gear
  D_P = Pitch diameter of pinion or gear
  RPM = Speed of pinion or gear
  ϕ = Pinion or gear tooth pressure angle

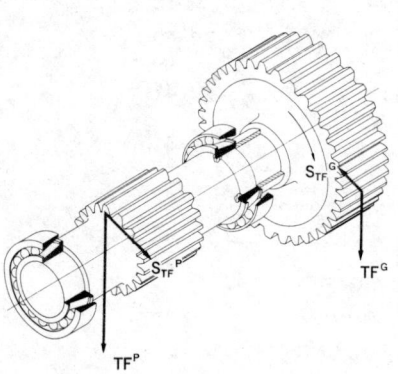

Single Helical Gearing Formulae

Tangential Force, TF $= \dfrac{126{,}000 \times HP}{D_P \times RPM}$

Separating Force, $S_{TF} = \dfrac{TF \times \tan \phi}{\cos \lambda}$

Thrust Force, $T_{TF} = TF \times \tan \lambda$

Where:
  D_P = Pitch diameter of pinion or gear
  ϕ = Pinion or gear tooth pressure angle
  λ = Pinion or gear tooth helix angle

Note: For **double helical** (herringbone) gearing, $T_{TF} = 0$

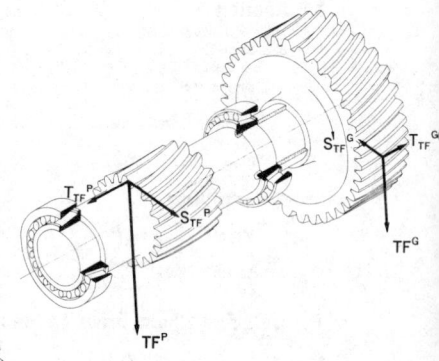

Bevel Gearing Formulae

Straight — Zerol — Spiral — Hypoid

In straight and 0° spiral angle Zerol bevel gearing, the gear forces always tend to push the pinion and gear out of mesh. In some forms of Zerol gearing, a spiral angled tooth form is used. In these, the gear forces are determined in the same manner as in spiral bevel gearing. In spiral and hypoid gearing, the direction of the thrust and radial forces depends upon the ratio, spiral angle, hand of spiral, direction of rotation and whether the gear involved is driving or driven. The hand of the spiral is determined by the observer by noting whether the tooth curvature on the near face of the gear inclines away to the left or right from the shaft axis. The pinion hand usually determines the gear combination. Direction of rotation is determined by viewing toward the apex (cone center) as indicated on page 37.

Determination of Applied Loads

In calculating the tangential force, TF, in bevel and hypoid gearing, the pinion or gear mean working diameter, D_M, is used instead of the pitch diameter, D_P.

The mean working diameter D_M is obtained as follows:

$$D_M = D_P - (b \times \sin \gamma)$$

Where:

γ = Gear or pinion pitch angle
b = Tooth length

Equations for determining thrust and radial force components for various bevel and hypoid gear problems are shown on succeeding pages.

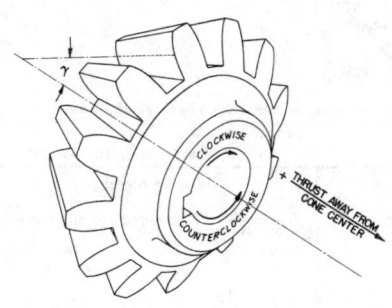

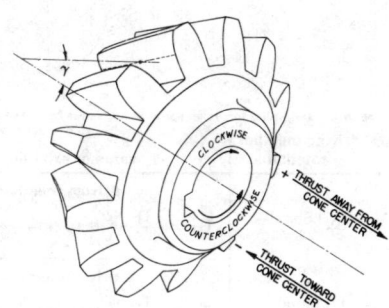

Straight Bevel and Zerol with 0° Spiral, Gearing Formulae

Pinion

Tangential Force, $TF^P = \dfrac{126,000 \times HP}{D_M^P \times RPM^P}$

Axial Thrust Force, $T_{TF}^P = TF^P \tan \phi \sin \gamma^P$

Separating Force, $S_{TF}^P = TF^P \tan \phi \cos \gamma^P$

Gear

Tangential Force, $TF^G = \dfrac{126,000 \times HP}{D_M^G \times RPM^G}$

Axial Thrust Force, $T_{TF}^G = TF^G \tan \phi \sin \gamma^G$

Separating Force, $S_{TF}^G = TF^G \tan \phi \cos \gamma^G$

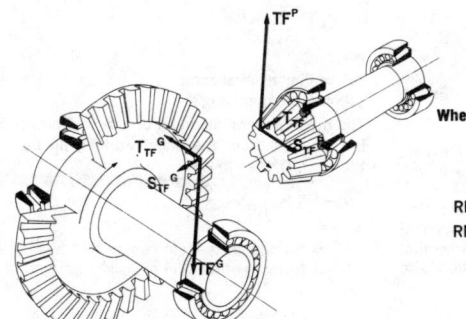

Where:

HP = Input horsepower to pinion or gear
D_M^P = Mean working diameter of pinion
D_M^G = Mean working diameter of gear
RPM^P = Speed of pinion
RPM^G = Speed of gear
ϕ = Normal tooth pressure angle
γ^P = Pitch angle of pinion
γ^G = Pitch angle of gear

Spiral Bevel, Spiral Zerol and Hypoid Gearing Formulae

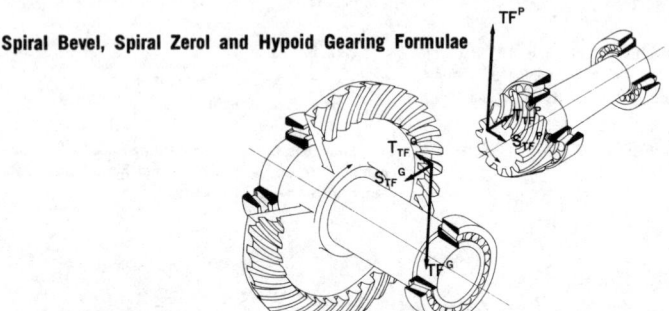

The thrust and radial forces on spiral bevel, spiral Zerol and hypoid gearing may be determined from the equations below.

driving member rotation	value of axial thrust	value of separating component
	driving member	**driving member**
RH Spiral—Clockwise	$T_{TF} = \dfrac{TF}{\cos\psi}\left(\tan\phi\sin\gamma - \sin\psi\cos\gamma\right)$	$S_{TF} = \dfrac{TF}{\cos\psi}\left(\tan\phi\cos\gamma + \sin\psi\sin\gamma\right)$
or	**driven member**	**driven member**
LH Spiral—Counterclockwise	$T_{TF} = \dfrac{TF}{\cos\psi}\left(\tan\phi\sin\gamma + \sin\psi\cos\gamma\right)$	$S_{TF} = \dfrac{TF}{\cos\psi}\left(\tan\phi\cos\gamma - \sin\psi\sin\gamma\right)$
	driving member	**driving member**
RH Spiral—Counterclockwise	$T_{TF} = \dfrac{TF}{\cos\psi}\left(\tan\phi\sin\gamma + \sin\psi\cos\gamma\right)$	$S_{TF} = \dfrac{TF}{\cos\psi}\left(\tan\phi\cos\gamma - \sin\psi\sin\gamma\right)$
or	**driven member**	**driven member**
LH Spiral—Clockwise	$T_{TF} = \dfrac{TF}{\cos\psi}\left(\tan\phi\sin\gamma - \sin\psi\cos\gamma\right)$	$S_{TF} = \dfrac{TF}{\cos\psi}\left(\tan\phi\cos\gamma + \sin\psi\sin\gamma\right)$

note: (Use the value of the angles ψ, ϕ and γ for the particular gear for which the force is determined.)

Where:
TF = Tangential force
T_{TF} = Axial thrust load
S_{TF} = Separating component
ϕ = Normal pressure angle taken on the driving side of the tooth
ψ = Spiral angle
γ = Pitch angle on spiral gears but in hypoid gears it is taken as the face angle of the pinion or root angle of the gear

In straight, Zerol and spiral bevel gearing the pinion tangential force, TF^P, is equal to the gear tangential force, TF^G. However, in hypoid gearing the tangential force on the pinion, TF^P, is determined from the following equation:

$$TF^P = \frac{TF^G \cos\psi^P}{\cos\psi^G}$$

Where:
ψ^P = Pinion spiral angle
ψ^G = Gear spiral angle

The mean working diameter of a hypoid pinion, D_M^P, is calculated from the mean working diameter of the gear, D_M^G, as follows:

$$D_M^P = D_M^G \times \frac{N^P}{N^G} \times \frac{\cos\psi^G}{\cos\psi^P}$$

Where:
N^P = Number of teeth in pinion
N^G = Number of teeth in gear

Determination of Applied Loads

Straight Worm Gearing Formulae

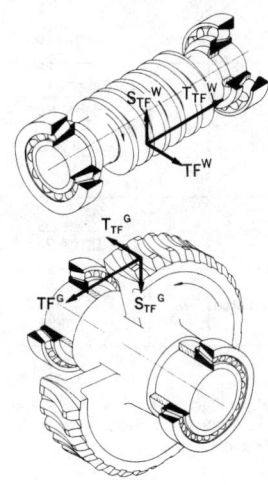

Worm Gear	symbol	equation
Tangential Force	TF^G	$\dfrac{126{,}000 \times HP \times m \times \eta}{D_P^G \times RPM^W}$ Or, $\dfrac{126{,}000 \times HP \times \eta}{D_P^G \times RPM^G}$ Or, $\dfrac{TF^W \times \eta}{\tan \lambda}$ Or, $\dfrac{TF^W}{\tan (\lambda + f)}$
Thrust Force	T_{TF}^G	$\dfrac{126{,}000 \times HP}{D_P^W \times RPM^W}$
Separating Force	S_{TF}^G	$\dfrac{TF^W \tan \phi}{\sin (\lambda + f)}$ Or, $\dfrac{TF^W \tan \phi_x}{\tan (\lambda + f)}$

Worm	symbol	equation
Tangential Force	TF^W	$\dfrac{126{,}000 \times HP}{D_P^W \times RPM^W}$
Thrust Force	T_{TF}^W	$\dfrac{126{,}000 \times HP \times \eta}{D_P^G \times RPM^G}$ Or, $\dfrac{TF^W \times \eta}{\tan \lambda}$ Or, $\dfrac{TF^W}{\tan (\lambda + f)}$
Separating Force	S_{TF}^W	$\dfrac{TF^W \tan \phi}{\sin (\lambda + f)}$ Or, $\dfrac{TF^W \tan \phi_x}{\tan (\lambda + f)}$

Where:

HP = Input horsepower to worm

D_P^W = Worm pitch diameter

D_P^G = Worm gear pitch diameter

RPM^W = RPM of worm

RPM^G = RPM of worm gear

λ = Lead angle

$\quad = Tan^{-1}\left(\dfrac{D_P^G}{m \times D_P^W}\right)$

$\quad = Tan^{-1}\left(\dfrac{Lead\ in\ inches}{\pi \times D_P^W}\right)$

m = Gearing ratio

ϕ = Normal tooth pressure angle

ϕ_x = Axial tooth pressure angle

η = Gearing efficiency, (for straight worms)

$\quad = \dfrac{\tan \lambda}{\tan (\lambda + f)}$

Where:

f = Friction angle

$$= \left(\frac{1250}{V_R}\right)^{6/10}$$

(The above is approximately correct over 40 FPM and under 1150 FPM).

V_R = Rubbing velocity in FPM

$$= \frac{D_P^W \times RPM^W}{3.82 \cos \lambda}$$

For values of V_R, under 40 FPM, $f = 8°$

For values of V_R over 1150 FPM, $f = 1° \, 4'$

Double Enveloping Worm Gearing Formulae

Worm	symbol	equation
Tangential Force	TF^W	$\dfrac{126{,}000 \times HP}{D_M^W \times RPM^W}$
Thrust Force	T_{TF}^W †	$0.98 \, TF^G$
Separating Force	S_{TF}^W	$\dfrac{0.98 \, TF^G \tan \phi}{\cos \lambda}$

Worm Gear	symbol	equation
Tangential Force	TF^G ‡	$\dfrac{126{,}000 \times HP \times m \times \eta}{D_P^G \times RPM^W}$ Or, $\dfrac{126{,}000 \times HP \times \eta}{D_P^G \times RPM^G}$
Thrust Force	T_{TF}^G	$\dfrac{126{,}000 \times HP}{D_M^W \times RPM^W}$
Separating Force	S_{TF}^G	$\dfrac{0.98 \, TF^G \tan \phi}{\cos \lambda}$

Where:

η = The manufacturers value for efficiency based on their published average helix angle

D_M^W = Worm effective pitch diameter

$$= (2 \times CD) - (0.98 \, D_P^G)$$

$$\text{Average Helix Angle} = \text{Tan}^{-1}\left[\frac{0.97}{m\left(0.03 + \dfrac{D_P^W}{D_P^G}\right)}\right]$$

CD = Distance between worm and worm gear centers

λ = Lead angle (See previous equations)

† Use this value for TF^G for bearing loading calculations on worm gear shaft.

‡ Use this value for calculating torque in subsequent gears and shafts.

Determination of Applied Loads

B. Belt and Chain Drive Factors

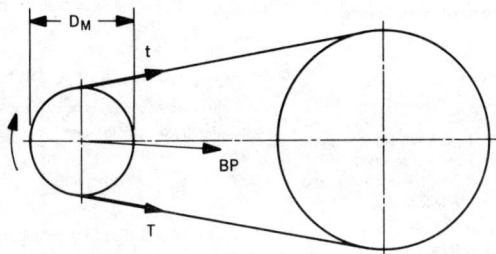

The general formula used to determine the total belt pull (T + t) from the tension "T" on the tight side and tension "t" on the slack side has received much investigation. Due to the variations of belt tightness as set up by various operators, exact formulae are difficult to establish. Most manufacturers establish effective belt pull (T − t) on the basis of HP per inch of belt width for single, double and triple ply belts at various belt velocities. The latest editions of Machinery Handbook give much data on the factors mentioned above.

Belt tensions, as they affect bearing loadings, are difficult to predict but experience has indicated that the following formula may be safely used to calculate the total pull from various types of belt and pulley designs as well as chain sprockets:

$$BP = \frac{126,000 \times HP \times F_x}{D_M \times RPM}$$

Where:

BP = The total belt or chain pull

HP = Horse power transmitted

D_M = Working outside diameter of pulleys and pitch diameter of sprockets

$$D_M \left(\begin{array}{c}\text{Standard Roller}\\\text{Chain Sprocket}\end{array}\right) = \frac{\text{Pitch (in)}}{\sin\left(\dfrac{180}{\text{No. of Teeth}}\right)}$$

F_x = Belt or chain pull factors as follows:

Type	F_x
Chains, single	1.00
Chains, double	1.25
"V" belts	1.50
Single ply belts	2.00
Double ply belts	2.50
Triple ply belts	3.00

C. Shock Loads

It is difficult to determine the exact effect that shock loading has on bearing life. The magnitude of the shock load depends on the masses of the colliding bodies and their velocity and deformation at impact. The effect on the bearing depends on how much of the shock is absorbed between the point of impact and the bearings and whether the shock load is great enough to cause bearing damage. It is also dependent on frequency and duration of shock loads. As a minimum, a suddenly applied load is equivalent to twice its static value and may be considerably more than this, depending on the velocity of impact.

Shock involves a number of variables that generally are not known nor easily determined on an application, therefore, it remains good practice to rely on experience. The Timken Company has many years of experience with all types of equipment under most severe loading conditions. It is suggested that a Timken Company sales engineer be consulted on any application involving unusual loading or service requirements.

D. General Formulae

The following conversion units and formulae will be of value to the designer:

Power Conversion Units

1 Kilowatt (Kw)
 = 1000 watts (w)
 = 1.341 horsepower (HP)
 = 737.6 pound-foot/second (lb-ft/sec)

1 Horsepower (HP) = 0.7457 Kw
 = 550 lb-ft/sec

Centrifugal Force

Unbalance in a rotating member results in a centrifugal force that affects bearing life and is calculated from the following equation:

$$CF = \frac{W \times r \times (RPM)^2}{35200}$$

Where:

W = Weight of unbalance (lb)
r = Radius to center of mass (in)

Tractive Effort and Wheel Speed

The horsepower at a driving wheel may be calculated from vehicle speed and tractive effort as follows:

$$HP = \frac{TE \times MPH}{375}$$

The wheel speed in terms of vehicle speed is given by:

$$RPM = \frac{336 \times MPH}{D_M}$$

Where:

TE = Tractive effort (lb)
MPH = Vehicle speed (miles/hour)
D_M = Mean wheel diameter (in)
 = 2 times loaded radius for rubber tires (in)

Bearing Selection

PAGE

A. **Effective Spread of Tapered Roller Bearings** . . **44, 45**

B. **Bearing Reactions** **45**
   1. Shaft on Two Supports **45**
   2. Shaft on Three or More Supports **45**

C. **Bearing Thrust Reaction** **45, 46**

D. **Dynamic Equivalent Radial Load** **46, 47**
   1. Single-Row Mounting **47**
   2. Two-Row Mounting With External Thrust **47**
   3. Two-Row Mounting No External Thrust **47**
   4. Rotating or Stationary Cone **47**

E. **Application Factors** **48**

F. **Speed Factors and Life Factors in Life Calculations** **48**
   1. Speed and Speed Factors **48**
   2. Life and Life Factors **48**

G. **Weighted Average Bearing Load, Life and Speed** **48, 49**

H. **Ratios of Bearing Life to Loads, Horsepower and Speeds** **49**

I. **Typical Bearing Analysis and Selection** **50-59**
   1. Single-Row Bearings **50-54**
      a. Radial Load Only **51**
      b. Combined Radial and Thrust Loads **52**
      c. Thrust Load Only **53**
      d. Slow Oscillating Application **54**
   2. Two-Row Bearings **55-59**
      a. Radial Load Only **55**
      b. Combined Radial and Thrust Loads - Identical Series **56**
      c. Combined Radial and Thrust Loads - Dissimilar Series **57**
   3. Weighted Average Loading and Life **58, 59**

When the external forces that act on a shaft are known or have been calculated as described in the previous section, a satisfactory tapered roller bearing can be selected. This involves establishing the bearing spread, bearing reactions and equivalent bearing loads. The final selection will depend on required mounting dimensions and required life of the bearing.

This section contains the equations and procedures for selecting bearings.

A. Effective Spread of Tapered Roller Bearings

Single-Row Bearings

Tapered roller bearings are mounted in pairs and can be mounted in one of two distinct ways, which are referred to as either **indirect** or **direct** mountings. Each of these designs will provide certain desirable operating characteristics depending upon the type of application and operation in which they are used. Although economy in the manufacture of the machine part is an important item in the selection of the mounting used, the importance of **rigidity** provided by one arrangement or the other is in many cases the determining factor. The design required to obtain this rigidity can be best illustrated by an inspection of the two arrangements.

Figure 12 shows an **indirect** mounting where the bearings are applied with the included angles of the conical members of the bearings open away from each other. In this case, the large diameter ends of the rollers of the bearings point out or away from each other.

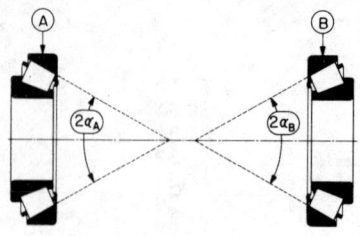

Figure 12

Figure 13 shows a **direct** mounting where the bearings are applied with the included angles of the conical members of the bearings open toward each

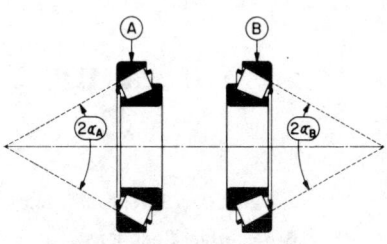

Figure 13

other. In this case the large diameter ends of the rollers of the bearings point in or toward each other.

The stability afforded by these two arrangements is best demonstrated by figure 14 which shows the indirect mounting above the shaft center line and the direct mounting below.

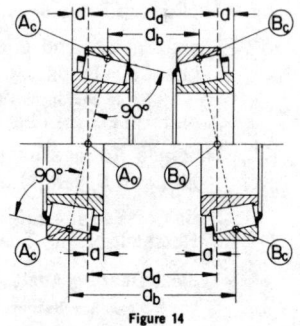

Figure 14

By striking perpendiculars "A_c-A_o" from the center of the "roller-cup" contact line, "A_c", to the shaft center line, "A_o", for bearing "A", and a similar line "B_c-B_o" for bearing "B", and using the intersections "A_o" and "B_o", the distance "a_a" is obtained.

This is the measure of bearing mounting stability. It will be observed that the actual bearing spacing "a_b" for the direct mounting is considerably greater than the actual bearing spacing "a_b" for the indirect mounting to give the same system stability.

To obtain the most accurate bearing loading, points "A_0" and "B_0" should be used as the true **effective load centers** of all resisting forces set up by the rollers in the bearing. It is about these points that all moments should be calculated when determining bearing loading and shaft stresses.

The Bearing Tables in Section 1 of The Timken Company Engineering Journal give the location of this point in all single-row bearing assemblies as a dimension (a) from the cone back face.

All typical calculations shown in this journal use the effective load centers for the bearing spacing. This distance is designated as the effective spread, a_a.

B. Bearing Reactions

1. Shaft on Two Supports

The familiar static beam equations are used to translate the external forces applied to a shaft into bearing reactions. Generally a shaft is subjected to several forces. The individual forces on each bearing are determined by taking moments about each bearing position. The various forces are then combined into a single radial resultant reaction on each bearing and one thrust reaction on the locating bearing. Forces applied are resolved into orthogonal planes for convenience. (Refer to examples for details).

Single-row tapered roller bearing supports are considered acting at the effective load centers (see figure 14). In two-row supports, the geometric center of the two-row bearing is considered to be the support except when the thrust force is great enough to seat one row. Then the effective load center of the seated row can be used as the point about which more accurate bearing load reactions should be calculated.

2. Shaft on Three or More Supports

The equations of static equilibrium are insufficient to solve for reactions on a shaft having more than two supports. Such problems are statically indeterminate.

In such problems, the elastic deflection of the shaft and the rigidity of each support significantly affect the distribution of reactions. The rigidity of the supports takes into consideration the deformation of the bearing and housing support as well as any clearance due to loose fits of the cone or cup.

If the necessary information is supplied, the bearing reactions can be calculated with reasonable accuracy. It should be kept in mind that variances in the above information may result in significant variances in the calculated reactions.

C. Bearing Thrust Reaction

A tapered roller bearing is ideally suited to carry all types of loadings—radial, thrust and any combination of both. Due to the tapered design of the bearing, any radial load will create an induced thrust reaction within the bearing. In order to prevent the races and rollers from separating or unseating, this thrust must be counteracted by an equal and opposite thrust force. Conversely, any applied external thrust creates an equal and opposite thrust reaction within the bearing. For example, with constant radial load, as external thrust is increased, the cone and cup will be pushed together until the thrust reaction within the bearing equals the applied thrust.

Thus the thrust reaction varies with each combination of radial and thrust load. This change in thrust reaction is a result of the number of rollers that are in contact with both the cone and cup and is referred to as the **load zone** of the bearing.

It is not practical to calculate exact thrust reactions for every application. The following equations are used for simplicity:

For a condition of radial load only and when the load zone is 180° or less, the thrust reaction is

$$\frac{0.47 \, F_r}{K}$$

When the load zone is greater than 180°, but less than approximately 300°, the thrust reaction is

$$\frac{0.6 \, F_r}{K}$$

These yield slightly conservative values.

Thrust on Housings and Shafts

Some applications require that the forces exerted on housing walls, backing ring flanges, cap screws, adjusting nuts, end plates and backing shoulders be known. This data will aid in the determination of stresses and estimated possible deflections of some of the more critical machine elements.

The following formulae are for the thrust force a bearing will exert on the housing and shaft where the shaft is mounted on two single-row bearings and there is **no external thrust**, T_e. The test or condition should be taken in the order shown to determine which of the two equations should be used.

Thrust On Housing With No External Thrust, T_e

Design	Condition	Thrust on Bearing "A"	Thrust on Bearing "B"
No external thrust ⒶⒷ	If $\dfrac{0.47\,F_rA}{K_A} > \dfrac{0.47\,F_rB}{K_B}$	$\dfrac{0.47\,F_rA}{K_A}$	$\dfrac{0.47\,F_rA}{K_A}$
	If $\dfrac{0.47\,F_rA}{K_A} < \dfrac{0.47\,F_rB}{K_B}$	$\dfrac{0.47\,F_rB}{K_B}$	$\dfrac{0.47\,F_rB}{K_B}$

The following formulae are for the thrust force a bearing will exert on the housing and shaft, where the shaft is mounted on two single-row bearings and there is **external thrust**, T_e. The test or condition should be taken in the order shown to decide which of the three equations should be used.

Thrust On Housing With External Thrust, T_e

Design	Condition	Thrust on Bearing "A"	Thrust on Bearing "B"
With external thrust ⒶⒷ	If $\dfrac{0.47\,F_rA}{K_A} > \dfrac{0.47\,F_rB}{K_B} + T_e$	$\dfrac{0.47\,F_rA}{K_A}$	$\dfrac{0.47\,F_rA}{K_A} - T_e$
	If $\dfrac{0.6\,F_rA}{K_A} > \dfrac{0.47\,F_rB}{K_B} + T_e$	$\dfrac{0.6\,F_rA}{K_A}$	$\dfrac{0.6\,F_rA}{K_A} - T_e$
	If $\dfrac{0.6\,F_rA}{K_A} < \dfrac{0.47\,F_rB}{K_B} + T_e$	$\dfrac{0.47\,F_rB}{K_B} + T_e$	$\dfrac{0.47\,F_rB}{K_B}$

D. Dynamic Equivalent Radial Load

The dynamic equivalent radial load on a bearing is defined as that radial load only, which, if applied to a bearing, would give the same life as that which the bearing will obtain under the actual condition of combined loading.

The radial rating of the bearing is based on radial loads only. In order to determine life for combined loading where the thrust exceeds the thrust reaction at 180° load zone, it becomes necessary to calculate a dynamic equivalent radial load.

Using bearing thrust reactions as discussed above, the following expressions yield dynamic equivalent radial loads for Timken tapered roller bearings:

$$P = X\,F_r + Y\,F_a$$

Where:
   P = Dynamic equivalent radial load
   X = Radial factor
   Y = Thrust factor
   F_r = Radial load
   F_a = Total thrust load

The following gives the dynamic equivalent radial load formulae in a convenient form for shafts mounted on single and two-row tapered roller bearings.

Dynamic Equivalent Radial Load Formulae

1. Single-Row Mounting (With External Thrust, T_e, on Bearing A)

Design	Dynamic Equivalent Radial Load Formulae	
	$P_A = 0.4\, F_rA + K_A \left(\dfrac{0.47\, F_rB}{K_B} + T_e \right)$	If $P_A < F_rA$, then use $P_A = F_rA$
	$P_B = 0.4\, F_rB + K_B \left(\dfrac{0.47\, F_rA}{K_A} - T_e \right)$	If $P_B < F_rB$, then use $P_B = F_rB$

The above equations should be used first to determine the dynamic equivalent radial loads on bearings A and B. If these yield values less than the radial reactions, then the radial reactions should be used to calculate bearing life.

2. Two-Row Mounting (With External Thrust, T_e)

IDENTICAL BEARING SERIES, $K_A = K_B$

Design	Condition	Dynamic Equivalent Radial Load Formulae
	$T_e \leq \dfrac{0.6\, F_r}{K_A}$	$P_A = 0.5\, F_r + 0.83\, K_A\, T_e$
		$P_B = 0.5\, F_r - 0.83\, K_A\, T_e$
	$T_e > \dfrac{0.6\, F_r}{K_A}$	$P_A = 0.4\, F_r + K_A\, T_e$
		$P_B = 0$

DISSIMILAR BEARING SERIES, $K_A \neq K_B$

Design	Condition	Dynamic Equivalent Radial Load Formulae
	$T_e \leq \dfrac{0.6\, F_r}{K_A}$	$P_A = \dfrac{K_A}{K_A + K_B} (F_r + 1.67\, K_B\, T_e)$
		$P_B = \dfrac{K_B}{K_A + K_B} (F_r - 1.67\, K_A\, T_e)$
	$T_e > \dfrac{0.6\, F_r}{K_A}$	$P_A = 0.4\, F_r + K_A\, T_e$
		$P_B = 0$

F_r is the radial load on the two-row assembly. The **single-row** basic dynamic radial load rating, C(90), is to be applied when calculating life based on the above formulae.

3. Two-Row Mounting (No External Thrust)

Under this loading condition no dynamic equivalent radial load is calculated. Therefore, the bearing load, F_r, is that applied to the two-row assembly and the **two-row** basic dynamic radial load rating, C(90)₂, is used to calculate life.

4. Rotating or Stationary Cone

All of the calculations for selection of bearings illustrate rotating cone applications only. The rotation factor for a stationary cone is 1.0, the same as it is for a rotating cone. Therefore the dynamic equivalent radial load formulae for stationary cone applications are the same as they are for rotating cone applications.

E. Application Factors

On some types of equipment it is known from experience that the service conditions are generally more severe than theoretically anticipated. In such cases application factors have been adopted to reflect the actual load or actual condition as they affect bearing life.

The application factor is a factor by which the bearing equivalent load is multiplied for fatigue life determination.

As more information becomes available from Timken Research, field tests and additional experience, these application factors will be replaced by more exact analyses of environmental influences on bearing life.

Application factors based on field experience for various types of equipment are tabulated in the Reference Tables.

F. Speed Factors and Life Factors in Life Calculations

1. Speed and Speed Factors

The speed of a bearing is the rotational speed of one bearing race relative to the other bearing race. The speed factor is a factor by which the basic rating at 500 RPM is multiplied to obtain the rating at the prevailing speed. It is defined by:

$$SF = \left(\frac{500}{S}\right)^{3/10}$$

Where:

SF = Speed factor
S = Relative RPM of cone/cup

Speed factors for speeds up to 35,000 RPM are tabulated in the Reference Tables.

2. Life and Life Factors

The life factor is a factor by which the basic dynamic load rating at 3000 hours L_{10} is divided to obtain the rating for a required number of hours. It is defined by:

$$LF = \left(\frac{L_{10}}{3000}\right)^{3/10}$$

Where:

LF = Life factor
L_{10} = Bearing life (hr)

Life factors for 100 hours to 100,000 hours are tabulated in the Reference Tables.

G. Weighted Average Bearing Load, Life and Speed

On many applications the bearings are subjected to variable conditions of loading. Under such conditions, the selection is many times made on the basis of maximum load and speed. However, a more economical selection may be made by analysing the loading cycle to determine the weighted averages of load, speed and time. The averages are weighted according to the relationship of load and speed to life as discussed above.

Doubling the load would reduce the life to 10%, whereas doubling the speed would reduce the life to 50%. We cannot safely select the bearing on the basis of average loading but we should select it on the basis of weighted average loading which will properly take into account variations in speed, load and percentage of time during which the variable loads and speeds occur during a loading cycle.

The available life of a bearing operating at a given speed may be used up by a heavy load applied for a short time or by a light load applied for a long time. Each period of load application uses up a certain portion of the bearing life, leaving a reduced number of hours for subsequent loads.

The following are the weighted average formulae:

General Case
Variable Loading — Variable Speed —
Variable % Time

$$F_{wt} @ 500RPM = F_{max}\left[T_1\left(\frac{F_1}{F_{max} \cdot SF_1}\right)^{10/3} \right.$$

$$+ T_2\left(\frac{F_2}{F_{max} \cdot SF_2}\right)^{10/3}$$

$$\left. + \ldots T_n\left(\frac{F_n}{F_{max} \cdot SF_n}\right)^{10/3}\right]^{3/10}$$

Variable Loading — Variable Speed —
Variable % Time

$$L_{10} = \frac{1}{\dfrac{T_1}{L_{10_1}} + \dfrac{T_2}{L_{10_2}} + \ldots \dfrac{T_n}{L_{10_n}}}$$

Variable Loading — Constant Speed — Variable % Time

$$F_{wt} = F_{max} \left[T_1 \left(\frac{F_1}{F_{max}} \right)^{10/3} + T_2 \left(\frac{F_2}{F_{max}} \right)^{10/3} \right.$$

$$\left. + \ldots T_n \left(\frac{F_n}{F_{max}} \right)^{10/3} \right]^{3/10}$$

Constant Loading — Variable Speed — Variable % Time

$$S_{av} = \frac{S_1 t_1 + S_2 t_2 + \ldots S_n t_n}{t_t}$$

Uniformly Increasing Load — Constant Speed

$$F_{wt} = F_{min} + 0.645 \, (F_{max} - F_{min})$$

Constant Loading — Constant or Average Speed

$$F_{wt} \text{ @ 500RPM} = \frac{F}{SF}$$

In the above:

L_{10} = Bearing life (hr)

F = Bearing load (F_1, F_2 .. F_n are the magnitudes of bearing loading during the loading cycle)

F_{max} = Maximum bearing load during a loading cycle

F_{min} = Minimum bearing load during a loading cycle

S = Bearing speed (RPM), (S_1, S_2 .. S_n are the speeds during which F_1, F_2 .. F_n occur)

SF = Speed factor, (SF_1, SF_2 .. SF_n are the speed factors during which F_1, F_2 .. F_n occur)

T_1, T_2 .. T_n = The fraction of time in a loading cycle which F_1, F_2 .. F_n occur

t_1, t_2 .. t_n = Actual time in hours during which speeds S_1, S_2 .. S_n occur

t_t = Total number of hours in loading cycle

In applications where bearings are subjected to cyclic loading involving varying load direction, oscillation and such, a Timken Company sales engineer should be consulted.

H. Ratios of Bearing Life to Loads, Horsepower and Speeds

In applications subjected to variable conditions of loading, once bearing life is calculated for one condition, life for any other condition can conveniently be calculated by taking the ratio of certain variables. The following relationships hold under the specific conditions:

Condition	Equation
Variable Load and Variable Speed	$L_2 = L_1 \left(\frac{P_1}{P_2} \right)^{10/3} \left(\frac{S_1}{S_2} \right)$
Variable Horsepower and Variable Speed	$L_2 = L_1 \left(\frac{HP_1}{HP_2} \right)^{10/3} \left(\frac{S_2}{S_1} \right)^{7/3}$
Constant Load and Variable Speed	$L_2 = L_1 \left(\frac{S_1}{S_2} \right)$
Constant Horsepower and Variable Speed	$L_2 = L_1 \left(\frac{S_2}{S_1} \right)^{7/3}$
Variable Load and Constant Speed	$L_2 = L_1 \left(\frac{P_1}{P_2} \right)^{10/3}$
Variable Horsepower and Constant Speed	$L_2 = L_1 \left(\frac{HP_1}{HP_2} \right)^{10/3}$

Where:

HP = Horsepower
P = Dynamic equivalent radial load
L = L_{10} (hr)
S = Speed (RPM)

If ratios of life factors instead of L_{10} are desired, the ratios in the above equations with appropriate exponents should be taken to the 3/10 power. For example:

$$LF_2 = LF_1 \left(\frac{P_1}{P_2} \right) \left(\frac{S_1}{S_2} \right)^{3/10}$$

and, $$LF_2 = LF_1 \left(\frac{HP_1}{HP_2} \right) \left(\frac{S_2}{S_1} \right)^{7/10}$$

I. Typical Bearing Analysis and Selection

The designer must determine the magnitude of the radial and thrust loads, estimate the required hours of life of the bearing, and define the conditions of operation. Then the bearing selection is made from the basic dynamic load ratings established by The Timken Company's research and experience. In general, where thrust loads predominate in an application, bearings with lower K-factors should be selected.

The basic dynamic load ratings, both radial, C(90), and thrust, CA(90), for Timken bearings are published for a speed of 500 RPM and an L_{10} of 3000 hours. For various conditions of operation involving radial load (F_r) and thrust load (F_a), the following formulae apply:

$$C(90)R = \frac{P \times LF \times AF}{SF}$$

Where:

C(90)R = Required dynamic radial load rating at 500 RPM and 3000 hours L_{10}

P = Dynamic equivalent radial load from a combination of radial and thrust loads

LF = Life factor, corresponding to the desired L_{10} hours of life expectancy of the bearing, selected from the Reference Tables

AF = Application factor, compensating for characteristics of operating conditions, such as shock, continuous duty and inequality of loading, selected from the Reference Tables

SF = Speed factor, depending upon the operating speed in RPM, selected from the Reference Tables

Where only thrust loads are involved, the bearing may be selected on the basis of thrust load only and the above equation becomes:

$$CA(90)R = \frac{F_a \times LF \times AF}{SF}$$

Where:

CA(90)R = Required dynamic thrust load rating at 500 RPM and 3000 hours L_{10}

F_a = Total thrust load

After the value of C(90)R has been calculated, the specific bearing may be selected from the tables. The cone bore of the bearing is usually established by the strength and stiffness requirements of the shaft, hence bearing sizes are listed according to the size of the cone bore.

The bearing selected may have a basic dynamic radial load rating slightly different from the required dynamic radial load rating. The L_{10} expectancy of the selected bearing may then be determined by first calculating the **actual** life factor value from:

$$LF = \frac{C(90) \times SF}{P \times AF}$$

Where:

P = The calculated dynamic equivalent radial load on the bearing

In the case where only thrust loads are involved:

$$LF = \frac{CA(90) \times SF}{F_a \times AF}$$

The life factor table in the Reference Tables then gives the relationship between this L_{10} expectancy and the life factor, LF. As an alternative, the following formula can be used to determine the life instead of referring to the life factor tables:

$$L_{10} = (LF)^{10/3} \times 3000 \text{ Hours}$$

Various combinations of bearing types, installation and load applications are illustrated on pages 51 through 59 and are classified as follows:

(1) Single-Row Bearings

a. Radial Load Only
b. Combined Radial and Thrust Loads
c. Thrust Load Only
d. Slow Oscillating Application

(2) Two-Row Bearings

a. Radial Load Only
b. Combined Radial and Thrust Loads - Identical Series
c. Combined Radial and Thrust Loads - Dissimilar Series

(3) Weighted Average Loading and Life

Selection of Single-Row Vs. Two-Row Bearings

When the rating of a single-row bearing is insufficient for a specific bearing position, a two-row bearing is selected.

If the distance between two bearing positions is large and a satisfactory initial bearing setting cannot be made to compensate for thermal expansions and contractions between two single-row bearings, then two-row bearings are applied with one bearing position fixed while the other is allowed free axial float.

Some applications also require maximum rigidity, in which case two-row bearings are used.

Bearing Selection

1. Single-Row Bearings

a. Radial Load Only

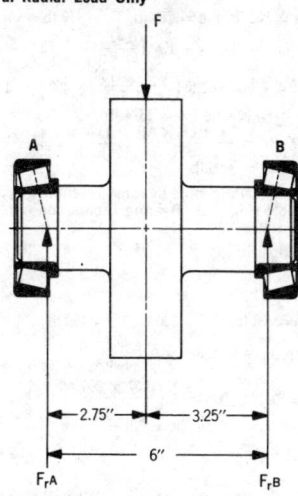

Given Conditions

Application—Support Roller
Bearing Mounting—Direct, with unequal spacing from load
Radial Load, $F = 1500$ lb
Thrust Load, $T_e = 0$
Speed, $S = 3500$ RPM
Required Life = 10,000 hr, L_{10}
Desired Shaft Diameter = 1.375 in, minimum

Analysis

Life Factor, $LF = \left(\dfrac{10,000}{3,000}\right)^{3/10} = 1.435$

Application Factor, $AF = 1.0$ (assumed)

Speed Factor, $SF = \left(\dfrac{500}{3500}\right)^{3/10} = 0.558$

Load Per Bearing,

$F_{rA} = \dfrac{1500 \times 3.25}{6} = 812$ lb

$F_{rB} = \dfrac{1500 \times 2.75}{6} = 688$ lb

For preliminary check, assume $K_A = K_B = 1.50$

SELECTION (based on assumed K-factor)

Bearing "A"

$F_{rA} = 812$ lb, $F_{rB} = 688$ lb, $T_e = 0$

$P_{A(trial)} = 0.4\, F_{rA} + K_A\left(\dfrac{0.47\, F_{rB}}{K_B} + T_e\right)$

$\quad = 0.4 \times 812 + 1.5\left(\dfrac{0.47 \times 688}{1.5} + 0\right) = 648$ lb

$P_A < F_{rA}$ ∴ Use $P_A = F_{rA} = 812$ lb

$C(90)R_A = \dfrac{P_A \times LF \times AF}{SF} = \dfrac{812 \times 1.435 \times 1.0}{0.558}$

$\quad = 2088$ lb

Select 1.375 in bore bearing assembly, type TS, refer to single-row Bearing Tables, cone LM48548, cup LM48510.
$C(90) = 2140$ lb, $K = 1.55$

Bearing "B"

$F_{rB} = 688$ lb, $F_{rA} = 812$ lb, $T_e = 0$

$P_{B(trial)} = 0.4\, F_{rB} + K_B\left(\dfrac{0.47\, F_{rA}}{K_A} + T_e\right)$

$\quad = 0.4 \times 688 + 1.5\left(\dfrac{0.47 \times 812}{1.55} + 0\right) = 645$ lb

$P_B < F_{rB}$ ∴ Use $P_B = F_{rB} = 688$ lb

$C(90)R_B = \dfrac{P_B \times LF \times AF}{SF} = \dfrac{688 \times 1.435 \times 1.0}{0.558}$

$\quad = 1769$ lb

Select 1.375 in bore bearing assembly, type TS, refer to single-row Bearing Tables, cone LM48548, cup LM48510.
$C(90) = 2140$ lb, $K = 1.55$

SELECTION RECHECK (based on actual K-factor)

Bearing "A"

$P_{A(actual)} = 0.4 \times 812 + 1.55\left(\dfrac{0.47 \times 688}{1.55} + 0\right)$

$\quad = 648$ lb

$P_A < F_{rA}$ ∴ use $P_A = 812$ lb

$LF_A = \dfrac{C(90) \times SF}{P_A \times AF} = \dfrac{2140 \times 0.558}{812 \times 1.0} = 1.471$

For LF of 1.471—$L_{10} = 10,850$ hr, this is satisfactory.

Bearing "B"

$P_{B(actual)} = 0.4 \times 688 + 1.55\left(\dfrac{0.47 \times 812}{1.55} + 0\right)$

$\quad = 657$ lb

$P_B < F_{rB}$ ∴ use $P_B = F_{rB} = 688$ lb

$LF_B = \dfrac{C(90)_B \times SF}{P_B \times AF} = \dfrac{2140 \times 0.558}{688 \times 1.0} = 1.736$

For LF of 1.736—$L_{10} = 18,850$ hr, this is satisfactory.

b. Combined Radial and Thrust Loads

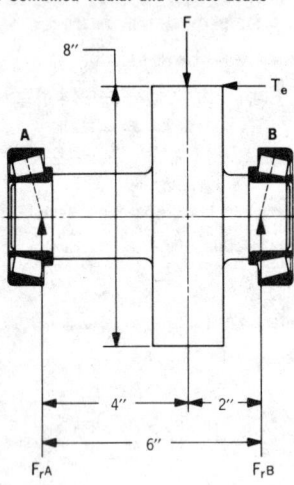

Given Conditions

Application—Support Roller
Bearing Mounting—Direct, with unequal spacing from load
Radial Load, $F = 1500$ lb
Thrust Load, $T_e = 450$ lb
Speed, $S = 3500$ RPM
Support Roller O.D. $= 8$ in
Required Life $= 10,000$ hr, L_{10}
Desired Shaft Diameter $= 1.375$ in

Analysis

Life Factor, $LF = \left(\dfrac{10,000}{3,000}\right)^{3/10} = 1.435$

Application Factor, $AF = 1.0$ (assumed)

Speed Factor, $SF = \left(\dfrac{500}{3500}\right)^{3/10} = 0.558$

Load Per Bearing,

$F_{rA} = \dfrac{1500 \times 2}{6} + \dfrac{450 \times 8}{2 \times 6} = 800$ lb

$F_{rB} = \dfrac{1500 \times 4}{6} - \dfrac{450 \times 8}{2 \times 6} = 700$ lb

For preliminary check assume $K_A = K_B = 1.5$

SELECTION (based on assumed K-factor)

Bearing "A"

$F_{rA} = 800$ lb, $F_{rB} = 700$ lb, $T_e = 450$ lb

$P_{A\,(trial)} = 0.4 F_{rA} + K_A \left(\dfrac{0.47\,F_{rB}}{K_B} + T_e\right)$

$= 0.4 \times 800 + 1.5 \left(\dfrac{0.47 \times 700}{1.5} + 450\right) = 1324$ lb

$P_A > F_{rA} \therefore$ Use $P_A = 1324$ lb

$C(90)R_A = \dfrac{P_A \times LF \times AF}{SF} = \dfrac{1324 \times 1.435 \times 1.0}{0.558}$
$= 3405$ lb

Select 1.375 in bore bearing assembly, Type TS, refer to single-row Bearing Tables, cone HM88649, cup HM88610.
$C(90) = 3190$ lb, $K = 1.07$

Bearing "B"

$F_{rB} = 700$ lb, $F_{rA} = 800$ lb, $T_e = 450$ lb

$P_{B\,(trial)} = 0.4 F_{rB} + K_B \left(\dfrac{0.47\,F_{rA}}{K_A} - T_e\right)$

$= 0.4 \times 700 + 1.5 \left(\dfrac{0.47 \times 800}{1.07} - 450\right) = 132$ lb

$P_B < F_{rB} \therefore$ Use $P_B = F_{rB} = 700$ lb

$C(90)R_B = \dfrac{P_B \times LF \times AF}{SF} = \dfrac{700 \times 1.435 \times 1.0}{0.558}$
$= 1800$ lb

Select same part number as selected for bearing "A" for reasons of economy.

SELECTION RECHECK (based on actual K-factor)

Bearing "A"

$P_{A\,(actual)} = 0.4 \times 800 + 1.07 \left(\dfrac{0.47 \times 700}{1.07} + 450\right)$

$= 1130$ lb

$LF_A = \dfrac{C(90)_A \times SF}{P_A \times AF} = \dfrac{3190 \times 0.558}{1130 \times 1.0} = 1.575$

For LF of $1.575 - L_{10} = 13,650$ hr, this is satisfactory.

Bearing "B"

$P_{B\,(actual)} = 0.4 \times 700 + 1.07 \left(\dfrac{0.47 \times 800}{1.07} - 450\right)$

$= 175$ lb

$P_B < F_{rB} \therefore$ Use $P_B = F_{rB} = 700$ lb

$LF_B = \dfrac{C(90)_B \times SF}{P_B \times AF} = \dfrac{3190 \times 0.558}{700 \times 1.0} = 2.543$

For LF of $2.543 - L_{10} = 67,350$ hr, this is satisfactory.

Single-Row Bearings (continued)

c. Thrust Load Only

(Calculate the bearing loading and use the basic dynamic thrust load rating of the bearing.)

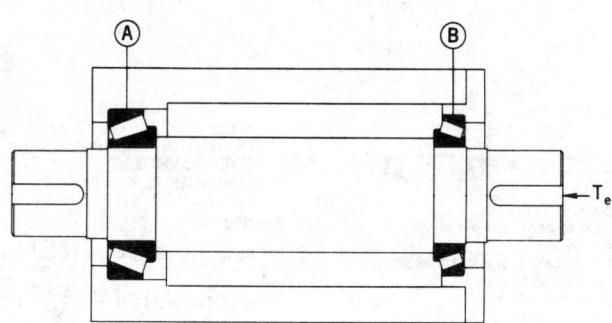

Given Conditions

Application—Plastic Extruder
Bearing Mounting—Single-Row, direct mounting
Thrust Load, $T_e = 62,500$ lb
Speed, $S = 60$ RPM
Required Life = 15,000 hr, L_{10}
Desired Shaft Diameter = 7.500 in
Direct Coupled Driven

Analysis

Life Factor, $LF = \left(\dfrac{15,000}{3,000}\right)^{3/10} = 1.621$

Application Factor, $AF = 1.0$ (assumed)

Speed Factor, $SF = \left(\dfrac{500}{60}\right)^{3/10} = 1.889$

Load Per Bearing,

$F_rA = F_rB = 0$

$F_aA = T_e = 62,500$ lb

SELECTION

Bearing "A"

$CA(90)R_A = \dfrac{F_aA \times LF \times AF}{SF} = \dfrac{62,500 \times 1.621 \times 1.0}{1.889}$

$= 53,633$ lb

Select 7.500 in bore bearing assembly, type TS, refer to single-row Bearing Tables, cone HH840249, cup HH840210.

$CA(90) = 54,500$ lb, $K = 1.01$

$LF_A = \dfrac{CA(90)_A \times SF}{F_aA \times AF} = \dfrac{54,500 \times 1.889}{62,500 \times 1.0} = 1.647$

For LF of $1.647 - L_{10} = 15,825$ hr, this is satisfactory.

Bearing "B"

Select 7.500 in bore bearing assembly type TS, refer to single-row Bearing Tables. Since there is theoretically no load on this mating bearing, it is selected on basis of economy and size in proportion to opposing bearing, cone 93750, cup 93125.

$CA(90) = 29,400$ lb, $K = 1.12$

d. Slow Oscillating Application

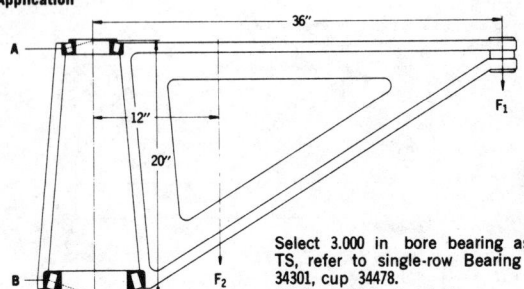

Given Conditions

Application—Jib Crane
Arrangement of bearings—As shown
Load $F_1 = 6000$ lb
Load $F_2 = 1800$ lb = crane dead weight
Speed, S = Slow oscillation
Desired mast diameters
    Bearing A = 3.000 in
    Bearing B = 5.750 in

Analysis

Since this type of application operates with a slow oscillatory motion and the service is usually intermittent, experience indicates that selecting bearings on a fatigue basis is unnecessary. Therefore the bearing selections are normally based on a dynamic equivalent radial load which is not to exceed 4 times C(90).

Load Per Bearing:

$$F_rA = F_rB = \frac{6000 \times 36}{20} + \frac{1800 \times 12}{20} = 11,880 \text{ lb}$$

$$T_e = F_1 + F_2 = 6000 + 1800 = 7800 \text{ lb}$$

SELECTION (based on assumed K-factor)

Bearing "A"

Trial check to establish dynamic equivalent radial load formula
Assume $K_A = K_B = 1.50$

$$P_A = 0.4 \times F_rA + K_A \left(\frac{0.47 \, F_rB}{K_B} - T_e \right)$$

$$= 0.4 \times 11,880 + 1.50 \left(\frac{0.47 \times 11,880}{1.50} - 7800 \right) = 1364 \text{ lb}$$

$P_A < F_rA$ ∴ Use $P_A = F_rA = 11,880$ lb

$$C(90)R_A = \frac{P_A}{4} = \frac{11,880}{4} = 2970 \text{ lb}$$

Select 3.000 in bore bearing assembly, type TS, refer to single-row Bearing Tables, cone 34301, cup 34478.
C(90) = 4250 lb, K = 1.30

Bearing "B"

$$P_{B \text{ (trial)}} = 0.4 \, F_rB + K_B \left(\frac{0.47 \, F_rA}{K_A} + T_e \right)$$

$$= 0.4 \times 11,880 + 1.50 \left(\frac{0.47 \times 11,880}{1.30} + 7800 \right) = 22,895 \text{ lb}$$

$$C(90)R_B = \frac{P_B}{4} = \frac{22,895}{4} = 5724 \text{ lb}$$

Select 5.750 in bore bearing assembly, type TS, refer to single-row Bearing Tables, cone 36690, cup 36620.
C(90) = 9700 lb, K = 1.59

SELECTION RECHECK (based on actual K-factor)

Bearing "A"

$P_{A(actual)}$

$$= 0.4 \times 11,880 + 1.30 \left(\frac{0.47 \times 11,880}{1.59} - 7800 \right)$$

$$= 823 \text{ lb}$$

$P_A < F_rA$ ∴ $P_A = F_rA = 11,880$ lb

$\dfrac{P_A}{C(90)A} = \dfrac{11880}{4250} = 2.80$, this is satisfactory.

Bearing "B"

$P_{B \text{ (actual)}}$

$$= 0.4 \times 11,880 + 1.59 \left(\frac{0.47 \times 11,880}{1.30} + 7800 \right)$$

$$= 23,983 \text{ lb}$$

$\dfrac{P_B}{C(90)B} = \dfrac{23,983}{9700} = 2.47$, this is satisfactory.

Bearing Selection

2. Two-Row Bearings

a. Radial Load Only
(Identical series bearings)

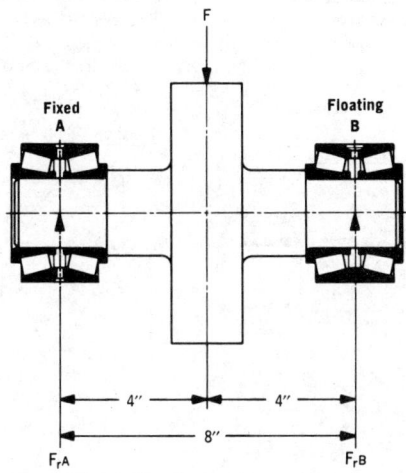

Given Conditions

Application—Support Roller
Bearing Mounting—Two-row with equal spacing
from bearing centers to load
Radial Load, F = 2900 lb
Speed, S = 2750 RPM
Required Life = 15,000 hr, L₁₀
Desired Shaft Diameter = 1.8125 in, minimum

Analysis

Life Factor, $LF = \left(\dfrac{15,000}{3,000}\right)^{3/10} = 1.621$

Application Factor, $AF = 1.0$ (assumed)

Speed Factor, $SF = \left(\dfrac{500}{2750}\right)^{3/10} = 0.600$

Load Per Bearing,

$F_rA = F_rB = \dfrac{2900 \times 4}{8} = 1450$ lb

SELECTION

Bearings "A" and Bearing "B"

Since $F_rA = F_rB$, select same bearing series for positions "A" and "B".
$P_A = P_B = F_rA = F_rB = 1450$ lb
$C(90)R_A = C(90)R_B = \dfrac{P_A \times LF \times AF}{SF} = \dfrac{P_B \times LF \times AF}{SF}$
$= \dfrac{1450 \times 1.621 \times 1.0}{0.600} = 3917$ lb

Bearing "A"

Select 1.8125 in bore bearing assembly, type TDO, refer to two-row Bearing Tables, cone 18690, cup 18620D.

$C(90)_{2A} = 3990$ lb, K = 1.56
$LF_A = \dfrac{C(90)_{2A} \times SF}{P_A \times AF} = \dfrac{3990 \times 0.600}{1450 \times 1.0} = 1.651$
For LF of 1.651 — L₁₀=15,950 hr, this is satisfactory.

Bearing "B"

Select 1.8125 in bore bearing assembly, type TDODC, refer to two-row Bearing Tables, cone 18690, cup 18620DC.
$C(90)_2 = 3990$ lb, K = 1.56
$LF_B = LF_A = 1.651$, this is satisfactory.

b. Combined Radial and Thrust Loads

(Identical series bearings at fixed position.)

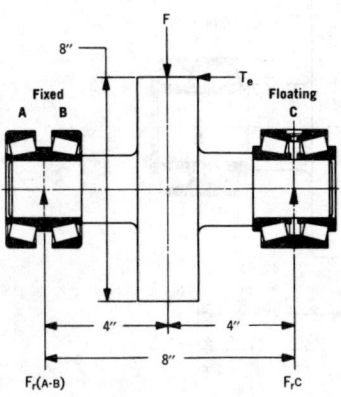

Given Conditions

Application—Support Roller
Bearing Mounting—Two-row, with equal spacing
  from bearing centers to load
Radial Load, F = 2000 lb
Thrust Load, T_e = 600 lb
Speed, S = 2500 RPM
Required Life = 15,000 hr, L_{10}
Support Roller O.D. = 8 in
Desired shaft diameters
  = 2.000 in, minimum at position "A-B"
  = 1.500 in, minimum at position "C"

Analysis

Life Factor, $LF = \left(\dfrac{15,000}{3000}\right)^{3/10} = 1.621$

Application Factor, AF = 1.0 (assumed)

Speed Factor, $SF = \left(\dfrac{500}{2500}\right)^{3/10} = 0.617$

Load Per Bearing,

$$F_r(A\text{-}B) = \frac{2000 \times 4}{8} + \frac{600 \times 8}{2 \times 8} = 1300 \text{ lb}$$

$$F_rC = \frac{2000 \times 4}{8} - \frac{600 \times 8}{2 \times 8} = 700 \text{ lb}$$

SELECTION (based on assumed K-factor)

Bearings "A" and "B" (fixed position)

Trial check to establish dynamic equivalent radial load formula

T_e = 600 lb, assume $K_A = K_B = 1.50$

then, $\dfrac{0.6\, F_r(A\text{-}B)}{K} = \dfrac{0.6 \times 1300}{1.50} = 520$ lb

$T_e > \dfrac{0.6\, F_r(A\text{-}B)}{K} \therefore P_A = 0.4\, F_r(A\text{-}B) + K_A\, T_e$

and $P_B = 0$

$P_A = 0.4 \times 1300 + 1.50 \times 600 = 1420$ lb

$C(90)R_A = \dfrac{P_A \times LF \times AF}{SF} = \dfrac{1420 \times 1.621 \times 1.0}{0.617}$

$= 3731$ lb

Select 2.1654 in bore bearing assembly, two type TS, refer to single-row Bearing Tables, cone JLM506849, cup JLM506810.

$C(90) = 3790$ lb, K = 1.45

SELECTION RECHECK (based on actual K-factor)

$\dfrac{0.6 \times F_r(A\text{-}B)}{K_A} = \dfrac{0.6 \times 1300}{1.45} = 538$ lb $< T_e$

$P_A = 0.4 \times 1300 + 1.45 \times 600 = 1390$ lb

$LF_A = \dfrac{C(90)_A \times SF}{P_A \times AF} = \dfrac{3790 \times 0.617}{1390 \times 1.0} = 1.682$

For LF of 1.682—L_{10}=16,975 hr, this is satisfactory.

Bearing "C" (floating position)

Since there is no external thrust imposed on this bearing, $P_C = F_rC = 700$ lb

$C(90)R_C = \dfrac{P_C \times LF \times AF}{SF} = \dfrac{700 \times 1.621 \times 1.0}{0.617}$

$= 1839$ lb

Select 1.500 in bore bearing assembly, type TDODC, refer to two-row Bearing Tables, cone 13685, cup 13621DC.
$C(90)_2 = 4250$ lb, K = 1.45

$LF_C = \dfrac{C(90)_{2C} \times SF}{P_C \times AF} = \dfrac{4250 \times 0.617}{700 \times 1.0} = 3.746$

This is satisfactory.

Bearing Selection

2. Two-Row Bearings (continued)

c. Combined Radial and Thrust Load
(Dissimilar series bearings at fixed position.)

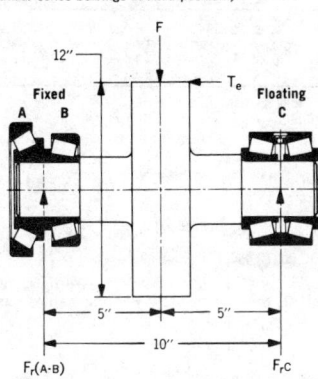

Given Conditions

Application—Support Roller
Bearing Mounting—Two-row with equal spacing from bearing centers to load. (Bearing row "A" and "B" at fixed position are dissimilar series. Bearing "C" at floating position is a two-row bearing.)
Radial Load, $F = 2500$ lb
Thrust Load, $T_e = 750$ lb
Speed, $S = 2400$ RPM
Required Life = 15,000 hr, L_{10}
Support Roller O.D. = 12 in
Desired Shaft Diameters
  = 2.500 in, minimum at position "A-B"
  = 1.500 in, minimum at position "C"

Analysis

Life Factor, $LF = \left(\dfrac{15,000}{3000}\right)^{3/10} = 1.621$

Application Factor, $AF = 1.0$ (assumed)

Speed Factor, $SF = \left(\dfrac{500}{2400}\right)^{3/10} = 0.625$

Load Per Bearing,

$F_r(A-B) = \dfrac{2500 \times 5}{10} + \dfrac{750 \times 12}{2 \times 10} = 1700$ lb

$F_rC = \dfrac{2500 \times 5}{10} - \dfrac{750 \times 12}{2 \times 10} = 800$ lb

---

SELECTION (based on assumed K-factor)

Bearings "A" and "B" (fixed position)
Trial check to establish dynamic equivalent radial load formula
$T_e = 750$ lb, assume $K_A = 1.00$ and $K_B = 1.50$
then, $\dfrac{0.6\,F_r(A-B)}{K_A} = \dfrac{0.6 \times 1700}{1.00} = 1020$ lb

$T_e < \dfrac{0.6 F_r(A-B)}{K_A}$

$\therefore P_A = \dfrac{K_A}{K_A + K_B}\left[F_r(A-B) + 1.67\,K_A\,T_e\right]$

and $P_B = \dfrac{K_B}{K_A + K_B}\left[F_r(A-B) - 1.67\,K_A\,T_e\right]$

$P_A = \dfrac{1.00}{1.00+1.50}\left[1700 + 1.67 \times 1.50 \times 750\right] = 1432$ lb

$P_B = \dfrac{1.50}{1.00+1.50}\left[1700 - 1.67 \times 1.00 \times 750\right] = 269$ lb

$C(90)R_A = \dfrac{P_A \times LF \times AF}{SF} = \dfrac{1432 \times 1.621 \times 1.0}{0.625} = 3714$ lb

Select 2.5591 in bore bearing assembly, type TS, refer to single-row Bearing Tables, cone JLM710949, cup JLM710910.
$C(90) = 4450$ lb, $K = 1.29$

$C(90)R_B = \dfrac{P_B \times LF \times AF}{SF} = \dfrac{269 \times 1.621 \times 1.0}{0.625} = 698$ lb

Select 2.625 in bore bearing assembly, type TS, refer to sngle-row Bearing Tables, cone 395A, cup 394A.
$C(90) = 4000$ lb, $K = 1.45$

SELECTION RECHECK (based on actual K-factor)

$\dfrac{0.6\,F_r(A-B)}{K_A} = \dfrac{0.6 \times 1700}{1.29} = 791$ lb $> T_e$

$P_A = \dfrac{1.29}{1.29+1.45}\left[1700 + 1.67 \times 1.45 \times 750\right] = 1655$ lb

$LF_A = \dfrac{C(90)A \times SF}{P_A \times AF} = \dfrac{4450 \times 0.625}{1655 \times 1.0} = 1.681$

For LF of 1.681 — $L_{10} = 16,950$ hr, this is satisfactory.

$P_B = \dfrac{1.45}{1.29+1.45}\left[1700 - 1.67 \times 1.29 \times 750\right] = 45$ lb

$LF_B = \dfrac{C(90)B \times SF}{P_B \times AF} = \dfrac{4000 \times 0.625}{45 \times 1.0} = 55.6$

This is satisfactory.

Bearing "C" (floating position)
Since there is no external thrust imposed on this bearing, $P_C = F_rC = 800$ lb
$C(90)R_C = \dfrac{P_C \times LF \times AF}{SF} = \dfrac{800 \times 1.621 \times 1.0}{0.625} = 2075$ lb

Select 1.500 in bore bearing assembly, type TDODC, refer to two-row Bearing Tables, cone 13685, cup 13621DC.
$C(90)_2 = 4250$ lb, $K = 1.45$
$LF_C = \dfrac{C(90)_2C \times SF}{P_C \times AF} = \dfrac{4250 \times 0.625}{800 \times 1.0} = 3.32$
This is satisfactory.

3. Weighted Average Loading and Life

The following cases illustrate the use of the weighted average loading formulae tabulated on pages 48 and 49.

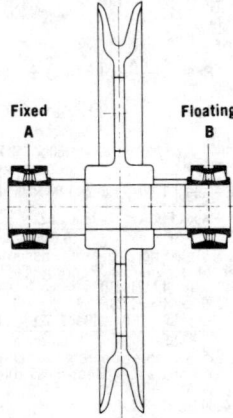

Fixed A   Floating B

Case 1

Variable Loading — Variable Speed — Variable % Time

This is the general case, and the weighted average load is expressed as:

$$F_{wt} @ \ 500RPM = F_{max} \left[T_1 \left(\frac{F_1}{F_{max} \cdot SF_1} \right)^{10/3} \right.$$

$$+ T_2 \left(\frac{F_2}{F_{max} \cdot SF_2} \right)^{10/3}$$

$$\left. + \cdots T_n \left(\frac{F_n}{F_{max} \cdot SF_n} \right)^{10/3} \right]^{3/10}$$

Given Conditions

Application — Crane Sheave
Arrangement of Bearings—as above
Required Life = 5000 hr, L_{10}
Desired Shaft Diameter = 1.875 in, or greater

Analysis Factors

Life Factor, LF = 1.166
Application Factor, AF = 1.0

Loads and Speeds

$$F_rA = F_rB = F_{max} = F_1 = 10,000 \ lb$$
$$F_rA = F_rB \quad = F_2 = \ 8,000 \ lb$$
$$F_rA = F_rB \quad = F_3 = \ 5,000 \ lb$$

Period	Loading Pounds	Speed RPM	SF	Time Minutes	% Time
1	10,000	100	1.621	15	30
2	8,000	50	1.995	25	50
3	5,000	10	3.233	10	20
Total Time				50	

SELECTION

$$F_{wt} @ \ 500RPM = 10,000 \left[0.30 \left(\frac{10,000}{10,000 \times 1.621} \right)^{10/3} + \right.$$

$$\left. 0.50 \left(\frac{8000}{10,000 \times 1.995} \right)^{10/3} + 0.20 \left(\frac{5000}{10,000 \times 3.233} \right)^{10/3} \right]^{3/10}$$

$$= 10,000 \ (0.0842)^{3/10} = 4759 \ lb$$

Select 1.9685 in bore bearing assembly, type TNADC, refer to two-row Bearing Tables, cone NA366, cup 363DC.

$C(90)_2 = 6300 \ lb, \ K = 1.83$

Life Factor, $LF = \dfrac{C(90)_2 \times SF}{F_{wt} \times AF} = \dfrac{6300 \times 1}{4759 \times 1} = 1.324$

For LF of 1.324 — $L_{10} = 7650$ hr, this is satisfactory.

Case 2

Variable Loading — Variable Speed — Variable % Time — Weighted L_{10} from Calculated Life Factors

In some cases it is advantageous to calculate the L_{10} for each of a set of cases in a loading cycle. The weighted L_{10} may then be calculated from these lives by the use of the following formula:

$$L_{10} = \frac{1}{\dfrac{T_1}{L_{10_1}} + \dfrac{T_2}{L_{10_2}} + \cdots \dfrac{T_n}{L_{10_n}}}$$

Given Conditions

Sheave of Case 1 with data on cycle tabulated as follows:

Period	Loading	RPM	SF	Bearing Rating at Given Speed	LF	L_{10}	Time in Minutes	% Time
1	10,000	100	1.621	10,212	1.02	3,200	15	30
2	8,000	50	1.995	12,569	1.57	13,500	25	50
3	5,000	10	3.233	20,368	4.07	322,900	10	20
Total time.							50	

$$L_{10} = \frac{1}{\dfrac{0.3}{3200} + \dfrac{0.5}{13,500} + \dfrac{0.2}{322,900}} = 7610 \ hr$$

Case 3

Variable Loading — Constant Speed — Variable % Time

This is a simplification of Case 1, in that the speed is constant, and the weighted average load at that speed becomes:

$$F_{wt} = \left[(T_1 \times F_1^{10/3}) + (T_2 \times F_2^{10/3}) \right.$$

$$\left. + \ldots (T_n \times F_n^{10/3}) \right]^{3/10}$$

$$= F_{max} \left[T_1 \left(\frac{F_1}{F_{max}} \right)^{10/3} + T_2 \left(\frac{F_2}{F_{max}} \right)^{10/3} \right.$$

$$\left. + \ldots T_n \left(\frac{F_n}{F_{max}} \right)^{10/3} \right]^{3/10}$$

Given Conditions

Sheave of Case 1, with constant speed of 100 RPM and same bearing:

$$F_{wt} = 10,000 \times \left[0.30 \left(\frac{10,000}{10,000} \right)^{10/3} \right.$$

$$\left. + 0.50 \left(\frac{8000}{10,000} \right)^{10/3} + 0.20 \left(\frac{5000}{10,000} \right)^{10/3} \right]^{3/10}$$

$$= 10,000 (0.557)^{3/10} = 10,000 \times 0.839 = 8390 \text{ lb}$$

$$LF = \frac{C(90)_2 \times SF}{F_{wt} \times AF} = \frac{6300 \times 1.621}{8390 \times 1.0} = 1.217$$

For LF of 1.217 — $L_{10} = 5770$ hr

Case 4

Constant Loading — Variable Speed — Variable % Time

This is another simplification of Case 1, in that the load is constant while the speed changes over a cycle. Since the speed and duration are each known the average speed can be calculated as follows:

$$S_{av} = \frac{S_1 t_1 + S_2 t_2 + \ldots S_n t_n}{t_t}$$

Given Conditions

Sheave in Case 1 with a constant load of 10,000 lb

$$S_{av} = \frac{(100 \times 15) + (50 \times 25) + (10 \times 10)}{50} = 57$$

SF @ 57 RPM = 1.918

$$LF = \frac{C(90)_2 \times SF}{P \times AF} = \frac{6300 \times 1.918}{10,000 \times 1.0} = 1.208$$

For LF of 1.208 — $L_{10} = 5630$ hr, this is satisfactory.

Case 5

Uniformly Increasing Load—Constant Speed

This is a variation of previous examples in that the loading varies from a minimum value "F_{min}" to a maximum value "F_{max}" at a uniform rate of increase. When the speed is constant the weighted average load is approximately equal to:

$$F_{wt} = F_{min} + 0.645 (F_{max} - F_{min})$$

Given Conditions

Assume that the sheave illustrated in Case 3 has a minimum load, $F_{min} = 5000$ pounds and a maximum load, $F_{max} = 10,000$ pounds. Assuming that the load varies from F_{min} to F_{max} at a constant rate of increase, then the weighted average loading, F_{wt}, from the previous equation will be:

$$F_{wt} = F_{min} + 0.645 (F_{max} - F_{min})$$

$$= 5000 + 0.645 (10,000 - 5000) = 8225 \text{ lb}$$

$$\text{Then } LF = \frac{C(90)_2 \times SF}{F_{wt} \times AF} = \frac{6300 \times 1.621}{8225 \times 1.0} = 1.242$$

For LF of 1.242 — $L_{10} = 6180$ hr, this is satisfactory.

Case 6

Constant Loading—Constant or Average Speed

For constant load and speed the general formula of Case 1 becomes:

$$F_{wt} @ 500 \text{RPM} = \frac{F}{SF}$$

Given Conditions

If bearing cone NA366, cup 363DC as selected for the sheave in Case 1 is checked on the basis of the maximum load, $F_{max} = 10,000$ pounds, and the maximum speed, 100 RPM, we arrive at the life factor in the usual way:

$$LF = \frac{C(90)_2 \times SF}{F_{max} \times AF} = \frac{6300 \times 1.621}{10,000 \times 1.0} = 1.021$$

For LF of 1.021 — $L_{10} = 3220$ hr

This method would tend to indicate that the bearing would be inadequate whereas in Case 1 the bearing is actually satisfactory for 7650 hours when calculated on the basis of weighted average loading.

LOADING ANALYSIS FOR
PASSENGER CARS AND HIGHWAY TRUCKS

Tractive Effort

Tractive effort is the tangential force between the driving wheels and the road necessary to propel a vehicle at a given speed against the combined grade, air and rolling resistances.

1. Passenger Car Tractive Effort at 50 MPH (Empirical)

The passenger car tractive effort (TE) is an empirical value of 60 pounds per 1,000 pounds of gross vehicle weight at 50 mph.

$$TE @ 50 \text{ MPH} = \text{Tractive effort (Empirical)}$$
$$\text{passenger car}$$
$$= \frac{GW \times 60}{1000} \quad \ldots \ldots \ldots \ldots \ldots (20)$$

When this tractive effort is used as an applied load in the bearing loading analysis for passenger cars operating in a normal highway environment, the bearing loading of 100% results in acceptable reliability when using the application factors (AF) and life factors (LF) tabulated in The Timken Company Engineering Journal page A-6.

2. Highway Truck Tractive Effort (Analytical)

To relate the calculated bearing life of the axle center more accurately to the actual on-the-road fatigue life, an approach to estimating highway truck vehicle tractive effort at the ground under various conditions has been established. It consists of establishing a tractive effort based on gross weight and frontal area for each condition of the operating cycle, taking into consideration grade resistance, rolling resistance and air resistance using the following formulas and tables:

a. Grade Resistance

TE (Grade) = Gross Weight × Sine of grade angle

Where: Gross Weight = Total vehicle weight
Tan. (grade angle) = % grade/100

b. Rolling Resistance

TE (Rolling) = Rolling resistance × (1 + road factor)

Where: Rolling resistance = $\dfrac{RrHP \times 375}{MPH}$

RrHP = Rolling resistance HP
375 = Constant

MPH = Miles per hour

RrHP = Rolling factor × $\dfrac{\text{Total gross weight}}{1000}$

Where: Rolling factor =
$$\frac{(7.6 + 0.09 \text{ MPH}) \times \text{MPH}}{375}$$

ROAD FACTOR TABLE

Road Class	Road Surface Type	Factor Condition of Surface		
		Good	Fair	Poor
I	Cement concrete Brick Asphalt block Asphalt plank Granite block Sheet asphalt Asphaltic concrete Bituminous macadam (high type) Wood block	0.0	0.1	0.2
II	Bituminous macadam (low type) Bituminous (tar) Oil mats (oiled macadam) Treated gravel	0.2	0.6	1.0
III	Sand clay Gravel Crushed stone Cobbles	0.5	1.0	1.5
IV	Earth Sand	1.0	1.5	2.5

c. Air Resistance

$$TE \text{ (Air)} = \frac{RaHP \times 375}{MPH}$$

Where: RaHP = Air Resistance in HP
375 = Constant
MPH = Miles per hour
RaHP = (area factor) × (velocity factor) × (altitude factor)

Where: Area factor =
$$\frac{(\text{height (ft)} - 3/4) \times \text{width (ft)}}{375}$$

Velocity Factor = 0.002 $(MPH)^3$
Altitude Factor = (See Table)

d. Summation of Resistances

The vehicle tractive effort for each condition and speed of the operating cycle is the sum of the resistance forces:

$$TE = TE \text{ (Grade)} + TE \text{ (Rolling)} + TE \text{ (Air)} . .(21)$$

ALTITUDE FACTOR TABLE (For Air Resistance)			
Altitude ft	Altitude Factor	Altitude ft	Altitude Factor
0	1.00	8,000	0.78
1,000	0.97	9,000	0.76
2,000	0.94	10,000	0.74
3,000	0.91	11,000	0.71
4,000	0.89	12,000	0.69
5,000	0.86	13,000	0.67
6,000	0.83	14,000	0.65
7,000	0.81	15,000	0.63

With these tractive effort values, two approaches to analyzing bearing life expectancy can be followed. First, a separate bearing loading analysis can be prepared for each condition of operation, and then the "% load" or "actual LF" combined into a weighted bearing life analysis (see equation on page 48). This approach permits analyzing the respective bearing life in each load condition to see where major life reductions occur. In the sec-

ond approach the tractive efforts of the loading cycle are consolidated into a single weighted average tractive effort @ 500 RPM. Use the formula on page 48 substituting tractive effort (TE) for F which in turn is used to determine the bearing weighted load and weighted life for the operating cycle.

3. Highway Trucks Tractive Effort (Empirical)

Sufficient data is not always readily available to use the **analytical** TE approach to bearing loading analysis on axle center applications. The end use of the axle usually covers a considerable range of vehicle weights. Also, environmental conditions, variable gross loads, driver attitudes and economics of operations have a major effect on the amount of available power that is put through the axle center bearings at any given time. Therefore, an **"empirical approach"** to tractive effort for bearing loading analysis is also shown.

In this **empirical** approach to select the proper bearing, highway trucks and buses have been divided into five groups by weight assigned a reliability that would be expected of these vehicles if they were to operate at a designated speed on approximately a level road their entire life.

An **empirical** tractive effort curve was developed by using the resistance formula and assumed vehicle frontal areas.

HIGHWAY TRUCK AND BUS WEIGHT AND RELIABILITY GROUPINGS

				(ASSUMED CONDITIONS)			
GROUP	GROSS WEIGHT	TYPE VEHICLE	MPH	L-10 (HOURS) MILES	LIFE FACTOR	DESIRED MILES LIFE 98% RELIABILITY	
I	UP TO 6,500 LBS⁰	PICKUP PANEL	40	(8,800) 220,000	1.200	70,000	
II	UP TO 15,000 LBS.	VAN PANEL PICKUP RECREATIONAL VEHICLE TRUCK (TWO AXLES)	40	(7,800) 310,000	1.332	100,000	
III	15000 LBS. TO 26000 LBS.	SCHOOL BUS TRACTOR TRAILER (THREE AXLES) TRUCK (THREE AXLES)	40	(11,800) 465,000	1.500	150,000	
IV	26,000 LBS. AND UP	TRACTOR TRAILER (FIVE OR MORE AXLES) TRACTOR TRAILER (FOUR AXLES)	40	(23,800) 940,000	1.884	300,000	
V	26,000 LBS. AND UP	TRANSIT and SUBURBAN BUS	40	(23,800) 940,000	1.884	300,000	
		INTER-CITY BUS	60	(18,800) 940,000	1.730		

FIGURE 17   ⁰LIGHT TRUCKS USING PASSENGER CAR COMPONENTS

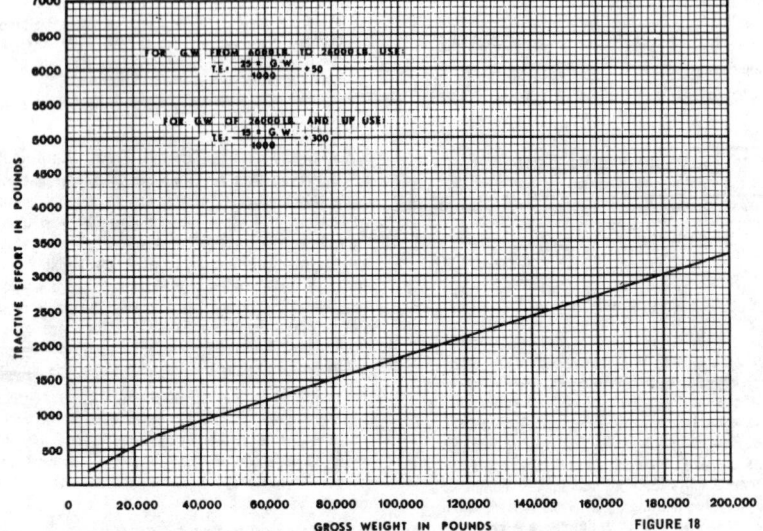

FIGURE 18

**TRACTIVE EFFORT CURVE (EMPIRICAL) FOR HIGHWAY TRUCKS
AND COMBINATIONS TRANSIT AND SUBURBAN BUSES**

With the **empirical** approach the gross weight of the vehicle establishes the tractive effort at 40 mph either from the curve Figure 18 or calculated as follows:

TE @ 40 MPH = Tractive Effort (Empirical)
for highway trucks
(6,000 to 26,000 lb Gross Weight)

$$= \frac{25 \times GW}{1000} + 50 \quad \ldots \ldots (22)$$

TE @ 40 MPH = Tractive Effort (Empirical)
for highway trucks
(26,000 lb up Gross Weight)

$$= \frac{15 \times GW}{1000} + 300 \quad \ldots \ldots (23)$$

A bearing loading analysis can be prepared using this **empirical** tractive effort (TE) as an applied load to the wheels at the ground in conjunction with the axle center gear data. Use the appropriate weight related application factors (AF) and life factors (LF) tabulated on page A-6. Acceptable bearing loading is 100%.

4. Buses - Tractive Effort

When considering tractive effort for buses it is preferable to use the **analytical** approach (page A-1) if sufficient data is available. This is especially important in the case of inter-city buses because the calculated tractive effort values will reflect the effect of the sustained higher speeds.

In the event sufficient data is not available, the same general values for **empirical** tractive effort (figure 18, page A-3) relative to gross weight groups and desired reliability exist for transit and suburban buses as those used for highway trucks for similar gross weights at 40 mph Figure 17, page A-2.

5. Off-Highway Tractive Effort (Empirical)

It is preferable when calculating off-highway truck axle centers that some type of load, speed, time cycle schedule be known from which a "weighted life" bearing loading analysis can be made.

If a detailed cycle is lacking, an **empirical** tractive

$$\text{effort of} \quad \frac{80 \text{ lb} \times \text{Gross Weight}}{1000} \quad \text{at}$$

18 mph may be used as a tractive effort from which to calculate axle center bearing loadings and make tentative bearing selections.

TE @ 18 MPH = Tractive effort **empirical**

Off-highway trucks

$$= \frac{80 \times \text{GW}}{1000} \quad \dots \dots \dots \dots \quad (24)$$

A bearing loading of 100% is considered normal.

Bearing Loading

Bearing selection for automotive applications are made on the basis of imposed loads, operating speeds, type of mounting and desired reliability.

The effective load center method is used to locate the true center of pressure of all the resistance forces on the bearings.

Wheel bearing loading calculations are based on the gross weight of the axle less tire and wheel weight.

Axle center bearing loading calculations are based on gross weight of the vehicle and tractive effort, either on an analytical or empirical basis, as described on pages A-1 through A-4.

Transmission and transfer case bearing load and life calculations are based on the engine torque, the engine speed at that torque, and an operating cycle. When the operating cycle is not given, a typical cycle and life requirement is used as shown on page A-6.

Application factors and initial life factors are tabulated on page A-6.

In the bearing life analysis the L_{10} life is usually calculated and represents 90% reliability. Other degrees of reliability may be established using the values shown on the graph on page 24.

Front Wheels - Non-Driving

In making calculations of the front wheel bearing loads it is usually found that the load reaction line will pass close to the inner bearing. The major portion of the load will be carried as a radial load on the inner bearing while comparatively little radial load will be on the outer bearing.

The outer bearing reacts in the nature of a stabilizer carrying its own radial load combined with the induced thrust resulting from the inner bearing radial load.

The selection of a front wheel bearing set is a matter of hub and spindle design and of proper bearing combination.

For passenger car applications the effective load center spread of the bearings should be a minimum of .10 times the rolling diameter of the tire. The proportion of the spindle outer seat diameter is generally not less than 60% of the spindle inner cone seat diameter.

For highway trucks the effective bearing spread is at least .12 times the tire diameter.

Bearings for this application should be selected on the basis of 100 percent maximum loading at nominal speeds of 50 m.p.h. for passenger cars and intercity buses and 40 m.p.h. for highway trucks and transit or suburban buses.

Application factors and initial life factors are shown on page A-6.

Rear Wheels

Semi-Floating Axles on Passenger Cars

The selection of rear wheel bearings is dependent upon the safe axle shaft diameter, axle housing rigidity and the gross axle weight of the vehicle. The live shaft semifloating design can incorporate a UNIT-BEARING (TSU), or a shallow angle single tapered roller bearing (TS), on each wheel.

The UNIT-BEARING is pressed onto the flanged axle and clamped in position by means of a solid locking collar, or other locking device, (No center block is required with the UNIT-BEARING design.)

Calculations of the radial bearing loads using the effective load center of the UNIT-BEARING are based on one-half the gross axle weight on the tires at the ground less the unsprung weight of the wheel and hub assembly. Bearing loading on this application should not exceed 100% for a L_{10} life of 3,000 hours.

When a TS type bearing is used the splined end of the axle shaft is supported in the differential side gear and is butted against a floating center block. The center or thrust block is located in the center of the differential so that the thrust load on one wheel is freely transmitted through the thrust block to the bearing of the opposite wheel.

Rear Wheel

Full Floating Axle on Truck and Buses, Trailer Wheels

Bearings are selected on the basis of bore size, capacity and K factor relationship. On wheel applications the effective bearing load center spread should be at least .12 times the rolling diameter of the tire for highway trucks, buses and trailers.

The radial bearing loads are based on one-half the gross axle load on the tires at the ground less the unsprung weight of the wheel and hub assembly. The load line is usually located between the bearing effective load centers. The magnitude of the radial load on the bearings and the "K" factors determine which bearing will carry the combined radial and induced trust loading.

The nominal life expectancy for various vehicles are shown on page A-6. Based on gross weight, general groupings of trucks form service categories, each having a L_{10} life expectancy and corresponding initial life factor. The bearing sizes should be selected so that the percent loading on either bearing will not exceed 100% for a highway vehicle.

Spiral Bevel Axle Center

Single Reduction Straddle-Mounted Pinion

The bearing loads for spiral bevel axle centers are calculated from the tangential force at the ring gear mean pitch diameter. The magnitude of this applied load tangential force is determined on a tractive effort basis by using either the empirical tractive effort and speed as shown on pages A-1 - A-3 or an analytical tractive effort based on the vehicle speed, grade, frontal area, etc., supplied by the manufacturer (eq 21, page A-2).

In the spiral bevel gearing, there are three forces acting at the point of gear tooth contact, tangential driving force, a separating force and a thrust force. Mechanical Drive Element formulae for determining the gear load components are shown on page 38.

The tangential force used in calculating the coast bearing loads is assumed to be 70% of the tangential force in drive. (Where retarders may be used, suggest 100% of tangential force.)

Bearing selections are based on bore size, capacity and angularity. For both pinion and differential bearings, 100% is the maximum acceptable load on the empirical tractive effort (TE) basis for normal automotive applications.

Hypoid Axle Center

Single Reduction Overhung Pinion

The bearing loads for hypoid axle centers are calculated from the tangential force at the ring gear mean pitch diameter. The magnitude of this tangential force is determined on a tractive effort basis, from the gross weight, for either empirical or analytical tractive effort (TE) bearing loading analysis, as described on pages A-1 thru A-4.

In the hypoid gearing there are three forces acting at the point of gear tooth contact, a tangential driving force, a separating force and a thrust force. These are resolved into axial and radial components

which are parallel and perpendicular to the axis of the pinion shaft and parallel and perpendicular to the gear shaft axis in a plane formed by a line between the center of the gear and the intersections of the pinion and gear mean pitch diameters. Equations for determining the gear load components are shown on page 38. The direction of offset determines the hand of spiral.

The tangential force used in calculating the coast bearing loads is assumed to be 70% of the tangential force in drive, except when a retarder is in the drive train, in which case 100% of the drive load is used in coast.

The selection of bearings for any position of a rear axle center must be of sufficient capacity and proper angularity to provide for proper alignment of the hypoid gear set under all conditions of loading. If proper deflection characteristics are to be retained for the gear set, the relationship of the bearing effective load centers to the load line overhang should not drop below certain limits.

On passenger cars where shaft sizes and bearing angularity are reasonably constant, the load line overhang is taken from the effective load center of the bearing adjacent to the pinion head. The minimum effective load center spread of the bearings should range between 3 to 3.75 times the load line overhang dependent upon the gross weight. As a guide up to a 3550 lbs. gross weight passenger car, the bearing effective load center spread should be three times the load line overhang. Up to 4950 lbs. gross weight it should be 3.5 times and up to 7,000 lbs. it should be 3.75 times.

On highway trucks there is a wider range of shaft sizes and bearing angularities; therefore, the pinion load line overhang is measured from the geometric center of the inner bearing adjacent to the pinion head, and the bearing geometric center spread should be a minimum of 1¾ times the overhang.

Maximum bearing loading for normal automotive applications is 100% for both the differential and pinion bearings under the empirical tractive effort approach.

Transmission

Transmission bearing loadings are based on an estimated weighted percent of the maximum engine torque at a given RPM operating through a transmission shifting cycle.

An input torque of 70% or 85% of the maximum engine torque was chosen as a realistic operating engine torque that would be maintained during normal vehicle operation. For vehicles not exceeding 15,000 pounds gross weight, 70% of the maximum engine torque is used for bearing loading calculations. A value of 85% of the maximum engine torque is used when the gross weight is over 15,000 pounds. Bearing loadings are then determined in each of the transmission ratios, and these are used to calculate the weighted life. The torque transmitted through the transmission in the lower gears **may** be limited by the skid torque developed between the driving wheel and the road.

TYPICAL TRUCK TRANSMISSION CYCLES

Percent Operating Time for Empirical

Automotive Transmissions

Forward Speeds in Transmissions

Gear Increments	4	5	6	7	8	9	10
1st	1	1	1	1	1	.5	.5
2nd	4	3	2.5	2	2	1.0	1.0
3rd	25	12	6.0	4	3.5	2.0	1.5
4th	70	24	12.0	8	5.0	3.5	2.5
5th		60	23.5	12	7.5	5.5	4
6th			55	23	13	9.0	6.5
7th				50	23	15.0	10
8th					45	23.5	15
9th						40	24
10th							35

Torque greater than this will only skid the wheels. If the manufacturer requests that we consider wheel skid limitation, he should supply us with the wheel diameter and the axle center ratio.

If the transmission shifting cycle is not available for use in determining the applied load and the relative time applied on the bearings, an empirical value based on the following table may be used.

The life requirement for a transmission varies from one model transmission to another. In general, as the weight of the vehicle increases, the life requirement or reliability also increases. The following table shows four general truck groupings based on gross weight and their corresponding life factors to be used in calculating transmission bearing loadings.

Transfer Cases

This same approach is applied to transfer cases. The input torque and speed to the transfer case is the same as to the transmission except that it is modified by the transmission shifting cycle and ratios. When the transfer case is two speed and a cycle is not given, a typical operating time is 90% in high range and 10% in low range.

RECOMMENDED LIFE FACTORS AND APPLICATION FACTORS FOR AUTOMOTIVE APPLICATIONS

Vehicle	Life Factor (LF)	Application Factors (AF)									Empirical Speed mph
			differential				pinion		transmission and transfer case	
		cross shaft	pedestal or carrier type	trans-axle	wheel	semi-floating axle rear wheel	over hung	straddle mounted		
Passenger Cars	1.00	—	2.00	1.00	1.0	1.15	1.0	.667	1.0	50
Light Trucks (Passenger Car Chassis)	1.20	—	1.65	1.00	1.15	1.15	1.0	.667	1.0	40
Highway Trucks (Up to 15,000 Lbs.)	1.332	1.15	1.65	—	1.15	—	1.0	.667	1.0	40
Highway Trucks, Tractor Trailers, School Buses (Over 15,000 Lbs. - 26,000 Lbs.)	1.50	1.15	1.65	—	1.15	—	1.0	.667	1.0	40
Highway Trucks, Tractor Trailers, Transit and Suburban Buses (26,000 Lbs. and Up)	1.854	1.15	1.65	—	1.15*	—	1.0	.667	1.0	40
Inter-city Buses (26,000 Lbs. and Up)	1.730	1.15	1.65	—	1.15*	—	1.0	.667	1.0	50
Commercial Highway Trailers	1.854	—	—	—	1.15*	—	—	—	—	40
House Trailers - U Haul	.77	—	—	—	1.0	—	—	—	—	—
Off-highway Trucks	1.00	1.15	1.65	—	2.0	—	1.0	.667	1.0	18

*1.0 if oil lubricated

AUTOMOTIVE FITTING PRACTICE

(Inch System and Inch Conversion of Metric System)

CONES

RESULTANT FIT AND DEVIATION FROM BASIC BORE SIZE

					ROTATING CONE									STATIONARY CONE				

(Pinion / rear wheels (semi-floating axles) / transmissions cross shafts transfer cases / rear wheels [UNIT BEARING] (semi-floating axles) / differential / front wheels rear wheels (full-floating axles) trailer wheels)

CONE BORE

basic size	range over	incl.	toler-ance
INCH SYSTEM OF TOLERANCING NORMALLY USES MINIMUM DIAMETER FOR BASIC CONE BORE SIZE. †Indicates maximum bore is shown. (See footnote.)	0	3.0000 76.2	+.0005 0
	0	3.0000 76.2	0 Δ +.0008
	3.0000 76.2	12.0000 304.8	0 +.0010
METRIC SYSTEM OF TOLERANCING USES MAXIMUM DIAMETER FOR BASIC BORE SIZE. Metric system tolerances are used on all "µ" prefix part numbers (the bore dimensions are proceeded by an "µ" in the bearing tables and dimension sheets.)	.7087 18	1.1811 30	−.0005 0
	1.1811 30	1.9685 50	−.0005 0
	1.9685 50	3.1496 80	−.0006 0
	3.1496 80	4.7244 120	−.0008 0
	4.7244 120	7.0866 180	−.0010 0

RECOMMENDED FITTING PRACTICE (INCH SYSTEM)

INCH CONVERSION OF METRIC FITTING PRACTICE

CUPS

RESULTANT FIT AND DEVIATION FROM BASIC O.D. SIZE

					STATIONARY CUP								ROTATING CUP				

CUP O.D.

basic size	range over	incl.	toler-ance
INCH SYSTEM OF BEARING TOLERANCING NORMALLY USES MINIMUM DIAMETER FOR BASIC CUP O.D. SIZE. †Indicates Maximum O.D. is shown. (See footnote.)	0	3.0000 76.2	+.0010 0
	3.0000 76.2	5.0000 127.0	+.0010 0
	5.0000 127.0	12.0000 304.8	+.0010 0
METRIC SYSTEM OF BEARING TOLERANCING USES MAXIMUM DIAMETER FOR BASIC CUP O.D. SIZE. Metric system tolerances are used on all "µ" prefix part numbers (the O.D. dimensions are proceeded by an "µ" in the bearing tables and dimension sheets.)	1.1811 30	1.9685 50	0 −.0008
	1.9685 50	3.1496 80	0 −.0008
	3.1496 80	4.7244 120	0 −.0008
	4.7244 120	7.0866 180	0 −.0010
	7.0866 180	9.8425 250	0 −.0012
	9.8425 250	12.4016 315	0

RECOMMENDED FITTING PRACTICE

INCH CONVERSION OF METRIC FITTING PRACTICE

*Non-standard tolerances.

†Dimension shown is maximum value.

When the (†) symbol appears on (inch system) bore and O.D. dimensions the basic size is maximum. The tolerance is minus by the same magnitude for a given bore or O.D. range as the standard and inch system. The resulting fit is held by modifying the seat deviation.

*Dimension shown is maximum value (metric system).

R7 symbols for I.S.O. standard system of limits and fits are shown where they apply.

Mounting of Bearings

PAGE

A. Factory Pre-Set Bearing Assemblies   62

B. Backing Designs 62-67

C. Bearing Setting Devices 68-75
   1. End Play Vs. Preload   68
   2. Spacers   69
   3. Automated Bearing Setting Methods   70
      a. Set-Right   70
      b. Acro-Set   70
      c. Torque-Set   70
   4. Adjusting Devices 71-75

D. Closure Designs 76-80
   1. Metal Stampings 76-79
   2. Machined Flingers 76-79
   3. Annular Grooves 76, 78, 80
   4. Radial Lip Seals 76, 79, 80
   5. Piston Rings   80
   6. Vertical Shaft Closures   80

E. Typical Mountings 81-87

F. Lubrication 88-90
   1. Oil 88, 89
   2. Grease 89, 90

A. Factory Pre-Set Bearing Assemblies

All bearings which are provided with spacers at the factory are pre-set assemblies. This involves all types of two-row and four-row bearings that are furnished with spacers properly ground for the requirements of the application in which the bearings are to be used. The spacers are finished to size for each bearing assembly and component parts from one assembly are not interchangeable with a similar assembly. In some large bearing assemblies, to aid you so that these parts do not become mixed before use, an identifying "serial number" is marked on each cup, cone and spacer. **All parts with the same serial number should be kept together.** Some small pre-set assemblies are not marked with a serial number but they are **still not interchangeable** and component parts should be assembled as received. (An exception to this restriction is the "SR" assembly described on page 14.

Type TQITS four-row bearings—especially adaptable to high speed rolling mills—are also pre-set assemblies. See page 19.

On the other hand, type TNA bearings shown on pages 15 and 16 are ground for complete interchangeability of parts.

In factory pre-set assemblies or non-adjustable type TNA interchangeable parts bearings, a certain fixed internal axial setting is built into the bearing when it is manufactured. This setting is referred to as "bench end play" and is used to compensate for the following variations:

(1) Minimum mounted end play or preload required to assure satisfactory bearing performance for the specific service requirements.

(2) End play removed when either outer or inner races, or both, are applied in or on their supporting members with the recommended interference fits.

(3) Temperature differentials and other service conditions.

Failure to use standard fitting tolerances in all installations using the above types of bearings can result in premature bearing damage and possible damage to the related machine parts as well. Since a bearing cone will expand when it is applied with an interference fit on a shaft, the bench end play with which the bearing is manufactured is reduced. The amount of reduction depends on the interference fit.

Interference fits of cups have a corresponding effect on bench end play since the cups will tend to contract to the housing bore dimension.

If interference fits are either greater or less than those specified, the bearing might be required to operate with insufficient looseness—or too much looseness—and be unsatisfactory in actual performance.

Bench end plays are carefully determined by Timken Company engineers after analyzing the possible operating temperature differentials, problems of gear mesh tolerances, rigidity, and other operating variations and requirements. Therefore, it is important that the bearing be used in accordance with mounting specifications.

B. Backing Designs

The height of the shoulders for cups and cones should follow the recommendations for the particular bearing given in the Bearing Tables. Along with having the dimension specified, it is essential that the shoulder be square with the shaft O.D. or housing bore. The shoulder should extend beyond the radius against the flat backing surface of the raceway and be of sufficient height to support the thrust loads encountered by the bearing.

Numerous typical backing designs are shown on pages 63 to 68 for both the back face and the front face of the cones and cups. A brief explanation is given for each figure shown.

Mounting of Bearings

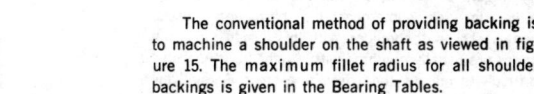

Shaft Design - Cone Backings

Cone Back Face

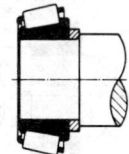

Figure 15

The conventional method of providing backing is to machine a shoulder on the shaft as viewed in figure 15. The maximum fillet radius for all shoulder backings is given in the Bearing Tables.

Figure 16

In some applications it may be necessary to provide proper support for the cone by introducing a backing ring between the cone and the shaft shoulder as shown in figure 16. This permits using a smaller shaft diameter.

Figure 17

In many applications where straight shafting is used and where it is desired to eliminate threading, drilling or tapping, a snap ring can be used as shown in figure 17.

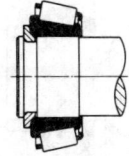

Figure 18

If operating conditions might dislodge the snap ring from its groove, then a shroud should be installed over the snap ring or a split ring applied and held in place by the cone as illustrated in figure 18.

Cone Front Face

Figure 19 indicates how the cone front face in either single or double cones may be mounted directly against a shaft shoulder. With this design, since the cones are usually mounted with a tight fit, it becomes difficult to remove them from the shaft. A relatively sharp radius is also required, thereby weakening the shaft.

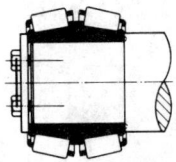

Figure 19

In figure 20, knock-out slots are provided in the shaft at 180° spacing to facilitate removing the cones. These slots may be used in either single or double cone mountings where they are applied with a tight fit.

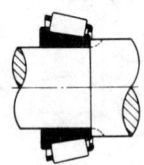

Figure 20

Where it is important to provide a fillet radius larger than the cone radius in order to avoid stress concentration and a weakened shaft, a backing ring and two knock-out slots as shown in figure 21 may be used.

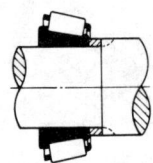

Figure 21

Figure 22 illustrates how the cone front face in either single or double cone bearings may be mounted against a backing ring which in turn is located against the shaft shoulder. The backing ring outside diameter is made larger than the shaft to provide a shoulder which may be used as a puller for cone removal.

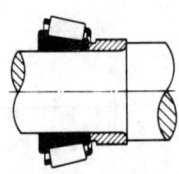

Figure 22

Mounting of Bearings

Housing Design - Cup Backings

Cup Back Face

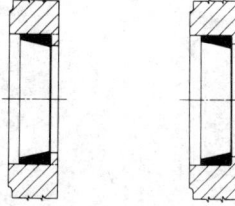

Figure 23 **Figure 24**

The design used in figure 23 is quite common in rough cast installations such as wheels where the shoulder diameter in the casting may not be concentric with the shaft axis. The shoulder diameter is made small to assure proper cup backing. Knock-out slots are provided at 180° for cup removal. Where the casting shoulder is concentric with the shaft axis, the recommended backings are indicated in the Bearing Tables and the design shown in figure 24 may be used.

The fillet radius for all shoulder backings must clear the cup radius. These values are tabulated in the Bearing Tables.

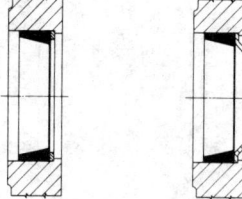

Figure 25 **Figure 26**

If a small shoulder is available but is inadequate to give the cup proper backing due to the size of the cup radius, a shoulder spacer may be used as shown in figure 25. Where a stamped closure may be necessary, the cup can be backed against the closure as shown in figure 26 as long as its thickness is adequate to properly support the cup.

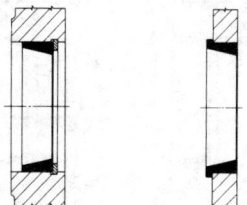

Figure 27 **Figure 28**

Figure 27 shows the cup backed against a snap ring. The through-bored housing provides accurate alignment of cup seats.

Figure 28 shows a flanged cup mounting. The housing may be through-bored and its face finished square with the bore to provide proper backing for the cup.

Figures 29 and 30 show alternate designs using cup followers held in position with cap screws. The piloted follower design is used to obtain concentricity of closures with the shaft. A pilot is also recommended where heavy followers are used with large bearings.

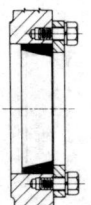 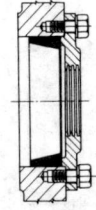

Figure 29   Figure 30

Figures 31 and 32 show cup carrier mountings where it is necessary to have a large housing bore for assembly of internal parts. Carriers are also used in somes cases of split housing designs where it is not practical or possible to have an accurate finish in the housing bore.

Figure 31   Figure 32

Figures 33 and 34 show two type TS cups backed by a snap ring. In figure 33, both cups are backed directly against the snap ring. When a snap ring does not separate the cups sufficiently to assure adequate axial clearance between the bearing cages, a stepped spacer can be employed as shown in figure 34.

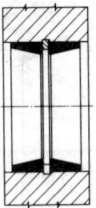 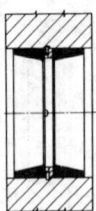

Figure 33   Figure 34

Mounting of Bearings

Cup Front Face

Figure 35

Figure 36

Figure 35 shows a type TS cup located against a shoulder integral with the housing. In some applications it may be more advantageous to use a snap ring as illustrated in figure 36.

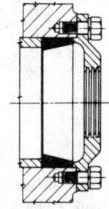

Figure 37

Figure 38

A flat clamping ring as shown in figure 37 or the pilot of a machined closure as shown in figure 38 is frequently utilized to assure positive positioning of the cups in the housing.

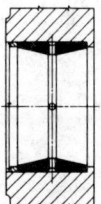

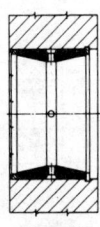

Figure 39

Figure 40

A fixed bearing requires positive positioning of the cup in the housing. Figure 39 shows a double cup located against a shoulder in the housing. Instead of an integral shoulder in the housing, some applications can use a snap ring as shown in figure 40.

C. Bearing Setting Devices

Tapered roller bearings offer an important convenience feature in determining proper bearing setting. The tapered raceways are separable—cone and roller assemblies easily separated from the cup. This permits axial movement of cone and rollers relative to the cup and thus allows any desired clearance or preload to be set between raceways and rollers.

1. End Play Vs. Preload

End play, the term used to refer to the axial movement of the bearing assembly, is necessary where speed and/or thermal expansion of related parts must be accommodated. The ideal bearing setting under operating conditions is metal-to-metal or zero end play. This setting is an attempt to reach that optimum point of operation. Such factors as size of parts, speed, any external heat conditions, lubrication and relative stiffness of the housing are considered when making the bearing setting.

Radial clearance versus end play is a function of the bearing included cup angle and can be determined by multiplying the end play by 0.39/K. For example, an initial cold setting of 0.006″ end play for a bearing having a K-factor of 1.17 would result in a radial clearance of 0.002″ within that bearing assembly. In making this initial end play setting, the objective is that under operating conditions, where both radial and axial thermal expansion have already taken place, this bearing would be running at zero end play or under metal-to-metal conditions.

Preload, the term used to refer to a bearing setting that is tighter than metal-to-metal, is utilized when increased rigidity is required. The basic purpose of preload is to stabilize housing walls, shafts, and the bearings themselves such that when external loads are applied, movement of all three will be reduced to a minimum. As is the case in any initial setting of the bearing—whether it be with preload or end play—the goal is to attain a metal-to-metal rotating condition after radial and axial expansions and housing deflection have taken place.

Optimum Preload is the minimum preload that will provide maximum stability of the shaft, bearings and housing walls. When subjected to forces, any material will compress, bend or deflect. Bearing housings are no exception. When a housing moves, the shaft and all related parts on the shaft also move. Rigid bearing mountings are necessary to maintain correct gear mesh when subjected to heavy forces. This rigidity is essential to assure minimal fatigue and wear, as well as maximum gear life. Gear movements can be minimized by setting the bearings with optimum preload.

A typical example of this concept is the mounting of the pinion and ring gear set used in a hypoid drive axle. To illustrate, consider the effects of a thrust force only on the housing walls.

With no load applied, figure 41 shows the system with no housing deflection and the gears are in perfect mesh.

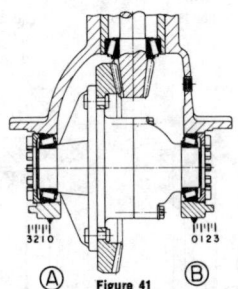

Ⓐ   **Figure 41**   Ⓑ

When an external thrust force "X" is applied to the shaft, as illustrated in figure 42, it is restrained by bearing "A" whose housing deforms elastically by what can be called one unit of distance. This disturbs the gear mesh and also unseats bearing "B".

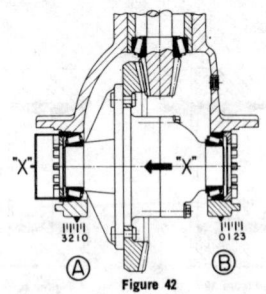

Ⓐ   **Figure 42**   Ⓑ

With the thrust force still applied, reseat bearing "B" by advancing bearing "A" cup follower one unit of distance as shown in figure 43. This moves bearing "A", the gear, shaft and cone "B"—re-establishing the seating of bearing "B", and putting the gears back into proper mesh.

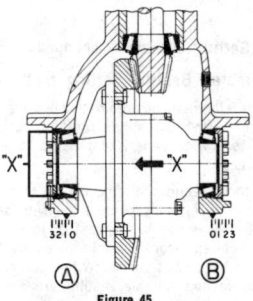

Figure 45

duce bearing life. Applications requiring preload should be analyzed to determine the optimum amount necessary. Recommended settings are available from The Timken Company's engineering department.

An adjusting device is required to accurately position the cone and roller assembly relative to the cup and maintain this position.

Various adjusting devices for moving the cone or cup are shown on pages 71 to 75. A brief explanation of each device shown is provided.

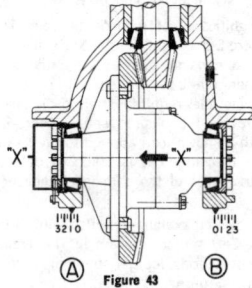

Figure 43

If the external thrust force "X" is removed, the housing now exerts a force of "X/2" on bearings "B" and "A" in an effort to return to its original shape. The gears, without any force applied to them, are half a unit too deeply in mesh and the mounting now has optimum preload as shown in figure 44.

2. Spacers

Many multiple-row tapered roller bearings are preset with spacers at time of manufacture, thereby permitting assembly into applications without requiring manual setting at time of installation. A clamping device is required to retain the raceways in position so that the bearing setting is permanently maintained.

Bearing types AP, TDI, TDIT, TDO, TDODC, TQO, TQITS and "SS" must be assembled with the spacers that are assigned to each bearing assembly at time of manufacture. The cones, cups and spacers of these types are **not interchangeable.**

The "SR" assembly is made up of two single cones, two single cups, a cone spacer and a cup spacer. This bearing is not a matched assembly. Any two cones, two cups, cone spacer and cup spacer having the same relative part numbers may be assembled to make up a complete "SR" assembly having the correct mounted bearing setting. This is assuming that the cone and cup seats are finished to the recommended dimensions. The bearings used in these assemblies, together with the fixed length spacers, utilize statistical quality control techniques for establishing the desired range of mounted bearing settings.

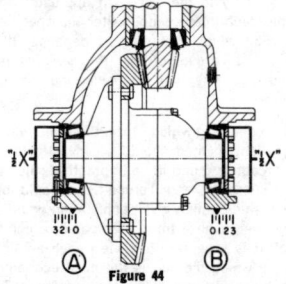

Figure 44

If the external thrust force is reapplied, there is a force "X" on bearing "A", none on bearing "B", but bearing "B" is still seated and the gears are in proper mesh. Figure 45 illustrates this operational condition with optimum preload.

Preload beyond the point of optimum preload serves no useful purpose and does nothing but re-

Bearing Setting Devices—Continued

3. Automated Bearing Setting Methods

The development of automated bearing assembly and setting techniques has brought economy and reliability to a wide variety of tapered roller bearing applications.

With these techniques, the choice is available to the designer to either provide a bearing setting device as he always has in the past or to specify more closely controlled machining tolerances and/or one of these assembly procedures. With such techniques, fast, accurate and reliable results are assured. Human error is minimized. Three such automated methods are **Set-Right, Acro-Set, and Torque-Set.**

a. Set-Right

Set-Right establishes the bearing setting by controlling tolerances in the radial as well as the axial direction. By applying statistical quality control analysis to these tolerances, manual adjustment is eliminated. The Set-Right method generally requires closer control of some machining operations.

A detailed description of Set-Right and a mathematical analysis is contained in "Engineering Bulletin No. 6" published by The Timken Company. Additional information is contained in The Timken Company Engineering Journal supplement "Automated Bearing Settings".

Semi-Set-Right is the name that has been coined to describe bearing setup procedures that require a closer setting than can be achieved by Set-Right. This method can be adopted for most shim-adjusted arrangements and offers a substantial savings in setup time compared to conventional methods.

b. Acro-Set

Acro-Set is a method of setting tapered roller bearings that is generally achieved through measurement of a shim gap with a specified setup load applied.

This setup technique is based on Hooke's Law which states that within the elastic limit, deformation or deflection is proportional to the load applied. It is applicable to either end play or preloaded bearing settings.

A detailed explanation with descriptive data and actual applications is contained in The Timken Company Engineering Journal supplement "Automated Bearing Settings".

c. Torque-Set

The Torque-Set technique is a method of obtaining correct bearing settings by using bearing rolling torque as a basis for determining the amount of deformation or deflection of the assembly parts affecting bearing settings. This technique is applicable regardless of whether the final bearing setting is preload or end play.

The significant difference between Torque-Set and Acro-Set is that Torque-Set starts off with a known dimension such as an initial shim pack, and then the bearing torque is measured to determine the required shim pack change that will provide the desired setting. Acro-Set starts off with a known load applied to the bearings and then a measurement is taken to determine the final thickness of the shim pack, spacer or snap ring.

A step-by-step explanation of the utilization of the Torque-Set method is given in The Timken Company Engineering Journal supplement "Automated Bearing Settings".

The decision as to which automated bearing setting technique should be used must be made early in the design sequence. The designer should not merely design the machine and then leave it to the assembly department to determine the assembly procedure that should be used. This admonition obviously does not apply to the Set-Right approach, since the assembly department cannot alter the specified tolerances upon which this method depends. It is with Acro-Set and Torque-Set that the designer needs to meet his responsibility of selecting the assembly procedure.

When deciding which of the three methods to use, the Set-Right method should be investigated first. If that approach is found to be impractical, the other two systems, Acro-Set and Torque-Set, should be given equal consideration. A given application could possibly use any one of these three methods or a combination of them. It is necessary to review each application to determine which method is the most economical and what fixtures and tools are to be employed. The final decision will be based on the physical size and weight of the unit, present machining tolerances, production volume, access to retaining devices (locknuts, end plates, cup followers, etc.), and available tools.

Timken Company sales engineers and service engineers are readily available to assist you in determining the best method to obtain the correct bearing settings.

Mounting of Bearings

4. Adjusting Devices

Cone

In cone-adjusted mountings, the cup backing may be any fixed shoulder such as shown in figures 46 through 55. One cone may be backed against any fixed shoulder and the other adjusted by some satisfactory adjusting device.

In some cases it may be necessary to use a cone adjusting device at more than one bearing position on a common shaft to provide axial adjustment.

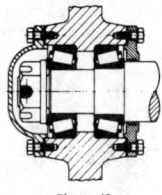

Figure 46

Figure 46 shows a slotted nut used for obtaining the bearing setting. The nut is locked in place with a cotter pin. Both the nut and washer should be of sufficient size to give adequate backing to the cone. Two cotter pin holes spaced at 90° are used to obtain twice as many locking positions per revolution of the nut and a corresponding closer bearing setting.

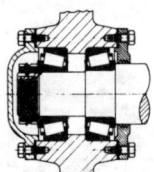

Figure 47

Figure 47 shows two standard locknuts and a lock washer serving as the adjusting device. These nuts are commercially available in sizes from 0.391″ to 7.847″ thread diameter as shown in the Auxiliary Parts Section. These nuts and washers are offered by The Timken Company and a substantial stock of these is planned at all times for your purchase.

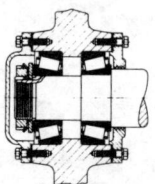

Figure 48

Where sufficient space is not available to permit the use of two standard locknuts and a lock washer, a single locknut, lock washer and tongued washer as shown in figure 48 have been found practical.

Cone Adjusting Devices—Continued

A special nut, often called a stake nut, figure 49, can be used for adjustment and locked by peening the thin section into a keyway slot.

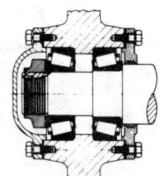

Figure 49

In applications requiring precision class bearings, a special nut containing a soft metal shoe, which is clamped against the threads with a set screw, can be used. See figure 50.

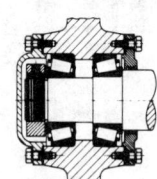

Figure 50

Figure 51 shows how a threaded split nut is sometimes used for bearing setting.

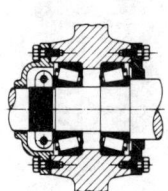

Figure 51

In figure 52 the set-up is made with shims and an end-plate held in place by cap screws applied to the end of the shaft. A slot may be provided in the end plate to measure the shim gap. Standard shim sizes for use with this mounting arrangement can be found in the Auxiliary Parts Section.

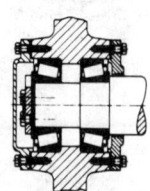

Figure 52

Mounting of Bearings

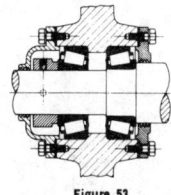

Figure 53

Another adjusting device for maximum shaft extension diameter or straight shafting is shown in figure 53. Here two screws spaced at 90° clamp the collar against the shaft. Adjusting devices such as shown here should only be used in applications having light loads and low speeds.

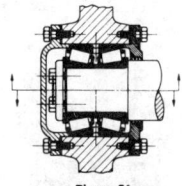

Figure 54

Figure 54 shows a two-row double cup mounting. A type TDO bearing with cone spacer is shown above the centerline and a type TNA bearing below the centerline. These bearings are manufactured with the correct running clearances built into the bearing. A type TDO bearing is shown assembled on the shaft with a cone spacer and clamped against a shoulder by an end plate or nut. A type TNA bearing is assembled on the shaft with the cones butted together and similarly clamped against the shoulder. No further setup provision is required in either case.

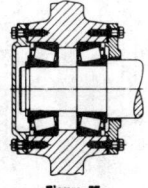

Figure 55

A selective snap ring is illustrated in figure 55. After installing the snap ring in its groove, the cone must be moved back against the snap ring to assure that the desired bearing setting is attained.

Adjusting Devices—Continued

Cup

In cup-adjusted mountings, the cone backing may be any fixed shoulder such as shown in figures 56 through 62. One cup may be backed against any fixed shoulder and the other cup set by some satisfactory adjusting device.

In some cases, it may be necessary to use a cup positioning device at more than one bearing position in a common housing to provide axial adjustment.

Figure 56 shows alternate designs above and below the centerline. A cup carrier is shown above the centerline while a cup follower is shown below. Both designs use shims for adjustment and the carrier or follower is held in place by cap screws.

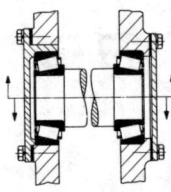

Figure 56

In figure 57 the cup is adjusted by an unpiloted plate with the shims held in place by cap screws. Care must be taken to provide cage clearance and sufficient cup backing. See the Auxiliary Parts Section for standard shim sizes.

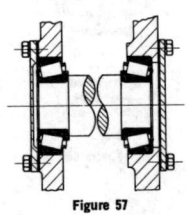

Figure 57

A threaded cup carrier is shown above the centerline in figure 58 while a threaded cup follower is shown in the alternate design below. The carrier and follower are locked by a plate and a cap screw located between the lugs on the carrier or follower and into a slot in the housing.

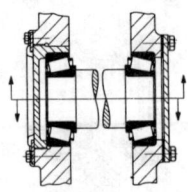

Figure 58

Mounting of Bearings

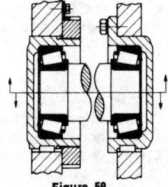

Figure 59

Figure 59 shows an arrangement through which one cup can be adjusted from the inside of the housing. Here a threaded nut is used to adjust one cup carrier and locked by a key and cap screw. Both cup carriers must be fixed against rotation. The fixed carrier is bolted in place in the design shown above the shaft centerline and pressed in place against the flange and keyed in the design shown below the shaft centerline.

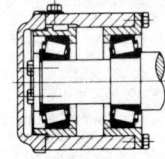

Figure 60

In an indirect mounting with a through-bored housing, figure 60 shows how the bearing setting can be made with a threaded end cap locked by a plate and cap screw. The plate fits into slots in the end cap. The threaded cup carrier must be fixed against rotation in the housing.

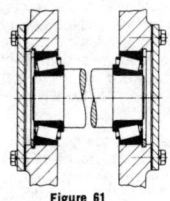

Figure 61

Figure 61 illustrates a beveled snap ring as the setting device. The cup that is adjacent the beveled snap ring is advanced by expanding the snap ring into its groove until the desired setting is obtained. These beveled snap rings are commercially available.

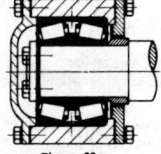

Figure 62

Figure 62 shows a type TDI bearing with a cup spacer. This bearing is supplied with the cup spacer providing the correct internal bearing clearance. The bearing is clamped by a cup follower through the cups and spacer against the housing shoulder.

D. Closure Designs

The selection of the proper closure design for any Timken bearing application should consider the type of lubricant, the foreign material to be kept out of the bearing chamber, the speed of the application and general operating conditions. Foreign material such as dust, scale or any hard, gritty substance will act as a lapping agent and cause rapid bearing wear. Water, acid or deteriorated lubricant may etch the finely-finished raceways and roller surfaces and result in bearing damage.

Because of the damage these injurious environmental factors can create, due consideration must be given to proper closure designs that will most effectively protect the bearings.

Several closure arrangements are given starting on the following page to assist the designer in developing the most satisfactory arrangement. These designs are relatively simple in construction and by combining the basic elements into more sophisticated arrangements, effective closures can be constructed to protect bearings against even the most harmful environmental conditions.

Closure Components	Operating Conditions	
Annular grooves Stampings Radial lip seal	Clean	
Annular grooves and stampings Radial lip seal and stampings	Fairly Clean	Low Speed
Radial lip seal with external machined dust seal Stampings and machined parts	Dirty	
Internal Flingers with annular grooves	Clean	
Internal flingers, annular grooves and outer stamping dust shields	Fairly Clean	High Speed
Internal flingers, annular grooves and outer machined dust shields	Dirty	

1. Metal Stampings

Metal stamping closures are effective in low speed and clean applications. Where environmental conditions are dirty, stampings are used in combination with other closure elements to provide an effective labyrinth against the entrance of foreign matter into the bearing chamber.

Stampings should be designed to provide a clearance of 0.020" to 0.025" on diameter between rotating and stationary parts. A minimum axial clearance of 1/16" should be provided between adjacent rotating and stationary parts. These stampings are shown in figures 63, 64 and 65.

2. Machined Flingers

Machined parts used with other closure elements are recommended in place of stampings where closer closure clearances are desired. This results in a more efficient retention of lubricant and exclusion of foreign matter from the bearing housing. Examples are shown in figures 65, 66 and 67.

3. Annular Grooves

Annular groove closures are primarily used with grease lubrication in place of radial lip seals where considerable grit and dust are encountered. This type of closure is also effective in high speed oil lubricated applications when used with an internal umbrella type flinger illustrated in figure 67.

Annular groove closures are most effective when applied with close-running clearances. On closure diameters up to 2", a clearance of 0.010" to 0.015" on diameter is recommended. For larger diameters, these clearances may be increased to as much as 0.040" to 0.050" on diameter.

The closure usually has several grooves machined in the bore or on the outside diameter depending on the design. When used with oil, these grooves tend to interrupt the capillary action. Used with grease, the grooves become filled with a mixture of dust and grease which tends to harden and provide a tight closure.

The grooves are usually cut with a round nose tool the sides of which are ground to an included angle of 30°. The width of the groove at the widest part should be about 1/8" to 3/16" and the land between the grooves should be about one-half the width of the groove. The depth should be 5/32" to 3/16". At least three grooves are recommended and a greater number will make the closure that much more effective.

4. Radial Lip Seals

Many types and styles of radial lip seals are commercially available to satisfy many sealing requirements.

In clean environments where the primary requirement is the retention of lubricant in the bearing housing, a single lip seal with the lip pointing inward is often used.

Where the critical concern is exclusion of contaminants, the lip is usually pointed out, as shown in figure 69.

These single lip seals are available with or without a spring-loaded lip. The spring maintains a constant pressure of the lip on the sealing surface, thereby providing a more efficient seal for a longer period of time.

When environmental conditions require a seal to prevent contaminants from entering the bearing chamber as well as retaining the lubricant, a double lip seal is often used. Usually the lips face opposite each other.

External flingers or shrouds should be used where extremely dirty conditions are present so that the seal lip and sealing surface are protected to avoid rapid wear and premature seal failures. See figure 70.

The particular style and type of seal selected for an application should be based on recommendations of the seal supplier.

Sealing surface hardness and finish should also follow the recommendations of the seal supplier. In general, surface hardness should be Rockwell C-30 minimum and surface finish should be within the range of 10 to 30 micro-inch arithmetical average. A finish much smoother than this will not support a lubricant film to adequately lubricate the seal lip. The result is usually premature seal failure.

Polished or plunge ground finish without lead is preferred to prevent pumping of lubricant out of the bearing housing past the seal lip. Guidelines of the seal supplier should be followed in determining allowable seal seat runout.

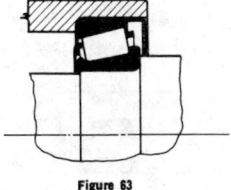

Figure 63

The stamping shown in figure 63 is effective for applications that are grease lubricated and operating under clean conditions.

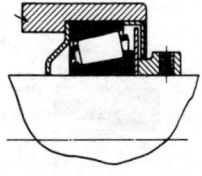

Figure 64

The design in figure 64 uses stampings on both sides of the bearing in order to keep the grease in close proximity to the bearing. Only a small amount of grease is required for adequate lubrication. The flinger mounted at the outer side of the bearing adds a labyrinth effect.

Closure Designs—Continued

Flingers can also be made as machined parts as illustrated in figures 65 and 66.

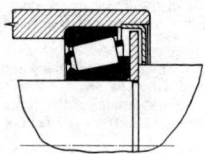

Figure 65

The outer member of the closure in figure 66 has annular grooves machined into the I.D. to make it more effective than a stamping.

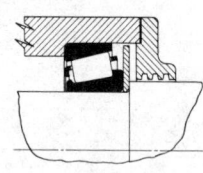

Figure 66

An umbrella shaped flinger is shown in figure 67 along with an annular grooved outer member. At high shaft speeds this closure effectively retains oil.

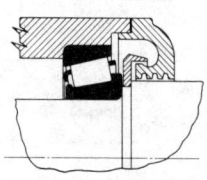

Figure 67

Annular grooves with a machined labyrinth effectively protect a grease lubricated bearing when the unit is required to operate in an extremely dirty environment. See figure 68.

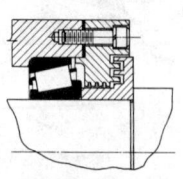

Figure 68

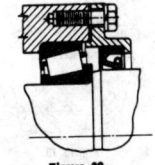

Figure 69

The radial lip seal in figure 69 is effective for sealing either a grease or oil lubricated application.

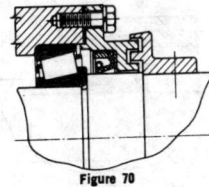

Figure 70

The combination of a labyrinth with a radial lip seal—figure 70—effectively protects a grease or oil lubricated bearing that is operating in a unit in an extremely dirty environment.

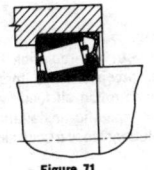

Figure 71

The "Duo-Face" seal shown in figure 71 has proven satisfactory in many different types of grease lubricated applications.

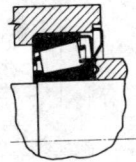

Figure 72

A metal stamping seal as shown in figure 72 is commercially available. One lip rubs against the front face of the cup while the other rubs against the face of the housing. Another style of this seal consisting only of the inner member is available.

Closure Designs—Continued

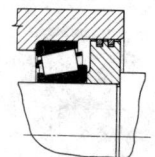

Figure 73

5. Piston Rings

In some applications, existing operating conditions make annular groove closures or radial lip seals unsatisfactory. Piston rings as shown in figures 73 and 74 have been used. These rings satisfactorily retain grease. When used singly they do not hold oil in or keep foreign liquids out of the bearing chamber. A piston ring expands into the housing bore, thereby forming a labyrinth with the groove in the shaft or adapter member used. The axial clearance of the ring in the groove should be 0.006″ to 0.008″.

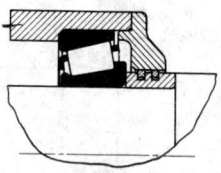

Figure 74

6. Vertical Shaft Closures

The problem of properly sealing housings where vertical shafts and oil lubrication are used has received considerable study. In spite of all efforts toward the development of good effective vertical operating seals, the problem usually resolves itself into one of trying to provide internal flinger closures in combination with a circulating oil system. Where such lubricating provisions are impractical, a mist or other carefully controlled oil feed system must be developed for the specific installation. Figures 75-77 show a few solutions to vertical sealing problems.

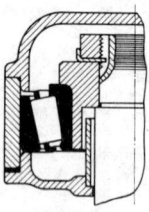

Figure 75

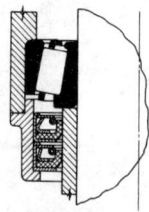

Figure 76

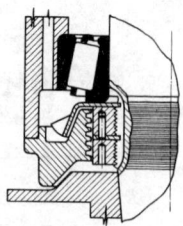

Figure 77

Mounting of Bearings

Typical Mountings
Single-Row Arrangements

Applications illustrating direct and indirect bearing mountings are covered in the figures that follow.

The indirect mounting is nearly always recommended in wheel applications and any other applications where maximum rigidity and stability is required in a minimum of width.

The direct mounting often has some advantage in reducing machining and application costs. Typical applications include gear reduction units, pillow blocks and journal boxes.

Indirect Mounting

Rotating Cone - Stationary Cup

Two type TS bearings in figure 78 support the pinion shaft in this spiral bevel gear drive. Both cups and cones are applied with tight fits. The cups are pressed into the cartridge and backed against a shoulder.

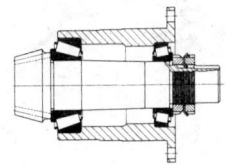

Figure 78

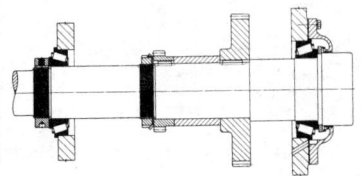

Figure 79

Figure 79 is a flanged cup bearing, type TSF, mounting using single-row bearings on a milling machine spindle. The flanged cups permit the use of accurate through-bored housings.

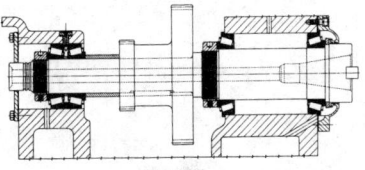

Figure 80

Figure 80 is an arrangement of two flanged cup bearings in the nose of a milling machine spindle with a floating type TDODC bearing in the rear position. Both housing bores can be simultaneously machined to permit accurate alignment between the nose and rear cup seats.

Single-Row Arrangements—Continued

Stationary Cone - Rotating Cup

A typical pneumatic-tired wheel hub, mounted on type TS bearings, is shown in figure 81. The cups are pressed against the wheel hub shoulders which have been provided with knock-out slots. The cups are applied tight in the hub while the cones are mounted with a loose fit on the shaft.

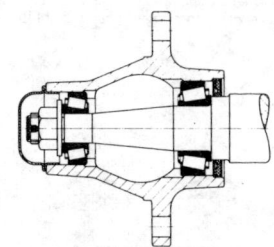

Figure 81

Figure 82 shows the "Duo-Face" seal type TSL bearing in a wheel hub. The seal is attached to the cone rib so that assembly of the cone and seal is performed in one operation. Since no other sealing elements are required for this application, less parts are required for inventory.

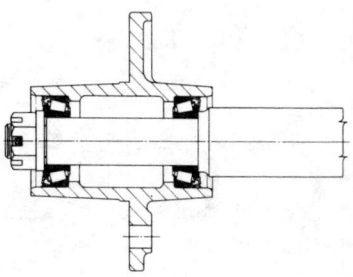

Figure 82

Figure 83 shows flanged cup type TSF single-row bearings in idler gears on paper mill dryer drives. Through-bored gear hubs are permitted with the use of flanged cups.

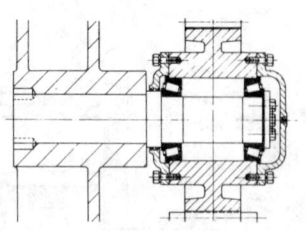

Figure 83

Mounting of Bearings

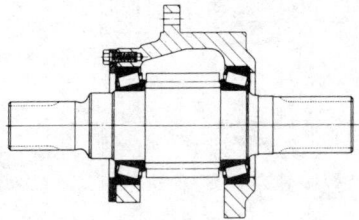

Figure 84

Rotating Cone - Stationary Cup

This tractor final drive pinion illustrated in figure 84 is mounted on two type TS bearings with the cones backed against shoulders on the pinion shaft. One cup is backed against a shoulder in the housing and the other cup is held in position by a bolted-on backing ring.

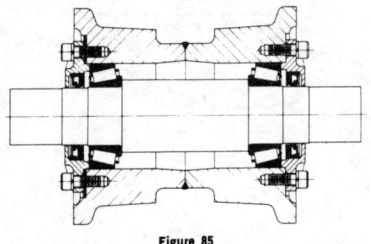

Figure 85

Stationary Cone - Rotating Cup

The mounting of two type TS bearings in a crawler tractor track support roller as shown in figure 85 is similar to figure 84. The cups rotate and must be mounted with an interference fit to prevent creepage and possible damage to the cup seats.

Two-Row Arrangements

Rotating Cone - Stationary Cup

The "SR" assembly in figure 86 is manufactured with cone and cup spacers. The O.D. configuration of the cup spacer permits the entry of lubricant to the area between the two rows of rollers.

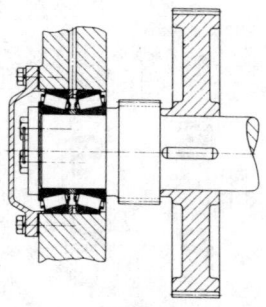

Figure 86

Two types of bearings are shown in figure 87. A type TDO is used at the fixed position and a type TDODC cup is used at the floating position.

The gear shaft is fixed axially by clamping the type TDO cup against a shoulder in the housing. A pin is inserted into the large hole in the O.D. of the type TDODC cup to prevent it from creeping and damaging the cup seat.

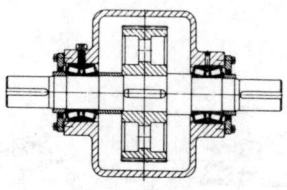

Figure 87

The mounting of the type TNA and TNADC bearings in figure 88 is similar to the mounting in figure 87. The only difference is that the type TNA bearing does not use a spacer between the two single cones to establish the bearing setting.

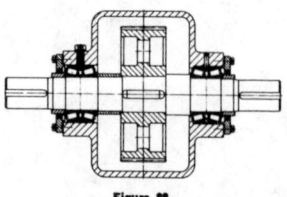

Figure 88

Mounting of Bearings

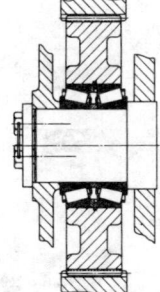

Figure 89

Stationary Cone - Rotating Cup

The "SR" assembly in figure 89 shows how the O.D. profile of the cup spacer permits the use of a snap ring to locate this idler gear axially.

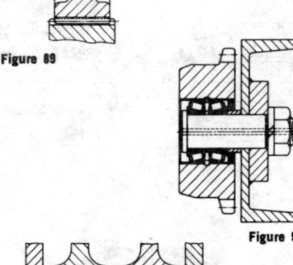

Figure 90

The "SS" assembly shown in figure 90 is also manufactured with cone and cup spacers. The snap ring cup spacer permits positive location of the cups in the housing without the use of any shoulders or clamping rings.

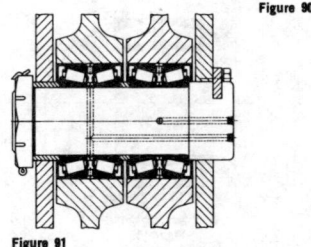

Figure 91

Figure 91 shows a type TNASW bearing applied to a multiple sheave block. The cups are tight fitted in the sheave bore and do not need a cup clamping device. The cones are applied with loose fits. The inside cone faces are provided with slots and chamfers to permit lubricant to pass into the bearings through the holes drilled in the shaft.

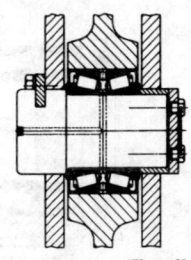

Figure 92

Figure 92 shows a type TNASWE bearing which is slightly wider than the TNASW shown in figure 91. The outside diameter of the extended cone rib on each side of the bearing is ground to permit the use of a closure. The bearing mounting is otherwise similar to figure 91.

Two-Row Arrangements—Continued

Direct Mounting

Rotating Cone - Stationary Cup

The cups in figure 93 are direct mounted in cartridges. One cartridge is allowed to float in the housing while the other is fixed against axial displacement by the seal carrier plate and cap screws.

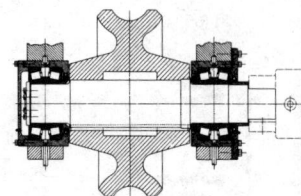

Figure 93

The bearing mounting in figure 94 is similar to figure 93. The cups at the floating position are mounted in a cartridge while the cups at the fixed position are mounted directly into the main housing. The sleeve with tapered I.D., on which the cones at the floating position are mounted, is used to facilitate disassembly of the bearings and cartridge from the shaft.

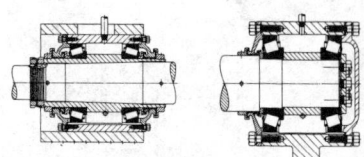

Figure 94

Figure 95 shows a type TDI bearing applied to a rolling mill roll neck. In most of these applications the bearing cones are mounted on the roll necks with a loose fit to permit easy removal of chocks and bearings from the rolls.

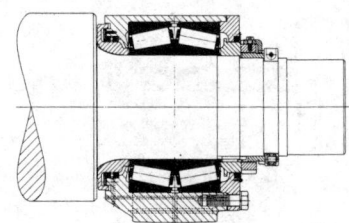

Figure 95

Figure 96 shows a type TDIT bearing mounted on a rolling mill roll neck. This tapered bore bearing is applied with an interference fit, thereby permitting high speeds without cone creepage. The bearing assembly is held in place by a nut applied over a threaded sleeve. This sleeve is held in place by a hinged backing ring. The roll necks are provided with axial and radial holes as shown so that the cone may be expanded and removed from the taper of the neck by hydraulic pressure.

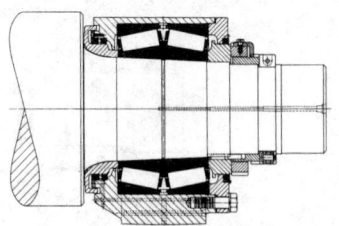

Figure 96

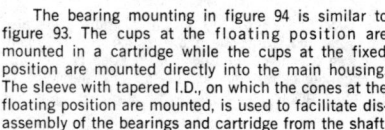

Mounting of Bearings

Thrust Bearing Arrangements

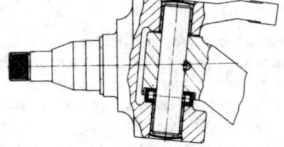

Figure 97

Figure 97 shows the application of a type TTSP bearing in a truck steering pivot. This type is also used in such applications as floor jacks and crane hooks.

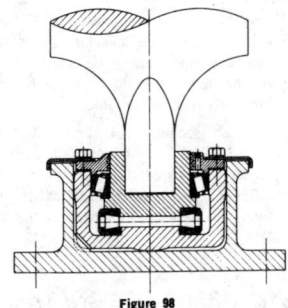

Figure 98

Figure 98 shows a type TTCS bearing mounted in the bottom or step position of a jib crane mast. The retainer can be provided either with or without holes about its outside diameter, depending on the lubrication requirements of the design. The type TTCS assembly is identical to the type TTC with the exception of retainer construction.

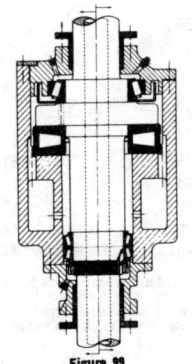

Figure 99

The type TTHD bearing is an accurately ground precision product which may be used for heavy continuously-applied thrust loads at moderately high speeds.

Figure 99 shows a type TTHD bearing used to take the thrust on oil well swivels.

F. Lubrication

Adequate lubrication is essential to the successful performance of Timken tapered roller bearings in any application. "Adequate" describes lubricants which have the physical and chemical properties required by the application. It also includes the proper amount of lubricant and the proper application of the lubricant to the bearing.

Bearing lubricants perform three fundamental functions:

(1) Lubricate by separating mating surfaces and reducing friction.

(2) Transfer heat.

(3) Protect from corrosion and dirt.

When the mating surfaces of a bearing are lubricated, the surfaces are actually separated by a thin film of lubricant (less than 0.000050") which prevents metal-to-metal contact and resultant friction and wear. Lubricants are also used to transfer heat away from the contact surfaces of the bearing to cooler surfaces of the housing or to a heat exchanger. Lubricants must also protect the precision ground bearing surfaces from corrosion or attack by undesirable environments. Proper lubricant selection must give consideration to each of the fundamental functions to insure adequate lubrication.

There are three **basic types** of lubricants: **oil, grease** and **solid.**

Oils and greases are commonly used in Timken bearing applications. At the present state of the art, solid film lubricants are not practical for most conventional applications and will be given no further consideration in this discussion.

1. Oil

Commercially used lubricating oils are available in many forms for automotive, industrial, aircraft and other uses. Oils are classified as petroleum types, which are refined from crude oil, or synthetic types, which are produced by chemical synthesis.

Many varieties of synthetic oils such as silicones, diesters, polybutenes and polyglycols are available. However, for practical industrial lubrication the use of synthetic oils is usually limited to specialized applications which exceed the temperature capabilit of petroleum oils. The Timken Company engineeri department should be consulted regarding the app cation of synthetic lubricants.

Petroleum oils are used for nearly all oil lub cated applications. These oils have physical a chemical properties that can be used to help sel the correct oil for any bearing application. The dor nant property in the selection of any oil is viscosi Since viscosity varies inversely with temperature, t viscosity value must always be stated along with temperature at which it was determined.

Industrial users commonly report viscosity Saybolt Universal Seconds, abbreviated as SSU or S at 100°F and/or 210°F. The measure of the rate change of viscosity with temperature is called viscos index or VI. The higher the VI, the lower the rate change in viscosity with temperature.

The American Society for Testing and Materi (ASTM) has published a recommended practice "Viscosity System for Industrial Fluid Lubricant designated D2422. The viscosity classification numb as listed below is the normal viscosity of the fluid SUS at 100°F.

ASTM GRADE DESIGNATIONS

ASTM Viscosity Classification Number	Viscosity Range SUS at 100°F*
3150	2835-3465
2150	1935-2365
1500	1350-1650
1000	900-1100
700	630-770
465	419-511
315	284-346
215	194-236
150	135-165
105	95-115
75	68-82
60	54-66

*Rounded off to nearest whole number.

PRINTED BY PERMISSION OF THE AMERICAN SOCIETY FOR TESTING AND MATERIALS.

Figure 100

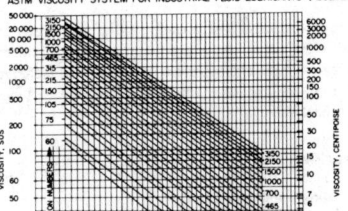

ASTM VISCOSITY SYSTEM FOR INDUSTRIAL FLUID LUBRICANTS (ASSUME 90 V.I.)

PRINTED BY PERMISSION OF THE AMERICAN
SOCIETY FOR TESTING AND MATERIALS.

Figure 101

Figure 101 shows a partial listing of the ASTM viscosity system plotted on a viscosity-temperature chart. From these charts the viscosity of a lubricant can be approximated for a wide temperature range.

The selection of correct oil viscosity for any bearing application requires careful study of operational and environmental factors. From the elastohydrodynamic (EHD) theory, bearing operating speed is the primary consideration in selecting proper oil viscosity at any operating temperature. Secondary consideration is given to load, type of oil and environmental factors. Accordingly, it is necessary to use high viscosity oil on low speed applications, and low viscosity oil on high speed applications.

The Timken Company engineering department can provide specific viscosity recommendations based on the EHD theory for specific applications. However, as a good rule of thumb the oil viscosity should be 60 SUS minimum at the bearing operating temperature.

Many oil lubricated bearing applications are operated satisfactorily without the benefit of filters. However, where environmental contamination has a detrimental effect on bearing performance, filtration equipment is recommended. Experience has shown that nominally rated 40 micron filters are satisfactory for most Timken bearing industrial applications.

2. Grease

Conventionally, greases used in Timken bearing applications are petroleum oils of some specific vis-

cosity which are thickened to the desired consistency by some form of metallic soap. Greases are available in many soap types (sometimes called base type) such as sodium (soda), calcium (lime), lithium, calcium-complex and aluminum-complex. Organic and inorganic type non-soap thickeners are also used in some products.

Calcium greases are inexpensive, have good water resistance, but are limited to temperatures below 150°F. Sodium greases generally have good stability and will operate at higher temperatures, but absorb water and cannot be used where moisture is present. Lithium, calcium-complex and aluminum-complex greases generally combine the higher temperature properties and stability of sodium grease with the water resistance of calcium grease. These greases are often referred to as "multi-purpose" greases since they combine the two most important lubricant advantages into one product.

Important grease properties to remember:

1. Soap type qualities (outlined above).

2. Viscosity of the base oil.

3. Grease consistency.

4. Ability to remain stable both mechanically and chemically during use.

Tapered roller bearings generally use NLGI No. 1 or No. 2 greases. In some cases, where cold weather pumping in automatic greasing systems is required, No. 0 greases are used. No. 3 and heavier greases are seldom used in Timken bearings because they tend to channel and cause lubricant starvation.

Typical grease lubricated industrial bearing applications can be satisfied with an NLGI No. 2 consistency multi-purpose type grease (like lithium 12 hydroxy stearate soap) with a 300 SUS to 1200 SUS at 100°F petroleum type base oil which also contains added rust and oxidation inhibitors. The lower viscosity base oils are used for higher speed applications where heat generation must be kept to a minimum. The higher viscosity base oils are used in the more heavily loaded or slow speed applications. EP (extreme pressure) additives may also be included, but they are not required except where abnormal loads are possible or where particular combinations of load and speed are likely to cause scoring.

Lubrication—Continued

Lubricant additives are materials, usually chemicals, which are added to oils or greases to improve specific properties of the lubricant. Additives, when properly formulated into a lubricant, can increase lubricant life, resist corrosion, increase anti-score and anti-wear capacity, and enhance other properties to increase the value of the product. However, additives are very complex and therefore should not be included indiscriminately in lubricants as a cure-all for all lubrication problems.

The more common lubricant additives are:

1. Oxidation inhibitors for increasing the product's service life.

2. Rust or corrosion inhibitors to protect bearing surfaces from rust or corrosion.

3. Demulsifiers to promote oil and water separation.

4. Viscosity index improvers to decrease viscosity sensitivity to temperature change.

5. Pour point depressants to lower the pouring point at low temperatures.

6. Lubricity agents to modify friction.

7. Anti-wear agents to retard wear.

8. Extreme pressure additives to prevent scoring under boundary lubrication conditions.

9. Detergents and dispersants to maintain cleanliness.

10. Anti-foam agents to reduce foam.

11. Tackiness agents to improve adhesive properties.

Inorganic additives such as molybdenum disulfide, graphite and zinc oxide are sometimes included in lubricants. In most tapered roller bearing applications these inorganic additives are of no significant benefit. Conversely, as long as the concentration is low and the particle size small, they are not harmful. Therefore, we neither recommend nor discourage their use.

Additional discussions on lubrication of Timken bearings are found under Heat Generation on page 31 and in Speed Capabilities of Tapered Roller Bearings on pages 32, 33 and 34.

Bearing Analysis and Loading Symbols

a = Axial distance from cone back face to "effective load center"

a_a = Effective bearing spread

a_b = Actual bearing spread

AF = Application factor - A factor compensating for variations in operating conditions, such as shock, continuous duty, inequality of loading, etc. (example Clay Working Machinery — AF = 2) Selection of application factor is based on experience or an assumed value is used. (See Reference Tables)

b = Tooth length

BP = Belt or chain pull

BTU = British thermal units

c_p = Specific heat of lubricant in BTU/lb_m/°F

C(N) = Basic dynamic radial load rating for (N) million revolutions

C(90) = The basic dynamic radial load rating of a single-row bearing at a speed of 500 RPM and for a life of 3000 hours L_{10} or 90 million revolutions

$C(90)_2$ = Basic dynamic radial load rating of a two-row bearing

C(90)R = Required dynamic radial load rating at 500 RPM and 3000 hours L_{10} (See page 50)

CA(N) = Basic dynamic thrust load rating for (N) million revolutions

CA(90) = The basic dynamic thrust load rating of a bearing at a speed of 500 RPM and for a life of 3000 hours L_{10} or 90 million revolutions

CA(90)R = Required dynamic thrust load rating at 500 RPM and 3000 hours L_{10} (See page 50)

CD = Distance between worm and worm gear centers

CF = Centrifugal force

D_M = Mean diameter, in inches, or effective working diameter of pinions, gears, sprockets, wheels or pulleys. Mean rolling diameter of tires

daN = decanewton, the unit of force within the International System of Units (SI) adopted as official units for bearing ratings in the metric system. It is the force required to give a mass of ten kilograms an acceleration of one meter/second^2. See reference tables for conversion factors.

D_P = Pitch diameter, in inches of pinions, gears, sprockets, etc.

f_t = Torque combined loading factor

F = General term for applied bearing load

F_a = Total thrust load

F_{max} = Maximum load during a loading cycle

F_{min} = Minimum load during a loading cycle

F_r = Radial component of applied bearing load

F_{wt} = Weighted average load from a loading cycle (p. 48 and p. 58)

FPM = Feet per minute

F_x = Belt and chain pull factors

G = Bearing geometry factor (See p. 28 to p. 30)

hr = Hours

HP = Horsepower

in = Inches

kw = Kilowatt

K = K-factor = Ratio of basic dynamic radial load rating C(90) to basic dynamic thrust load rating CA(90) in a single-row bearing

$$K = \frac{C(90)}{CA(90)} \text{ (See p. 22)}$$

L = General term for bearing life in hours

L_{10} = Bearing life in hours. The life expectancy that 90% of a group of apparently identical bearings will attain or exceed under a specific loading condition

$$L_{10} = \left(\frac{C(90) \times SF}{P \times AF}\right)^{10/3} \times 3000 \text{ hr} =$$
$$(LF)^{10/3} \times 3000 \text{ hr}$$
$$= \left(\frac{C(90)}{P \times AF}\right)^{10/3} \times 90 \times 10^6 \text{ revolutions}$$

L_{av} = Average life expectancy, in hours, of a number of bearings under a specific loading condition

$L_{av} \sim 5 \times L_{10}$

lb = Pounds (#)

lb_m = Pound (mass)

LF = Life Factor = $\dfrac{C(90) \times SF}{P \times AF}$

A factor which corresponds to the L_{10} hours of life desired from, or provided by, a bearing. It is used in selecting the bearing, or in calculating the L_{10} which a given bearing will provide under certain loading conditions.
(Example: when LF = 1, L_{10} = 3000 hr, See Reference Tables)

$$LF = \left(\frac{L_{10}}{3000}\right)^{3/10}$$

LH = Left hand

m = Ratio of gearing

mm = Millimeter

M = Running torque

M_b = Bending moment

M_t = Torsional moment

MPH = Miles per hour

N = Number of teeth in gears, pinions and sprockets

NLGI = National Lubricating Grease Institute

P = Dynamic equivalent radial load (Example: P_A = Dynamic equivalent radial load on bearing "A")

P_o = Static equivalent radial load

PSI = Pounds per square inch

Q = Heat (BTU/minute)

r = Radius to center of mass

R = Reliability, in percent

RH = Right hand

RPM = Revolutions per minute

S = Bearing speed in RPM
(Example: S_1, S_2 ⋯ S_n indicate RPM during applied bearing loads F_1, F_2 ⋯ F_n respectively)

SF = Speed factor at bearing speed "S" in RPM (Example: SF = 1 when speed, RPM = 500, See Reference Tables)

$$SF = \left(\frac{500}{S}\right)^{3/10}$$

S_{TF} = Gear tooth separating force

SUS = Saybolt universal seconds

t_1, t_2 ⋯ t_n = Actual time in hours during which bearing speeds S_1, S_2 ⋯ S_n occur during a loading cycle

T_1, T_2 ⋯ T_n = The % of time during which the applied bearing loading F_1, F_2 ⋯ F_n occur during the loading cycle, expressed as a decimal fraction

T_e = Calculated or given external thrust load on bearing (Example: $T_e A$ = 450 lb p. 52)

t_t = Total time of loading cycle ($t_1 + t_2$ ⋯ t_n)

T_{TF} = Gear tooth thrust

TE = Tractive effort on vehicle wheels

TF = Tangential force on gears, sprockets or pinions

W = Weight of unbalance (lb)

ϕ = (phi) = Normal tooth pressure angle in gearing, in degrees

ϕ_x = (phi$_x$) = Axial tooth pressure angle in degrees

θ_i = (theta$_i$) = Temperature of oil entering bearing, (degrees Fahrenheit)

θ_o = (theta$_o$) = Temperature of oil exiting bearing, (degrees Fahrenheit)

α = (alpha) = ½ included cup angle, in degrees

γ = (gamma) = Bevel gearing - Pitch angle, in degrees. Hypoid gearing - Face angle of pinion and root angle of gear, in degrees

ψ = (psi) = Angle in degrees

λ = (lambda) = Helix angle in helical gears and lead angle in worm gearing, in degrees, (in double enveloping worm gears the lead angle λ is taken at the center of worm and gear contact.)

f = Friction angle in worm gearing, in degrees

π = (pi) = 3.1416

η = (eta) = Efficiency, expressed as a decimal

μ = (mu) = Viscosity of oil in centipoise

ρ = (rho) = Density of lubricant in lb_m/cubic ft

° = Degrees

′ = Minutes

∴ = Therefore

% = Percent

⟨ or < = Less than

⟩ or > = Greater than

≠ = Not equal to

≤ = Less than or equal to

REFERENCE TABLES

	PAGE
Life Factor Table	Back of Tab
Speed Factor Table	1
Cone and Cup Fitting Practice	2-17
Inch System Bearings Fitting Practice	4, 5, 12, 13
Metric System Bearings Fitting Practice	6-11, 14-17
Bearing Tolerances	18-23
Life and Application Factors	24-27
Conversion Tables	28

Life Factor Table

hours life (L_{10}) versus life factor (LF)

$$\text{life} = LF^{10/3} \times 3000 \text{ (hours}$$

The basic dynamic load rating of a Timken bearing is based on an L_{10} of 3000 hours at 500 RPM or 90 million revolutions.

hours	factor	hours	factor	hours	factor	hours	factor	hours	factor	hours	fac
100	0.360	660	0.635	2900	0.990	8000	1.342	17750	1.705	31000	2.0
110	0.371	680	0.641	**3000**	**1.000**	8100	1.347	18000	1.712	31500	2.02
120	0.381	700	0.646	3100	1.010	8200	1.352	18250	1.719	32000	2.03
130	0.390	720	0.652	3200	1.020	8300	1.357	18500	1.726	32500	2.04
140	0.399	740	0.657	3300	1.029	8400	1.362	18750	1.733	33000	2.0
150	0.407	760	0.662	3400	1.038	8500	1.367	19000	1.740	33500	2.0
160	0.415	780	0.668	3500	1.047	8600	1.372	19250	1.747	34000	2.07
170	0.423	800	0.673	3600	1.056	8700	1.376	19500	1.753	34500	2.0
180	0.430	820	0.678	3700	1.065	8800	1.381	19750	1.760	35000	2.0
190	0.437	840	0.683	3800	1.073	8900	1.386	20000	1.767	35500	2.0
200	0.444	860	0.687	3900	1.082	9000	1.390	20250	1.773	36000	2.1
210	0.450	880	0.692	4000	1.090	9100	1.395	20500	1.780	36500	2.1
220	0.457	900	0.697	4100	1.098	9200	1.400	20750	1.786	37000	2.1
230	0.463	920	0.701	4200	1.106	9300	1.404	21000	1.793	37500	2.1
240	0.469	940	0.706	4300	1.114	9400	1.409	21250	1.799	38000	2.1
250	0.475	960	0.710	4400	1.122	9500	1.413	21500	1.805	38500	2.1
260	0.480	980	0.715	4500	1.129	9600	1.418	21750	1.812	39000	2.1
270	0.486	1000	0.719	4600	1.137	9700	1.422	22000	1.818	39500	2.1
280	0.491	1050	0.730	4700	1.144	9800	1.426	22250	1.824	40000	2.1
290	0.496	1100	0.740	4800	1.151	9900	1.431	22500	1.830	41000	2.1
300	0.501	1150	0.750	4900	1.159	10000	1.435	22750	1.836	42000	2.2
310	0.506	1200	0.760	5000	1.166	10250	1.446	23000	1.842	43000	2.2
320	0.511	1250	0.769	5100	1.173	10500	1.456	23250	1.848	44000	2.2
330	0.516	1300	0.778	5200	1.179	10750	1.467	23500	1.854	45000	2.2
340	0.520	1350	0.787	5300	1.186	11000	1.477	23750	1.860	46000	2.2
350	0.525	1400	0.796	5400	1.193	11250	1.487	24000	1.866	47000	2.2
360	0.529	1450	0.804	5500	1.199	11500	1.496	24250	1.872	48000	2.2
370	0.534	1500	0.812	5600	1.206	11750	1.506	24500	1.878	49000	2.3
380	0.538	1550	0.820	5700	1.212	12000	1.516	24750	1.883	50000	2.3
390	0.542	1600	0.828	5800	1.219	12250	1.525	25000	1.889	52500	2.3
400	0.546	1650	0.836	5900	1.225	12500	1.534	25250	1.895	55000	2.3
410	0.550	1700	0.843	6000	1.231	12750	1.544	25500	1.900	57500	2.4
420	0.554	1750	0.851	6100	1.237	13000	1.553	25750	1.906	60000	2.4
430	0.558	1800	0.858	6200	1.243	13250	1.561	26000	1.911	62500	2.4
440	0.562	1850	0.865	6300	1.249	13500	1.570	26250	1.917	65000	2.5
450	0.566	1900	0.872	6400	1.255	13750	1.579	26500	1.922	67500	2.5
460	0.570	1950	0.879	6500	1.261	14000	1.587	26750	1.928	70000	2.5
470	0.573	2000	0.885	6600	1.267	14250	1.596	27000	1.933	72500	2.6
480	0.577	2050	0.892	6700	1.273	14500	1.604	27250	1.939	75000	2.6
490	0.581	2100	0.899	6800	1.278	14750	1.613	27500	1.944	77500	2.6
500	0.584	2150	0.905	6900	1.284	15000	1.621	27750	1.949	80000	2.7
510	0.588	2200	0.911	7000	1.289	15250	1.629	28000	1.954	82500	2.7
520	0.591	2250	0.917	7100	1.295	15500	1.637	28250	1.960	85000	2.7
530	0.594	2300	0.923	7200	1.300	15750	1.645	28500	1.965	87500	2.7
540	0.598	2350	0.929	7300	1.306	16000	1.652	28750	1.970	90000	2.
550	0.601	2400	0.935	7400	1.311	16250	1.660	29000	1.975	92500	2.
560	0.604	2450	0.941	7500	1.316	16500	1.668	29250	1.980	95000	2.
580	0.611	2500	0.947	7600	1.322	16750	1.675	29500	1.985	97500	2.
600	0.617	2600	0.958	7700	1.327	17000	1.683	29750	1.990	100000	2.
620	0.623	2700	0.969	7800	1.332	17250	1.690	30000	1.995		
640	0.629	2800	0.980	7900	1.337	17500	1.697	30500	2.005		

Reference Tables

Speed Factor Table

speed (RPM) versus speed factor (SF)

$$SF = \left(\frac{500}{RPM}\right)^{3/10}$$

rpm	factor	rpm	factor	rpm	factor	rpm	factor	rpm	factor	rpm	factor
< 5	4.000	62	1.871	280	1.190	800	0.868	2600	0.610	11000	0.396
5	3.981	64	1.853	290	1.178	825	0.861	2650	0.606	11250	0.393
6	3.769	66	1.836	300	1.166	850	0.853	2700	0.603	11500	0.390
7	3.599	68	1.819	310	1.154	875	0.845	2750	0.600	11750	0.388
8	3.458	70	1.804	320	1.143	900	0.838	2800	0.596	12000	0.385
9	3.337	72	1.789	330	1.133	925	0.831	2850	0.593	12250	0.383
10	3.234	74	1.774	340	1.123	950	0.825	2900	0.590	12500	0.381
11	3.142	76	1.760	350	1.113	975	0.818	2950	0.587	12750	0.378
12	3.062	78	1.746	360	1.104	1000	0.812	3000	0.584	13000	0.376
13	2.989	80	1.733	370	1.095	1025	0.806	3100	0.578	13250	0.374
14	2.923	82	1.720	380	1.086	1050	0.800	3200	0.573	13500	0.372
15	2.863	84	1.708	390	1.077	1075	0.795	3300	0.568	13750	0.370
16	2.808	86	1.696	400	1.069	1100	0.789	3400	0.563	14000	0.368
17	2.758	88	1.684	410	1.061	1125	0.784	3500	0.558	14250	0.366
18	2.711	90	1.673	420	1.054	1150	0.779	3600	0.553	14500	0.364
19	2.667	92	1.662	430	1.046	1175	0.774	3700	0.549	14750	0.362
20	2.627	94	1.651	440	1.039	1200	0.769	3800	0.544	15000	0.360
21	2.588	96	1.641	450	1.032	1225	0.764	3900	0.540	15250	0.359
22	2.552	98	1.631	460	1.025	1250	0.760	4000	0.536	15500	0.357
23	2.519	100	1.621	470	1.019	1275	0.755	4100	0.532	15750	0.355
24	2.487	105	1.597	480	1.012	1300	0.751	4200	0.528	16000	0.354
25	2.456	110	1.575	490	1.006	1325	0.746	4300	0.524	16250	0.352
26	2.428	115	1.554	500	1.000	1350	0.742	4400	0.521	16500	0.350
27	2.400	120	1.534	510	0.994	1375	0.738	4500	0.517	16750	0.349
28	2.374	125	1.516	520	0.988	1400	0.734	4600	0.514	17000	0.347
29	2.349	130	1.498	530	0.983	1425	0.730	4700	0.511	17500	0.344
30	2.326	135	1.481	540	0.977	1450	0.727	4800	0.507	18000	0.341
31	2.303	140	1.465	550	0.972	1475	0.723	4900	0.504	18500	0.338
32	2.281	145	1.450	560	0.967	1500	0.719	5000	0.501	19000	0.336
33	2.260	150	1.435	570	0.961	1525	0.716	5250	0.494	19500	0.333
34	2.240	155	1.421	580	0.956	1550	0.712	5500	0.487	20000	0.331
35	2.221	160	1.408	590	0.952	1575	0.709	5750	0.481	20500	0.328
36	2.202	165	1.395	600	0.947	1600	0.705	6000	0.475	21000	0.326
37	2.184	170	1.382	610	0.942	1650	0.699	6250	0.469	21500	0.324
38	2.166	175	1.370	620	0.938	1700	0.693	6500	0.463	22000	0.321
39	2.150	180	1.359	630	0.933	1750	0.687	6750	0.458	22500	0.319
40	2.133	185	1.348	640	0.929	1800	0.681	7000	0.453	23000	0.317
41	2.118	190	1.337	650	0.924	1850	0.675	7250	0.448	23500	0.315
42	2.102	195	1.326	660	0.920	1900	0.670	7500	0.444	24000	0.313
43	2.088	200	1.316	670	0.916	1950	0.665	7750	0.439	24500	0.311
44	2.073	205	1.307	680	0.912	2000	0.660	8000	0.435	25000	0.309
45	2.059	210	1.297	690	0.908	2050	0.655	8250	0.431	26000	0.306
46	2.046	215	1.288	700	0.904	2100	0.650	8500	0.427	27000	0.302
47	2.033	220	1.279	710	0.900	2150	0.646	8750	0.424	28000	0.299
48	2.020	225	1.271	720	0.896	2200	0.641	9000	0.420	29000	0.296
49	2.007	230	1.262	730	0.893	2250	0.637	9250	0.417	30000	0.293
50	1.995	235	1.254	740	0.889	2300	0.633	9500	0.413	31000	0.290
52	1.972	240	1.246	750	0.885	2350	0.629	9750	0.410	32000	0.287
54	1.950	245	1.239	760	0.882	2400	0.625	10000	0.407	33000	0.285
56	1.929	250	1.231	770	0.879	2450	0.621	10250	0.404	34000	0.282
58	1.908	260	1.217	780	0.875	2500	0.617	10500	0.401	35000	0.280
60	1.889	270	1.203	790	0.872	2550	0.613	10750	0.398		

Cone and Cup Fitting Practice

The tapered construction of a Timken bearing is an advantage since it permits setting of the bearing internal clearance during installation to meet the operating requirements of the application involved. In addition, this feature permits greater machining tolerances for the housing bores into which the cups are mounted and greater machining and grinding tolerances for the shaft on which the cones are mounted.

General industrial application fitting practice standards for cones and cups are shown in the following tables. When using adjustable mountings, some latitude in diameters is permitted where strict adherence to these standards is impractical or impossible. If your application calls for other than standard fits, the problem should be submitted to your Timken Company sales engineer for recommendations.

Precision class bearings must be mounted on shafts and in housings which are similarly finished to at least the same precision limits as the bearing bore and O.D. High quality surface finishes should also be provided.

The bearing races will in all cases tend to take the shape of the part with which they are mated. Therefore, the mounted bearing will not be any more accurate than the surface on which it is mounted. Thus, all shafts and housings should be accurately made to the tolerances shown in the following fitting practice tables. Concentricity, shoulder squareness and surface finish are equally important in assuring optimum operating characteristics.

1. Cones

Rotating cones should always be applied with an interference fit. The term "rotating cone" is used to describe a condition in which the cone rotates relative to the load. This may occur with a rotating cone under a stationary load or a stationary cone with a rotating load. Loose fits will permit the cones to creep and wear the shaft as well as the backing shoulder. This will result in excessive bearing looseness and possible premature bearing and shaft damage.

Stationary cone fitting practice depends on the application. Under conditions of high speed and heavy loads or shock, interference fits using heavy duty fitting practice should be used. With cones mounted on unground shafts subjected to moderate shock loads and moderate speeds, a metal-to-metal or zero average fit is used. In single sheave and wheel applications using unground shafts—or in cases using ground shafts with moderate shock loads—a minimum of zero to a maximum looseness of two times the cone bore tolerance is recommended. In stationary cone applications requiring hardened and ground spindles, a slightly looser fit is permitted. Special fits may also

be necessary on installations such as multiple sheave crane blocks subjected to moderate shock loads and low speeds. In such cases, a slightly looser cone fit is satisfactory.

a. Ground Shaft Fitting Practice

To maintain the recommended fit, all cone shaft seats should be ground whenever possible to a maximum surface finish of 63 micro-inches arithmetical average. In cases where the surface finish of the bearing seat is good and the application is not subjected to high shock loads, the interference fits shown in the table for ground shaft fitting practice are satisfactory.

b. Heavy Duty Fitting Practice

Where it is impractical to grind the shaft O.D. for the cone seats, a tighter heavy duty fitting practice should be followed. In this case the shaft O.D. should be turned to a maximum surface finish of 125 micro-inches arithmetical average. The average interference cone fit should be 0.0005" per inch (0,5 μm per mm) of bearing bore. This figure applies to bearings up to 24" (609,6 mm) bore. If the shaft diameter is held to the same tolerance as the bearing bore, then the average interference fit, for example, between a 24" (609,6 mm) bore cone and shaft will be 0.012" (305 μm). The fit range will be 0.012" (305 μm) plus or minus the bearing bore tolerance. For bearings over 24" (609,6 mm) bore, the fitting practice indicated in the tables for unground shaft finish should be used.

In cases where heavy shock loads and high speeds are involved, this heavy duty fitting practice also should be used, regardless of whether the cone seats are ground or unground.

2. Cups

Housing bores should generally be finished to a maximum surface finish of 125 micro-inches arithmetical average. A rougher finish than this may permit rapid wear of the cup seat surface—resulting in a looser cup fit than desired. The housings must be properly aged or normalized before they are machined for size and surface finish.

Rotating cup applications should always use an interference fit. This is no problem when the bearing setting is obtained through the cones. When bearing setting cannot be accomplished through the cones, it may be necessary to apply the cups with a tight fit in a closely-fitted carrier which is fastened to the housing. Then the bearing settings, as well as assembly and disassembly, can be accomplished by means of the carrier.

In normal designs of single or double cups which are non-adjustable or non-moveable, cups over 3" (76.2 mm) outside diameter are mounted with a minimum fit of 0.001" (25 μm) tight to a maximum tightness of 0.001" (25 μm) plus two times the cup outside diameter tolerance. In unclamped double cup mountings, as used in sheaves, a minimum tightness of 0.002" (50 μm) is used.

Stationary, non-adjustable and fixed single-row cup applications should be applied with a tight fit wherever practical. Loose fits may be used where the bearing setup is obtained by sliding the cup through the housing bore.

When the outside diameter of single-row bearings mounted at each end of a shaft are equal and one is adjustable and the other fixed, it is recommended that the same adjustable fit be used at both ends to permit through-boring.

Two-row double cup bearings are mounted with loose fits to permit assembly and disassembly. The loose fit also permits float when the bearing is mounted in conjunction with an axially fixed bearing on the other end of the shaft.

a. Aluminum or Magnesium Housings

Unless a special lubricant is used, cups should not be pressed into an aluminum or magnesium housing without first contracting them by freezing or expanding the housing by heating—or both. If this is not done, metal may be picked up as the cup is pressed in place and result in an unsatisfactory fit. In many cases, cups are mounted in steel inserts which are attached to the aluminum and magnesium housings. Standard fits may then be used. Where the cup is fitted directly into an **aluminum** housing, it is recommended that a tight fit of **0.0010" per inch** (1 μm per mm) of cup diameter be used. For a **magnesium** housing, a tight fit of **0.0015" per inch** (1,5 μm per mm) of diameter is recommended.

3. Thrust Bearings

Types **TTC, TTCS,** and **TTSP** thrust bearings are generally mounted with a fit range on the inside diameter of 0.005" (127 μm) loose to 0.015" (381 μm) loose. Sufficient clearance is provided on the outside diameter to permit free centering of the bearing without interference.

When type **TTHD** thrust bearings are subjected to continuous rotation, the rotating race should be applied with a minimum interference fit of 0.001" (25μm).

4. Types TNA, TNASW and TNASWE Bearings

The fitting practice for types TNA, TNASW and TNASWE bearings is tabulated along with the other dimensions in the two-row bearing tables. The basic cone fitting practice for these types of bearings used in rotating cone applications is heavy duty fitting practice as described above. The fitting practice for type TNA bearings is given for both rotating and stationary cone applications. The fitting practice for types TNASW and TNASWE bearings is given only for stationary cone applications. **When a type TNASW or TNASWE bearing is used in a rotating cone application, sizes above 3.500" (88,90 mm) cone bore cannot be used** because insufficient mounted internal bearing clearance will be obtained.

Since these are factory pre-set bearings, this recommended fitting practice must be followed so that the bearing is not required to operate with insufficient looseness—or too much looseness.

5. Fitting Practice Tables

The fitting practice tables that follow have been prepared for both **inch** (in black) and **metric** (in red) dimensions.

For the inch system bearings, Classes 4 and 2 (standard) and Classes 3, 0 and 00 (precision) have been included. The maximum available size in Class 0 product is a bearing O.D. of 12.0000" (304,800 mm) and in Class 00 product is a bearing O.D. of 10.5000" (266,700 mm).

Various metric system bearings have been covered. These include Classes K and N (metric system standard bearings) and Classes C and B (metric system precision bearings). The metric value shown for the **tolerances** and **resultant fit** is given in micrometers where 1 micrometer = 0,001 millimeter.

The following tables are included:

a. Inch system bearings in inches and millimeters.

b. Metric system bearings in inches and millimeters.

In the resultant fit columns of all tables, L = Loose and T = Tight.

Rolling Mill Roll Neck fitting practice is contained in the Rolling Mill Equipment Supplement to The Timken·Company Engineering Journal. For all other equipment associated with the rolling mill industry, the fitting practice recommendations in the tables that follow should be used.

INDUSTRIAL EQUIPMENT—CONE FITTING PRACTICE (Inches)
INCH SYSTEM BEARINGS

CLASS: 4 AND 2 PRODUCT*

RESULTANT FIT AND DEVIATION FROM MINIMUM CONE BORE

CONE BORE range		Tolerance †	ROTATING CONE — ground seat (constant loads with moderate shock)		ROTATING CONE — unground seat (heavy loads, or high speed or shock)		STATIONARY CONE — unground seat (moderate loads, no shock)		STATIONARY CONE — ground seat (moderate loads, no shock)		STATIONARY CONE — unground seat (sheaves, wheels, idlers)		STATIONARY CONE — hardened and ground seat (wheel spindles)	
over	inclusive		cone seat deviation	resultant fit	cone seat deviation	resultant fit	cone seat deviation	resultant fit	cone seat deviation	resultant fit	cone seat deviation	resultant fit	cone seat deviation	resultant fit
0	3.0000	0 / +0.0005	+0.0015 / +0.0010	0.0015T / 0.0010T	+0.0025 / +0.0015	0.0025T / 0.0010T	+0.0005 / 0	0.0005T / 0.0005L	0 / −0.0005	0 / 0.0010L	0 / −0.0005	0 / 0.0010L	−0.0002 / −0.0007	0.0002L / 0.0012L
3.0000	12.0000	0 / +0.0010	+0.0025 / +0.0015	0.0025T / 0.0005T	Use Heavy Duty Fitting Practice, See P. 2		+0.0010 / 0	0.0010T / 0.0010L	0 / −0.0010	0 / 0.0020L	0 / −0.0010	0 / 0.0020L	−0.0002 / −0.0012	0.0002L / 0.0022L
12.0000	24.0000	0 / +0.0020	+0.0050 / +0.0030	0.0050T / 0.0010T	Use Heavy Duty Fitting Practice, See P. 2		+0.0020 / 0	0.0020T / 0.0020L	0 / −0.0020	0 / 0.0040L	0 / −0.0020	0 / 0.0040L	—	—
24.0000	36.0000	0 / +0.0030	+0.0075 / +0.0045	0.0075T / 0.0015T	+0.0150 / +0.0120	0.0150T / 0.0090T	+0.0030 / 0	0.0030T / 0.0030L	0 / −0.0030	0 / 0.0060L	0 / −0.0030	0 / 0.0060L	—	—

CLASS: 3 AND 0₁₀ PRODUCT*

RESULTANT FIT AND DEVIATION FROM MINIMUM CONE BORE

CONE BORE range		Tolerance †	ROTATING CONE — ground seat (precision machine tool spindles)		ROTATING CONE — unground seat (heavy loads, or high speed or shock)	STATIONARY CONE — ground seat (precision machine tool spindles)	
over	inclusive		cone seat deviation	resultant fit		cone seat deviation	resultant fit
0	12.0000	0 / +0.0005	+0.0012 / +0.0007	0.0012T / 0.0002T	Use Minimum Cone Fit of .00025" Per Inch of Cone Bore	+0.0012 / +0.0007	0.0012T / 0.0002T
12.0000	24.0000	0 / +0.0010	+0.0025 / +0.0015	0.0025T / 0.0005T		+0.0025 / +0.0015	0.0025T / 0.0005T
24.0000	36.0000	0 / +0.0015	+0.0040 / +0.0025	0.0040T / 0.0010T		+0.0040 / +0.0025	0.0040T / 0.0010T

CLASS: 00 PRODUCT*

RESULTANT FIT AND DEVIATION FROM MINIMUM CONE BORE

CONE BORE range		Tolerance †	ROTATING CONE — ground seat (precision machine tool spindles)		STATIONARY CONE — ground seat (precision machine tool spindles)	
over	inclusive		cone seat deviation	resultant fit	cone seat deviation	resultant fit
0	8.0000	0 / +0.0003	+0.0008 / +0.0005	0.0008T / 0.0002T	+0.0008 / +0.0005	0.0008T / 0.0002T

cone bore tolerance	cone seat deviation	resultant fit
−0.0005	+0.0010	0.0015T
0	+0.0005	0.0005T

*See Bearing Tolerance Chart, page 18.

†For minus tolerance bearings indicated in bearing tables, same fit applies. For example:

⓪ Maximum cone bore for Class 0 Product is 9.5000".

INDUSTRIAL EQUIPMENT—CUP FITTING PRACTICE (Inches)
INCH SYSTEM BEARINGS

CLASS: 4 AND 2 PRODUCT*

RESULTANT FIT AND DEVIATION FROM MINIMUM CUP O.D.

Cup O.D. over	Cup O.D. inclusive	tolerance †	STATIONARY CUP — floating or clamped — cup seat deviation	— resultant fit	STATIONARY CUP — adjustable — cup seat deviation	— resultant fit	STATIONARY CUP — non-adjustable or in carriers — cup seat deviation	— resultant fit	ROTATING CUP — non-adjustable or in carriers or sheaves-clamped — cup seat deviation	— resultant fit	ROTATING CUP — sheaves-unclamped — cup seat deviation	— resultant fit
0	3.0000	+0.0010 / 0	+0.0020 / +0.0030	0.0010L / 0.0030L	0 / +0.0010	0.0010T / 0.0010L	−0.0015 / −0.0005	0.0025T / 0.0005T	−0.0015 / −0.0005	0.0025T / 0.0005T	−0.0030 / −0.0020	0.0040T / 0.0020T
3.0000	5.0000	+0.0010 / 0	+0.0020 / +0.0030	0.0010L / 0.0030L	0 / +0.0010	0.0010T / 0.0010L	−0.0020 / −0.0010	0.0030T / 0.0010T	−0.0020 / −0.0010	0.0030T / 0.0010T	−0.0030 / −0.0020	0.0040T / 0.0020T
5.0000	12.0000	+0.0010 / 0	+0.0020 / +0.0030	0.0010L / 0.0030L	0 / +0.0020	0.0010T / 0.0020L	−0.0020 / −0.0010	0.0030T / 0.0010T	−0.0020 / −0.0010	0.0030T / 0.0010T	−0.0030 / −0.0020	0.0040T / 0.0020T
12.0000	24.0000	+0.0020 / 0	+0.0040 / +0.0060	0.0020L / 0.0060L	+0.0010 / +0.0030	0.0010T / 0.0030L	−0.0030 / −0.0010	0.0050T / 0.0010T	−0.0030 / −0.0010	0.0050T / 0.0010T	−0.0040 / −0.0020	0.0060T / 0.0020T
24.0000	36.0000	+0.0030 / 0	+0.0060 / +0.0090	0.0030L / 0.0090L	+0.0020 / +0.0050	0.0010T / 0.0050L	−0.0040 / −0.0010	0.0070T / 0.0010T	−0.0040 / −0.0010	0.0070T / 0.0010T	—	—

CLASS: 3 AND 0⊚ PRODUCT*

RESULTANT FIT AND DEVIATION FROM MINIMUM CUP O.D.

Cup O.D. over	Cup O.D. inclusive	tolerance †	STATIONARY CUP — clamped — cup seat deviation	— resultant fit	STATIONARY CUP — adjustable — cup seat deviation	— resultant fit	STATIONARY CUP — non-adjustable or in carriers — cup seat deviation	— resultant fit	ROTATING CUP — non-adjustable or in carriers — cup seat deviation	— resultant fit
0	6.0000	+0.0005 / 0	+0.0005 / +0.0010	0 / 0.0010L	0 / +0.0005	0.0005T / 0.0005L	−0.0005 / 0	0.0010T / 0	−0.0010 / −0.0005	0.0015T / 0.0005T
6.0000	12.0000	+0.0005 / 0	+0.0005 / +0.0010	0 / 0.0010L	0 / +0.0005	0.0005T / 0.0005L	−0.0010 / 0	0.0015T / 0	−0.0015 / −0.0005	0.0020T / 0.0005T
12.0000	24.0000	+0.0010 / 0	+0.0010 / +0.0020	0 / 0.0020L	0 / +0.0010	0.0010T / 0.0010L	−0.0010 / 0	0.0020T / 0	−0.0015 / −0.0005	0.0025T / 0.0005T
24.0000	36.0000	+0.0015 / 0	+0.0015 / +0.0030	0 / 0.0030L	0 / +0.0015	0.0015T / 0.0015L	−0.0015 / 0	0.0030T / 0	−0.0020 / −0.0005	0.0035T / 0.0005T

CLASS: 00 PRODUCT*

RESULTANT FIT AND DEVIATION FROM MINIMUM CUP O.D.

Cup O.D. over	Cup O.D. inclusive	tolerance †	STATIONARY CUP — clamped — cup seat deviation	— resultant fit	STATIONARY CUP — adjustable — cup seat deviation	— resultant fit	STATIONARY CUP — non-adjustable — cup seat deviation	— resultant fit
0	10.5000	+0.0003 / 0	+0.0003 / +0.0006	0 / 0.0006L	0 / +0.0003	0.0003T / 0.0003L	−0.0003 / 0	0.0006T / 0

cup o.d. tolerance	cup seat deviation	resultant fit
0 / −0.0010	+0.0010 / +0.0020	0.0010L / 0.0030L

*See Bearing Tolerance Chart, page 18.

†For minus tolerance bearing indicated in bearing tables, same fit applies. For example: →

⊚Maximum cup o.d. for Class 0 Product is 12.000".

INDUSTRIAL EQUIPMENT—CONE FITTING PRACTICE (Inches)
METRIC SYSTEM BEARINGS (For "J" Prefix Parts)

CLASS: K AND N PRODUCT*

RESULTANT FIT AND DEVIATION FROM MAXIMUM CONE BORE

CONE BORE — range over	inclusive	tolerance	ROTATING CONE — ground seat / constant loads with moderate shock — cone seat deviation	resultant fit	symbol	unground or ground seat / heavy loads, or high speeds or shock — cone seat deviation	resultant fit	symbol	unground or ground seat / heavy loads, high speeds or shock — cone seat deviation	resultant fit	symbol	STATIONARY CONE — ground seat / moderate loads, no shock — cone seat deviation	resultant fit	symbol	unground seat / moderate loads, no shock — cone seat deviation	resultant fit	symbol	ground seat / sheaves, wheels, idlers — cone seat deviation	resultant fit	symbol	unground seat / sheaves, wheels, idlers — cone seat deviation	resultant fit	symbol	hardened and ground seat / wheel spindles — cone seat deviation	resultant fit	symbol
0.3937	0.7087	-0.0005 / 0	+0.0007 / +0.0003	0.0012T / 0.0003T	m6	+0.0009 / +0.0005	0.0014T / 0.0005T	n6	+0.0009 / +0.0005	0.0014T / 0.0005T	n6	-0.00025 / -0.00065	0.00025T / 0.00065L	g6	0 / -0.0004	0.0005T / 0.0004L	h6	-0.00025 / -0.00065	0.00025T / 0.00065L	g6	-0.00025 / -0.00065	0.00025T / 0.00065L	g6	-0.0006 / -0.0010	0.0001L / 0.0010L	f6
0.7087	1.1811	-0.0005 / 0	+0.0008 / +0.0003	0.0013T / 0.0003T	m6	+0.0011 / +0.0006	0.0016T / 0.0006T	n6	+0.0011 / +0.0006	0.0016T / 0.0006T	n6	-0.0003 / -0.0008	0.0002T / 0.0008L	g6	0 / -0.0005	0.0005T / 0.0005L	h6	-0.0003 / -0.0008	0.0002T / 0.0008L	g6	-0.0003 / -0.0008	0.0002T / 0.0008L	g6	-0.0008 / -0.0013	0.0003L / 0.0013L	f6
1.1811	1.9685	-0.0005 / 0	+0.0010 / +0.0004	0.0015T / 0.0004T	m6	+0.0013 / +0.0007	0.0018T / 0.0007T	n6	+0.0013 / +0.0007	0.0018T / 0.0007T	n6	-0.0004 / -0.0010	0.0001T / 0.0010L	g6	0 / -0.0006	0.0005T / 0.0006L	h6	-0.0004 / -0.0010	0.0001T / 0.0010L	g6	-0.0004 / -0.0010	0.0001T / 0.0010L	g6	-0.0010 / -0.0016	0.0005L / 0.0016L	f6
1.9685	3.1496	-0.0006 / 0	+0.0012 / +0.0005	0.0018T / 0.0005T	m6	+0.0015 / +0.0008	0.0021T / 0.0008T	n6	+0.0015 / +0.0008	0.0021T / 0.0008T	n6	-0.0004 / -0.0011	0.0002T / 0.0011L	g6	0 / -0.0007	0.0006T / 0.0007L	h6	-0.0004 / -0.0011	0.0002T / 0.0011L	g6	-0.0004 / -0.0011	0.0002T / 0.0011L	g6	-0.0012 / -0.0019	0.0006L / 0.0019L	f6
3.1496	4.7244	-0.0008 / 0	+0.0014 / +0.0005	0.0022T / 0.0005T	m6	+0.0019 / +0.0010	0.0027T / 0.0010T	n6	+0.0019 / +0.0010	0.0027T / 0.0010T	n6	-0.0005 / -0.0014	0.0003T / 0.0014L	g6	0 / -0.0009	0.0008T / 0.0009L	h6	-0.0005 / -0.0014	0.0003T / 0.0014L	g6	-0.0005 / -0.0014	0.0003T / 0.0014L	g6	-0.0014 / -0.0023	0.0006L / 0.0023L	f6
4.7244	7.0866	-0.0010 / 0	+0.0022 / +0.0012	0.0032T / 0.0012T	n6	+0.0028 / +0.0018	0.0038T / 0.0018T	p6	+0.0028 / +0.0018	0.0038T / 0.0018T	p6	-0.0006 / -0.0016	0.0004T / 0.0016L	g6	0 / -0.0010	0.0010T / 0.0010L	h6	-0.0006 / -0.0016	0.0004T / 0.0016L	g6	-0.0006 / -0.0016	0.0004T / 0.0016L	g6	-0.0016 / -0.0026	0.0006L / 0.0026L	f6
7.0866	9.8425	-0.0012 / 0	+0.0026 / +0.0014	0.0038T / 0.0014T	n6	+0.0042 / +0.0030	0.0054T / 0.0030T	r6	+0.0042 / +0.0030	0.0054T / 0.0030T	r6	-0.0006 / -0.0018	0.0006T / 0.0018L	g6	0 / -0.0012	0.0012T / 0.0012L	h6	-0.0006 / -0.0018	0.0006T / 0.0018L	g6	-0.0006 / -0.0018	0.0006T / 0.0018L	g6	-0.0020 / -0.0032	0.0008L / 0.0032L	f6
9.8425	12.4016	-0.0014 / 0	+0.0026 / +0.0014	0.0040T / 0.0014T	r7	+0.0055 / +0.0035	0.0069T / 0.0035T	r7	+0.0055 / +0.0035	0.0069T / 0.0035T	r7	-0.0007 / -0.0019	0.0007T / 0.0019L	g6	0 / -0.0014	0.0014T / 0.0014L	h6	-0.0007 / -0.0019	0.0007T / 0.0019L	g6	-0.0007 / -0.0019	0.0007T / 0.0019L	g6	-0.0022 / -0.0034	0.0008L / 0.0034L	f6
12.4016	15.7480	-0.0016 / 0	+0.0030 / +0.0016	0.0046T / 0.0016T	r7	+0.0067 / +0.0045	0.0083T / 0.0045T	r7	+0.0067 / +0.0045	0.0083T / 0.0045T	r7	-0.0007 / -0.0029	0.0009T / 0.0029L	g7	0 / -0.0016	0.0016T / 0.0016L	h6	-0.0007 / -0.0029	0.0009T / 0.0029L	g7	-0.0007 / -0.0029	0.0009T / 0.0029L	g7	—	—	—
15.7480	19.6850	-0.0018 / 0	+0.0034 / +0.0018	0.0052T / 0.0018T	r7	+0.0075 / +0.0050	0.0093T / 0.0050T	r7	+0.0075 / +0.0050	0.0093T / 0.0050T	r7	-0.0008 / -0.0033	0.0010T / 0.0033L	g7	0 / -0.0018	0.0018T / 0.0018L	h6	-0.0008 / -0.0033	0.0010T / 0.0033L	g7	-0.0008 / -0.0033	0.0010T / 0.0033L	g7	—	—	—
19.6850	24.8031	-0.0020 / 0	+0.0040 / +0.0020	0.0060T / 0.0020T	—	+0.0080 / +0.0050	0.0100T / 0.0050T	—	+0.0080 / +0.0050	0.0100T / 0.0050T	—	-0.0020 / -0.0040	0 / 0.0040L	—	0 / -0.0020	0.0020T / 0.0020L	—	-0.0020 / -0.0040	0 / 0.0040L	—	-0.0020 / -0.0040	0 / 0.0040L	—	—	—	—
24.8031	31.4961	-0.0030 / 0	+0.0050 / +0.0020	0.0080T / 0.0020T	—	+0.0090 / +0.0060	0.0120T / 0.0060T	—	+0.0090 / +0.0060	0.0120T / 0.0060T	—	-0.0030 / -0.0060	0 / 0.0060L	—	0 / -0.0030	0.0030T / 0.0030L	—	-0.0030 / -0.0060	0 / 0.0060L	—	-0.0030 / -0.0060	0 / 0.0060L	—	—	—	—
31.4961	39.3700	-0.0040 / 0	+0.0060 / +0.0020	0.0100T / 0.0020T	—	+0.0110 / +0.0070	0.0150T / 0.0070T	—	+0.0110 / +0.0070	0.0150T / 0.0070T	—	-0.0040 / -0.0080	0 / 0.0080L	—	0 / -0.0040	0.0040T / 0.0040L	—	-0.0040 / -0.0080	0 / 0.0080L	—	-0.0040 / -0.0080	0 / 0.0080L	—	—	—	—

INDUSTRIAL EQUIPMENT—CUP FITTING PRACTICE (Inches)
METRIC SYSTEM BEARINGS (For "J" Prefix Parts)

CLASS: K AND N PRODUCT*

RESULTANT FIT AND DEVIATION FROM MAXIMUM CUP O.D.

CUP O.D. over	CUP O.D. inclusive	tolerance	STATIONARY CUP floating or clamped — cup seat deviation	resultant fit	symbol	adjustable — cup seat deviation	resultant fit	symbol	non-adjustable or in carriers — cup seat deviation	resultant fit	symbol	ROTATING CUP non-adjustable or in carriers or sheaves-clamped — cup seat deviation	resultant fit	symbol	sheaves-unclamped — cup seat deviation	resultant fit	symbol
0.7087	1.1811	0 / −0.0008	+0.0003 / +0.0011	0.0003L / 0.0019L	G7	−0.0003 / +0.0005	0.0003T / 0.0013L	J7	−0.0013 / −0.0005	0.0013T / 0.0003L	P7	−0.0017 / −0.0009	0.0017T / 0.0001T	R7	−0.0024 / −0.0012	0.0024T / 0.0004T	R8
1.1811	1.9685	0 / −0.0008	+0.0004 / +0.0014	0.0004L / 0.0022L	G7	−0.0004 / +0.0006	0.0004T / 0.0014L	J7	−0.0016 / −0.0006	0.0016T / 0.0002L	P7	−0.0020 / −0.0010	0.0020T / 0.0002T	R7	−0.0030 / −0.0014	0.0030T / 0.0006T	R8
1.9685	3.1496	0 / −0.0008	+0.0004 / +0.0016	0.0004L / 0.0024L	G7	−0.0004 / +0.0008	0.0004T / 0.0016L	J7	−0.0021 / −0.0009	0.0021T / 0.0001L	P7	−0.0023 / −0.0011	0.0023T / 0.0003T	R7	−0.0035 / −0.0018	0.0035T / 0.0010T	—
3.1496	4.7244	0 / −0.0008	+0.0005 / +0.0019	0.0005L / 0.0027L	G7	−0.0005 / +0.0009	0.0005T / 0.0017L	J7	−0.0025 / −0.0011	0.0025T / 0.0003T	P7	−0.0029 / −0.0015	0.0029T / 0.0007T	R7	−0.0040 / −0.0020	0.0040T / 0.0012T	—
4.7244	7.0866	0 / −0.0010	+0.0006 / +0.0022	0.0006L / 0.0032L	G7	−0.0006 / +0.0010	0.0006T / 0.0020L	J7	−0.0028 / −0.0012	0.0028T / 0.0002T	P7	−0.0035 / −0.0019	0.0035T / 0.0009T	R7	−0.0045 / −0.0025	0.0045T / 0.0015T	—
7.0866	9.8424	0 / −0.0012	+0.0006 / +0.0024	0.0006L / 0.0036L	G7	−0.0007 / +0.0011	0.0007T / 0.0023L	J7	−0.0032 / −0.0014	0.0032T / 0.0002T	P7	−0.0042 / −0.0024	0.0042T / 0.0012T	R7	−0.0050 / −0.0030	0.0050T / 0.0018T	—
9.8424	12.4016	0 / −0.0016	+0.0007 / +0.0027	0.0007L / 0.0043L	G7	−0.0007 / +0.0013	0.0007T / 0.0029L	J7	−0.0034 / −0.0014	0.0034T / 0.0002T	P7	−0.0047 / −0.0027	0.0047T / 0.0011T	R7	−0.0055 / −0.0035	0.0055T / 0.0019T	—
12.4016	15.7480	0 / −0.0016	+0.0025 / +0.0039	0.0025L / 0.0055L	F6	−0.0007 / +0.0015	0.0007T / 0.0031L	J7	−0.0039 / −0.0017	0.0039T / 0.0001T	P7	−0.0059 / −0.0037	0.0059T / 0.0021T	R7	−0.0059 / −0.0037	0.0059T / 0.0021T	R7
15.7480	19.6850	0 / −0.0020	+0.0028 / +0.0038	0.0028L / 0.0058L	F5	−0.0009 / +0.0016	0.0009T / 0.0036L	J7	−0.0044 / −0.0019	0.0044T / 0.0001L	P7	−0.0066 / −0.0041	0.0066T / 0.0021T	R7	−0.0066 / −0.0041	0.0065T / 0.0021T	R7
19.6850	24.8031	0 / −0.0020	+0.0025 / +0.0045	0.0025L / 0.0065L	—	−0.0009 / +0.0018	0.0009T / 0.0038L	J7	−0.0048 / −0.0020	0.0048T / 0	—	−0.0070 / −0.0042	0.0070T / 0.0022T	—	−0.0070 / −0.0042	0.0070T / 0.0022T	—
24.8031	31.4961	0 / −0.0030	+0.0030 / +0.0060	0.0030L / 0.0090L	—	−0.0010 / +0.0020	0.0010T / 0.0050L	—	−0.0060 / −0.0030	0.0060T / 0	—			—			—
31.4961	39.3700	0 / −0.0040	+0.0030 / +0.0070	0.0030L / 0.0110L	—	−0.0010 / +0.0030	0.0010T / 0.0070L	—	−0.0080 / −0.0040	0.0080T / 0	—			—			—

*See Bearing Tolerance Chart, page 20.

INDUSTRIAL EQUIPMENT—CONE FITTING PRACTICE (Inches)
METRIC SYSTEM BEARINGS (For "J" Prefix Parts)

CLASS: C PRODUCT*

RESULTANT FIT AND DEVIATION FROM MAXIMUM CONE BORE

CONE BORE range over	CONE BORE range inclusive	tolerance	ROTATING CONE — ground seat, precision machine tool spindles: cone seat deviation	resultant fit	symbol	ROTATING CONE — ground seat, heavy loads, or high speed or shock: cone seat deviation	resultant fit	symbol	STATIONARY CONE — ground seat, precision machine tool spindles: cone seat deviation	resultant fit	symbol
0.3937	0.7087	−0.0004 / 0	+0.0004 / +0.0001	0.0008T / 0.0001T	k5	+0.0007 / +0.0003	0.0011T / 0.0003T	m6	+0.0004 / +0.0001	0.0008T / 0.0001T	k5
0.7087	1.1811	−0.0004 / 0	+0.0005 / +0.0001	0.0009T / 0.0001T	k5	+0.0007 / +0.0003	0.0011T / 0.0003T	m5	+0.0005 / +0.0001	0.0009T / 0.0001T	k5
1.1811	1.9685	−0.0004 / 0	+0.0005 / +0.0001	0.0009T / 0.0001T	k5	+0.0008 / +0.0004	0.0012T / 0.0004T	m5	+0.0005 / +0.0001	0.0009T / 0.0001T	k5
1.9685	3.1496	−0.0005 / 0	+0.0006 / +0.0001	0.0011T / 0.0001T	k5	+0.0013 / +0.0008	0.0018T / 0.0008T	n5	+0.0006 / +0.0001	0.0011T / 0.0001T	k5
3.1496	4.7244	−0.0005 / 0	+0.0007 / +0.0001	0.0012T / 0.0001T	k5	+0.0016 / +0.0010	0.0021T / 0.0010T	n5	+0.0007 / +0.0001	0.0012T / 0.0001T	k5
4.7244	7.0866	−0.0005 / 0	+0.0008 / +0.0001	0.0013T / 0.0001T	k5	+0.0023 / +0.0018	0.0028T / 0.0018T	p4	+0.0008 / +0.0001	0.0013T / 0.0001T	k5
7.0866	9.8425	−0.0006 / 0	+0.0010 / +0.0002	0.0016T / 0.0002T	k5	+0.0036 / +0.0030	0.0042T / 0.0030T	r4	+0.0010 / +0.0002	0.0016T / 0.0002T	k5
9.8425	12.4016	−0.0007 / 0	+0.0011 / +0.0002	0.0018T / 0.0002T	k5	+0.0044 / +0.0035	0.0051T / 0.0035T	r5	+0.0011 / +0.0002	0.0018T / 0.0002T	k5
12.4016	15.7480	−0.0008 / 0	+0.0012 / +0.0002	0.0020T / 0.0002T	k5	+0.0055 / +0.0045	0.0063T / 0.0045T	r5	+0.0012 / +0.0002	0.0020T / 0.0002T	k5
15.7480	19.6850	−0.0010 / 0	+0.0012 / +0.0002	0.0022T / 0.0002T	k5	+0.0060 / +0.0050	0.0070T / 0.0050T	r5	+0.0012 / +0.0002	0.0022T / 0.0002T	k5
19.6850	24.8031	−0.0012 / 0	+0.0014 / +0.0002	0.0026T / 0.0002T	k5	+0.0072 / +0.0060	0.0084T / 0.0060T	—	+0.0014 / +0.0002	0.0025T / 0.0002T	—
24.8031	31.4961	−0.0016 / 0	+0.0025 / +0.0005	0.0041T / 0.0005T	—	+0.0086 / +0.0070	0.0102T / 0.0070T	—	+0.0025 / +0.0005	0.0041T / 0.0005T	—
31.4961	39.3700	−0.0020 / 0	+0.0025 / +0.0005	0.0045T / 0.0005T	—	+0.0100 / +0.0080	0.0120T / 0.0080T	—	+0.0025 / +0.0005	0.0045T / 0.0005T	—

*See Bearing Tolerance Chart, page 20.

INDUSTRIAL EQUIPMENT—CUP FITTING PRACTICE (Inches)
METRIC SYSTEM BEARINGS (For "J" Prefix Parts)

CLASS: C PRODUCT*

RESULTANT FIT AND DEVIATION FROM MAXIMUM CUP O.D.

CUP O.D. range over	inclusive	tolerance	STATIONARY CUP — floating cup seat deviation	floating resultant fit	symbol	clamped cup seat deviation	clamped resultant fit	symbol	adjustable cup seat deviation	adjustable resultant fit	symbol	non-adjustable in carriers cup seat deviation	non-adjustable resultant fit	symbol	ROTATING CUP non-adjustable or adjustable in carriers cup seat deviation	resultant fit	symbol
0.7087	1.1811	0 / -0.0003	+0.0003 / +0.0007	0.0003L / 0.0010L	G5	0 / +0.0004	0 / 0.0007L	H5	-0.0004	0.0004T / 0.0003L	K5	-0.00085 / -0.00045	0.00085T / 0.00015T	N5	-0.0010 / -0.0005	0.0010T / 0.0002T	N6
1.1811	1.9685	0 / -0.0004	+0.0004 / +0.0008	0.0004L / 0.0012L	G5	0 / +0.0004	0 / 0.0008L	H5	-0.0004 / 0	0.0004T / 0.0004L	K5	-0.0010 / -0.0006	0.0010T / 0.0002T	N5	-0.0011 / -0.0005	0.0011T / 0.0001T	N6
1.9685	3.1496	0 / -0.0004	+0.0004 / +0.0009	0.0004L / 0.0013L	G5	0 / +0.0005	0 / 0.0009L	H5	-0.0004 / +0.0001	0.0004T / 0.0005L	K5	-0.0011 / -0.0006	0.0011T / 0.0002T	N5	-0.0013 / -0.0006	0.0013T / 0.0002T	N6
3.1496	4.7244	0 / -0.0005	+0.0005 / +0.0011	0.0005L / 0.0016L	G5	0 / +0.0006	0 / 0.0011L	H5	-0.0005 / +0.0001	0.0005T / 0.0006L	K5	-0.0014 / -0.0008	0.0014T / 0.0003T	N5	-0.0016 / -0.0007	0.0016T / 0.0002T	N6
4.7244	7.0866	0 / -0.0005	+0.0006 / +0.0013	0.0006L / 0.0018L	G5	0 / +0.0007	0 / 0.0012L	H5	-0.0005 / +0.0005	0.0005T / 0.0010L	Js6	-0.0017 / -0.0010	0.0017T / 0.0005T	N5	-0.0019 / -0.0009	0.0019T / 0.0004T	N6
7.0866	9.8425	0 / -0.0006	+0.0006 / +0.0014	0.0006L / 0.0020L	G5	0 / +0.0008	0 / 0.0014L	H5	-0.0006 / +0.0006	0.0006T / 0.0012L	Js6	-0.0020 / -0.0012	0.0020T / 0.0006T	N5	-0.0022 / -0.0010	0.0022T / 0.0004T	N6
9.8425	12.4016	0 / -0.0008	+0.0007 / +0.0016	0.0007L / 0.0024L	G5	0 / +0.0009	0 / 0.0017L	H5	-0.0008 / +0.0001	0.0008T / 0.0009L	K5	-0.0020 / -0.0011	0.0020T / 0.0003T	N5	-0.0023 / -0.0011	0.0023T / 0.0003T	N6
12.4016	15.7480	0 / -0.0008	+0.0007 / +0.0017	0.0007L / 0.0025L	G5	0 / +0.0010	0 / 0.0018L	H5	-0.0009 / +0.0001	0.0009T / 0.0009L	K5	-0.0023 / -0.0013	0.0023T / 0.0005T	N5	-0.0026 / -0.0012	0.0026T / 0.0004T	N6
15.7480	19.6850	0 / -0.0010	+0.0008 / +0.0018	0.0008L / 0.0028L	G5	0 / +0.0010	0 / 0.0020L	H5	-0.0010 / 0	0.0010T / 0.0010L	K5	-0.0026 / -0.0016	0.0026T / 0.0006T	N5	-0.0028 / -0.0012	0.0028T / 0.0002T	N6
19.6850	24.8031	0 / -0.0010	+0.0010 / +0.0020	0.0010L / 0.0030L	—	0 / +0.0010	0 / 0.0020L	—	-0.0010	0.0010T / 0.0010L	—	-0.0026 / -0.0016	0.0026T / 0.0006T	—	-0.0030 / -0.0015	0.0030T / 0.0005T	—
24.8031	31.4961	0 / -0.0016	+0.0010 / +0.0025	0.0010L / 0.0041L	—	0 / +0.0016	0 / 0.0032L	—	-0.0016 / 0	0.0016T / 0.0016L	—	-0.0035 / -0.0020	0.0035T / 0.0004T	—	-0.0037 / -0.0021	0.0037T / 0.0005T	—
31.4961	39.3700	0 / -0.0020	+0.0010 / +0.0030	0.0010L / 0.0050L	—	0 / +0.0020	0 / 0.0040L	—	-0.0020	0.0020T / 0.0020L	—	-0.0040 / -0.0020	0.0040T / 0	—	-0.0045 / -0.0025	0.0045T / 0.0005T	—

*See Bearing Tolerance Chart, page 20.

INDUSTRIAL EQUIPMENT—CONE FITTING PRACTICE (Inches)
METRIC SYSTEM BEARINGS (For "J" Prefix Parts)

CLASS: B PRODUCT*

CONE BORE			RESULTANT FIT AND DEVIATION FROM MAXIMUM CONE BORE								
range		tolerance	ROTATING CONE						STATIONARY CONE		
			ground seat precision machine tool spindles			ground seat heavy loads, or high speed or shock			ground seat precision machine tool spindles		
over	inclusive		cone seat deviation	resultant fit	symbol	cone seat deviation	resultant fit	symbol	cone seat deviation	resultant fit	symbol
0.3937	0.7087	−0.0003 / 0	+0.0004 / +0.0001	0.0007T / 0.0001T	k5	+0.0006 / +0.0003	0.0009T / 0.0003T	m5	+0.0004 / +0.0001	0.0007T / 0.0001T	k5
0.7087	1.1811	−0.0003 / 0	+0.0005 / +0.0001	0.0008T / 0.0001T	k5	+0.0007 / +0.0003	0.0010T / 0.0003T	m5	+0.0005 / +0.0001	0.0008T / 0.0001T	k5
1.1811	1.9685	−0.0004 / 0	+0.0005 / +0.0001	0.0009T / 0.0001T	k5	+0.0008 / +0.0004	0.0012T / 0.0004T	m5	+0.0005 / +0.0001	0.0009T / 0.0001T	k5
1.9685	3.1496	−0.0004 / 0	+0.0006 / +0.0001	0.0010T / 0.0001T	k5	+0.0013 / +0.0008	0.0017T / 0.0008T	n5	+0.0006 / +0.0001	0.0010T / 0.0001T	k5
3.1496	4.7244	−0.0004 / 0	+0.0007 / +0.0001	0.0011T / 0.0001T	k5	+0.0014 / +0.0010	0.0018T / 0.0010T	n4	+0.0007 / +0.0001	0.0011T / 0.0001T	k5
4.7244	7.0866	−0.0004 / 0	+0.0008 / +0.0001	0.0012T / 0.0001T	k5	+0.0023 / +0.0018	0.0027T / 0.0018T	p4	+0.0008 / +0.0001	0.0012T / 0.0001T	k5
7.0866	9.8425	−0.0005 / 0	+0.0010 / +0.0002	0.0015T / 0.0002T	k5	+0.0036 / +0.0030	0.0041T / 0.0030T	r4	+0.0010 / +0.0002	0.0015T / 0.0002T	k5
9.8425	12.4016	−0.0005 / 0	+0.0011 / +0.0002	0.0016T / 0.0002T	k5	+0.0041 / +0.0035	0.0046T / 0.0035T	r4	+0.0011 / +0.0002	0.0016T / 0.0002T	k5

*See Bearing Tolerance Chart, page 20.

INDUSTRIAL EQUIPMENT—CUP FITTING PRACTICE (Inches)
METRIC SYSTEM BEARINGS (For "J" Prefix Parts)

CLASS: B PRODUCT*

RESULTANT FIT AND DEVIATION FROM MAXIMUM CUP O.D.

CUP O.D. range (over)	(inclusive)	tolerance	floating cup seat deviation	floating resultant fit	sym-bol	clamped cup seat deviation	clamped resultant fit	sym-bol	adjustable cup seat deviation	adjustable resultant fit	sym-bol	STATIONARY CUP non-adjustable or in carriers cup seat deviation	resultant fit	sym-bol	ROTATING CUP non-adjustable or in carriers cup seat deviation	resultant fit	sym-bol
0.7087	1.1811	0 / − 0.0003	+ 0.0003 / + 0.0007	0.0003L / 0.0010L	G5	0 / + 0.00025	0 / 0.00055L	H4	− 0.0004 / 0	0.0004T / 0.0003L	K5	− 0.00055 / − 0.00015	0.00055T / 0.00015L	M5	− 0.00085 / − 0.00045	0.00085T / 0.00015T	N5
1.1811	1.9685	0 / − 0.0003	+ 0.0004 / + 0.0008	0.0004L / 0.0011L	G5	0 / + 0.0003	0 / 0.0006L	H4	− 0.0004 / 0	0.0004T / 0.0003L	K5	− 0.0007 / − 0.0003	0.0007T / 0	M5	− 0.0010 / − 0.0006	0.0010T / 0.0003T	N5
1.9685	3.1496	0 / − 0.00035	+ 0.0004 / + 0.0009	0.00040L / 0.00125L	G5	0 / + 0.0003	0 / 0.00065L	H4	− 0.0004 / + 0.0001	0.00040T / 0.00045L	K5	− 0.0008 / − 0.0003	0.00080T / 0.00005L	M5	− 0.0011 / − 0.0006	0.00110T / 0.00025T	N5
3.1496	4.7244	0 / − 0.0004	+ 0.0005 / + 0.0011	0.0005L / 0.0015L	G5	0 / + 0.0004	0 / 0.0008L	H4	− 0.0005 / + 0.0001	0.0005T / 0.0005L	K5	− 0.0009 / − 0.0003	0.0009T / 0.0001L	M5	− 0.0014 / − 0.0008	0.0014T / 0.0004T	N5
4.7244	7.0866	0 / − 0.0004	+ 0.0006 / + 0.0013	0.0006L / 0.0017L	G5	0 / + 0.0005	0 / 0.0009L	H4	− 0.0005 / + 0.0005	0.0005T / 0.0009L	J45	− 0.0011 / − 0.0004	0.0011T / 0	M5	− 0.0017 / − 0.0010	0.0017T / 0.0006T	N5
7.0866	9.8425	0 / − 0.0005	+ 0.0006 / + 0.0014	0.0006L / 0.0019L	G5	0 / + 0.0006	0 / 0.0011L	H4	− 0.0004 / + 0.0004	0.0004T / 0.0009L	J45	− 0.0012 / − 0.0004	0.0012T / 0.0001L	M5	− 0.0020 / − 0.0012	0.0020T / 0.0007T	N5
9.8425	12.4016	0 / − 0.0006	+ 0.0007 / + 0.0016	0.0007L / 0.0021L	G5	0 / + 0.0006	0 / 0.0012L	H4	− 0.0004 / + 0.0004	0.0004T / 0.0010L	J45	− 0.0014 / − 0.0005	0.0014T / 0.0001L	M5	− 0.0020 / − 0.0011	0.0020T / 0.0005T	N5

*See Bearing Tolerance Chart, page 20.

INDUSTRIAL EQUIPMENT—CONE FITTING PRACTICE (Micrometers, μm)
INCH SYSTEM BEARINGS

CLASS: 4 AND 2 PRODUCT*

RESULTANT FIT AND DEVIATION FROM MINIMUM CONE BORE

CONE BORE			ROTATING CONE								STATIONARY CONE										
			ground seat		unground or ground seat		unground or ground seat				unground seat		ground seat		ground seat		unground seat		hardened and ground seat		wheel spindles
range mm		tolerance + μm	constant loads with moderate shock		heavy loads, or high speed or shock		heavy loads, or high speed or shock				moderate loads, no shock		moderate loads, no shock		moderate loads, no shock		sheaves, wheels, idlers				
over	inclusive		cone seat deviation	resultant fit	cone seat deviation	resultant fit	cone seat deviation	resultant fit			cone seat deviation	resultant fit	cone seat deviation	resultant fit	cone seat deviation	resultant fit	cone seat deviation	resultant fit	cone seat deviation	resultant fit	
0	76,2	0 +13	+ 38 + 26	38T 13T	+ 64 + 38	64T 25T	+ 64 + 38	64T 25T			+13 0	13T 13L	+13 0	0 26L	0 −13	0 26L	0 −13	−5 −18	5L 31L	
76,2	304,8	0 +25	+ 64 + 38	64T 13T	Use Heavy Duty Fitting Practice, See P. 2		Use Heavy Duty Fitting Practice, See P. 2				+25 0	25T 25L	+25 0	0 51L	0 −25	0 51L	0 −25	−5 −31	5L 56L	
304,8	609,6	0 +51	+127 + 76	127T 25T	+381 +305	381T 229T	+381 +305	381T 229T			+51 0	51T 51L	+51 0	0 102L	0 −51	0 102L	0 −51	—	—	
609,6	914,4	0 +76	+191 +114	191T 38T	+381 +305	381T 229T	+381 +305	381T 229T			+76 0	76T 76L	+76 0	0 152L	0 −76	0 152L	0 −76	—	—	

CLASS: 3 AND 0₀ PRODUCT*

RESULTANT FIT AND DEVIATION FROM MINIMUM CONE BORE

CONE BORE			ROTATING CONE				STATIONARY CONE			
			ground seat		ground seat		ground seat		ground seat	
range mm		tolerance + μm	precision machine tool spindles		heavy loads, or high speed or shock		precision machine tool spindles		precision machine tool spindles	
over	inclusive		cone seat deviation	resultant fit	cone seat deviation	resultant fit	cone seat deviation	resultant fit	cone seat deviation	resultant fit
0	304,8	0 +13	+ 31 + 18	31T 5T	Use Minimum Cone Fit of 0,25 μm Per mm of Cone Bore		+ 31 + 18	31T 5T		
304,8	609,6	0 +25	+ 64 + 38	64T 13T			+ 64 + 38	64T 13T		
609,6	914,4	0 +38	+102 + 63	102T 25T			+102 + 63	102T 25T		

CLASS: 00 PRODUCT*

RESULTANT FIT AND DEVIATION FROM MINIMUM CONE BORE

CONE BORE				ROTATING CONE		STATIONARY CONE	
				ground seat		ground seat	
range mm		tolerance + μm		precision machine tool spindles		precision machine tool spindles	
over	inclusive			cone seat deviation	resultant fit	cone seat deviation	resultant fit
0	203,8	0 +8		+20 +13	20T 5T	+20 +13	20T 5T

cone bore tolerance	cone seat deviation	resultant fit
−13 0	+25 +13	38T 13T

*See Bearing Tolerance Chart, page 18.

†For minus tolerance bearings indicated in bearing tables, same fit applies. For example:

⓪Maximum cone bore for Class 0 Product is 241,3 mm.

INDUSTRIAL EQUIPMENT—CUP FITTING PRACTICE (Micrometers, μm) INCH SYSTEM BEARINGS

CLASS: 4 AND 2 PRODUCT*

RESULTANT FIT AND DEVIATION FROM MINIMUM CUP O.D.

CUP O.D. range mm		tolerance ± μm	STATIONARY CUP floating or clamped		STATIONARY CUP adjustable		STATIONARY CUP non-adjustable or in carriers		ROTATING CUP non-adjustable or in carriers, sheaves-clamped		ROTATING CUP sheaves-unclamped	
over	inclusive		cup seat deviation	resultant fit	cup seat deviation	resultant fit	cup seat deviation	resultant fit	cup seat deviation	resultant fit	cup seat deviation	resultant fit
0	76.2	+25 / 0	+50 / +76	25L / 76L	0 / +25	25T / 25L	−39 / −13	64T / 13T	−39 / −13	64T / 13T	−77 / −51	102T / 51T
76.2	127	+25 / 0	+50 / +76	25L / 76L	0 / +25	25T / 25L	−51 / −25	76T / 25T	−51 / −25	76T / 25T	−77 / −51	102T / 51T
127	304.8	+25 / 0	+50 / +76	25L / 76L	0 / +51	25T / 51L	−51 / −25	76T / 25T	−51 / −25	76T / 25T	−77 / −51	102T / 51T
304.8	609.6	+51 / 0	+102 / +152	51L / 152L	+26 / +76	25T / 76L	−76 / −25	127T / 25T	−76 / −25	127T / 25T	−102 / −51	153T / 51T
609.6	914.4	+76 / 0	+152 / +229	76L / 229L	+51 / +127	25T / 127L	−102 / −25	178T / 25T	−102 / −25	178T / 25T	—	—

CLASS: 3 AND 0⓪ PRODUCT*

RESULTANT FIT AND DEVIATION FROM MINIMUM CUP O.D.

CUP O.D. range mm		tolerance ± μm	STATIONARY CUP floating		STATIONARY CUP clamped		STATIONARY CUP adjustable		ROTATING CUP non-adjustable or in carriers		ROTATING CUP non-adjustable or in carriers	
over	inclusive		cup seat deviation	resultant fit	cup seat deviation	resultant fit	cup seat deviation	resultant fit	cup seat deviation	resultant fit	cup seat deviation	resultant fit
0	152.4	+13 / 0	+26 / +38	13L / 38L	+13 / +25	0 / 25L	0 / +13	13T / 13L	−12 / 0	25T / 0	−25 / −13	38T / 13T
152.4	304.8	+13 / 0	+26 / +38	13L / 38L	+13 / +25	0 / 25L	0 / +25	13T / 25L	−25 / 0	38T / 0	−38 / −13	51T / 13T
304.8	609.6	+25 / 0	+38 / +64	13L / 64L	+25 / +51	0 / 51L	0 / +25	25T / 25L	−26 / 0	51T / 0	−39 / −13	64T / 13T
609.6	914.4	+38 / 0	+51 / +89	13L / 89L	+38 / +76	0 / 76L	0 / +38	38T / 38L	−38 / 0	76T / 0	−51 / −13	89T / 13T

CLASS: 00 PRODUCT*

RESULTANT FIT AND DEVIATION FROM MINIMUM CUP O.D.

CUP O.D. range mm		tolerance ± μm	STATIONARY CUP floating		STATIONARY CUP clamped		STATIONARY CUP adjustable		STATIONARY CUP non-adjustable	
over	inclusive		cup seat deviation	resultant fit	cup seat deviation	resultant fit	cup seat deviation	resultant fit	cup seat deviation	resultant fit
0	266.7	+8 / 0	+16 / +23	8L / 23L	+8 / +15	0 / 15L	0 / +8	8T / 8L	−7 / 0	15T / 0

cup o.d. tolerance	cup seat deviation	resultant fit
0 / −25	+25 / +51	25L / 76L

*See Bearing Tolerance Chart, page 18.

†For minus tolerance bearing indicated in bearing tables, same fit applies. For example: →

⓪Maximum cup o.d. for Class O Product is 304.8 mm.

13

INDUSTRIAL EQUIPMENT—CONE FITTING PRACTICE (Micrometers, μm)
METRIC SYSTEM BEARINGS (For "J" Prefix Parts)

CLASS: K AND N PRODUCT*

RESULTANT FIT AND DEVIATION FROM MAXIMUM CONE BORE

Each group cell below is given as: cone seat deviation / resultant fit / symbol. (T = interference, L = clearance; dimensions in μm.)

Cone bore range (mm) over	incl.	Tolerance μm	ROTATING CONE — ground seat, constant loads w/ moderate shock	ROTATING CONE — unground or ground seat, heavy loads, high speed or shock	STATIONARY CONE — unground or ground seat, heavy loads, high speed or shock	STATIONARY CONE — ground seat, moderate loads, no shock	STATIONARY CONE — unground seat, moderate loads, no shock	Sheaves, wheels, idlers (unground seat)	Hardened & ground seat — wheel spindles
10	18	−13/0	+18/+7 · 31T/7T · m6	+23/+12 · 36T/12T · n6	+23/+12 · 36T/12T · n6	0/−11 · 13T/11L · h6	0/−11 · 13T/11L · h6	−6/−17 · 7T/17L · g6	−16/−27 · 3L/27L · f6
18	30	−13/0	+21/+8 · 34T/8T · m6	+28/+15 · 41T/15T · n6	+28/+15 · 41T/15T · n6	0/−13 · 13T/13L · h6	0/−13 · 13T/13L · h6	−7/−20 · 6T/20L · g6	−20/−33 · 7L/33L · f6
30	50	−13/0	+25/+9 · 38T/9T · m6	+33/+17 · 46T/17T · n6	+33/+17 · 46T/17T · n6	0/−16 · 13T/16L · h6	0/−16 · 13T/16L · h6	−9/−25 · 4T/25L · g6	−25/−41 · 12L/41L · f6
50	80	−15/0	+30/+11 · 45T/11T · m6	+39/+20 · 54T/20T · n6	+39/+20 · 54T/20T · n6	0/−19 · 15T/19L · h6	0/−19 · 15T/19L · h6	−10/−29 · 5T/29L · g6	−30/−49 · 15L/49L · f6
80	120	−20/0	+35/+13 · 55T/13T · m6	+45/+23 · 65T/23T · n6	+45/+23 · 65T/23T · n6	0/−22 · 20T/22L · h6	0/−22 · 20T/22L · h6	−12/−34 · 8T/34L · g6	−36/−58 · 16L/58L · f6
120	180	−25/0	+52/+27 · 77T/27T · n6	+68/+43 · 93T/43T · p6	+68/+43 · 93T/43T · p6	0/−25 · 25T/25L · h6	0/−25 · 25T/25L · h6	−14/−39 · 11T/39L · g6	−43/−68 · 18L/68L · f6
180	200	−30/0	+60/+31 · 90T/31T · n6	+106/+77 · 136T/77T · r6	+106/+77 · 136T/77T · r6	0/−29 · 30T/29L · h6	0/−29 · 30T/29L · h6	−15/−44 · 15T/44L · g6	−50/−79 · 20L/79L · f6
200	225	−30/0	+60/+31 · 90T/31T · n6	+109/+80 · 139T/80T · r6	+109/+80 · 139T/80T · r6	0/−29 · 30T/29L · h6	0/−29 · 30T/29L · h6	−15/−44 · 15T/44L · g6	−50/−79 · 20L/79L · f6
225	250	−30/0	+60/+31 · 90T/31T · n6	+113/+84 · 143T/84T · r6	+113/+84 · 143T/84T · r6	0/−29 · 30T/29L · h6	0/−29 · 30T/29L · h6	−15/−44 · 15T/44L · g6	−50/−79 · 20L/79L · f6
250	280	−35/0	+66/+34 · 101T/34T · n6	+146/+94 · 181T/94T · r7	+146/+94 · 181T/94T · r7	0/−32 · 35T/32L · h6	0/−32 · 35T/32L · h6	−17/−49 · 18T/49L · g6	−56/−88 · 21L/88L · f6
280	315	−35/0	+66/+34 · 101T/34T · n6	+150/+98 · 185T/98T · r7	+150/+98 · 185T/98T · r7	0/−32 · 35T/32L · h6	0/−32 · 35T/32L · h6	−17/−49 · 18T/49L · g6	−56/−88 · 21L/88L · f6
315	355	−40/0	+73/+37 · 113T/37T · n6	+165/+108 · 205T/108T · r7	+165/+108 · 205T/108T · r7	0/−36 · 40T/36L · h6	0/−36 · 40T/36L · h6	−18/−75 · 22T/75L · g7	—
355	400	−40/0	+73/+37 · 113T/37T · n6	+171/+114 · 211T/114T · r7	+171/+114 · 211T/114T · r7	0/−36 · 40T/36L · h6	0/−36 · 40T/36L · h6	−18/−75 · 22T/75L · g7	—
400	450	−45/0	+80/+40 · 125T/40T · n6	+189/+126 · 234T/126T · r7	+189/+126 · 234T/126T · r7	0/−40 · 45T/40L · h6	0/−40 · 45T/40L · h6	−20/−83 · 25T/83L · g7	—
450	500	−45/0	+80/+40 · 125T/40T · n6	+195/+132 · 240T/132T · r7	+195/+132 · 240T/132T · r7	0/−40 · 45T/40L · h6	0/−40 · 45T/40L · h6	−20/−83 · 25T/83L · g7	—
500	630	−50/0	+100/+50 · 150T/50T · —	+200/+125 · 250T/125T · —	+200/+125 · 250T/125T · —	0/−50 · 50T/50L · —	0/−50 · 50T/50L · —	−50/−100 · 0/100L · —	—
630	800	−75/0	+125/+50 · 200T/50T · —	+225/+150 · 300T/150T · —	+225/+150 · 300T/150T · —	0/−75 · 75T/75L · —	0/−75 · 75T/75L · —	−75/−150 · 0/150L · —	—
800	1000	−100/0	+150/+50 · 250T/50T · —	+275/+175 · 375T/175T · —	+275/+175 · 375T/175T · —	0/−100 · 100T/100L · —	0/−100 · 100T/100L · —	−100/−200 · 0/200L · —	—

*See Bearing Tolerance Chart, page 20.

INDUSTRIAL EQUIPMENT CUP FITTING PRACTICE (Micrometers, μm)
METRIC SYSTEM BEARINGS (For "J" Prefix Parts)

CLASS: K AND N PRODUCT*

RESULTANT FIT AND DEVIATION FROM MAXIMUM CUP O.D.

CUP O.D. range mm over	inclusive	tolerance μm	STATIONARY CUP — floating or clamped cup seat dev	resultant fit	symbol	adjustable cup seat dev	resultant fit	symbol	non-adjustable or in carriers cup seat dev	resultant fit	symbol	ROTATING CUP — non-adjustable or in carriers or sheaves-clamped cup seat dev	resultant fit	symbol	sheaves-unclamped cup seat dev	resultant fit	symbol
18	30	0 / -20	+7 / +28	7L / 48L	G7	-9 / +12	9T / 32L	J7	-35 / -14	35T / 6L	P7	-41 / -20	41T / 0	R7	-61 / -28	61T / 8T	R8
30	50	0 / -20	+9 / +34	9L / 54L	G7	-11 / +14	11T / 34L	J7	-42 / -17	42T / 3L	P7	-50 / -25	50T / 5T	R7	-73 / -34	73T / 14T	R8
50	65	0 / -20	+10 / +40	10L / 60L	G7	-12 / +18	12T / 38L	J7	-51 / -21	51T / 1T	P7	-60 / -30	60T / 10T	R7	-90 / -45	90T / 25T	—
65	80	0 / -20										-62 / -32	62T / 12T		-100 / -50	100T / 30T	—
80	100	0 / -20	+12 / +47	12L / 67L	G7	-13 / +22	13T / 42L	J7	-59 / -24	59T / 4T	P7	-73 / -38	73T / 18T	R7	-115 / -65	115T / 40T	—
100	120	0 / -20										-76 / -41	76T / 21T		-125 / -75	125T / 45T	—
120	140	0 / -25	+14 / +54	14L / 79L	G7	-14 / +26	14T / 51L	J7	-68 / -28	68T / 3T	P7	-88 / -48	88T / 23T	R7	-140 / -90	140T / 50T	—
140	160	0 / -25										-90 / -50	90T / 25T				
160	180	0 / -25										-93 / -53	93T / 28T				
180	200	0 / -30	+15 / +61	15L / 91L	G7	-16 / +30	16T / 60L	J7	-79 / -33	79T / 3T	P7	-106 / -60	106T / 30T	R7			
200	225	0 / -30										-109 / -63	109T / 33T				
225	250	0 / -30										-113 / -67	113T / 37T				
250	280	0 / -40	+17 / +69	17L / 109L	G7	-16 / +36	16T / 76L	J7	-88 / -36	88T / 4L	P7	-126 / -74	126T / 34T	R7			
280	315	0 / -40										-130 / -78	130T / 38T				
315	355	0 / -40	+62 / +98	62L / 138L	F6	-18 / +39	18T / 79L	J7	-98 / -41	98T / 1T	P7	-144 / -87	144T / 47T	R7	-144 / -87	144T / 47T	R7
355	400	0 / -40										-150 / -93	150T / 53T		-150 / -93	150T / 53T	R7
400	450	0 / -50	+68 / +95	68L / 145L	F5	-20 / +43	20T / 93L	J7	-108 / -45	108T / 5L	P7	-166 / -103	166T / 53T	R7	-166 / -103	166T / 53T	R7
450	500	0 / -50										-172 / -109	172T / 59T		-172 / -109	172T / 59T	R7
500	630	0 / -50	+65 / +115	65L / 165L	—	-22 / +46	22T / 96L	—	-118 / -50	118T / 0	—	-190 / -120	190T / 70T	R7	-190 / -120	190T / 70T	—
630	800	0 / -75	+75 / +150	75L / 225L	—	-25 / +50	25T / 125L	—	-150 / -75	150T / 0	—						
800	1000	0 / -100	+75 / +175	75L / 275L	—	-25 / +75	25T / 175L	—	-200 / -100	200T / 0	—						

*See Bearing Tolerance Chart, page 20.

INDUSTRIAL EQUIPMENT—
CONE FITTING PRACTICE (Micrometers, μm)
METRIC SYSTEM BEARINGS (For "J" Prefix Parts)

CLASS: C PRODUCT*

CONE BORE range mm over	inclusive	tolerance μm	ROTATING CONE ground seat precision machine tool spindles — cone seat deviation	resultant fit	symbol	ROTATING CONE ground seat heavy loads, or high speed or shock — cone seat deviation	resultant fit	symbol	STATIONARY CONE ground seat precision machine tool spindles — cone seat deviation	resultant fit	symbol
10	18	−10 / 0	+ 9 / + 1	19T / 1T	k5	+ 18 / + 7	28T / 7T	m6	+ 9 / + 1	19T / 1T	k5
18	30	−10 / 0	+11 / + 2	21T / 2T	k5	+ 17 / + 8	27T / 8T	m5	+11 / + 2	21T / 2T	k5
30	50	−10 / 0	+13 / + 2	23T / 2T	k5	+ 20 / + 9	30T / 9T	m5	+13 / + 2	23T / 2T	k5
50	80	−13 / 0	+15 / + 2	28T / 2T	k5	+ 33 / + 20	46T / 20T	n5	+15 / + 2	28T / 2T	k5
80	120	−13 / 0	+18 / + 3	31T / 3T	k5	+ 38 / + 23	51T / 23T	n5	+18 / + 3	31T / 3T	k5
120	180	−13 / 0	+21 / + 3	34T / 3T	k5	+ 55 / + 43	68T / 43T	p4	+21 / + 3	34T / 3T	k5
180	200	−15 / 0				+ 91 / + 77	106T / 77T				
200	225		+24 / + 4	39T / 4T	k5	+ 94 / + 80	109T / 80T	r4	+24 / + 4	39T / 4T	k5
225	250					+ 98 / + 84	113T / 84T				
250	280	−18 / 0				+117 / + 94	135T / 94T				
280	315		+27 / + 4	45T / 4T	k5	+121 / + 98	139T / 98T	r5	+27 / + 4	45T / 4T	k5
315	355	−20 / 0				+133 / +108	153T / 108T				
355	400		+29 / + 4	49T / 4T	k5	+139 / +114	159T / 114T	r5	+29 / + 4	49T / 4T	k5
400	450	−25 / 0				+153 / +126	178T / 126T				
450	500		+32 / + 5	57T / 5T	k5	+159 / +132	184T / 132T	r5	+32 / + 5	57T / 5T	k5
500	630	−30 / 0	+40 / +10	70T / 10T	—	+185 / +150	215T / 150T	—	+40 / +10	70T / 10T	—
630	800	−40 / 0	+55 / +15	95T / 15T	—	+220 / +175	260T / 175T	—	+55 / +15	95T / 15T	—
800	1000	−50 / 0	+65 / +15	115T / 15T	—	+255 / +200	305T / 200T	—	+65 / +15	115T / 15T	—

CLASS: B PRODUCT*

over	inclusive	tolerance μm	cone seat deviation	resultant fit	symbol	cone seat deviation	resultant fit	symbol	cone seat deviation	resultant fit	symbol
10	18	− 8 / 0	+ 9 / + 1	17T / 1T	k5	+ 15 / + 7	23T / 7T	m5	+ 9 / + 1	17T / 1T	k5
18	30	− 8 / 0	+11 / + 2	19T / 2T	k5	+ 17 / + 8	25T / 8T	m5	+11 / + 2	19T / 2T	k5
30	50	−10 / 0	+13 / + 2	23T / 2T	k5	+ 20 / + 9	30T / 9T	m5	+13 / + 2	23T / 2T	k5
50	80	−10 / 0	+15 / + 2	25T / 2T	k5	+ 33 / + 20	43T / 20T	n5	+15 / + 2	25T / 2T	k5
80	120	−10 / 0	+18 / + 3	28T / 3T	k5	+ 33 / + 23	43T / 23T	n4	+18 / + 3	28T / 3T	k5
120	180	−10 / 0	+21 / + 3	31T / 3T	k5	+ 55 / + 43	65T / 43T	p4	+21 / + 3	31T / 3T	k5
180	200	−13 / 0				+ 91 / + 77	104T / 77T				
200	225		+24 / + 4	37T / 4T	k5	+ 94 / + 80	107T / 80T	r4	+24 / + 4	37T / 4T	k5
225	250					+ 98 / + 84	111T / 84T				
250	280	−13 / 0				+110 / + 94	123T / 94T				
280	315		+27 / + 4	40T / 4T	k5	+114 / + 98	127T / 98T	r4	+27 / + 4	40T / 4T	k5

*See Bearing Tolerance Chart, page 20.

INDUSTRIAL EQUIPMENT—
CUP FITTING PRACTICE (Micrometers, μm)
METRIC SYSTEM BEARINGS (For "J" Prefix Parts)

CLASS: C PRODUCT*

CUP O.D. range mm ever	inclusive	toler-ance μm	floating cup seat deviation	resultant fit	symbol	clamped cup seat deviation	resultant fit	symbol	adjustable cup seat deviation	resultant fit	symbol	non-adjustable or in carriers cup seat deviation	resultant fit	symbol	rotating non-adjustable or in carriers cup seat deviation	resultant fit	symbol
18	30	0 / − 8	+ 7 / +16	7L / 24L	G5	0 / + 9	0 / 17L	H5	− 8 / + 1	8T / 9L	K5	− 21 / − 12	21T / 4T	N5	− 24 / − 11	24T / 3T	N6
30	50	0 / −10	+ 9 / +20	9L / 30L	G5	0 / +11	0 / 21L	H5	− 9 / + 2	9T / 12L	K5	− 24 / − 13	24T / 3T	N5	− 28 / − 12	28T / 2T	N6
50	80	0 / −10	+10 / +23	10L / 33L	G5	0 / +13	0 / 23L	H5	−10 / + 3	10T / 13L	K5	− 28 / − 15	28T / 5T	N5	− 33 / − 14	33T / 4T	N6
80	120	0 / −13	+12 / +27	12L / 40L	G5	0 / +15	0 / 28L	H5	−13 / + 2	13T / 15L	K5	− 33 / − 18	33T / 5T	N5	− 38 / − 16	38T / 3T	N6
120	180	0 / −13	+14 / +32	14L / 45L	G5	0 / +18	0 / 31L	H5	−12,5 / +12,5	12,5T / 25,5L	JS6	− 39 / − 21	39T / 8T	N5	− 45 / − 20	45T / 7T	N6
180	250	0 / −15	+15 / +35	15L / 50L	G5	0 / +20	0 / 35L	H5	−14,5 / +14,5	14,5T / 29,5L	JS6	− 45 / − 25	45T / 10T	N5	− 51 / − 22	51T / 7T	N6
250	315	0 / −20	+17 / +40	17L / 60L	G5	0 / +23	0 / 43L	H5	−20 / + 3	20T / 23L	K5	− 50 / − 27	50T / 7T	N5	− 57 / − 25	57T / 5T	N6
315	400	0 / −20	+18 / +43	18L / 63L	G5	0 / +25	0 / 45L	H5	−22 / + 3	22T / 23L	K5	− 55 / − 30	55T / 10T	N5	− 62 / − 26	62T / 6T	N6
400	500	0 / −25	+20 / +47	20L / 72L	G5	0 / +27	0 / 52L	H5	−25 / + 2	25T / 27L	K5	− 60 / − 33	60T / 8T	N5	− 67 / − 27	67T / 2T	N6
500	630	0 / −25	+25 / +50	25L / 75L	—	0 / +25	0 / 50L	—	−25 / 0	25T / 25L	—	− 65 / − 40	65T / 15T	—	− 75 / − 38	75T / 13T	—
630	800	0 / −40	+25 / +65	25L / 105L	—	0 / +40	0 / 80L	—	−40 / 0	40T / 40L	—	− 90 / − 50	90T / 10T	—	− 95 / − 50	95T / 10T	—
800	1000	0 / −50	+25 / +75	25L / 125L	—	0 / +50	0 / 100L	—	−50 / 0	50T / 50L	—	−100 / − 50	100T / 0	—	−115 / − 65	115T / 15T	—

CLASS: B PRODUCT*

CUP O.D. range mm ever	inclusive	toler-ance μm	floating cup seat deviation	resultant fit	symbol	clamped cup seat deviation	resultant fit	symbol	adjustable cup seat deviation	resultant fit	symbol	non-adjustable or in carriers cup seat deviation	resultant fit	symbol	rotating non-adjustable or in carriers cup seat deviation	resultant fit	symbol
18	30	0 / − 8	+ 7 / +16	7L / 24L	G5	0 / + 6	0 / 14L	H4	− 8 / + 1	8T / 9L	K5	− 14 / − 5	14T / 3L	M5	− 21 / − 12	21T / 4T	N5
30	50	0 / − 8	+ 9 / +20	9L / 28L	G5	0 / + 7	0 / 15L	H4	− 9 / + 2	9T / 10L	K5	− 16 / − 5	16T / 3L	M5	− 24 / − 13	24T / 5T	N5
50	80	0 / − 9	+10 / +23	10L / 32L	G5	0 / + 8	0 / 17L	H4	−10 / + 3	10T / 12L	K5	− 19 / − 6	19T / 3L	M5	− 28 / − 15	28T / 6T	N5
80	120	0 / −10	+12 / +27	12L / 37L	G5	0 / +10	0 / 20L	H4	−13 / + 2	13T / 12L	K5	− 23 / − 8	23T / 2L	M5	− 33 / − 18	33T / 8T	N5
120	180	0 / −10	+14 / +32	14L / 42L	G5	0 / +12	0 / 22L	H4	−12,5 / +12,5	12,5T / 22,5L	Js6	− 27 / − 9	27T / 1L	M5	− 39 / − 21	39T / 11T	N5
180	250	0 / −13	+15 / +35	15L / 48L	G5	0 / +14	0 / 27L	H4	−10 / +10	10T / 23L	Js5	− 31 / − 11	31T / 2L	M5	− 45 / − 25	45T / 12T	N5
250	315	0 / −15	+17 / +40	17L / 55L	G5	0 / +16	0 / 31L	H4	−11,5 / +11,5	11,5T / 26,5L	Js5	− 36 / − 13	36T / 2L	M5	− 50 / − 27	50T / 12T	N5

*See Bearing Tolerance Chart, page 20.

INCH SYSTEM
BEARING TOLERANCES

CONE BORE TOLERANCE †

				CLASS									
				4 All Sizes		**2** 24.0000 609,600 Max. Cone Bore		**3** All Sizes		**0** 12.0000 304,800 Max. Cup O.D.		**00** 10.5000 266,700 Max. Cup O.D.	
				DEVIATION IN .0001 INCH AND MICROMETERS									
BEARING TYPES	CONE BORE OVER	INCL.	CUP O.D. OVER	INCL.	HIGH	LOW	HIGH	LOW	HIGH	LOW	HIGH	LOW	HIGH	LOW
TS	—	3.0000 76,200			+ 5 ▲ + 13	0 0	+ 5 +13	0 0	+ 5 +13	0 0	+ 5 +13	0 0	+3 +8	0 0
TSF TSL SS ASSEM	3.0000 76,200	12.0000 304,800			+ 10 + 25	0 0	+10 +25	0 0	+ 5 +13	0 0	+ 5 +13	0 0	+3 +8	0 0
TDI TDIT	12.0000 304,800	24.0000 609,600			+ 20 + 51	0 0	+20 +51	0 0	+10 +25	0 0	—		—	
TDO TDODC TNA	24.0000 609,600	36.0000 914,400			+ 30 + 76	0 0	—		+15 +38	0 0	—		—	
TNADC TNASW	36.0000 914,400	48.0000 1219,200			+ 40 +102	0 0	—		+20 +51	0 0	—		—	
TNASWE	48.0000 1219,200	—			+ 50 +127	0 0	—		+30 +76	0 0	—		—	

▲Cone bore deviation = 8 High, 0 Low (20 High, 0 Low) for cones in series LM11700, LM11900, M12600, LM12700, L44600, L45400, LM48500, LM67400 and L68100.

†Inch system bearings in the dimension tables with this sign (†) are shown with maximum cone bore; the tolerance is minus by the same magnitude as shown.

CUP O.D. TOLERANCE †

BEARING TYPES	CONE BORE OVER	INCL.	CUP O.D. OVER	INCL.	HIGH	LOW	HIGH	LOW	HIGH	LOW	HIGH	LOW	HIGH	LOW
TS TSF TSL SS ASSEM. TDI			—	12.0000 304,800	+ 10 + 25	0 0	+10 +25	0 0	+ 5 +13	0 0	+ 5 +13	0 0	+3 +8	0 0
			12.0000 304,800	24.0000 609,600	+ 20 + 51	0 0	+20 +51	0 0	+10 +25	0 0	—		—	
TDIT TDO			24.0000 609,600	36.0000 914,400	+ 30 + 76	0 0	+30 +76	0 0	+15 +38	0 0	—		—	
TDODC TNA TNADC			36.0000 914,400	48.0000 1219,200	+ 40 +102	0 0	—		+20 +51	0 0	—		—	
TNASW TNASWE			48.0000 1219,200	—	+ 50 +127	0 0	—		+30 +76	0 0	—		—	

†Inch system bearings in the dimension tables with this sign (†) are shown with maximum cup O.D.; the tolerance is minus by the same magnitude as shown.

CUP FLANGE O.D. TOLERANCE

BEARING TYPES	CONE BORE OVER	INCL.	CUP O.D. OVER	INCL.	HIGH	LOW	HIGH	LOW	HIGH	LOW	HIGH	LOW	HIGH	LOW
TSF			—	12.0000 304,800	+ 20 + 51	0 0	+ 20 + 51	0 0	+ 20 + 51	0 0	+20 +51	0 0	+20 +51	0 0
			12.0000 304,800	24.0000 609,600	+ 30 + 76	0 0	+ 30 + 76	0 0	+ 30 + 76	0 0	—		—	
			24.0000 609,600	36.0000 914,400	+ 40 +102	0 0	+ 40 +102	0 0	+ 40 +102	0 0	—		—	
			36.0000 914,400	—	+ 50 +127	0 0	—		+ 50 +127	0 0	—		—	

CONE STAND TOLERANCE

BEARING TYPES	CONE BORE OVER	INCL.	CUP O.D. OVER	INCL.	HIGH	LOW	HIGH	LOW	HIGH	LOW	HIGH	LOW	HIGH	LOW
SINGLE CONES	—	4.0000 101,600			+ 40 ▲ +102	0 0	+ 40 +102	0 0	+ 40 +102	− 40 −102	+ 40 +102	− 40 −102	+ 40 +102	− 40 −102
	4.0000 101,600	12.0000 304,800			+ 60 +152	− 60 −152	+ 40 +102	0 0	+ 40 +102	− 40 −102	+ 40 +102	− 40 −102	+ 40 +102	− 40 −102
	12.0000 304,800	24.0000 609,600	—	20.0000 508,000	+ 70 +178	− 70 −178	+ 70 +178	− 70 −178	+ 40 +102	− 40 −102	—		—	
	12.0000 304,800	24.0000 609,600	20.0000 508,000	—	+ 70 +178	− 70 −178	+ 70 +178	− 70 −178	+ 70 +178	− 70 −178	—		—	
	24.0000 609,600	—			+ 70 +178	− 70 −178	—		+ 70 +178	− 70 −178	—		—	

▲Cone stand deviation = 70 High, 0 Low (178 High, 0 Low) for cones in series LM11700, LM11900, M12600, LM12700, L44600, L45400, LM48500, LM67400 and L68100.

18

INCH SYSTEM
BEARING TOLERANCES

CUP STAND TOLERANCE *

Each value cell shows: top = deviation in .0001 inch, bottom = micrometers.

					CLASS 4 All Sizes		CLASS 2 24.0000 609,600 Max. Cone Bore		CLASS 3 All Sizes		CLASS 0 12.0000 304,800 Max. Cup O.D.		CLASS 00 10.5000 266,700 Max. Cup O.D.	
BEARING TYPES	CONE BORE OVER	CONE BORE INCL.	CUP O.D. OVER	CUP O.D. INCL.	HIGH	LOW	HIGH	LOW	HIGH	LOW	HIGH	LOW	HIGH	LOW
SINGLE CUPS	—	4.0000 101,600			+40▲ +102	0 0	+40 +102	0 0	+40 +102	−40 −102	+40 +102	−40 −102	+40 +102	−40 −102
	4.0000 101,600	12.0000 304,800			+80 +203	−40 −102	+40 +102	0 0	+40 +102	−40 −102	+40 +102	−40 −102	+40 +102	−40 −102
	12.0000 304,800	24.0000 609,600	—	20.0000 508,800	+80 +203	−80 −203	+80 +203	−80 −203	+40 +102	−40 −102	—	—	—	—
	12.0000 304,800	24.0000 609,600	20.0000 508,000	—	+80 +203	−80 −203	+80 +203	−80 −203	+80 +203	−80 −203	—	—	—	—
	24.0000 609,600	—			+80 +203	−80 −203	—	—	+80 +203	−80 −203	—	—	—	—

*Cup stand for flanged cups is measured from flange backface.

▲Cup stand deviation = 70 High, 0 Low (178 High, 0 Low) for cups in series LM11700, LM11900, M12600, LM12700, L44600, L45400, LM48500, LM67000 and L68100.

OVERALL BEARING WIDTH TOLERANCE

					4 HIGH	4 LOW	2 HIGH	2 LOW	3 HIGH	3 LOW	0 HIGH	0 LOW	00 HIGH	00 LOW
BEARING TYPES	CONE BORE OVER	CONE BORE INCL.	CUP O.D. OVER	CUP O.D. INCL.										
TS TSF TSL (1)	—	4.0000 101,600			+80▲ +203	0 0	+80 +203	0 0	+80 +203	−80 −203	+80 +203	−80 −203	+80 +203	−80 −203
	4.0000 101,600	12.0000 304,800			+140 +356	−100 −254	+80 +203	0 0	+80 +203	−80 −203	+80 +203	−80 −203	+80 +203	−80 −203
	12.0000 304,800	24.0000 609,600	—	20.0000 508,000	+150 +381	−150 −381	+150 +381	−150 −381	+80 +203	−80 −203	—	—	—	—
	12.0000 304,800	24.0000 609,600	20.0000 508,000	—	+150 +381	−150 −381	+150 +381	−150 −381	+150 +381	−150 −381	—	—	—	—
	24.0000 609,600	—			+150 +381	−150 −381	—	—	+150 +381	−150 −381	—	—	—	—
TNA TNADC TNASW TNASWE	—	5.0000 127,000			+100 +254	0 0	+100 +254	0 0	+100 +254	0 0	—	—	—	—
	5.0000 127,000	—			+300 +762	0 0	+300 +762	0 0	+300 +762	0 0	—	—	—	—
TDI TDIT TDO TDODC	—	4.0000 101,600			+160 +406	0 0	+160 +406	0 0	+160 +406	−160 −406	+160 +406	−160 −406	+160 +406	−160 −406
	4.0000 101,600	12.0000 304,800			+280 +711	−200 −508	+160 +406	−80 −203	+160 +406	−160 −406	+160 +406	−160 −406	+160 +406	−160 −406
	12.0000 304,800	24.0000 609,600	—	20.0000 508,000	+300 +762	−300 −762	+300 +762	−300 −762	+160 +406	−160 −406	—	—	—	—
	12.0000 304,800	24.0000 609,600	20.0000 508,000	—	+300 +762	−300 −762	+300 +762	−300 −762	+300 +762	−300 −762	—	—	—	—
	24.0000 609,600	—			+300 +762	−300 −762	—	—	+300 +762	−300 −762	—	—	—	—
SS ASSEM.	—	4.0000 101,600			+180♦ +459	−20 −51	+180 +459	−20 −51	—	—	—	—	—	—

▲Overall bearing width deviation = 140 High, 0 Low (356 High, 0 Low) for series LM11700, LM11900, M12600, LM12700, L44600, L45400, LM48500, LM67000 and L68100.

♦Overall bearing width deviation = 300 High, 20 Low (762 High, 51 Low) for SS assemblies in series LM11700, LM11900, M12600, LM12700, L44600, L45400, LM48500, LM67000 and L68100.

(1) For TSF type bearings, the tolerance applies to the dimension from the backface of the flange to the backface of the cone.

ASSEMBLED BEARING MAXIMUM RADIAL RUNOUT

BEARING TYPES	CONE BORE OVER	CONE BORE INCL.	CUP O.D. OVER	CUP O.D. INCL.	4	2	3	0	00
TS TSF TSL			—	12.0000 304,800	20 51	15 38	3 8	1.5 4	0.75 2
SS ASSEM. TDI TDIT			12.0000 304,800	24.0000 609,600	20 51	15 38	7 18	—	—
TDO TDODC TNA			24.0000 609,600	36.0000 914,400	30 76	20 51	20 51	—	—
TNADC TNASW TNASWE			36.0000 914,400	—	30 76	—	30 76	—	—

METRIC SYSTEM BEARING TOLERANCES (FOR "J" PREFIX PARTS)

CONE BORE TOLERANCE

BEARING TYPES	CONE BORE OVER	CONE BORE INCL.	K ALL SIZES HIGH	K LOW	N 19.6850 500 Max. Cone Bore & Max. Cup O.D. HIGH	N LOW	C 62.9921 1600 Max. Cone Bore & Max. Cup O.D. HIGH	C LOW	B 12.4016 315 Max. Cone Bore & Max. Cup O.D. HIGH	B LOW
	0.3937 / 10	0.7087 / 18	0 / 0	− 5 / −13	0 / 0	− 5 / −13	0 / 0	− 4 / −10	0 / 0	− 3 / − 8
	0.7087 / 18	1.1811 / 30	0 / 0	− 5 / −13	0 / 0	− 5 / −13	0 / 0	− 4 / −10	0 / 0	− 3 / − 8
	1.1811 / 30	1.9685 / 50	0 / 0	− 5 / −13	0 / 0	− 5 / −13	0 / 0	− 4 / −10	0 / 0	− 4 / −10
	1.9685 / 50	3.1496 / 80	0 / 0	− 8 / −15	0 / 0	− 6 / −15	0 / 0	− 5 / −13	0 / 0	− 4 / −10
	3.1496 / 80	4.7244 / 120	0 / 0	− 8 / −20	0 / 0	− 8 / −20	0 / 0	− 5 / −13	0 / 0	− 4 / −10
	4.7244 / 120	7.0866 / 180	0 / 0	−10 / −25	0 / 0	−10 / −25	0 / 0	− 5 / −13	0 / 0	− 4 / −10
	7.0866 / 180	9.8425 / 250	0 / 0	−12 / −30	0 / 0	−12 / −30	0 / 0	− 6 / −15	0 / 0	− 5 / −13
TS SR ASSEM. TDO	9.8425 / 250	12.4016 / 315	0 / 0	−14 / −35	0 / 0	−14 / −35	0 / 0	− 7 / −18	0 / 0	− 5 / −13
	12.4016 / 315	15.7480 / 400	0 / 0	−16 / −40	0 / 0	−16 / −40	0 / 0	− 8 / −20	−	−
	15.7480 / 400	19.6850 / 500	0 / 0	−18 / −45	0 / 0	−18 / −45	0 / 0	−10 / −25	−	−
	19.6850 / 500	24.8031 / 630	0 / 0	−20 / −50	−	−	0 / 0	−12 / −30	−	−
	24.8031 / 630	31.4961 / 800	0 / 0	−31 / −80	−	−	0 / 0	−16 / −40	−	−
	31.4961 / 800	39.3700 / 1000	0 / 0	−39 / −100	−	−	0 / 0	−20 / −50	−	−
	39.3700 / 1000	47.2441 / 1200	0 / 0	−51 / −130	−	−	0 / 0	−24 / −60	−	−
	47.2441 / 1200	62.9921 / 1600	0 / 0	−59 / −150	−	−	0 / 0	−31 / −80	−	−
	62.9921 / 1600	78.7402 / 2000	0 / 0	−79 / −200	−	−	−	−	−	−
	78.7402 / 2000		0 / 0	−98 / −250	−	−	−	−	−	−

CUP O.D. TOLERANCE

BEARING TYPES	CUP O.D. OVER	CUP O.D. INCL.	K HIGH	K LOW	N HIGH	N LOW	C HIGH	C LOW	B HIGH	B LOW
	0.7087 / 18	1.1811 / 30	0 / 0	− 8 / −20	0 / 0	− 8 / −20	0 / 0	− 3 / − 8	0 / 0	− 3 / − 8
	1.1811 / 30	1.9685 / 50	0 / 0	− 8 / −20	0 / 0	− 8 / −20	0 / 0	− 4 / −10	0 / 0	− 3 / − 8
	1.9685 / 50	3.1496 / 80	0 / 0	− 8 / −20	0 / 0	− 8 / −20	0 / 0	− 4 / −10	0 / 0	− 3.5 / − 9
	3.1496 / 80	4.7244 / 120	0 / 0	− 8 / −20	0 / 0	− 8 / −20	0 / 0	− 5 / −13	0 / 0	− 4 / −10
	4.7244 / 120	5.9055 / 150	0 / 0	−10 / −25	0 / 0	−10 / −25	0 / 0	− 5 / −13	0 / 0	− 4 / −10
	5.9055 / 150	7.0866 / 180	0 / 0	−10 / −25	0 / 0	−10 / −25	0 / 0	− 5 / −13	0 / 0	− 4 / −10
	7.0866 / 180	9.8425 / 250	0 / 0	−12 / −30	0 / 0	−12 / −30	0 / 0	− 6 / −15	0 / 0	− 5 / −13
TS SR ASSEM. TDO	9.8425 / 250	12.4016 / 315	0 / 0	−16 / −40	0 / 0	−16 / −40	0 / 0	− 8 / −20	0 / 0	− 6 / −15
	12.4016 / 315	15.7480 / 400	0 / 0	−16 / −40	0 / 0	−16 / −40	0 / 0	− 8 / −20	−	−
	15.7480 / 400	19.6850 / 500	0 / 0	−20 / −50	0 / 0	−20 / −50	0 / 0	−10 / −25	−	−
	19.6850 / 500	24.8031 / 630	0 / 0	−20 / −50	−	−	0 / 0	−10 / −25	−	−
	24.8031 / 630	31.4961 / 800	0 / 0	−31 / −80	−	−	0 / 0	−16 / −40	−	−
	31.4961 / 800	39.3700 / 1000	0 / 0	−39 / −100	−	−	0 / 0	−20 / −50	−	−
	39.3700 / 1000	47.2441 / 1200	0 / 0	−51 / −130	−	−	0 / 0	−24 / −60	−	−
	47.2441 / 1200	62.9921 / 1600	0 / 0	− 65 / −165	−	−	0 / 0	−31 / −80	−	−
	62.9921 / 1600	78.7402 / 2000	0 / 0	−79 / −200	−	−	−	−	−	−
	78.7402 / 2000		0 / 0	−98 / −250	−	−	−	−	−	−

METRIC SYSTEM
BEARING TOLERANCES
(FOR "J" PREFIX PARTS)

Each cell shows two stacked values: top = .0001 Inch, bottom = Micrometers.

CONE WIDTH TOLERANCE

BEARING TYPES	CONE BORE OVER	INCL.	K ALL SIZES HIGH	K LOW	N 19.6850 / 500 HIGH	N LOW	C 62.9921 / 1600 HIGH	C LOW	B 12.4016 / 315 HIGH	B LOW
	0.3937 / 10	0.7087 / 18	0 / 0	−39 / −100	0 / 0	−20 / −50	0 / 0	−79 / −200	0 / 0	−79 / −200
	0.7087 / 18	1.1811 / 30	0 / 0	−39 / −100	0 / 0	−20 / −50	0 / 0	−79 / −200	0 / 0	−79 / −200
	1.1811 / 30	1.9685 / 50	0 / 0	−39 / −100	0 / 0	−20 / −50	0 / 0	−79 / −200	0 / 0	−79 / −200
	1.9685 / 50	3.1496 / 80	0 / 0	−59 / −150	0 / 0	−20 / −50	0 / 0	−118 / −300	0 / 0	−118 / −300
	3.1496 / 80	4.7244 / 120	0 / 0	−59 / −150	0 / 0	−20 / −50	0 / 0	−118 / −300	0 / 0	−118 / −300
	4.7244 / 120	7.0866 / 180	0 / 0	−79 / −200	0 / 0	−20 / −50	0 / 0	−118 / −300	0 / 0	−118 / −300
	7.0866 / 180	9.8425 / 250	0 / 0	−79 / −200	0 / 0	−20 / −50	0 / 0	−138 / −350	0 / 0	−138 / −350
SINGLE CONES	9.8425 / 250	12.4016 / 315	0 / 0	−79 / −200	0 / 0	−20 / −50	0 / 0	−138 / −350	0 / 0	−138 / −350
	12.4016 / 315	15.7480 / 400	0 / 0	−98 / −250	0 / 0	−20 / −50	0 / 0	−138 / −350	−	−
	15.7480 / 400	19.6850 / 500	0 / 0	−98 / −250	0 / 0	−20 / −50	0 / 0	−138 / −350	−	−
	19.6850 / 500	24.8031 / 630	0 / 0	−98 / −250	−	−	0 / 0	−138 / −350	−	−
	24.8031 / 630	31.4961 / 800	0 / 0	−118 / −300	−	−	0 / 0	−138 / −350	−	−
	31.4961 / 800	39.3700 / 1000	0 / 0	−118 / −300	−	−	0 / 0	−138 / −350	−	−
	39.3700 / 1000	47.2441 / 1200	0 / 0	−118 / −300	−	−	0 / 0	−138 / −350	−	−
	47.2441 / 1200	62.9921 / 1600	0 / 0	−138 / −350	−	−	0 / 0	−138 / −350	−	−
	62.9921 / 1600	78.7402 / 2000	0 / 0	−138 / −350	−	−	−	−	−	−
	78.7402 / 2000		0 / 0	−138 / −350	−	−	−	−	−	−

CUP WIDTH TOLERANCE

BEARING TYPES	CUP O.D. OVER	INCL.	K HIGH	K LOW	N HIGH	N LOW	C HIGH	C LOW	B HIGH	B LOW
	0.7087 / 18	1.1811 / 30	0 / 0	−59 / −150	0 / 0	−39 / −100	0 / 0	−59 / −150	0 / 0	−59 / −150
	1.1811 / 30	1.9685 / 50	0 / 0	−59 / −150	0 / 0	−39 / −100	0 / 0	−59 / −150	0 / 0	−59 / −150
	1.9685 / 50	3.1496 / 80	0 / 0	−59 / −150	0 / 0	−39 / −100	0 / 0	−59 / −150	0 / 0	−59 / −150
	3.1496 / 80	4.7244 / 120	0 / 0	−79 / −200	0 / 0	−39 / −100	0 / 0	−79 / −200	0 / 0	−79 / −200
	4.7244 / 120	5.9055 / 150	0 / 0	−79 / −200	0 / 0	−39 / −100	0 / 0	−79 / −200	0 / 0	−79 / −200
	5.9055 / 150	7.0866 / 180	0 / 0	−79 / −200	0 / 0	−39 / −100	0 / 0	−98 / −250	0 / 0	−98 / −250
	7.0866 / 180	9.8425 / 250	0 / 0	−98 / −250	0 / 0	−39 / −100	0 / 0	−98 / −250	0 / 0	−98 / −250
SINGLE CUPS	9.8425 / 250	12.4016 / 315	0 / 0	−98 / −250	0 / 0	−39 / −100	0 / 0	−118 / −300	0 / 0	−118 / −300
	12.4016 / 315	15.7480 / 400	0 / 0	−98 / −250	0 / 0	−39 / −100	0 / 0	−118 / −300	−	−
	15.7480 / 400	19.6850 / 500	0 / 0	−118 / −300	0 / 0	−39 / −100	0 / 0	−138 / −350	−	−
	19.6850 / 500	24.8031 / 630	0 / 0	−118 / −300	−	−	0 / 0	−138 / −350	−	−
	24.8031 / 630	31.4961 / 800	0 / 0	−118 / −300	−	−	0 / 0	−138 / −350	−	−
	31.4961 / 800	39.3700 / 1000	0 / 0	−138 / −350	−	−	0 / 0	−157 / −400	−	−
	39.3700 / 1000	47.2441 / 1200	0 / 0	−138 / −350	−	−	0 / 0	−157 / −400	−	−
	47.2441 / 1200	62.9921 / 1600	0 / 0	−157 / −400	−	−	0 / 0	−157 / −400	−	−
	62.9921 / 1600	78.7402 / 2000	0 / 0	−157 / −400	−	−	−	−	−	−
	78.7402 / 2000		0 / 0	−157 / −400	−	−	−	−	−	−

METRIC SYSTEM BEARING TOLERANCES (FOR "J" PREFIX PARTS)

CONE STAND TOLERANCE

SINGLE CONES

BEARING TYPES	CONE BORE OVER	CONE BORE INCL.	K (ALL SIZES) HIGH	K LOW	N 19.6850 / 500 (Max. Cone Bore & Max. Cup O.D.) HIGH	N LOW	C 62.9921 / 1600 (Max. Cone Bore & Max. Cup O.D.) HIGH	C LOW	B 12.4016 / 315 (Max. Cone Bore & Max. Cup O.D.) HIGH	B LOW
			DEVIATION—In .0001 Inch and Micrometers							
SINGLE CONES	0.3937 10	0.7087 18	+ 39 +100	0 0	+ 20 + 50	0 0	+ 39 +100	− 39 −100	+ 39 +100	− 39 −100
	0.7087 18	1.1811 30	+ 39 +100	0 0	+ 20 + 50	0 0	+ 39 +100	− 39 −100	+ 39 +100	− 39 −100
	1.1811 30	1.9685 50	+ 39 +100	0 0	+ 20 + 50	0 0	+ 39 +100	− 39 −100	+ 39 +100	− 39 −100
	1.9685 50	3.1496 80	+ 39 +100	0 0	+ 20 + 50	0 0	+ 39 +100	− 39 −100	+ 39 +100	− 39 −100
	3.1496 80	4.7244 120	+ 39 +100	− 39 −100	+ 20 + 50	0 0	+ 39 +100	− 39 −100	+ 39 +100	− 39 −100
	4.7244 120	7.0866 180	+ 39 +100	− 39 −100	+ 20 + 50	0 0	+ 39 +100	− 39 −100	+ 39 +100	− 39 −100
	7.0866 180	9.8425 250	+ 39 +100	− 39 −100	+ 20 + 50	0 0	+ 39 +100	− 59 −150	+ 39 +100	− 59 −150
	9.8425 250	12.4016 315	+ 39 +100	− 39 −100	+ 39 +100	0 0	+ 39 +100	− 59 −150	+ 39 +100	− 59 −150
	12.4016 315	15.7480 400	+ 39 +100	− 39 −100	+ 39 +100	0 0	+ 59 +150	− 59 −150	−	−
	15.7480 400	19.6850 500	+ 59 +150	− 59 −150	+ 39 +100	0 0	+ 59 +150	− 59 −150	−	−
	19.6850 500	24.8031 630	+ 59 +150	− 59 −150	−	−	+ 59 +150	− 79 −200	−	−
	24.8031 630	31.4961 800	+ 59 +150	− 59 −150	−	−	+ 59 +150	− 79 −200	−	−
	31.4961 800	39.3700 1000	+ 59 +150	− 59 −150	−	−	+ 59 +150	− 79 −200	−	−
	39.3700 1000	47.2441 1200	+ 59 +150	− 79 −200	−	−	+ 59 +150	− 79 −200	−	−
	47.2441 1200	62.9921 1600	+ 59 +150	− 79 −200	−	−	+ 59 +150	− 79 −200	−	−
	62.9921 1600	78.7402 2000	+ 59 +150	− 79 −200	−	−	−	−	−	−
	78.7402 2000		+ 59 +150	− 79 −200	−	−	−	−	−	−

CUP STAND TOLERANCE

SINGLE CUPS

BEARING TYPES	CONE BORE OVER	CONE BORE INCL.	K HIGH	K LOW	N HIGH	N LOW	C HIGH	C LOW	B HIGH	B LOW
SINGLE CUPS	0.3937 10	0.7087 18	+ 39 +100	0 0	+ 20 + 50	0 0	+ 39 +100	− 39 −100	+ 39 +100	− 39 −100
	0.7087 18	1.1811 30	+ 39 +100	0 0	+ 20 + 50	0 0	+ 39 +100	− 39 −100	+ 39 +100	− 39 −100
	1.1811 30	1.9685 50	+ 39 +100	0 0	+ 20 + 50	0 0	+ 39 +100	− 39 −100	+ 39 +100	− 39 −100
	1.9685 50	3.1496 80	+ 39 +100	0 0	+ 20 + 50	0 0	+ 39 +100	− 39 −100	+ 39 +100	− 39 −100
	3.1496 80	4.7244 120	+ 39 +100	− 39 −100	+ 20 + 50	0 0	+ 39 +100	− 39 −100	+ 39 +100	− 39 −100
	4.7244 120	7.0866 180	+ 39 +100	− 39 −100	+ 39 +100	0 0	+ 39 +100	− 59 −150	+ 39 +100	− 59 −150
	7.0866 180	9.8425 250	+ 39 +100	− 39 −100	+ 39 +100	0 0	+ 39 +100	− 59 −150	+ 39 +100	− 59 −150
	9.8425 250	12.4016 315	+ 39 +100	− 39 −100	+ 39 +100	0 0	+ 39 +100	− 59 −150	+ 39 +100	− 59 −150
	12.4016 315	15.7480 400	+ 39 +100	− 39 −100	+ 39 +100	0 0	+ 39 +100	− 59 −150	−	−
	15.7480 400	19.6850 500	+ 39 +100	− 59 −150	+ 39 +100	0 0	+ 59 +150	− 59 −150	−	−
	19.6850 500	24.8031 630	+ 39 +100	− 59 −150	−	−	+ 59 +150	− 79 −200	−	−
	24.8031 630	31.4961 800	+ 39 +100	− 59 −150	−	−	+ 59 +150	− 79 −200	−	−
	31.4961 800	39.3700 1000	+ 59 +150	− 59 −150	−	−	+ 79 +200	− 79 −200	−	−
	39.3700 1000	47.2441 1200	+ 59 +150	− 59 −150	−	−	+ 79 +200	− 98 −250	−	−
	47.2441 1200	62.9921 1600	+ 79 +200	− 79 −200	−	−	+ 79 +200	−118 −300	−	−
	62.9921 1600	78.7402 2000	+ 79 +200	− 79 −200	−	−	−	−	−	−
	78.7402 2000		+ 79 +200	− 79 −200	−	−	−	−	−	−

METRIC SYSTEM BEARING TOLERANCES (FOR "J" PREFIX PARTS)

OVERALL BEARING WIDTH TOLERANCE

BEARING TYPES	CONE BORE OVER	INCL.	K ALL SIZES HIGH	K LOW	N 19.6850 500 Max. Cone Bore & Max. Cup O.D. HIGH	N LOW	C 62.9921 1600 Max. Cone Bore & Max. Cup O.D. HIGH	C LOW	B 12.4016 315 Max. Cone Bore & Max. Cup O.D. HIGH	B LOW
			DEVIATION—In .0001 Inch and Micrometers							
TS	0.3937 / 10	0.7087 / 18	+ 79 / +200	0 / 0	+ 39 / +100	0 / 0	+ 79 / +200	− 79 / −200	+ 79 / +200	− 79 / −200
	0.7087 / 18	1.1811 / 30	+ 79 / +200	0 / 0	+ 39 / +100	0 / 0	+ 79 / +200	− 79 / −200	+ 79 / +200	− 79 / −200
	1.1811 / 30	1.9685 / 50	+ 79 / +200	0 / 0	+ 39 / +100	0 / 0	+ 79 / +200	− 79 / −200	+ 79 / +200	− 79 / −200
	1.9685 / 50	3.1496 / 80	+ 79 / +200	0 / 0	+ 39 / +100	0 / 0	+ 79 / +200	− 79 / −200	+ 79 / +200	− 79 / −200
	3.1496 / 80	4.7244 / 120	+ 79 / +200	0 / 0	+ 39 / +100	0 / 0	+ 79 / +200	− 79 / −200	+ 79 / +200	− 79 / −200
	4.7244 / 120	7.0866 / 180	+ 79 / +200	− 79 / −200	+ 59 / +150	0 / 0	+ 79 / +200	− 98 / −250	+ 79 / +200	− 98 / −250
	7.0866 / 180	9.8425 / 250	+ 79 / +200	− 79 / −200	+ 59 / +150	0 / 0	+ 79 / +200	−118 / −300	+ 79 / +200	−118 / −300
	9.8425 / 250	12.4016 / 315	+ 79 / +200	− 79 / −200	+ 79 / +200	0 / 0	+ 79 / +200	−118 / −300	+ 79 / +200	−118 / −300
	12.4016 / 315	15.7480 / 400	+ 79 / +200	− 79 / −200	+ 79 / +200	0 / 0	+ 98 / +250	−118 / −300	−	−
	15.7480 / 400	19.6850 / 500	+ 98 / +250	−118 / −300	+ 79 / +200	0 / 0	+118 / +300	−118 / −300	−	−
	19.6850 / 500	24.8031 / 630	+ 98 / +250	−118 / −300	−	−	+118 / +300	−157 / −400	−	−
	24.8031 / 630	31.4961 / 800	+ 98 / +250	−118 / −300	−	−	+118 / +300	−157 / −400	−	−
	31.4961 / 800	39.3700 / 1000	+118 / +300	−118 / −300	−	−	+138 / +350	−157 / −400	−	−
	39.3700 / 1000	47.2441 / 1200	+138 / +300	−138 / −350	−	−	+138 / +350	−177 / −450	−	−
	47.2441 / 1200	62.9921 / 1600	+138 / +350	−157 / −400	−	−	+138 / +350	−197 / −500	−	−
	62.9921 / 1600	78.7402 / 2000	+138 / +350	−157 / −400	−	−	−	−	−	−
	78.7402 / 2000		+138 / +350	−157 / −400	−	−	−	−	−	−
SR ASSEM.	0.3937 / 10	4.7244 / 120	−	−	0 / 0	− 59 / −150	−	−	−	−
	4.7244 / 120	9.8425 / 250	−	−	0 / 0	− 59 / −150	−	−	−	−
	9.8425 / 250	19.6850 / 500	−	−	0 / 0	− 59 / −150	−	−	−	−

ASSEMBLED BEARING MAXIMUM RADIAL RUNOUT

BEARING TYPES	CUP O.D. OVER	INCL.	K	N	C	B
	0.7087 / 18	1.1811 / 30	12 / 30	12 / 30	2 / 5	1 / 2,5
	1.1811 / 30	1.9685 / 50	12 / 30	12 / 30	2.4 / 6	1 / 2,5
	1.9685 / 50	3.1496 / 80	12 / 30	12 / 30	2.4 / 6	1.4 / 3,5
	3.1496 / 80	4.7244 / 120	16 / 40	16 / 40	2.4 / 6	1.4 / 3,5
	4.7244 / 120	5.9055 / 150	16 / 40	16 / 40	2.8 / 7	1.4 / 3,5
	5.9055 / 150	7.0866 / 180	16 / 40	16 / 40	3 / 8	1.5 / 4
	7.0866 / 180	9.8425 / 250	20 / 50	20 / 50	4 / 10	2 / 5
TS SR ASSEM. TDO	9.8425 / 250	12.4016 / 315	20 / 50	20 / 50	4.3 / 11	2 / 5
	12.4016 / 315	15.7480 / 400	20 / 50	20 / 50	5 / 13	−
	15.7480 / 400	19.6850 / 500	25 / 65	25 / 65	7 / 18	−
	19.6850 / 500	24.8031 / 630	25 / 65	−	10 / 25	−
	24.8031 / 630	31.4961 / 800	25 / 65	−	14 / 35	−
	31.4961 / 800	39.3700 / 1000	35 / 90	−	20 / 50	−
	39.3700 / 1000	47.2441 / 1200	35 / 90	−	24 / 60	−
	47.2441 / 1200	62.9921 / 1600	35 / 90	−	31 / 80	−
	62.9921 / 1600	78.7402 / 2000	35 / 90	−	−	−
	78.7402 / 2000		35 / 90	−	−	−

Life and Application Factors

application	life factor	application factor*
aerial cable tramways	1.5	1
aircraft - fixed wing		
wheels - (consult The Timken Company's engineering department)		
aircraft hangar doors		
(consult The Timken Company's engineering department)		
bakery and restaurant machinery		
bone cutters, dough mixers, etc.	2	1
bread slicers, grinders and meat slicers	1	1
bicycles	1	1
blowers	2	1
bottling equipment	2	1
calenders (see associated industry)		
cars (other than standard railway equipment)		
cane, clay, creosote, etc.	1	1
kiln cars	2	1.5
mine and ore (consult The Timken Company's engineering department)		
steel mill (consult The Timken Company's engineering department)		
clay working machinery		
brick machines, dry pans, maximullers, sand mixers, etc. ..	1.5	2

application	life factor	application factor*
compressors (calculated on M.E.P. of both H.P. and L.P. cylinders)		
garage	1.5	1
large stationary units	3	1
portable and refrigeration units	2	1
conveyors		
drives, conveyor rolls, pallet wheels, apron and pan conveyors	1.5	1
cranes		
bridge cranes roll shop, mill, mold yard, stripper, machine shop ...	2	1
power house, motor room ...	1.25	1
industrial storage, shipping .	1.5	1
locomotive, gantry and mobile .	1	1
dryers and kiln trunnion rollers		
(cement and chemical equipment) (consult The Timken Company's engineering department)		
elevators and moving stairways ..	2	1
engines		
for high speed gas and diesel engines use M.E.P. - for low speed (up to 500 rpm) use 40% of maximum pressure		
farm and industrial engines—gas or oil	1.5	1
oil field and logging engines—gas, oil or steam	2	1
outboard motors (see marine equipment)		
extractors	2	1

*for "stationary cone, rotating cup" industrial applications with poor seals and dirty conditions use AF × 1.20.

application	life factor	application factor*	application	life factor	application factor*
fans and blowers	2	1	industrial or shop trucks—continued		
farm machinery			lift trucks, trailers and industrial tractors (consult The Timken Company's engineering department)		
combines, cultivators and tillers, disc plows, ensilage and corn cutters, feed grinders, hammer mills, huskers, mowing machines, pickers, wind units, shellers, tractors, trailers, wagons, hay balers, threshers, etc.	1	1	laundry machinery — commercial	2	1
floor scrubbers and polishers	1	1	lawn mowers	1	1
			leather working machinery	2	1
flywheels — presses and shears (see machine tools)			locomotives—mine and industrial	2	1
gear reduction units			logging equipment		
general purpose units and geared motors	1.166	1	arches, blocks, hoists, donkeys, skidders, yarders, etc.	1	1
special drives (use same factor as equipment driven)			machine tools		
glass making machinery	2	1	factory	2	1
grain milling machinery (industrial)			portable	1	1
			press and shear flywheels:		
feed grinders, roller mills, elevator equipment, etc.	2	1	1 - stationary cones and rotating cups with circulating oil system	2	2
household appliances	1	1	2 - stationary and rotating cones with rotating cups with grease lubrication	2	2.4
I-beam trolleys and hoisting equipment			marine equipment		
hoists, winches, etc.	1	1	drives, thrust blocks, etc. heavy cargo vessels, liners, tankers	2	1
I-beam trolleys, chain blocks, etc.	1	1	naval ships (peace time)	1	1
industrial or shop trucks			naval ships (war time)	0.5	1
			pleasure craft, fishing boats	1.5	1
hand trucks	1	1	tugs, service boats	1.75	1

*for "stationary cone, rotating cup" industrial applications with poor seals and dirty conditions use AF × 1.20.

Life and Application Factors—continued

application	life factor	application factor*	application	life factor	application factor*
marine equipment—continued			**printing machinery**	2	1
outboard motors	1	1	**pulverizing and screening equipment**		
windlasses and capstans	1	1			
cargo blocks (consult The Timken Company's engineering department)			air separators, ball mills, cement plant equipment, pulverizers, roll crushers, vibrating or shaker screens, etc.	1.5	1.33
mining equipment			dryer trunnion rollers (consult The Timken Company's engineering department)		
classifiers, flotation cells, mine drum hoists, head sheaves ..	2	1	jaw crushers	1.25	1
mine cars (consult The Timken Company's engineering department)			**pumps**		
miscellaneous mining equipment	1.5	1	deep well pumps, fire pumps, pipe line pumps	2	1
portable rock drills, slope rollers, etc.	1	1	dredge pumps	2	1.5
			household pumps, spray pumps	1	1
motorcycles	1	1	paper mill pumps	3	1.33
			railway equipment		
oil field equipment			car drives	2	1
drilling engines, oil well countershafts, pitmans, reduction units, rotaries, sand reels, drawworks, pumping units, pumps, etc.	2	1	mowers, rail benders, tie drillers, etc.	1	1
			section cars	1.5	1
			refrigeration		
swivels, crown and traveling blocks (consult The Timken Company's engineering department)			compressors (see compressors)		
			refrigerator car drives	2	1
paper mill machinery			**restaurant machinery (see bakery and restaurant machinery)**		
agitator drives, barkers, beaters, chip screens, chippers and dryer rolls, couch, press, wire and felt rolls and associated drives	3	1	**road building, earth moving and street maintenance equipment**		
jordan engines, machine and super calenders	3	1	asphalt mixers, rippers, backfillers, bulldozers, concrete mixers and working machinery, graders, portable rock drills, rollers, scarifiers, shovels, snow plows, street cleaners, trenchers, truck-mixers, power control units, scrapers, prime movers, etc.	1	1
plastic calenders	2	1			

*for "stationary cone, rotating cup" industrial applications with poor seals and dirty conditions use AF × 1.20.

Reference Tables

application	life factor	application factor*
rubber machinery		
banbury mixers, rubber mills, refiners, strainers, tubing machines, tire building machines, calenders, line shafting, etc.	2	1
rubber mill screwdowns	1	1
sand blast machines	1.5	1.33
saw mill machinery		
arches, blocks, hoists, donkeys, skidders, yarders, etc.	1	1
screening equipment (see pulverizing and screening equipment)		
sewage screens	2	1.5
shop or industrial trucks		
hand	1	1
lift trucks, trailers and industrial tractors (consult The Timken Company's engineering department)		
shovels - power		
cone rollers (consult The Timken Company's engineering department)		
gear drives		
electric - use 100% of maximum rated requirements at average speeds		
gas or diesel - use 65% of maximum rated requirements at average speeds		
contractors equipment	1	1
strip mine operations	1.5	1
sheaves		
use 75% of maximum sheave loads	2	1

application	life factor	application factor*
steel mill machinery		
gear drives, pinion stands, edgers and combination drives (figure 100% overload except with flywheels use 200% overload at average speeds)	1.25	1
hot saws	1.5	1.33
roll necks (consult The Timken Company's engineering department)		
billet chargers, coilers, clay guns, furnace covers, levellers, straighteners, pinch rolls, reels, screwdowns, sheet scrubbers, slitters, trimmers, table rolls, uncoilers ..	1.25	1
stokers		
commercial	1.5	1.33
household	1	1
sugar mills		
drives	2	1
textile machinery		
calenders, looms, shears, warpers, etc.	2	1
tractors		
crawler	1	1
crawler track rollers	1.25	1
farm	1	1
wire forming or drawing machines, spring wire machines, etc.	2	1
woodworking machinery		
edgers, jointers, sanders, veneer lathes, saw mill carriages, etc.	2	1

*for "stationary cone, rotating cup" industrial applications with poor seals and dirty conditions use AF × 1.20.

Conversion Tables

1 decanewton = 1,0197 kiloponds = 2.2481 pounds
1 kilopond = 0,9807 decanewtons = 2.2046 pounds
1 pound = 0,4448 decanewtons = 0,4536 kiloponds
1 micrometer = 10^{-6} m = 1 μm

Refer to ISO recommendation **R1000** for rules for the use of units of the International System of Units and a selection of the decimal multiples and sub-multiples of the SI units.

The values in the following tables are based on 1 in = 25.4 mm (exactly).

INCHES TO MILLIMETERS

in	mm	in	mm	in	mm
0.0001	0,0025	0.0040	0,1016	0.0700	1,7780
0.0002	0,0051	0.0050	0,1270	0.0800	2,0320
0.0003	0,0076	0.0060	0,1524	0.0900	2,2860
0.0004	0,0102	0.0070	0,1778	0.1000	2,5400
0.0005	0,0127	0.0080	0,2032	0.2000	5,0800
0.0006	0,0152	0.0090	0,2286	0.3000	7,6200
0.0007	0,0178	0.0100	0,2540	0.4000	10,1600
0.0008	0,0203	0.0200	0,5080	0.5000	12,7000
0.0009	0,0229	0.0300	0,7620	0.6000	15,2400
0.0010	0,0254	0.0400	1,0160	0.7000	17,7800
0.0020	0,0508	0.0500	1,2700	0.8000	20,3200
0.0030	0,0762	0.0600	1,5240	0.9000	22,8600

inches		mm	inches		mm
1/64	0.015625	0,3969	33/64	0.515625	13,0969
1/32	0.03125	0,7937	17/32	0.53125	13,4937
3/64	0.046875	1,1906	35/64	0.546875	13,8906
1/16	0.0625	1,5875	9/16	0.5625	14,2875
5/64	0.078125	1,9844	37/64	0.578125	14,6844
3/32	0.09375	2,3812	19/32	0.59375	15,0812
7/64	0.109375	2,7781	39/64	0.609375	15,4781
1/8	0.125	3,1750	5/8	0.625	15,8750
9/64	0.140625	3,5719	41/64	0.640625	16,2719
5/32	0.15625	3,9687	21/32	0.65625	16,6687
11/64	0.171875	4,3656	43/64	0.671875	17,0656
3/16	0.1875	4,7625	11/16	0.6875	17,4625
13/64	0.203125	5,1594	45/64	0.703125	17,8594
7/32	0.21875	5,5562	23/32	0.71875	18,2562
15/64	0.234375	5,9531	47/64	0.734375	18,6531
1/4	0.25	6,3500	3/4	0.75	19,0500
17/64	0.265625	6,7469	49/64	0.765625	19,4469
9/32	0.28125	7,1437	25/32	0.78125	19,8437
19/64	0.296875	7,5406	51/64	0.796875	20,2406
5/16	0.3125	7,9375	13/16	0.8125	20,6375
21/64	0.328125	8,3344	53/64	0.828125	21,0344
11/32	0.34375	8,7312	27/32	0.84375	21,4312
23/64	0.350375	9,1281	55/64	0.859375	21,8281
3/8	0.375	9,5250	7/8	0.875	22,2250
25/64	0.390625	9,9219	57/64	0.890625	22,6219
13/32	0.40625	10,3187	29/32	0.90625	23,0187
27/64	0.421875	10,7156	59/64	0.921875	23,4156
7/16	0.4375	11,1125	15/16	0.9375	23,8125
29/64	0.453125	11,5094	61/64	0.953125	24,2094
15/32	0.46875	11,9062	31/32	0.96875	24,6062
31/64	0.484375	12,3031	63/64	0.984375	25,0031
1/2	0.5	12,7000			

MILLIMETERS

in	0	10	20	30	40	50
0		254,0	508,0	762,0	1016,0	1270,0
1	25,4	279,4	533,4	787,4	1041,4	1295,4
2	50,8	304,8	558,8	812,8	1066,8	1320,8
3	76,2	330,2	584,2	838,2	1092,2	1346,2
4	101,6	355,6	609,6	863,6	1117,6	1371,6
5	127,0	381,0	635,0	889,0	1143,0	1397,0
6	152,4	406,4	660,4	914,4	1168,4	1422,4
7	177,8	431,8	685,8	939,8	1193,8	1447,8
8	203,2	457,2	711,2	965,2	1219,2	1473,2
9	228,6	482,6	736,6	990,6	1244,6	1498,6

MILLIMETERS TO INCHES

mm	in	mm	in	mm	in	mm	in	mm	in	mm	in
0,001	0.00004	0,021	0.00083	0,041	0.00161	0,061	0.00240	0,081	0.00319	0,200	0.00787
0,002	0.00008	0,022	0.00087	0,042	0.00165	0,062	0.00244	0,082	0.00323	0,300	0.01181
0,003	0.00012	0,023	0.00091	0,043	0.00169	0,063	0.00248	0,083	0.00327	0,400	0.01575
0,004	0.00016	0,024	0.00094	0,044	0.00173	0,064	0.00252	0,084	0.00331	0,500	0.01969
0,005	0.00020	0,025	0.00098	0,045	0.00177	0,065	0.00256	0,085	0.00335	0,600	0.02362
0,006	0.00024	0,026	0.00102	0,046	0.00181	0,066	0.00260	0,086	0.00339	0,700	0.02756
0,007	0.00028	0,027	0.00106	0,047	0.00185	0,067	0.00264	0,087	0.00343	0,800	0.03150
0,008	0.00032	0,028	0.00110	0,048	0.00189	0,068	0.00268	0,088	0.00346	0,900	0.03543
0,009	0.00035	0,029	0.00114	0,049	0.00193	0,069	0.00272	0,089	0.00350		
0,010	0.00039	0,030	0.00118	0,050	0.00197	0,070	0.00276	0,090	0.00354		
0,011	0.00043	0,031	0.00122	0,051	0.00201	0,071	0.00280	0,091	0.00358		
0,012	0.00047	0,032	0.00126	0,052	0.00205	0,072	0.00283	0,092	0.00362		
0,013	0.00051	0,033	0.00130	0,053	0.00209	0,073	0.00287	0,093	0.00366		
0,014	0.00055	0,034	0.00134	0,054	0.00213	0,074	0.00291	0,094	0.00370		
0,015	0.00059	0,035	0.00138	0,055	0.00217	0,075	0.00295	0,095	0.00374		
0,016	0.00063	0,036	0.00142	0,056	0.00220	0,076	0.00299	0,096	0.00378		
0,017	0.00067	0,037	0.00146	0,057	0.00224	0,077	0.00303	0,097	0.00382		
0,018	0.00071	0,038	0.00150	0,058	0.00228	0,078	0.00307	0,098	0.00386		
0,019	0.00075	0,039	0.00154	0,059	0.00232	0,079	0.00311	0,099	0.00390		
0,020	0.00079	0,040	0.00157	0,060	0.00236	0,080	0.00315	0,100	0.00394		

INCHES

mm	0	10	20	30	40	50	60	70	80	90
0		0.39370	0.78740	1.18110	1.57480	1.96850	2.36220	2.75591	3.14961	3.54331
1	0.03937	0.43307	0.82677	1.22047	1.61417	2.00787	2.40157	2.79528	3.18898	3.58268
2	0.07874	0.47244	0.86614	1.25984	1.65354	2.04724	2.44094	2.83465	3.22835	3.62205
3	0.11811	0.51181	0.90551	1.29921	1.69291	2.08661	2.48031	2.87402	3.26772	3.66142
4	0.15748	0.55118	0.94488	1.33858	1.73228	2.12598	2.51969	2.91339	3.30709	3.70079
5	0.19685	0.59055	0.98425	1.37795	1.77165	2.16535	2.55906	2.95276	3.34646	3.74016
6	0.23622	0.62992	1.02362	1.41732	1.81102	2.20472	2.59843	2.99213	3.38583	3.77953
7	0.27559	0.66929	1.06299	1.45669	1.85039	2.24409	2.63780	3.03150	3.42520	3.81890
8	0.31496	0.70866	1.10236	1.49606	1.88976	2.28346	2.67717	3.07087	3.46457	3.85827
9	0.35433	0.74803	1.14173	1.53543	1.92913	2.32283	2.71654	3.11024	3.50394	3.89764

NUMERICAL SERIES LISTING

BEARING SELECTION INDEX

HOW TO USE THE BEARING SELECTION INDEX

The Bearing Selection Index provides a valuable tool to assist in the selection of popular bearing sizes. Basic bearing data is arranged to permit initial bearing selection to meet design requirements. Specific data (backing dimensions, radii, etc.) is tabulated in the dimension tables of the various bearing types. It is structured according to increasing cone bore size, then cup O.D. size, and then basic dynamic radial load ratings. Looking at each column specifically;

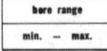

Bore Range—The minimum and maximum bores shown are actual bore sizes of specific cone part numbers in that bearing series.

Outside Diameter Range—The minimum and maximum O.D.'s shown are actual cup O.D.'s of specific cup part numbers in that bearing series.

Series Number—The number shown is the bearing series to which the cone and cup part numbers are assigned.

The "series" is a number made up of combinations of one to six digits with or without the prefixes A, LL, L, LM, M, HM, H, HH and EH. Any other prefixes and all suffixes appearing with any part number are not a basic part of the series number.

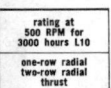

Ratings—Basic dynamic radial and thrust load ratings are given for each bearing series. They are stacked as shown—one-row radial, two-row radial and thrust. Where two or more bearing series have the same bore and O.D. range, the series having the lowest basic dynamic radial load rating is listed first.

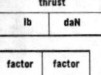

Factors—Factor "K" is shown for each bearing series to indicate the relationship of basic dynamic radial load rating to basic dynamic thrust load rating.

Factor "G" is a bearing geometry factor that is comprised of those internal bearing dimensions having an effect on bearing running torque and, in turn, heat generation within the bearing. **Making use of G-Factor**—Under **thrust load only**, bearing running torque is directly proportional to the G-factors. When two bearings are operating under identical conditions of loading, speed, temperature and lubrication, the bearing with the lower G-factor will exhibit lower rotational resistance.

Under **radial loads only**, bearing running torque is directly proportional to the ratio $\dfrac{G}{(K)^{1/3}}$

Under **combined loading**, bearing running torque is proportional to the G-factors, provided the bearings under consideration have approximately equal K-factors. In all other cases, the torque should be calculated as described on pages 28 through 31 in the Technical Data Section.

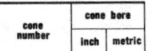

Cone Number and Bore—The cone numbers shown are listed by increasing bore size in the bearing series to which they are assigned. The bore shown is the minimum for inch system cones and maximum for metric system cones.

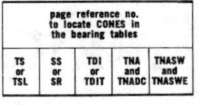

Page Reference Number to Locate Specific Cone Data—These columns show the bearing tables and page number where specific data is given for a particular cone number. This arrangement permits a quick determination of the bearing types available in the series selected.

In the "TS or TSL" column, cone part numbers having an "L" suffix are type "TSL".

In the "SS or SR" column, "SR" assemblies are made with only "J" prefix part numbers.

In the "TDI or TDIT" column, cone part numbers having a "D" suffix are type TDI, or cone part numbers having a "TD" suffix are type TDIT.

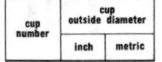

Cup Number and Outside Diameter—The cup numbers shown are listed by increasing outside diameter in the bearing series to which they are assigned. The outside diameter shown is the minimum for inch system cups and maximum for metric system cups.

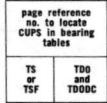

Page Reference Number to Locate Specific Cup Data—These columns show the bearing tables and page number where specific data is given for a particular cup number. This arrangement permits a quick determination of the bearing types available in the series selected.

In the "TS or TSF" column, cup part numbers having a "B" suffix are type TSF.

Dimension Sheets (Section 2)—The page number shown is a full size layout of the bearing series with selected cup or cups. Dimension sheets are provided where size limitations permit.

SELECTING BEARINGS FOR APPLICATION REQUIREMENTS

Knowing Only Bore Range, Rating and Bearing Type

Example: Design requires type TDO bearing, minimum shaft O.D. of 3.5000″ (88,900 mm), a maximum housing bore of 6.5000″ (165,100 mm), and a required basic dynamic radial load rating of at least 25,000 lbs.

Refer to bore range column in Bearing Selection Index. Scanning the bore range for each series which encompasses the required shaft size, check the two-row basic dynamic radial load rating and the cup O.D. range. Select the 755 series. Check bearing type column and select 752D cup with 6.3750″ (161,925 mm) O.D. Since single cones are used in type TDO bearings, refer to TS column for cone part number. Select cone 759 or 766, both have 3.5000″ (88,900 mm) bore. Use the type TS table for specific cone details to make final cone selection and the type TDO table for specific cup details and assembled bearing data.

Knowing Only Part Numbers and Bearing Type

Example: Knowing only single row (type TS) part number 766-753, you wish to know bearing size and rating. From the numerical Series Listing, the 755 series can be located in the Bearing Selection Index. Bore of 3.5000″ (88,900 mm) shown opposite cone 766. O.D. of 6.6250 (168,275 mm) shown opposite cup 753. The one-row basic dynamic radial load rating of 13,800 pounds for the 755 series is listed in the rating column. Specific cone or cup data can be obtained by referring to the bearing table pages shown for the cone and cup part numbers.

To locate the series in the Bearing Selection Index, find the part number range in the left hand column below. Reading across the tabulation provides the bearing series number and the page reference in the Bearing Selection Index.

The "series" numbers are made up of combinations of one to six digits with or without the following prefixes A, LL, L, LM, M, HM, H and HH. Any other prefixes and all suffixes appearing with any part number are not a basic part of the "series" number.

If Cone or Cup Number is between (Both numbers inclusive)	The Series number is	page no	If Cone or Cup Number is between (Both numbers inclusive)	The Series number is	page no	If Cone or Cup Number is between (Both numbers inclusive)	The Series number is	page no
4 — 6	5	2	832 — 850	835	21	4535 — 4595	4500	15
332 — 346	335	6	854 — 869	855	24	A5069 — A5144	A5000	2
350 — 359	355	10	892 — 898	895	30	5335 — 5395	5300	12
362 — 370	365	11	932 — 946	935	26	5535 — 5595	5500	15
372 — 377	375	15	1220 — 1280	1200	3	5735 — 5795	5700	22
382 — 389	385	14	1328 — 1380	1300	3	A6062 — A6162	A6000	1
390 — 399	395	15	1620 — 1680	1600	6	6220 — 6280	6200	13
414 — 420	415	8	1729 — 1780	1700	2	6320 — 6389	6300	17
432 — 449	435	6	1922 — 1997	1900	3	6420 — 6464	6400	18
452 — 469	455	11	A2037 — A2126	A2000	1	6525 — 6581	6500	23
472 — 487	475	17	2420 — 2475	2400	4	8520 — 8578	8500	37
492 — 498	495	21	2520 — 2585	2500	5	9121 — 9185	9100	19
522 — 529	525	10	2631 — 2691	2600	3	9220 — 9285	9200	19
532 — 543	535	10	2720 — 2796	2700	7	9320 — 9385	9300	23
552 — 560	555	16	2821 — 2876	2800	7	00050 — 00150	00000	1
562 — 570	565	19	2924 — 2984	2900	14	02420 — 02476	02400	4
572 — 582	575	22	3120 — 3198	3100	5	02820 — 02878	02800	5
590 — 598	595	23	3320 — 3387	3300	7	03062 — 03162	03000	1
612 — 624	615	13	3420 — 3490	3400	5	05062 — 05185	05000	1
632 — 645	635	17	3520 — 3586	3500	9	07079 — 07210	07000	2
652 — 665	655	20	3620 — 3659	3600	3	08118 — 08231	08000	5
672 — 691	675	24	3720 — 3784	3700	13	09062 — 09196	09000	1
740 — 750	745	19	3820 — 3880	3800	8	11162 — 11300	11000	11
752 — 767	755	22	3920 — 3994	3900	16	11520 — 11590	11500	1
772 — 787	775	25	A4049 — A4138	A4000	1	LM11710 — LM11749	LM11700	2
792 — 799	795	29	4335 — 4395	4300	9	LM11910 — LM11949	LM11900	2

NUMERICAL SERIES LISTING

If Cone or Cup Number is between (Both numbers inclusive)	The Series number is	page no
12168 — 12303	12000	12
12520 — 12580	12500	2
M12610 — M12649	M12600	2
LM12711 — LM12749	LM12700	2
13175 — 13318	13000	12
13620 — 13687	13600	8
13830 — 13889	13800	9
14116 — 14283	14000	5
14525 — 14585	14500	7
15100 — 15251	15000	4
15520 — 15590	15500	4
16150 — 16284	16000	9
17098 — 17245	17000	3
17520 — 17580	17500	1
18200 — 18337	18000	15
18520 — 18590	18500	10
18620 — 18690	18600	12
18720 — 18790	18700	14
19138 — 19283	19000	8
21063 — 21212	21000	1
L21511 — L21549	L21500	1
22168 — 22325	22000	12
22721 — 22778	22700	11
23092 — 23256	23000	3
23420 — 23491	23400	6
23621 — 23691	23600	8
24720 — 24780	24700	9
25519 — 25590	25500	9

If Cone or Cup Number is between (Both numbers inclusive)	The Series number is	page no
25820 — 25880	25800	7
26100 — 26284	26000	4
26820 — 26886	26800	8
27620 — 27691	27600	21
27820 — 27881	27800	7
28118 — 28318	28000	6
28521 — 28584	28500	13
28621 — 28682	28600	15
28820 — 28880	28800	38
28920 — 28995	28900	18
29520 — 29590	29500	18
29620 — 29688	29600	20
LM29710 — LM29749	LM29700	9
29820 — 29880	29800	39
31520 — 31597	31500	7
33225 — 33472	33000	18
33820 — 33895	33800	10
34274 — 34500	34000	21
35176 — 35326	35000	12
36137 — 36300	36000	7
36620 — 36691	36600	30
36920 — 36990	36900	33
37425 — 37626	37000	27
M38510 — M38549	M38500	7
38820 — 38885	38800	39
39236 — 39433	39000	18
39520 — 39591	39500	16
41100 — 41286	41000	4

If Cone or Cup Number is between (Both numbers inclusive)	The Series number is	page no
42346 — 42587	42000	24
42620 — 42690	42600	21
43096 — 43319	43000	3
44131 — 44363	44000	7
L44610 — L44649	L44600	3
45220 — 45291	45200	13
L45410 — L45449	L45400	5
46162 — 46368	46000	11
46720 — 46790	46700	31
47420 — 47490	47400	20
47620 — 47687	47600	21
47820 — 47896	47800	25
48506 — 48750	48000	29
48120 — 48190	48100	27
48220 — 48291	48200	28
48320 — 48393	48300	29
LM48510 — LM48548	LM48500	7
48620 — 48686	48600	30
49175 — 49368	49000	12
49520 — 49585	49500	12
52375 — 52637	52000	25
LL52510 — LL52549	LL52500	2
53150 — 53387	53000	9
55175 — 55444	55000	13
56418 — 56650	56000	27
59175 — 59425	59000	12
64433 — 64708	64000	27
65200 — 65500	65000	15

If Cone or Cup Number is between (Both numbers inclusive)	The Series number is	page no	If Cone or Cup Number is between (Both numbers inclusive)	The Series number is	page no	If Cone or Cup Number is between (Both numbers inclusive)	The Series number is	page no
65320 — 65390	65300	14	M86610 — M86649	M86600	4	EE132084 — 132125	132000	35
66200 — 66462	66000	15	87111 — 87762	87000	33	EE133137 — 133180	133000	43
66520 — 66589	66500	17	88126 — 88925	88000	36	EE134100 — 134144	134000	38
67425 — 67675	67000	27	M88010 — M88048	M88000	5	EE138131 — 138172	138000	42
LM67010 — LM67049	LM67000	6	HM88510 — HM88547	HM88500	6	HH144614 — HH144642	HH144600	35
67320 — 67391	67300	29	HM88610 — HM88649	HM88600	5	EE147112 — 147198	147000	40
67720 — 67791	67700	32	HM89410 — HM89449	HM89400	6	EE157337 — 157430	157000	50
67820 — 67887	67800	33	90334 — 90744	90000	24	EE161300 — 161900	160000	42
67920 — 67985	67900	35	93125 — 93826	93000	34	L163110 — L163149	L163100	43
68450 — 68712	68000	27	94113 — 94713	94000	32	EE168400 — 168500	168000	51
L68111 — L68149	L68100	8	95475 — 95927	95000	29	EE170950 — 171451	170000	37
71412 — 71751	71000	27	96140 — 96925	96000	35	EE192150 — 192201	192000	44
72187 — 72488	72000	14	98316 — 98789	98000	23	M201011 — M201047	M201000	10
LM72810 — LM72849	LM72800	3	99098 — 99600	99000	30	EE203136 — 203190	203000	43
73551 — 73876	73000	30	EE101103 — 101601	100000	40	JM205110 — JM205149	M205100	14
74472 — 74851	74000	28	L102810 — L102849	L102800	12	LL205410 — LL205449	LL205400	15
77350 — 77676	77000	25	LM102910 — LM102949	LM102900	13	JM207010 — JM207049	M207000	17
78214 — 78571	78000	17	LL103010 — LL103049	LL103000	12	JH211710 — JH211749	H211700	20
LM78310 — LM78349	LM78300	8	JLM104910 — LM104949	LM104900	14	HM212010 — HM212049	HM212000	19
80170 — 80217	80000	46	EE107057 — 107105	107000	31	JH217210 — JH217249	H217200	24
80325 — 80385	80300	45	EE109120 — 109163	109000	41	L217810 — L217849	L217800	25
HM81610 — HM81649	HM81600	2	EE113089 — 113171	113000	36	LL217810 — LL217849	LL217800	24
82550 — 82951	82000	30	EE114080 — 114161	114000	35	HM218210 — HM218248	HM218200	23
82720 — 82785	82700	34	L116110 — L116149	L116100	23	EE219068 — 219122	219000	33
84115 — 84155	84000	40	EE126096 — 126151	126000	38	EE221025 — 221576	220000	39
M84210 — M84249	M84200	3	EE127094 — 127138	127000	37	HH221410 — HH221449	HH221400	23
M84510 — M84548	M84500	3	EE128111 — 128160	128000	40	HH224310 — HH224346	HH224300	27
86100 — 86569	86000	32	EE130851 — 131401	130000	36	M224710 — M224749	M224700	28

NUMERICAL SERIES LISTING

If Cone or Cup Number is between (Both numbers inclusive)	The Series number is	page no	If Cone or Cup Number is between (Both numbers inclusive)	The Series number is	page no	If Cone or Cup Number is between (Both numbers inclusive)	The Series number is	page no
LL225710 — LL225749	LL225700	29	H244810 — H244849	H244800	36	LM272210 — LM272249	LM272200	46
L225810 — L225849	L225800	28	LM245110 — LM245149	LM245100	36	M272610 — M272647	M272600	47
HH228310 — HH228349	HH228300	28	M246910 — M246949	M246900	37	M272710 — M272749	M272700	46
H228610 — H228649	H228600	29	H247510 — H247549	H247500	35	M274110 — M274149	M274100	47
LM229110 — LM229146	LM229100	30	LM247710 — LM247748	LM247700	38	EE275095 — 275156	275000	38
EE231400 — 232025	230000	43	H249111 — H249148	H249100	37	M275310 — M275349	M275300	47
HM231110 — HM231149	HM231100	31	LM249710 — LM249748	LM249700	38	M276410 — M276449	M276400	47
HH231610 — HH231649	HH231600	29	M249710 — M249749	M249700	37	EE277455 — 277565	277000	51
M231610 — M231649	M231600	31	HH249910 — HH249949	HH249900	38	M278710 — M278749	M278700	48
EE234156 — 234220	234000	45	LM251610 — LM251649	LM251600	39	EE280700 — 281200	280000	33
HH234010 — HH234048	HH234000	30	HM252310 — HM252349	HM252300	39	M280010 — M280049	M280000	48
H234610 — H234649	H234600	31	M252310 — M252349	M252300	39	M281010 — M281049	M281000	49
M235113 — M235145	M235100	31	HH255110 — HH255149	HH255100	40	M281610 — M281649	M281600	49
LM236710 — LM236749	LM236700	34	M255410 — M255449	M255400	40	LM281810 — LM281849	LM281800	49
M236810 — M236849	M236800	33	HM256810 — HM256849	HM256800	41	LM283610 — LM283649	LM283600	49
HM237510 — HM237549	HM237500	31	M257110 — M257149	M257100	41	M284210 — M284249	M284200	49
H238110 — H238148	H238100	32	M257210 — M257248	M257200	42	NA285160 — 285228	285000	45
M238810 — M238849	M238800	33	HH258210 — HH258249	HH258200	41	LM286711 — LM286749	LM286700	50
EE239171 — 239250	239000	45	HM259010 — HM259049	HM259000	42	LM287610 — LM287649	LM287600	50
H239610 — H239649	H239600	33	HM261010 — HM261049	HM261000	42	LM287810 — LM287849	LM287800	51
EE241701 — 242375	240000	46	HM262710 — HM262749	HM262700	43	LM288210 — LM288249	LM288200	51
LM241110 — LM241149	LM241100	35	LM263110 — LM263145	LM263100	43	LM288910 — LM288949	LM288900	51
M241510 — M241549	M241500	35	LL264610 — LL264648	LL264600	44	EE289670 — 289815	289000	51
H242610 — H242649	H242600	35	HM265010 — HM265049	HM265000	43	EE291175 — 291751	290000	41
EE243190 — 243250	243000	47	HM266410 — HM266449	HM266400	44	EE292548 — EE292668	292000	51
EE244180 — 244236	244000	46	M268710 — M268749	M268700	44	EE295102 — EE295950	295000	38
M244210 — M244249	M244200	36	M270710 — M270749	M270700	46	LM300811 — LM300849	LM300800	10
LL244510 — LL244549	LL244500	37	M271610 — M271648	M271600	46	L305610 — L305649	L305600	15

If Cone or Cup Number is between (Both numbers inclusive)	The Series number is	page no	If Cone or Cup Number is between (Both numbers inclusive)	The Series number is	page no	If Cone or Cup Number is between (Both numbers inclusive)	The Series number is	page no
JH307710 — JH307749	H307700	17	HH421210 — HH421246	HH421200	26	JHM516810 — JHM516849	HM516800	24
JHM318410 — JHM318448	HM318400	25	LL428310 — LL428349	LL428300	30	L521910 — L521949	L521900	26
L319210 — L319249	L319200	25	EE430888 — 431576	430000	36	LM522510 — LM522549	LM522500	27
LL319310 — LL319349	LL319300	25	L432310 — L432349	L432300	31	JHM522610 — JHM522649	HM522600	27
HM321210 — HM321245	HM321200	26	EE433301 — 433512	433000	49	EE526130 — 526191	526000	42
EE324103 — 324160	324000	39	L433710 — L433749	L433700	31	EE529091 — 529157	529000	36
LL327010 — LL327049	LL327000	29	L435010 — L435049	L435000	32	LL529710 — LL529749	LL529700	31
L327210 — L327249	L327200	29	HH437510 — HH437549	HH437500	32	JHM534110 — JHM534149	HM534100	32
EE328167 — 328269	328000	45	LM446310 — LM446349	LM446300	37	HM535310 — HM535349	HM535300	33
LM328410 — LM328448	LM328400	30	EE450601 — 451215	450000	31	L540010 — L540049	L540000	34
EE329119 — 329173	329000	41	LM451310 — LM451349	LM451300	39	EE542220 — 542291	542000	48
EE333137 — 333203	333000	43	L467510 — L467549	L467500	45	543085 — 543114	543000	36
M348410 — M348449	M348400	38	EE470075 — 470128	470000	33	544090 — 544118	544000	36
M349510 — M349549	M349500	39	L476510 — L476549	L476500	47	545112 — 545141	545000	40
EE350701 — 351687	350000	33	EE480181 — 480340	480000	46	LM545810 — LM545849	LM545800	37
LL352110 — LL352149	LL352100	40	LL480710 — LL480749	LL480700	49	EE546220 — 546355	546000	47
L357010 — L357049	L357000	41	LL483418 — LL483449	LL483400	49	EE547341 — 547480	547000	50
LM361610 — LM361649	LM361600	43	LM501310 — LM501349	LM501300	10	EE551026 — 551700	550000	39
LL365310 — LL365348	LL365300	44	LM503310 — LM503349	LM503300	13	L555210 — L555249	L555200	40
LM377410 — LM377449	LM377400	48	HH506310 — HH506348	HH506300	14	LL562710 — LL562749	LL562700	44
LL379010 — LL379049	LL379000	48	JLM506810 — JLM506849	LM506800	17	LM565910 — LM565949	LM565900	44
EE380080 — 380875	380000	35	L507910 — L507949	L507900	18	LL566810 — LL566848	LL566800	45
EE390090 — 390200	390000	37	JLM508710 — JLM508748	LM508700	18	LM567910 — LM567949	LM567900	45
H414210 — H414249	H414200	19	LL510710 — LL510749	LL510700	19	L570610 — L570649	L570600	46
JH415610 — JH415647	H415600	22	JM511910 — JM511946	M511900	20	LL575310 — LL575349	LL575300	47
EE420651 — 421462	420000	32	JM515610 — JM515649	M515600	23	L580010 — L580049	L580000	48
L420410 — L420449	L420400	26	EE516050 — 516122	516000	29	LL582910 — LL582949	LL582900	49
LL420510 — LL420549	LL420500	26	HM516410 — HM516449	HM516400	23	LL584410 — LL584449	LL584400	50

If Cone or Cup Number is between (Both numbers inclusive)	The Series number is	page no
LL586018 — LL586049	LL586000	50
EE590675 — 591350	590000	33
LM603011 — LM603049	LM603000	13
EE607070 — 607140	607000	33
L610510 — L610549	L610500	19
JM612910 — JM612949	M612900	21
LM613410 — LM613449	LM613400	20
HM617010 — HM617049	HM617000	24
L623110 — L623149	L623100	27
L624510 — L624549	L624500	28
M624610 — M624649	M624600	28
HM624710 — HM624749	HM624700	28
L630310 — L630349	L630300	31
EE631305 — 631484	631000	50
EE634356 — 634510	634000	50
LM637310 — LM637349	LM637300	34
LL639210 — LL639249	LL639200	34
EE640192 — 640261	640000	47
LL641110 — LL641149	LL641100	35
EE647220 — 647285	647000	47
EE649240 — 649311	649000	48
LM654610 — LM654649	LM654600	40
EE655270 — 655346	655000	49
LM665910 — LM665949	LM665900	44
M667911 — M667947	M667900	45
680235 — 680270	680000	48
LL686910 — LL686947	LL686900	50
LL687910 — LL687949	LL687900	51

If Cone or Cup Number is between (Both numbers inclusive)	The Series number is	page no
JLM710910 — JLM710949	LM710900	20
L713010 — L713049	L713000	20
LL713010 — LL713049	LL713000	20
JLM714110 — JLM714149	LM714100	22
JM714210 — JM714249	M714200	22
LL714610 — LL714649	LL714600	22
EE715210 — 715380	715000	47
H715310 — H715348	H715300	19
JM716610 — JM716649	M716600	24
JM718110 — JM718149	M718100	25
LM718910 — LM718947	LM718900	25
JM719113 — JM719149	M719100	25
EE720125 — 720236	720000	42
JHM720210 — JHM720249	HM720200	26
JM720210 — JM720249	M720200	26
EE722110 — 722186	722000	40
EE724119 — 724195	724000	41
L724310 — L724349	L724300	28
L725311 — L725349	L725300	29
L730610 — L730649	L730600	31
JM734410 — JM734449	M734400	32
JM736110 — JM736149	M736100	33
JM738210 — JM738249	M738200	34
LM739710 — LM739749	LM739700	34
LM742710 — LM742749	LM742700	35
EE743240 — 743321	743000	48
HM743310 — HM743345	HM743300	35
HM746610 — HM746646	HM746600	36

If Cone or Cup Number is between (Both numbers inclusive)	The Series number is	page no
EE752300 — 752380	752000	49
EE755280 — 755361	755000	49
LM757010 — LM757049	LM757000	41
M757410 — M757447	M757400	41
LL758715 — LL758744	LL758700	42
LM761610 — LM761649	LM761600	43
LL762610 — LL762648	LL762600	44
EE763330 — 763410	763000	50
LM763410 — LM763449	LM763400	43
LM763811 — LM763848	LM763800	44
LM767710 — LM767749	LM767700	44
L770810 — L770849	L770800	46
LM770910 — LM770949	LM770900	46
LL771911 — LL771948	LL771900	46
LM772710 — LM772749	LM772700	47
EE776420 — 776520	776000	51
LL778110 — LL778149	LL778100	48
LL780210 — LL780249	LL780200	48
LL788310 — LL788349	LL788300	51
LL789910 — LL789949	LL789900	51
EE790114 — 790221	790000	40
HM801310 — HM801349	HM801300	9
M802011 — M802048	M802000	11
HM803110 — HM803149	HM803100	11
M804010 — M804049	M804000	14
HM804810 — HM804849	HM804800	11
LM806610 — LM806649	LM806600	16
HM807010 — HM807049	HM807000	11

If Cone or Cup Number is between (Both numbers inclusive)	The Series number is	page no	If Cone or Cup Number is between (Both numbers inclusive)	The Series number is	page no	If Cone or Cup Number is between (Both numbers inclusive)	The Series number is	page no
L812111 — L812148	L812100	20	LM869410 — LM869448	LM869400	45	HH923610 — HH923649	HH923600	26
JLM813010 — JLM813049	LM813000	21	LL876410 — LL876449	LL876400	47	H924010 — H924045	H924000	26
HM813810 — HM813849	HM813800	16	L879910 — L879947	L879900	48	HH924310 — HH924349	HH924300	27
HH814510 — HH814542	HH814500	18	L882410 — L882449	L882400	49	HH926710 — HH926749	HH926700	28
L814710 — L814749	L814700	22	LL889010 — LL889049	LL889000	51	HM926710 — HM926749	HM926700	28
LM814810 — LM814849	LM814800	21	HM903210 — HM903249	HM903200	9	HH932110 — HH932145	HH932100	29
EE820085 — 820161	820000	35	M903310 — M903345	M903300	11	H936310 — H936349	H936300	31
LM820012 — LM820048	LM820000	26	HM905810 — HM905843	HM905800	13	EE941205 — 941953	940000	41
EE821096 — 821165	821000	37	HM907614 — HM907643	HM907600	12	HH949510 — HH949549	HH949500	36
HM821511 — HM821547	HM821500	26	EE911600 — 912400	910000	45	HH953710 — HH953749	HH953700	38
EE822100 — 822176	822000	38	HM911210 — HM911245	HM911200	17	LL957010 — LL957049	LL957000	42
JM822010 — JM822049	M822000	27	H913810 — H913849	H913800	18	M959410 — M959442	M959400	42
EE833160 — 833233	833000	45	HH914412 — HH914449	HH914400	20	LM961510 — LM961548	LM961500	43
HH840210 — HH840249	HH840200	34	HM914510 — HM914549	HM914500	20	H961610 — H961649	H961600	42
JHM840410 — JHM840449	HM840400	35	H916610 — H916642	H916600	21	H969210 — H969249	H969200	45
EE843220 — 843291	843000	48	H917810 — H917849	H917800	23	EE971354 — 972100	970000	43
H852810 — H852849	H852800	39	M919010 — M919049	M919000	25	EE982051 — 982900	980000	47
L853010 — L853049	L853000	39	HM921310 — HM921343	HM921300	25	LL989310 — LL989349	LL989300	51
L860010 — L860049	L860000	42	LM921810 — LM921845	LM921800	26	LL990310 — LL990349	LL990300	51
L865512 — L865548	L865500	44	EE923095 — 923176	923000	37			

BEARING SELECTION INDEX

The following index of bearing series is listed by increasing bore size.

The bearing type and specific cone or cup dimensions are located on the page reference number indicated.

bore range min — max	OD range min — max	series no.	rating 500 RPM / 3000 hrs L10 — one-row radial thrust / two-row radial (lb)	(daN)	factor K	factor G	cone number	cone bore inch	cone bore metric	cone pg ref (TS/TSL · SS/SR · TDI/TDIT · TNA/TNADC · TNASW/TNASWE)	cup number	cup OD inch	cup OD metric	cup pg ref (TS/TSF · TDO/TDODC)	dim sheet pg no.
0.3750 — 0.4724 / 9.525 — 12.000	1.2000 — 1.2595 / 30.480 — 31.991	A2000	435 / 825 / 301	192 / 366 / 134	1.44	1.6	A2037	0.3750	9.525	TSL 1	A2120D	1.2000	30.480	TDODC 21	1
							A2047	†0.4724	†12.000	TSL 1	A2126	1.2595	31.991		
0.4992 — 0.5906 / 12.680 — 15.000	1.3775 / 34.988	A4000	500 / 950 / 387	222 / 422 / 172	1.29	2.1	A4049	0.4992	12.680	TSL 1	A4138	1.3775	34.988	TSF 1	2
							A4050	0.5000	12.700	TSL 1	A4138B	1.3775	34.988	TSF 61	
							A4059	†0.5906	†15.000	TSL 1	A4138D	1.3775	34.988	TDODC 21	
0.5000 / 12.700	1.5000 / 38.100	00000	760 / 1450 / 358	338 / 645 / 159	2.12	2.9	00050	0.5000	12.700	TSL 1	00150	1.5000	38.100	TSF 1	3
0.6250 / 15.875	1.3775 / 34.988	L21500	575 / 1090 / 314	256 / 485 / 140	1.83	2.8	L21549	0.6250	15.875	TSL 1	L21511	1.3775	34.988	TSF 1	5
0.6250 / 15.875	1.6250 / 41.275	03000	890 / 1700 / 475	396 / 755 / 210	1.88	3.9	03062	0.6250	15.875	TSL 1	03162	1.6250	41.275	TSF 1	7
0.6250 / 15.875	1.6875 / 42.862	11900	725 / 1390 / 875	324 / 615 / 390	0.83	3.1	11590	0.6250	15.875	TSL 1	11520	1.6875	42.862	TSF 1	6
0.6250 / 15.875	1.6875 / 42.862	17500	1150 / 2200 / 655	515 / 980 / 292	1.76	4.6	17580	0.6250	15.875	TSL 1	17520	1.6875	42.862	TSF 1	9
											17520B	1.6875	42.862	TSF 61	
0.6250 — 0.7500 / 15.875 — 19.050	1.5745 — 1.6250 / 39.992 — 41.275	A6000	503 / 1010 / 480	236 / 450 / 212	1.11	2.7	A6062	0.6250	15.875	TSL 1	A6157	1.5745	39.992	TSF 1	4
							A6067	0.6690	16.993	TSL 1	A6157B	1.5745	39.992	TSF 61	
							A6075	0.7500	19.050	TSL 2	A6162	1.6250	41.275	TSF 1	
0.6250 — 0.7500 / 15.875 — 19.050	2.1250 / 53.975	21000	1710 / 3260 / 1730	760 / 1450 / 770	0.99	6.1	21063	0.6250	15.875	TSL 1	21212	2.1250	53.975	TSF 1	11
							21075	0.7500	19.050	TSL 2					
0.6250 — 0.7874 / 15.875 — 20.000	1.7500 — 1.8504 / 44.450 — 47.000	A5000	1020 / 1940 / 620	450 / 860 / 276	1.64	5.2	A5062	0.6250	15.875	TSL 1	05175	1.7500	44.450	TSF 1	8
							A5068	0.6875	17.462	TSL 1	05185	1.8504	47.000	TSF 1	
							A5075	0.7500	19.050	SR 2	05185B	1.8504	47.000	TSF 61	
							A5075X	0.7500	19.050	SR 2	05185D	1.8504	47.000	TSF 1	
							NA05075EW	0.7500	19.050	TNASWE 43	05185S	1.8504	47.000	TDODC 21	
							A5079	†0.7874	†20.000	SR 2					
0.6250 — 0.8115 / 15.875 — 20.612	1.9380 / 49.225	09000	1600 / 3050 / 730	715 / 1360 / 324	2.20	7.1	09062	0.6250	15.875	TSL 1	09194	1.9380	49.225	TSF 2	10
							09067	0.7500	19.050	TSL 2	09195	1.9380	49.225	TSF 1	
							09074	0.7500	19.050	TSL 2	09195AB	1.9380	49.225	TSF 61	
							09078	0.7500	19.050	TSL 2	09196	1.9380	49.225	TSF 2	
							09081S	0.8115	20.612	TSL 2					

†Dimension shown is maximum value—see note at bottom of fitting practice table in Reference Tables.

BEARING SELECTION INDEX

The following index of bearing series is listed by increasing bore size.

The bearing type and specific cone or cup dimensions are located on the page reference number indicated.

Bore range in / mm	OD range in / mm	Series number	Rating lb (1‑row radial / 2‑row radial / thrust)	Rating daN	K	G	Cone number	Cone bore in	Cone bore mm	Cone page ref	Cup number	Cup OD in	Cup OD mm	Cup page ref	Dim. sheet page no.
0.6299 / 16.000	1.8504 / 47.000	HM81600	1560 / 2980 / 1460	695 / 1325 / 650	1.07	5.4	HM81649	0.6299	16.000	TS:1	HM81610	1.8504	47.000	TS:1	12
0.6872 / 17.455	1.4380 / 36.525	A5000	500 / 955 / 420	224 / 424 / 186	1.20	2.3	A5069	0.6872	17.455	TS:1	A5144	1.4380	36.525	TS:1	13
0.6875 / 17.462	1.5700 / 39.878	LM11700	935 / 1790 / 460	416 / 795 / 204	2.04	4.4	LM11749	0.6875	17.462	TS:1	LM11710	1.5700	39.878	TS:1	14
0.7500 / 19.050	1.7500 / 44.450	5	815 / 1560 / 670	364 / 690 / 298	1.22	4.1	4A	0.7500	19.050	SS/SR:1	6	1.7500	44.450	TS:2	15
0.7500 / 19.050	1.7810 / 45.237	LM11900	1230 / 2340 / 635	545 / 1040 / 282	1.94	5.8	LM11949	0.7500	19.050	TS:2	LM11910	1.7810	45.237	TS:2	16
							LM11949L	0.7500	19.050	SS/SR:69					
0.7500 — 1.0000 / 19.050 — 25.400	2.1250 — 2.2500 / 53.975 — 57.150	1700	1740 / 3320 / 915	775 / 1475 / 408	1.90	9.2	1775	0.7500	19.050	TS:2	1730	2.1250	53.975	TS:2	17
							1755	0.8750	22.225	TS:3	1729	2.2400	56.896	TS:3	
							1779	0.9375	23.812	TS:3	1729B	2.2400	56.896	TDO:61	
							1780	1.0000	25.400	TS:3	1738X	2.2500	57.150	TS:3	
0.7874 — 1.0000 / 20.000 — 25.400	1.9687 — 2.0472 / 50.000 — 52.000	07000	1130 / 2150 / 780	500 / 955 / 346	1.45	6.6	07079	0.7874	20.000	TS:2	07196	1.9687	50.005	TS:2	18
							07087	0.8750	22.225	TS:2	07196B	1.9687	50.005	TDO:61	
							07087X	0.8750	22.225	TS:2	07196D	1.9687	50.005	TDODC:21	
							07093	0.9375	23.812	TS:2	07196DC	2.0000	50.005	TDODC:21	
							07098	0.9843	24.981	TS:3	07210X	2.0000	50.800		
							07097	1.0000	25.000	TS:3	07204	2.0470	51.994	TS:2	
							07100	1.0000	25.400	TS:3	07204B	2.0470	51.994	TDO:61	
							07100L	1.0000	25.400	SS/SR:69	07205	2.0472	52.000	TS:3	
							07100S	1.0000	25.400	TS:3	07205B	2.0472	52.000	TDO:61	
							07100SA	1.0000	25.400	TS:2					
0.8125 / 20.638	1.9380 / 49.225	12500	1660 / 3160 / 915	740 / 1405 / 408	1.81	7.5	12580	0.8125	20.638	TS:2	12520	1.9380	49.225	TS:2	19
0.8437 — 0.8750 / 21.430 — 22.225	1.9687 / 50.005	M12600	1660 / 3160 / 790	740 / 1405 / 352	2.10	8.0	M12649	0.8437	21.430	TS:2	M12610	1.9687	50.005	TS:2	20
							M12649L	0.8437	21.430	SS/SR:69					
							M12648	0.8750	22.225	TS:2					
0.8661 / 22.000	1.8110 / 46.000	LM12700	1280 / 2430 / 670	570 / 1080 / 298	1.91	7.1	LM12749	0.8661	22.000	TS:1	LM12711	1.8110	46.000	TS:1	21
0.8750 / 22.225	1.6563 / 42.070	LL52500	670 / 1280 / 455	298 / 570 / 202	1.47	4.2	LL52549	0.8750	22.225	TS:2	LL52510	1.6563	42.070	TS:2	22

BEARING SELECTION INDEX

Bore (in / mm)	Cone No.	Cup No(s).	Cup O.D. (in / mm)	Factor (K)	Factor (G)	Rated Factor	Load Ratings	Load Ratings	Page
0.8750 / 22.225	1380[2]	1328[2], 13288[61], 1329[3]	2.0625 / 52.388, 2.0625 / 52.388, 2.1250 / 53.975	9.0	2.00	1300	810 / 1540 / 404	1820 / 3460 / 910	23
0.8750 / 22.225	1280[3]	1220[3]	2.2500 / 57.150	9.9	1.69	1200	935 / 1780 / 555	2100 / 4000 / 1240	25
0.8750 — 1.1250 / 22.225 — 28.575	1975[3], 1986[3], 1994X[4], 1987[4], 1997X[5], 1985[5], 1988[5]	1922[3], 1932[3], 19328[61], 1931[4], 19318[61]	2.2500 / 57.150, 2.3125 / 58.738, 2.3125 / 58.738, 2.3750 / 60.325, 2.3750 / 60.325	10.6	1.77	1900	825 / 1570 / 465	1850 / 3520 / 1050	24
0.8750 — 1.1250 / 22.225 — 29.367	2684[3], 2687[4], 2682[4], 2688[5], 2689[5], 2690[5], 2691[5]	2631[3], 26318[62]	2.6150 / 66.421, 2.6150 / 66.421	16.4	2.30	2800	1320 / 2520 / 575	2970 / 5650 / 1290	26
0.8900 / 22.606	LM72849[3]	LM72810[3]	1.8504 / 47.000	6.4	1.24	LM72800	535 / 1020 / 432	1210 / 2300 / 970	27
0.9375 / 23.812	3559[3]	3620[3], 36208[61]	2.4375 / 61.912, 2.4375 / 61.912	14.6	2.07	3800	1495 / 2860 / 725	3360 / 6400 / 1630	30
0.9375 — 1.0000 / 23.812 — 25.400	23092[3], 23100[4]	23256[3], 232568[62]	2.5625 / 65.088, 2.5625 / 65.088	9.3	0.80	23000	910 / 1740 / 1140	2050 / 3910 / 2560	29
0.9375 — 1.0625 / 23.812 — 26.988	L44640[3], L44643[3], L44643L[69], L44643LA[69], L44649[4]	L44610[3]	1.9800 / 50.292	7.7	1.56	L44600	535 / 1015 / 342	1200 / 2280 / 770	28
0.9600 — 1.3125 / 24.384 — 33.338	43096[3], 43112[5], 43118[6], 43125[7], 43131[8], 43132[9]	43300[3], 43312[5], 433128[62], 43319D[7][21], 43319DC[8][21]	3.0000 / 76.200, 3.1250 / 79.375, 3.1250 / 79.375, 3.1875 / 80.962, 3.1875 / 80.962	14.0	0.87	43000	1285 / 2440 / 1475	2880 / 5500 / 3320	31
0.9835 — 1.1875 / 24.981 — 30.162	17098[3], 17118S[6], 17117D[17], 17116D[6], 17119[6]	17244[3], 172448[61], 17245D[21]	2.4409 / 62.000, 2.4409 / 62.000, 2.4409 / 62.000	9.9	1.53	17000	720 / 1375 / 470	1620 / 3090 / 1060	32
1.0000 / 25.400	M84548[3]	M84510[3]	2.2500 / 57.150	9.4	1.07	M84500	845 / 1615 / 790	1900 / 3630 / 1760	34
1.0000 / 25.400	M84249[4]	M84210[4]	2.3437 / 59.530	10.5	1.07	M84200	1035 / 1960 / 965	2320 / 4450 / 2170	37

†Dimension shown is maximum value—see note at bottom of fitting practice table in Reference Tables.
*Non-standard tolerances, see Inch System bearing tolerances in Reference Tables.

BEARING SELECTION INDEX

The bearing type and specific cone or cup dimensions are located on the page reference number indicated.

The following index of bearing series is listed by increasing bore size.

bore range min. – max.	outside diameter range min. – max.	series number	rating at 500 RPM for 3000 hours L10 (one-row radial thrust / two-row radial thrust) lb	daN	factor K	factor G	cone number	cone bore inch	cone bore metric	TS or TSL	SS or TSL	TDI or TDIT	TNA and TNADC	TNASW or TNASWE	cup number	cup OD inch	cup OD metric	TS or TSF	TDO and TDODC	dim. sheet page no.
1.0000 – 1.1250 / 25,400 – 28,575	2.2500 – 2.3750 / 57,150 – 60,325	15500	1800 / 3440 / 1070	800 / 1530 / 475	1.69	10.8	15578	1.0000	25,400	3					15520	2.2500	57,150	3		33
							15580	1.0625	26,988	4					15520B	2.2500	57,150	61		
							15590	1.2187	28,575	5					15523	2.3750	60,325	4		
1.0000 – 1.1250 / 25,400 – 28,575	2.8593 / 72,626	41000	2550 / 4850 / 2620	1130 / 2160 / 1165	0.97	11.0	41100	1.0000	25,400	4					41286	2.8593	72,626	4		40
							41106	1.0625	26,988	5										
							41125	1.1250	28,575	5										
							41126	1.1250	28,575	5										
1.0000 – 1.2187 / 25,400 – 30,955	2.5312 / 64,292	M86600	2450 / 4650 / 2290	1090 / 2080 / 1020	1.07	13.7	M86643	1.0000	25,400	4					M86610	2.5312	64,292	4		38
							M86647	1.1250	28,575	5					M86610B	2.5312	64,292	62		
							M86649	1.1875	30,162	6										
							M86648A	1.2187	30,955	6										
1.0000 – 1.2500 / 25,400 – 31,750	2.4409 – 2.5000 / 62,000 – 63,500	15000	1990 / 3790 / 1190	885 / 1685 / 530	1.67	12.3	15100	1.0000	25,400	4					15245	2.4409	62,000	4		35
							15100S	1.0000	25,400	4					15250	2.5000	63,500	4		
							15100SR	1.0000	25,400	4					15250B	2.5000	63,500	61		
							15101	1.0000	25,400	4					15250R	2.5000	63,500	4		
							15102	1.0000	25,400	4					15250X	2.5000	63,500	4		
							15106	1.0625	26,988	5					15251D	2.5000	63,500		21	
							15112	1.1250	28,575	5										
							15113	1.1250	28,575	5										
							15117	†1.1811	†30,000	6										
							NA15117SW	1.1813	30,005	6				43						
							15116	1.1855	30,112	6										
							15118	1.1895	30,213	6										
							15119	1.1895	30,213	6										
							15120	1.1895	30,213	7										
							15123	1.2500	31,750	7										
							15125	1.2500	31,750	7										
							15126	1.2500	31,750	7										
1.0000 – 1.2500 / 25,400 – 31,750	2.6875 / 68,262	2400	2640 / 5050 / 1540	1175 / 2240 / 685	1.72	15.7	2473X	1.0000	25,400	4					2420	2.6875	68,262	4		41
							2474	1.1250	28,575	5										
							2475	1.2500	31,750	7										
1.0000 – 1.2598 / 25,400 – 32,000	2.6875 / 68,262	02400	2490 / 4750 / 1780	1110 / 2120 / 790	1.40	14.5	02473	1.0000	25,400	4					02420	2.6875	68,262	4		39
							02474	1.1250	28,575	5					02420B	2.6875	68,262	62		
							02475	1.2500	31,750	7										
							02476	1.2500	31,750	7										
							02476X	†1.2598	†32,000	8										
1.0000 – 1.3125 / 25,400 – 33,338	2.8125 – 2.8346 / 71,438 – 72,000	26000	2210 / 4200 / 1370	985 / 1880 / 605	1.62	13.6	26100	1.0000	25,000	4					262820	2.8125	71,438		21	36
							26112	1.1250	28,575	5					26284D	2.8338	71,979		21	
							26118	†1.1811	†30,000	6					26283	2.8346	72,000	4		
							NA26118SW	†1.1811	†30,000					43						
							26126	1.2600	32,004	8										
							26131	1.3125	33,338	8										

4

BEARING SELECTION INDEX

Group 43
Bore range: 1.0000 — 1.3125 / 25,400 — 33,338
Cone series: 3100 — 3700/7050/2100 · 1645/3140/935 · 1.76 · 19.4
Cup dim: 2.8593 / 72,626

Cone	Bore (in)	Bore (mm)	ref	Cup	O.D. (in)	O.D. (mm)	ref
3189	1.0000	25,400	4	3120	2.8593	72,626	5
3198	1.1250	28,575	5	31208	2.8593	72,626	62
3187	1.1875	30,162	6	3130	2.8593	72,626	4
3188	1.2500	31,750	7				
31885	1.2500	31,750	7				
3193	1.2500	31,750	7				
3196	1.3125	33,338	8				
3197	1.3125	33,338	8				

Group 42
Bore range: 1.0000 — 1.4062 / 25,400 — 35,717
Cone series: HM88500 — 3190/6050/2980 · 1415/2700/1325 · 1.07 · 18.6
Cup dim: 2.8438 / 72.233

Cone	Bore (in)	Bore (mm)	ref	Cup	O.D. (in)	O.D. (mm)	ref
HM88630	1.0000	25,400	4	HM88610	2.8438	72.233	4
HM88638	†1.2598	†32,000	8				
HM88649	1.3750	34,925	9				
HM88648	1.4062	35,717	10				

Group 46
Bore range: 1.1250 — 1.3125 / 28,575 — 33,338
Cone series: 2500 — 3280/6250/1530 · 1460/2780/685 · 2.14 · 19.7
Cup dim: 2.6150 — 2.7500 / 66.421 — 69.850

Cone	Bore (in)	Bore (mm)	ref	Cup	O.D. (in)	O.D. (mm)	ref
2578	1.1250	28,575	5	2520	2.6150	66.421	5
2558	1.1875	30,162	6	2523	2.7500	69.850	6
2559	1.1875	30,162	6	2523B	2.7500	69.850	62
2580	1.2500	31,750	7	2523D	2.7500	69.850	22
2582	1.2500	31,750	7	2523DC	2.7500	69.850	22
2581	1.3125	33,338	8	2523S	2.7500	69.850	6
2585	1.3125	33,338	8				

Group 45
Bore range: 1.1250 — 1.3125 / 28,575 — 33,338
Cone series: M88000 — 2620/5000/2450 · 1165/2220/1090 · 1.07 · 15.6
Cup dim: 2.6875 / 68.262

Cone	Bore (in)	Bore (mm)	ref	Cup	O.D. (in)	O.D. (mm)	ref
M88040	1.1250	28,575	5	M88010	2.6875	68.262	5
M88043	1.1875	30,162	6				
M88046	1.2500	31,750	7				
M88048	1.3125	33,338	8				
M88048A	1.3125	33,338	8				

Group 44
Bore range: 1.1250 — 1.3750 / 28,575 — 34,925
Cone series: 02800 — 2620/5000/2030 · 1165/2220/900 · 1.29 · 16.9
Cup dim: 2.8750 — 3.0000 / 73.025 — 76.200

Cone	Bore (in)	Bore (mm)	ref	Cup	O.D. (in)	O.D. (mm)	ref
02872	1.1250	28,575	5	02820	2.8750	73.025	5
02875	1.2500	31,750	7	02820D	3.0000	76.200	22
02876	1.2500	31,750	7				
02877	1.3750	34,925	9				
02878	1.3750	34,925	9				

Group 47
Bore range: 1.1417 / 29,000
Cone series: L45400 — 1250/2390/795 · 560/1065/352 · 1.58 · 9.1
Cup dim: 1.9800 / 50.292

Cone	Bore (in)	Bore (mm)	ref	Cup	O.D. (in)	O.D. (mm)	ref
A145449	1.1417	29,000	5	L45410	1.9800	50.292	5

Group 48
Bore range: 1.1811 — 1.3770 / 30,000 — 34,976
Cone series: 14000 — 2180/4150/1420 · 970/1840/635 · 1.53 · 14.9
Cup dim: 2.7148 — 2.8380 / 68.956 — 72.085

Cone	Bore (in)	Bore (mm)	ref	Cup	O.D. (in)	O.D. (mm)	ref
14117A	1.1811	30,000	6	14274A	2.7148	68.956	6
14118	1.1811	30,000	6	14274	2.7170	69.012	6
14116	1.1900	30,226	6	14276	2.7170	69.012	6
14124	1.2500	31,750	7	14276B	2.7170	69.012	62
14125A	1.2500	31,750	7	14276D	2.7170	69.012	22
14130	1.2500	31,750	7	14283	2.8380	72.085	7
14131	1.3125	33,338	8				
14137A	1.3750	34,925	9				
14138A	1.3750	34,925	9				
14139	1.3770	34,976	10				1

Group 49
Bore range: 1.1875 — 1.2500 / 30,162 — 31,750
Cone series: 08000 — 1280/2440/1040 · 570/1085/465 · 1.23 · 9.1
Cup dim: 2.3125 / 58.738

Cone	Bore (in)	Bore (mm)	ref	Cup	O.D. (in)	O.D. (mm)	ref
08118	1.1875	30,162	6	08231	2.3125	58.738	6
08125	1.2500	31,750	7	08231B	2.3125	58.738	61
				08231D	2.3125	58.738	22
				08231DC	2.3125	58.738	22

Group 51
Bore range: 1.1875 — 1.5000 / 30,162 — 38,100
Cone series: 3400 — 4150/7900/2590 · 1840/3520/1155 · 1.60 · 24.3
Cup dim: 3.1250 — 3.1562 / 79.375 — 80.167

Cone	Bore (in)	Bore (mm)	ref	Cup	O.D. (in)	O.D. (mm)	ref
3474	1.1875	30,162	6	3420	3.1250	79.375	6
3476	1.2500	31,750	8	34208	3.1250	79.375	63
3478	1.3750	34,925	10	3422	3.1562	80.167	8
3482	1.3750	34,925	10				
3479	1.4375	36,512	11				
3490	1.5000	38,100	12				

†Dimension shown is maximum value—see note at bottom of fitting practice table in Reference Tables.
*Non-standard tolerances, see Inch System bearing tolerances in Reference Tables.

BEARING SELECTION INDEX

The following index of bearing series is listed by increasing bore size.

The bearing type and specific cone or cup dimensions are located on the page reference number indicated.

bore range (inch / metric)	outside diameter range (inch / metric)	series number	rating at 500 RPM for 3000 hours L10 — lb (one-row radial / thrust / two-row radial)	daN	K	G	cone number	cone bore inch	cone bore metric	TS or TSL	SS or SR	cone pg (TNA or TNASW)	cup number	cup OD inch	cup OD metric	TS or TSF	TDO and TDODC	dim. sheet pg.
1.1875 — 1.5748 / 30,162 — 40,000	3.0000 — 3.1510 / 76,200 — 80,035	28000	2440 / 4650 / 1680	1085 / 2060 / 750	1.45	17.1	28118	1.1875	30,162	6			28300	3.0000	76,200	9		50
							28137	1.3750	34,925	9			28300X	3.0000	76,200	6		
							28138	1.3770	34,976	10			28315	3.1496	80,000	10		
							28150	1.5000	38,100	12			28315B	3.1496	80,000	63		
							28159	1.5740	39,980	13			28317	3.1510	80,035	12		
							28159	1.5748	40,000	13			28318D	3.1510	80,035		22	
1.2500 / 31,750	2.3280 — 2.4404 / 59,131 — 61,986	LM67000	1580 / 3000 / 1110	700 / 1335 / 495	1.42	10.8	LM67048	1.2500	31,750	7	- 1		LM67010	2.3280	59,131	7		52
							LM67048L	1.2500	31,750	69			LM67014	2.4404	61,986	7		
							LM67049A	1.2500	31,750	7								
1.2500 / 31,750	2.6875 / 68,262	23400	3210 / 6100 / 1940	1430 / 2720 / 860	1.66	18.1	23491	1.2500	31,750	7			23420	2.6875	68,262	7		54
1.2500 — 1.3125 / 31,750 — 33,338	2.8750 / 73,025	HM88500	3640 / 6950 / 3400	1620 / 3080 / 1515	1.07	20.8	HM88542	1.2500	31,750	7			HM88510	2.8750	73,025	7		55
							HM88547	1.3125	33,338	8								
1.2500 — 1.4375 / 31,750 — 36,512	3.0000 / 76,200	HM89400	3880 / 7400 / 3630	1725 / 3280 / 1615	1.07	22.7	HM89440	1.2500	31,750	7			HM89410	3.0000	76,200	9		56
							HM89443	1.3125	33,338	9			HM89411	3.0000	76,200	7		
							HM89444	1.3125	33,338	9								
							HM89446	1.3750	34,925	10								
							HM89446A	1.3750	34,925	10								
							HM89448	1.4375	36,512	11								
							HM89449	1.4375	36,512	11								
1.2500 — 1.6880 / 31,750 — 42,875	3.1496 / 80,000	335	3000 / 5700 / 1400	1335 / 2540 / 625	2.14	22.2	346	1.2500	31,750	8			332	3.1496	80,000	8		53
							335	1.3750	34,925	10			332A	3.1496	80,000	12		
							339	1.3780	35,000	10			332B	3.1496	80,000	63		
							337	1.5000	38,100	12			332US	3.1496	80,000	10		
							344	1.5748	40,000	13			333	3.1496	80,000	10		
							344A	1.5748	40,000	13								
							336	1.6250	41,275	14								
							342	1.6250	41,275	14								
							342S	1.6880	42,875	16								
1.2500 — 1.8125 / 31,750 — 46,038	3.7500 / 95,250	435	4950 / 9400 / 2410	2200 / 4180 / 1070	2.05	34.7	443	1.2500	31,750	8			432	3.7500	95,250	10		57
							449	1.3750	34,925	10			432A	3.7500	95,250	8		
							440	1.5000	38,100	13			432B	3.7500	95,250	63		
							444	1.5000	38,100	13			4320	3.7500	95,250		22	
							447	1.6250	41,275	15			4320C	3.7500	95,250		22	
							NA435SW	1.7500	44,450	17		43						
							438	1.7500	44,450	17								
							436	1.8125	46,038	19								
1.3125 / 33,338	2.6250 / 66,675	1600	2090 / 3980 / 1330	930 / 1770 / 590	1.57	13.9	1680	1.3125	33,338	8			1620	2.6250	66,675	8		58

BEARING SELECTION INDEX

Page	TS No.	Cup	Cone	Bore d (in)	Bore d (mm)	Cup OD (in)	Cup OD (mm)	T	—	rating A	rating B
59	2900	2821	2076	1.3125	33.338	2.8750	73.025	19.0	1.59	1295 / 2460 / 815	2910 / 5550 / 1830
62	31500	31520 / 31520B / 31521	31590 / 31593 / 31594 / 31597	1.3125 / 1.3750 / 1.3750 / 1.4375	33.338 / 34.925 / 34.925 / 36.512	3.0000	76.200	21.6	1.45	1680 / 3200 / 1155	3770 / 7200 / 2600
61	2700	2735X / 2720 / 2720B / 2729 / 2729X	2785 / 2790 / 2786 / 2793 / 2796 / 2780 / 2794 / 2776 / 2788 / 2788A / 2789	1.3125 / 1.3125 / 1.3750 / 1.3750 / 1.4365 / 1.4365 / 1.5000 / 1.5000 / 1.5000 / 1.5625	33.338 / 33.338 / 34.925 / 34.925 / 36.487 / 36.487 / 38.100 / 38.100 / 38.100 / 39.688	2.8750 / 3.0000	73.025 / 76.200	23.4	1.93	1540 / 2940 / 800	3460 / 6600 / 1790
60	44000	44348 / 44348B / 44363D	44131 / 44143 / NA44143 / 44150 / 44158 / 44157 / 44157X / 44162 / NA44163	1.3125 / 1.4375 / 1.5000 / 1.5625 / 1.5748 / 1.5748 / 1.6250 / 1.6250	33.338 / 36.512 / 38.100 / 39.688 / 40.000 / 40.000 / 41.275 / 41.275	3.4843 / 3.4843 / 3.6250	88.501 / 88.501 / 92.075	18.5	0.75	1410 / 2700 / 1880	3180 / 6050 / 4250
63	LM48500	LM48510 / LM48511A	LM48548 / LM48548A / LM48548L	1.3750 / 1.3750	34.925 / 34.925	2.5625	65.088	14.8	1.55	950 / 1820 / 615	2140 / 4100 / 1380
65	M38500	M38510	M38549	1.3750	34.925	2.6250	66.675	16.7	1.66	1120 / 2140 / 675	2520 / 4800 / 1520
64	14500	14525	14585	1.3750	34.925	2.6875	68.262	15.9	1.66	1040 / 1980 / 625	2330 / 4450 / 1410
68	36000	36300	36137	1.3750	34.925	3.0000	76.200	21.9	1.67	1750 / 3340 / 1045	3930 / 7500 / 2350
67	25800	25820 / 25821	25877 / 25878 / 25880	1.3750 / 1.3750 / 1.4365	34.925 / 34.925 / 36.487	2.8750	73.025	21.6	2.01	1485 / 2820 / 740	3340 / 6350 / 1660
66	27800	27820 / 27820D	27875 / 27880 / 27881	1.3750 / 1.5000 / 1.5000	34.925 / 38.100 / 38.100	3.1510	80.035	19.7	1.04	1370 / 2600 / 1315	3080 / 5850 / 2960
69	3300	3325 / 3339 / 3320 / 3320B / 3331 / 3329 / 3329B / 3328	3379 / 3381 / 3387 / 3382 / 3386	1.3750 / 1.5000 / 1.5000 / 1.5625 / 1.5625	34.925 / 38.100 / 38.100 / 39.688 / 39.688	3.1496 / 3.1510 / 3.1562 / 3.1562 / 3.2187 / 3.2187 / 3.3125	80.000 / 80.035 / 80.167 / 80.167 / 81.755 / 81.755 / 84.138	27.2	2.14	1900 / 3620 / 890	4300 / 8150 / 2000

Bore ranges (overall):
- 1.3125 / 33.338
- 1.3125 — 1.4375 / 33.338 — 36.512
- 1.3125 — 1.5625 / 33.338 — 39.688
- 1.3125 — 1.6250 / 33.338 — 41.275
- 1.3750 / 34.925
- 1.3750 / 34.925
- 1.3750 / 34.925
- 1.3750 / 34.925
- 1.3750 — 1.4365 / 34.925 — 36.487
- 1.3750 — 1.5000 / 34.925 — 38.100
- 1.3750 — 1.5625 / 34.925 — 39.688

Cup OD range (overall):
- 2.8750 / 73.025
- 3.0000 / 76.200
- 2.8750 — 3.0000 / 73.025 — 76.200
- 3.4843 — 3.6250 / 88.501 — 92.075
- 2.5625 / 65.088
- 2.6250 / 66.675
- 2.6875 / 68.262
- 3.0000 / 76.200
- 2.8750 / 73.025
- 3.1510 / 80.035
- 3.1496 — 3.3125 / 80.000 — 84.138

†Dimension shown is maximum value—see note at bottom of fitting practice table in Reference Tables.
▲Non-standard tolerances, see inch System bearing tolerances in Reference Tables.

The following index of bearing series is listed by increasing bore size.

BEARING SELECTION INDEX

The bearing type and specific cone or cup dimensions are located on the page reference number indicated.

bore range min — max	outside diameter range min — max	bore range min — max	fac-tor G	fac-tor K	rating at 500 RPM for 3000 hours L10 one-row radial thrust / two-row radial lb	daN	series number	cone number	cone bore inch	cone bore metric	cone TS or TSL	cone SS or SR	cone TDI or TDIT	cone TNA or TNADC	cone TNASW or TNASVE	cup number	cup O.D. inch	cup O.D. metric	cup TS or TSF	cup TDO and TDODC	dim. sheet page no.
1.3750 — 1.6250 34.925 — 41.275	3.3750 85.725	1.3750 — 1.6250 34.925 — 41.275	30.4	1.45	5000 9550 3450	2220 4240 1535	3800	3872	1.3750	34.925	10					3820	3.3750	85.725	11		71
								3878	1.4375	36.512	11					3820B	3.3750	85.725	63		
								3875	1.5000	38.100	12					3821	3.3750	85.725	10		
								3876	1.5000	38.100	12										
								3879	1.5748	40.000	13										
								3877	1.6250	41.275	15										
								3877A	1.6250	41.275	15										
								3880	1.6250	41.275	15										
1.3750 — 1.6250 34.925 — 41.275	3.4843 88.501	1.3750 — 1.6250 34.925 — 41.275	28.6	2.22	4450 8450 2000	1980 3760 890	415	417	1.3750	34.925	10					414	3.4843	88.501	10		70
								415	1.5000	38.100	12										
								418	1.5000	38.100	12										
								420	1.5748	40.000	14										
								419	1.6250	41.275	15										
1.3770 — 1.5000 34.976 — 38.100	2.6875 — 2.8346 68.262 — 72.000	1.3770 — 1.5000 34.976 — 38.100	14.6	1.31	2000 3810 1530	890 1695 680	19000	19138	1.3770	34.976	10					19268	2.6875	68.262	10		72
								191450	1.4375	36.512			9			19268B	2.6875	68.262	62		
								19146TD	1.4581	37.036			17			19281	2.8125	71.438	11		
								19150	1.5000	38.100	11					19283	2.8346	72.000	11		
																192838	2.8346	72.000	62		
																19283X	2.8346	72.000	11		
1.3780 35.000	2.3622 60.000	1.3780 35.000	12.8	1.40	1610 3060 1150	715 1360 510	L68100	L68149	†1.3780	†35.000	10					L68111	†2.3622	†60.000	10		73
1.3780 35.000	2.4409 62.000	1.3780 35.000	13.3	1.31	1780 3380 1360	790 1505 605	LM78300	LM78349	†1.3780	†35.000	10					LM78310A	†2.4409	†62.000	10		74
1.3780 35.000	2.8750 73.025	1.3780 35.000	20.1	1.58	3540 6750 2240	1575 3000 995	23600	23691	1.3780	35.000	10					23621	2.8750	73.025	10		75
1.3780 — 1.6880 35.000 — 42.875	3.0000 — 3.1562 76.200 — 80.167	1.3780 — 1.6880 35.000 — 42.875	26.5	1.83	3660 7000 2000	1630 3100 890	26800	26883	1.3780	35.000	10					26823	3.0000	76.200	10		76
								26877	1.4375	36.512	11					26822	3.1250	79.375	11		
								26878	1.5000	38.100	12					26822A	3.1250	79.375	12		
								26880	1.5625	39.688	13					26822B	3.1250	79.375	62		
								26881	1.5625	39.688	13					26824	3.1496	80.000	13		
								26882	1.6250	41.275	14					26820	3.1562	80.167	14		
								26885	1.6250	41.275	14					26821	3.1562	80.167	14		
								26884	1.6880	42.875	16					26830	3.1562	80.167	13		
								26886	1.6880	42.875	16										
1.4375 — 1.5000 36.512 — 38.100	2.7170 69.012	1.4375 — 1.5000 36.512 — 38.100	16.6	1.45	2230 4250 1540	990 1880 685	13600	13682	1.4375	36.512	11					13620	2.7170	69.012	11		77
								13685	1.5000	38.100	11					13621	2.7170	69.012	11		
								13685L	1.5000	38.100	69					13621D	2.7170	69.012		22	
								13687	1.5000	38.100	11					13621DC	2.7170	69.012		22	

BEARING SELECTION INDEX

Cone bore range (in)	Cone bore range (mm)	Cone series	Basic load ratings	Factor	Factor	Cups / cones detail	Page
1.4375 — 1.7960	36,512 — 45,618	29500	3680 / 7000 / 2110	1635 / 3120 / 940 — 1.74	28.2	28570 28572 28578 28577 28580 28581 28584 28590	78
3.2500 — 3.9050	82,550 — 99,187	29500				28519 28520 28520D 2552000C 28523 28521 28521B 28522 28526 28527 28545	
2.5000 — 2.5625	63,500 — 65,088	13800	1140 / 2180 / 675	510 / 970 / 300 — 1.69	12.5	13889 / 13830 13836 13836B	79
2.5625	65,088						
1.5000	38,100	LM29700	2020 / 3850 / 1150	900 / 1710 / 510 — 1.76	16.7	LM29748 LM29748L LM29749 / LM29710 LM29711	80
2.8346 — 2.8440	72,000 — 72,238	16000	2280 / 4350 / 1570	1015 / 1940 / 700 — 1.45	16.6	16150 / 16282 16283 16284 16284B	81
3.2500	82,550	HM801300	4300 / 8150 / 4000	1900 / 3640 / 1780 — 1.07	26.6	HM801346 HM801346X HM801349 / HM801310	83
3.0000 — 1.6250	76,200 — 41,275	24700	3040 / 5800 / 2040	1355 / 2580 / 910 — 1.49	21.5	M24778SW 24780 / 24720 24720D 24720DC 24721	96 (43)
3.5625	90,488	4300	6850 / 13100 / 3350	3060 / 5800 / 1490 — 2.05	42.6	4375 4388 4395 / 4335	88
3.7500 — 3.8750	95,250 — 98,425	53000	3850 / 7350 / 4900	1715 / 3260 / 2160 — 0.79	21.9	53150 53162 53176 53177 53178 / 53375 53376D 53387 53387X	82
3.7500 — 3.8750	95,250 — 98,425	HM903200	4500 / 8600 / 5700	2000 / 3820 / 2540 — 0.79	26.7	HM903241 HM903244 HM903245 HM903247 HM903249 HM903249A / HM903210 HM903216	84
3.3125 — 3.4375	84,138 — 87,312	3500	4550 / 8650 / 2380	2020 / 3860 / 1060 — 1.91	32.0	3560 3583 3576 3577 3585 3579 3578 3586 / 3520 3526 3525 3525B	85

†Dimension shown is maximum value—see note at bottom of fitting practice table in Reference Tables.
▲Non-standard tolerances, see Inch System bearing tolerances in Reference Tables.

BEARING SELECTION INDEX

The following index of bearing series is listed by increasing bore size.

The bearing type and specific cone or cup dimensions are located on the page reference number indicated.

bore range (inch)	bore range (metric)	OD range (inch)	OD range (metric)	series no.	rating @ 500 RPM 3000 hrs L10 — lb (1-row radial / 2-row radial / thrust)	daN	factor K	factor G	cone no.	cone bore (inch)	cone bore (metric)	cones TS/TSL	SS/SR	TDI/TDIT	TNA/TNADC	TNASW/TNASWE	cup no.	cup OD (inch)	cup OD (metric)	cups TS/TSF	TDO/TDODC	dim. sheet page
1.5000 — 2.0000	38.100 — 50.800	4.0000	101.600	525	6550 / 12500 / 3200	2920 / 5550 / 1425	2.05	46.9	525	1.5000	38.100	13					522	4.0000	101.600	13		87
									526	1.6250	41.275	15					522B	4.0000	101.600	64		
									527	1.7500	44.450	17										
									527S	1.7710	44.983	18										
									528	1.8750	47.625	19										
									528A	1.8750	47.625	19										
									529	2.0000	50.800	21										
									529X	2.0000	50.800	21										
1.5000 — 2.1250	38.100 — 53.975	3.6718 — 3.7500	93.264 — 95.250	33800	5250 / 9950 / 2960	2320 / 4440 / 1315	1.77	41.5	33880	1.5000	38.100	13					33820B	3.6718	93.264	63		86
									33885	1.7500	44.450	17					33821	3.7500	95.250	17		
									33889	2.0000	50.800	21					33821D	3.7500	95.250		23	
									33890	2.0625	52.388	23					33821DC	3.7500	95.250		23	
									33891	2.0625	52.388	23					33822	3.7500	95.250	13		
									33895	2.1250	53.975	23										
1.5625 39.688	1.5625 / 39.688	2.8750	73.025	M201000	2980 / 5650 / 1690	1325 / 2520 / 750	1.76	22.1	M201047	1.5625	39.688	13					M201011	2.8750	73.025	13		89
1.5748 — 1.8125	40.000 — 46.038	3.3465 — 3.5480	85.000 — 90.119	355	3140 / 6000 / 1640	1395 / 2660 / 730	1.91	24.7	350	1.5748	40.000	14					354A	3.3465	85.000	13		90
									350A	1.5748	40.000	13					354B	3.3465	85.000	63		
									357	1.5748	40.000	13					354X	3.3465	85.000	13		
									355	1.7500	44.450	16					352	3.5480	90.119	14		
									355A	1.7500	44.450	16					353D	3.5480	90.119		23	
									355X	1.8024	45.781			17			353DC	3.5480	90.119		23	
									359TD	1.8125	46.038	19										
									359A	1.8125	46.038	19										
									359S	1.8125	46.038	19										
1.5748 — 2.1250	40.000 — 53.975	4.2500 — 4.3750	107.950 — 111.125	535	6900 / 13100 / 3500	3060 / 5850 / 1560	1.97	51.6	543	1.5748	40.000	14					532X	4.2500	107.950	14		91
									535	1.7500	44.450	18					532A	4.3750	111.125	18		
									536	1.8750	47.625	19					532B	4.3750	111.125	64		
									537	2.0000	50.800	22				37	533D	4.3750	111.125		23	
									539	2.1250	53.975	24					533DC	4.3750	111.125		23	
									539A	2.1250	53.975	24										
1.6142 41.000	1.6142 / 41.000	2.6772	68.000	LM300800	2090 / 3980 / 1240	930 / 1770 / 555	1.68	18.3	LM300849	†1.6142	†41.000	14					LM300811	†2.6772	†68.000	14		92
1.6250 41.275	1.6250 / 41.275	2.8750	73.025	18500	2020 / 3840 / 1210	895 / 1710 / 535	1.67	17.3	18590	1.6250	41.275	14					18520	2.8750	73.025	14		94
1.6250 41.275	1.6250 / 41.275	2.8910	73.431	LM501300	2520 / 4800 / 1720	1120 / 2140 / 765	1.46	19.0	LM501349	1.6250	41.275	14					LM501310	2.8910	73.431	14		95
																	LM501311	2.8910	73.431	14		
																	LM501314	2.8910	73.431	14		

Bore in / mm	Cone	Cup(s)	Cup OD in / mm	Cup W	Assembly	Assembly OD in / mm	Width	Page
1.6250 / 41.275	11000	11182, 11183	3.0000 / 76.200	15.8	11300, 113008	3.0000 / 76.200	14, 62	93
1.6250 / 41.275	22700	22778	3.2500 / 82.550	27.1	22721	3.2500 / 82.550	14	100
1.6250 / 41.275	M802000	M802048	3.2500 / 82.550	24.5	M802011	3.2500 / 82.550	14	99
1.6250 / 41.275	M903300	M903345	3.6250 / 92.075	20.7	M903310	3.6250 / 92.075	15	97
1.6250 — 1.7500 / 41.275 — 44.450	HM803100	HM803145, HM803146, HM803149	3.5000 / 88.900	30.6	HM803110	3.5000 / 88.900	15	101
1.6250 — 1.7500 / 41.275 — 44.450	46000	46162, 46175, 46176	3.6875 / 93.662	35.3	46368	3.6875 / 93.662	15	103
1.6250 — 1.9060 / 41.275 — 48.412	HM804000	HM804840, HM804842, HM804843, HM804846, HM804848, HM804849	3.7500 / 95.250	35.0	HM804810	3.7500 / 95.250	15	102
1.6250 — 2.0312 / 41.275 — 51.592	365	365A, 367, 368A, 369S, 369, 360, 368, 370A, 368S	3.5000 — 3.5433 / 88.900 — 90.000	27.6	362A, 362, 362B, 363, 363D, 363DC	3.5000 — 3.5433 / 88.900 — 90.000	15, 18, 63, 19	98
1.6250 — 2.1250 / 41.275 — 53.975	HM807000	HM807035, HM807040, HM807044, JHM807045, JHM807046, HM807049	4.1250 — 4.1339 / 104.775 — 105.000	49.6	HM807010, HM807011, JHM807012	4.1250 — 4.1339 / 104.775 — 105.000	17, 15, 21	105
1.6250 — 2.2500 / 41.275 — 57.150	495	464A, 460, 467, 455, 455S, NA495, NA495SW, 468, 466, 462, 452A, 469	4.1250 — 4.3307 / 104.775 — 110.000	46.5	453X, 452, 452D, 452DC, 453A, 453AS, 453B, 454	4.1250 — 4.3307 / 104.775 — 110.000	15, 22, 23, 17, 19, 64	104

†Dimension shown is maximum value—see note at bottom of fitting practice table in Reference Tables.

*For "J" part tolerances—see metric tolerance and fitting practice in Reference Tables.

BEARING SELECTION INDEX

The following index of bearing series is listed by increasing bore size.

The bearing type and specific cone or cup dimensions are located on the page reference number indicated.

bore range min	bore range max	outside diameter range min	outside diameter range max	series number	rating at 500 RPM for 3000 hours L10 one-row radial / two-row radial thrust lb	daN	fac-tor K	fac-tor G	cone number	cone bore inch	cone bore metric	TS or TSL	SS or SR	TDI or TDIT	TNA and TNADC	TNASW or TNASWE	cup number	cup outside diameter inch	cup outside diameter metric	TS or TSF	TDO and TDODC	dimension sheet page no.
1.6875	42,862	3.2500	82,550	22000	2550 / 4850 / 1870	1135 / 2160 / 835	1.36	19.4	22168	1.6875	42.862	15					22325	3.2500	82.550	15		107
1.6875	42,862	3.0312	76,992	12000	2000 / 3810 / 1740	890 / 1695 / 775	1.15	17.1	12168	1.6875	42.862	15					12303	3.0312	76.992	15		106
1.7500	44,450								12175	1.7500	44.450	16										
1.7500	44,450	2.8125	71,438	LL103000	1420 / 2700 / 740	630 / 1200 / 330	1.91	16.2	LL103049	1.7500	44.450	16					LL103010	2.8125	71.438	16		108
																	LL103010B	2.8125	71.438	62		
1.7500	44,450	2.8750	73,025	L102800	2470 / 4700 / 1350	1095 / 2100 / 600	1.83	24.4	L102849	1.7500	44.450	16					L102810	2.8750	73.025	16		111
1.7500	44,450	3.1875	80,962	13000	2070 / 3940 / 1860	920 / 1750 / 830	1.11	18.5	13175	1.7500	44.450	16					13318	3.1875	80.962	16		109
1.7500	44,450	3.2650	82,931	35000	3150 / 6000 / 1610	1400 / 2660 / 715	1.96	24.1	35176	1.7500	44.450	16					35326	3.2650	82.931	16		112
1.7500	44,450	3.6875	93,662	49000	5250 / 10000 / 3230	2340 / 4440 / 1440	1.62	34.1	49175	1.7500	44.450	17					49368	3.6875	93.662	17		116
									49176	1.7500	44.450	17										
1.7500	44,450	3.1250	79,375	18600	2090 / 3990 / 1340	930 / 1775 / 595	1.56	19.5	18685	1.7500	44.450	16					18620	3.1250	79.375	16		110
1.8125	46,038								18690	1.8125	46.038	19					18620B	3.1250	79.375	62		
																	18620D	3.1250	79.375		23	
																	18620DC	3.1250	79.375		23	
1.7500	44,450	4.0625	103,188	5300	8800 / 16700 / 4450	3900 / 7450 / 1980	1.97	58.4	5356	1.7500	44.450	17					5335	4.0625	103.188	17		121
1.9375	49,212								5358	1.8750	47.625	19										
									5361	1.8750	47.625	19										
									5395	1.9375	49.212	20										
1.7500	44,450	4.0000	101,600	49500	5300 / 10100 / 3630	2360 / 4480 / 1615	1.46	39.2	49576	1.7500	44.450	17					49520	4.0000	101.600	21		117
2.0000	50,800								49585	2.0000	50.800	21					49522	4.0000	101.600	17		
1.7500	44,450	4.1250 — 4.2500	104,775 — 107,950	59000	6800 / 12900 / 4700	3020 / 5750 / 2080	1.45	45.7	59175	1.7500	44.450	17					59412	4.1250	104.775	17		119
2.0000	50,800								59176	1.7500	44.450	17					59425	4.2500	107.950	17		
									59187	1.8750	47.625	19										
									59200	2.0000	50.800	22										
									59201	2.0000	50.800	22										
1.7500	44,450	4.3750 — 4.4375	111,125 — 112,712	HM907600	5000 / 9500 / 7550	2220 / 4220 / 3360	0.66	36.1	HM907635	1.7500	44.450	18					HM907614	4.3750	111.125	18		115
2.0000	50,800								HM907639	1.8750	47.625	20					HM907616	4.4375	112.712	20		
									HM907643	2.0000	50.800	22										

BEARING SELECTION INDEX

Group 114 — Cone bore 1.7500 — 2.0625 / 44.450 — 52.388 mm; Cup O.D. 3.6718 — 3.8750 / 93.264 — 98.425 mm; Cup 3700; Ratings 5000 / 9500 / 2890 — 2220 / 4240 / 1285 — 1.73 — 39.6

Cone	Bore (in)	Bore (mm)	W	Cup	O.D. (in)	O.D. (mm)	W
3782	1.7500	44.450	16	3720	3.6718	93.264	18
3778	1.7710	44.983	18	37208	3.6718	93.264	63
3777	1.8125	46.038	19	37290	3.6718	93.264	23
3779	1.8750	47.625	19	37290DC	3.6718	93.264	23
3781	1.8750	47.625	19	3730	3.6718	93.264	16
3775	1.9375	49.212	20	3726	3.7500	95.250	19
3780	2.0000	50.800	21	3732	3.8750	98.425	19
MA37805W	2.0000	50.800	21	43			
3784	2.0000	50.800	21				
3787	2.0625	52.388	23				

Group 113 — Cone bore 1.7500 — 2.0625 / 44.450 — 52.388 mm; Cup O.D. 4.3750 — 4.4375 / 111.125 — 112.712 mm; Cup 55000; Ratings 4150 / 7900 / 6300 — 1840 / 3520 / 2800 — 0.66 — 29.0

Cone	Bore (in)	Bore (mm)	W	Cup	O.D. (in)	O.D. (mm)	W
55175	1.7500	44.450	18	55437	4.3750	111.125	17
55176	1.7500	44.450	17	55437B	4.3750	111.125	64
55187	1.8750	47.625	19	55443	4.4375	112.712	18
55196	1.9675	49.974	20	55444D	4.4375	112.712	23
55197	1.9675	49.974	20				
55200	2.0000	50.800	22				
55206	2.0625	52.388	23				

Group 122 — Cone bore 1.7500 — 2.1250 / 44.450 — 53.975 mm; Cup O.D. 5.0000 / 127.000 mm; Cup 6200; Ratings 12400 / 23700 / 6350 — 5550 / 10550 / 2820 — 1.96 — 81.8

Cone	Bore (in)	Bore (mm)	W	Cup	O.D. (in)	O.D. (mm)	W
6277	1.7500	44.450	18	6220	5.0000	127.000	18
6279	2.0000	50.800	23				
6280	2.1250	53.975	24				

Group 118 — Cone bore 1.7500 — 2.2500 / 44.450 — 57.150 mm; Cup O.D. 4.1250 / 104.775 mm; Cup 45200; Ratings 6200 / 11800 / 3520 — 2760 / 5250 / 1565 — 1.76 — 50.4

Cone	Bore (in)	Bore (mm)	W	Cup	O.D. (in)	O.D. (mm)	W
45280	1.7500	44.450	17	45220	4.1250	104.775	22
45284	2.0000	50.800	22	45221	4.1250	104.775	17
45285	2.0000	50.800	22				
45285A	2.0000	50.800	22				
45287	2.1250	53.975	23				
45289	2.2500	57.150	25				
45290	2.2500	57.150	25				
45291	2.2500	57.150	25				

Group 120 — Cone bore 1.7500 — 2.2500 / 44.450 — 57.150 mm; Cup O.D. 4.5276 — 4.7500 / 115.000 — 120.650 mm; Cup 615; Ratings 8300 / 15800 / 4450 — 3700 / 7050 / 1980 — 1.86 — 60.9

Cone	Bore (in)	Bore (mm)	W	Cup	O.D. (in)	O.D. (mm)	W
615	1.7500	44.450	18	614X	4.5276	115.000	18
619	2.0000	50.800	22	613X	4.7244	120.000	22
621	2.1250	53.975	24	612	4.7500	120.650	24
624	2.1250	53.975	24	612B	4.7500	120.650	64
622X	2.1654	55.000	25	6125	4.7500	120.650	24
623	2.2500	57.150	26				

Group 123 — Cone bore 1.7665 — 2.0625 / 44.869 — 52.388 mm; Cup O.D. 3.6250 / 92.075 mm; Cup 28500; Ratings 4100 / 7850 / 2660 — 1840 / 3500 / 1185 — 1.55 — 36.5

Cone	Bore (in)	Bore (mm)	W	Cup	O.D. (in)	O.D. (mm)	W
28576	1.7665	44.869	18	28521	3.6250	92.075	18
28579	†1.9685	†50.000	20	28521B	3.6250	92.075	63
28580	2.0000	50.800	21				
28584	2.0625	52.388	23	1			

Group 124 — Cone bore 1.7717 / 45.000 mm; Cup O.D. 4.1333 / 104.986 mm; Cup HM905800; Ratings 5550 / 10600 / 7400 — 2460 / 4700 / 3280 — 0.75 — 37.0

Cone	Bore (in)	Bore (mm)	W	Cup	O.D. (in)	O.D. (mm)	W
HM905843	†1.7717	†45.000	18	HM905810	4.1333	104.986	18

Group 125 — Cone bore 1.7812 / 45.242 mm; Cup O.D. 2.8910 / 73.431 mm; Cup LM102900; Ratings 2580 / 4900 / 1350 — 1150 / 2180 / 600 — 1.91 — 24.7

Cone	Bore (in)	Bore (mm)	W	Cup	O.D. (in)	O.D. (mm)	W
LM102949	1.7812	45.242	18	LM102910	2.8910	73.431	18
				LM102911	2.8910	73.431	18

Group 126 — Cone bore 1.7812 / 45.242 mm; Cup O.D. 3.0625 — 3.1496 / 77.788 — 80.000 mm; Cup LM603000; Ratings 2610 / 5000 / 1910 — 1160 / 2220 / 850 — 1.37 — 21.3

Cone	Bore (in)	Bore (mm)	W	Cup	O.D. (in)	O.D. (mm)	W
LM603049	1.7812	45.242	18	LM603011	3.0625	77.788	18
				LM603012	3.0625	77.788	18
				LM603014	†3.1496	†80.000	18

Group 127 — Cone bore 1.8110 / 46.000 mm; Cup O.D. 2.9528 / 75.000 mm; Cup LM503300; Ratings 2400 / 4600 / 1660 — 1070 / 2040 / 740 — 1.45 — 22.6

Cone	Bore (in)	Bore (mm)	W	Cup	O.D. (in)	O.D. (mm)	W
LM503349	†1.8110	†46.000	18	LM503310	†2.9528	†75.000	18
				LM503310A	†2.9528	†75.000	18

†Dimension shown is maximum value—see note at bottom of fitting practice table in Reference Tables.

BEARING SELECTION INDEX

The following index of bearing series is listed by increasing bore size.

The bearing type and specific cone or cup dimensions are located on the page reference number indicated.

bore range min	bore range max	OD range min	OD range max	series number	rating 500 RPM 3000 hr L10 (lb)	rating (daN)	factor K	factor G	cone bore inch	cone bore metric	TS or TSL	SS or SR	TDI or TDIT	TNA and TNADC	TNASW or TNASWE	cone number	cup number	cup OD inch	cup OD metric	TS or TSF	TDO and TDODC	dim. sheet page no.
1.8125	46.038	3.3465	85.000	2900	3830 / 7300 / 2270	1705 / 3240 / 1010	1.69	30.5	1.8125	46.038	19					2984	2924	3.3465	85.000	19		129
									1.8125	46.038	19					2984A	29248	3.3465	85.000	63		
1.8125	2.0000	3.3465	3.5000	18700	2240 / 4250 / 1550	995 / 1900 / 690	1.44	23.0	1.8125	46.038	19					18780	18720	3.3465	85.000	19		128
46.038	50.800	85.000	88.900						2.0000	50.800	21					18790	18720B	3.3465	85.000	63		
																	18724	3.5000	88.900	21		
1.8750	47.625	3.5000	88.900	M804000	3930 / 7500 / 3670	1745 / 3320 / 1635	1.07	26.9	1.8750	47.625	19					M804049	M804010	3.5000	88.900	19		131
1.8750	2.1875	4.8750	123.825	72000	6250 / 11900 / 7900	2780 / 5300 / 3520	0.79	38.1	1.8750	47.625	20					72187	72487	4.8750	123.825	20		132
47.625	55.562								2.0000	50.800	23					72200	724880	4.8750	123.825	23		
									2.1250	53.975	24					72212						
									2.1250	53.975				37		NA72212						
									2.1875	55.562	25					72218						
1.8750	2.2651	3.8125	3.9370	385	3590 / 6850 / 2180	1595 / 3040 / 970	1.65	33.7	1.8750	47.625	19					386A	382A	3.8125	96.838	19		130
47.625	57.534	96.838	100.000						2.0000	50.800	21					385A	382B	3.8125	96.838	63		
									2.1250	53.975	23					389A	382	3.8750	98.425	21		
									2.1250	53.975	23					389AS	383A	3.9370	100.000	23		
									2.1654	55.000	24					385	384D	3.9370	100.000		23	
									2.1654	55.000	25					385X	384DC	3.9370	100.000		23	
									2.1654	55.000				37		NA385	384ED	3.9370	100.000		23	
									2.1880	55.575	25					389	384EDC	3.9370	100.000		23	
									2.2500	57.150	25					387						
									2.2500	57.150	25					387A						
									2.2500	57.150	25					387AS						
									2.2500	57.150	25					387S						
									2.2650	57.531	26					388A						
									2.2651	57.534						388TD						
1.9375	49.212	4.5000	114.300	65300	8850 / 16800 / 6300	3940 / 7500 / 2900	1.36	50.7	1.9375	49.212	20					65390	65320	4.5000	114.300	20		133
													17			65390	653208	4.5000	114.300	64		
1.9375	49.212	4.5000	114.300	HH506300	9900 / 18800 / 6800	4400 / 8400 / 3040	1.45	57.4	1.9375	49.212	20					HH506348	HH506310	4.5000	114.300	20		134
																	HH506311	4.5000	114.300	20		
1.9685	2.0000	3.2283	3.2650	LM104900	3370 / 6400 / 1760	1500 / 2860 / 785	1.91	31.1	1.9685	50.000	20	2				LM104947A	LM104910	*3.2283	*82.000	20		135
50.000	50.800	82.000	82.931						1.9685	50.000	20					LM104948	LM104911	3.2500	82.550	20		
									2.0000	50.800	21					LM104949	LM104911A	3.2500	82.550	20		
																	LM104912	3.2650	82.931	21		
1.9685	50.000	3.5433	90.000	M205100	5000 / 9500 / 2800	2220 / 4220 / 1245	1.78	38.0	1.9685	50.000	20	2				JM205149	JM205110	*3.5433	*90.000	20		137

Assembly (TS) summary

TS No.	Bore range (in)	Bore range (mm)	OD range (in)	OD range (mm)	Factor	K	Page
(398 / 390 family)	2.0000 — 2.6875	50.800 — 68.262	4.3307 — 4.3750	110.000 — 111.125			136
LL205400	2.0000	50.800	3.0625	77.788	19.3	1.74	138
L305600	2.0000	50.800	3.1875	80.962	30.3	1.64	140
18000	2.0000	50.800	3.3750	85.725	20.8	1.03	139
375	2.0000 — 2.0625	50.800 — 52.388	3.6718 — 3.9370	93.264 — 100.000	30.4	1.73	141
4500	2.0000 — 2.1250	50.800 — 53.975	4.1250	104.775	57.5	1.74	146
28600	2.0000 — 2.2500	50.800 — 57.150	3.8125 — 3.8750	96.838 — 98.425	42.0	1.45	142
66000	2.0000 — 2.2500	50.800 — 57.150	4.6250	117.475	40.1	0.93	143
65000	2.0000 — 2.3750	50.800 — 60.325	5.0000	127.000	65.2	1.20	149
5500	2.0000 — 2.5938	50.800 — 65.883	4.8125	122.238	84.8	1.63	150

Cones

Cone No.	Bore (in)	Bore (mm)	Page
398	2.0000	50.800	136
390	2.2500	57.150	136
397	2.3622	60.000	136
392	2.4375	61.912	136
399D	2.5000	63.500	136
390A	2.5000	63.500	136
395	2.5579	64.971	136
395TD	2.6250	66.675	136
395A	2.6250	66.675	136
395S	2.6875	68.262	136
399A	2.6875	68.262	136
399AL	2.6875	68.262	136
399AS	2.6875	68.262	136
LL205449	2.0000	50.800	138
L305649	2.0000	50.800	140
18200	2.0000	50.800	139
375	2.0000	50.800	141
373D	2.0000	50.800	141
378S	2.0000	50.800	141
377TD	2.0541	52.174	141
377	2.0625	52.388	141
4580	2.0000	50.800	146
4595	2.1250	53.975	146
28678	2.0000	50.800	142
28680	2.1875	55.562	142
28682	2.2500	57.150	142
66200	2.0000	50.800	143
66212	2.1250	53.975	143
66225	2.2500	57.150	143
65200	2.0000	50.800	149
65212	2.1250	53.975	149
65225	2.2500	57.150	149
65231	2.3125	58.738	149
65235	2.3575	59.880	149
65237	2.3750	60.325	149
65237A	2.3750	60.325	149
5565	2.0000	50.800	150
5578	2.1250	53.975	150
5566	2.1875	55.562	150
5582	2.3750	60.325	150
5583	2.3750	60.325	150
5584	2.5000	63.500	150
5595	2.5938	65.883	150

Cups

Cup No.	OD (in)	OD (mm)	Page
394B	4.3307	110.000	136
394AS	4.3307	110.000	136
394D	4.3307	110.000	136
394DC	4.3307	110.000	136
393AS	4.3750	111.125	136
LL205410	3.0625	77.788	138
L305610	3.1875	80.962	140
L305610B	3.1875	80.962	140
18337	3.3750	85.725	139
374	3.6718	93.264	141
372A	3.8125	96.838	141
372	3.9370	100.000	141
373	3.9370	100.000	141
4535	4.1250	104.775	146
28621	3.8125	96.838	142
28622	3.8437	97.630	142
28622B	3.8437	97.630	142
28623	3.8750	98.425	142
66461	4.6250	117.475	143
66462	4.6250	117.475	143
66462B	4.6250	117.475	143
66462D	4.6250	117.475	143
66462DC	4.6250	117.475	143
65500	5.0000	127.000	149
65500B	5.0000	127.000	149
5535	4.8125	122.238	150

†Dimension shown is maximum value—see note at bottom of fitting practice table in Reference Tables.
*For "J" part tolerances—see metric tolerance and fitting practice in Reference Tables.

BEARING SELECTION INDEX

The following index of bearing series is listed by increasing bore size.

The bearing type and specific cone or cup dimensions are located on the page reference number indicated.

bore range min.–max. (inch / metric)	outside diameter range min.–max. (inch / metric)	series number	rating 500 RPM 3000 hrs L10 — one-row radial / two-row radial thrust (lb / daN)	factor K	factor G	cone number	cone bore inch	cone bore metric	page ref CONES (TS/TSL • SS/SR • TDI/TDIT • TNA/TNADC • TNASW/TNASWE)	cup number	cup OD inch	cup OD metric	page ref CUPS (TS/TSF • TDO/TDODC)	dim. sheet page no.
2.0000–2.6250 / 50.800–66.675	4.4375 / 112.712	3900	5900/2620; 11200/5000; 4050/1800	1.45	57.8	3975	2.0000	50.800	TS 22	3920	4.4375	112.712	TS 26	144
						3979	2.2500	57.150	26	3920B	4.4375	112.712	64	
						3981	2.3125	58.738	26	3925	4.4375	112.712	22	
						3977	2.3622	60.000	27	3926	4.4375	112.712	26	
						3980	2.3750	60.325	27					
						3982	2.5000	63.500	29					
						3984	2.6250	66.675	30					
						3994	2.6250	66.675	30					
2.0000–2.6250 / 50.800–66.675	4.4375–4.7238 / 112.712–119.985	39500	7000/3100; 13300/5900; 4050/1800	1.72	65.7	39573	2.0000	50.800	TS 22	39520	4.4375	112.712	TS 22	145
						39575	2.0000	50.800	22	39520B	4.4375	112.712	64	
						39578	2.1250	53.975	24	39521	4.4375	112.712	22	
						39580	2.2500	57.150	26	39528	4.7238	119.985	24	
						39581	2.2500	57.150	26					
						39585	2.5000	63.500	29					
						39585A	2.5000	63.500	29					
						39585D	2.5000	63.500	TDI 9					
						39586	†2.5591	65.001	30					
						39590	2.6250	66.675	30					
						39591	2.6250	66.675	SS/SR 1 • 30					
2.0000–2.6875 / 50.800–68.262	4.8125–4.8750 / 122.238–123.825	555	7900/3520; 15100/6700; 4700/2080	1.69	71.0	555	2.0000	50.800	TS 22	553X	4.8125	122.238	TS 22	147
						557S	2.1250	53.975	24	552A	4.8750	123.825	24	
						555S	2.2500	57.150	26	552B	4.8750	123.825	64 • TDO 23	
						558S	†2.3622	60.000	27	552D	4.8750	123.825	27 • TDO 23	
						557A	2.3750	60.325	27	552C	4.8750	123.825	27	
						558	2.3750	60.325	27					
						558A	2.3750	60.325	27					
						NA558SW	2.3750	60.325	TNASW 43					
						554	2.4375	61.912	28					
						559	2.5000	63.500	29					
						560	2.6250	66.675	31					
						560S	2.6875	68.262	31					
2.0000–2.8125 / 50.800–71.438	5.0000 / 127.000	HM813800	8050/3580; 15300/6800; 6950/3080	1.16	70.2	HM813836	2.0000	50.800	TS 23	HM813810	5.0000	127.000	TS 25	148
						HM813840	2.1875	55.562	25	HM813811	5.0000	127.000	23	
						HM813841	2.3750	60.325	27					
						HM813843	2.4375	61.912	28					
						HM813842	2.5000	63.500	29					
						HM813842A	2.5000	63.500	29					
						HM813844	2.6250	66.675	31					
						HM813846	2.7500	69.850	32					
						HM813849	2.8125	71.438	33					
2.1250 / 53.975	3.5000 / 88.900	LM806600	2690/1200; 5150/2280; 2520/1120	1.07	25.3	LM806649	2.1250	53.975	TS 23 • SS/SR 1	LM806610	3.5000	88.900	TS 23	151

Single-Row Tapered Roller Bearing Selection Index

Page 153 — Cone HM911200

Cone No.	Bore (in)	Bore (mm)	No.
HM911242	2.1250	53.975	24
HM911244	2.3622	60.000	27
HM911245	2.3750	60.325	27

Dim 44.9 — Factor 0.71 — Ratings 2900 / 5500 / 4080 — 6500 / 12400 / 9200

Cup No.	O.D. (in)	O.D. (mm)	No.
HM911210	5.1250	130.175	24
HM911216	5.3143	134.983	27

Page 154 — Cone 78000

Cone No.	Bore (in)	Bore (mm)	No.	
78214	2.1250	53.975	24	
78215	2.1250	53.975	24	
78216D	†2.1654	†55.000		9
78225	2.2500	57.150	26	
78250	2.5000	63.500	29	
78250D	†2.5000	†63.500		9
78293X	†2.5591	†65.000	30	9

Dim 49.4 — Factor 0.67 — Ratings 3000 / 5700 / 4480 — 6750 / 12990 / 10100

Cup No.	O.D. (in)	O.D. (mm)	No.
78537	5.3750	136.525	24
78549D	5.5000	139.700	
78551	5.5130	140.030	24
78571	5.7080	144.983	26

Page 155 — Cone 635

Cone No.	Bore (in)	Bore (mm)	No.	
636	2.1250	53.975	24	
635	2.2500	57.150	26	
637	2.3750	60.325	27	
639	2.5000	63.500	29	
641	2.6250	66.675	31	
643	2.7500	69.850	32	
M86435W	2.7500	69.850	33	
644	2.8125	71.438	33	
645	2.8125	71.438	33	44

Dim 83.0 — Factor 1.61 — Ratings 4260 / 8150 / 2640 — 9600 / 18300 / 5950

Cup No.	O.D. (in)	O.D. (mm)	No.
633	5.1250	130.175	24
632	5.3750	136.525	26
6328	5.3750	136.525	65
6320	5.3750	136.525	
6320C	5.3750	136.525	

Page 156 — Cone LM506800

Cone No.	Bore (in)	Bore (mm)	No.	
JLM506849	*2.1654	*55.000	24	2

Dim 35.2 — Factor 1.45 — Ratings 1685 / 3220 / 1165 — 3790 / 7200 / 2610

Cup No.	O.D. (in)	O.D. (mm)	No.
JLM506810	*3.5433	*90,000	24

Page 157 — Cone M207000

Cone No.	Bore (in)	Bore (mm)	No.	
JM207049	*2.1654	*55,000	24	2

Dim 44.5 — Factor 1.74 — Ratings 2400 / 4600 / 1380 — 5400 / 10300 / 3110

Cup No.	O.D. (in)	O.D. (mm)	No.
JM207010	*3.7402	*95,000	24

Page 159 — Cone H307700

Cone No.	Bore (in)	Bore (mm)	No.	
JH307749	*2.1654	*55,000	25	2

Dim 57.4 — Factor 1.69 — Ratings 3780 / 7200 / 2240 — 8500 / 16200 / 5050

Cup No.	O.D. (in)	O.D. (mm)	No.
JH307710	*4.3307	*110.000	25

Page 160 — Cone 6300

Cone No.	Bore (in)	Bore (mm)	No.
6381	*2.1654	*55,000	25
6361	2.3622	60.000	27
6376	2.3750	60.325	28
6382	2.5000	63.500	29
6379	2.5625	65.088	30
6386	2.6250	66.675	31
6389	2.6250	66.675	31

Dim 96.4 — Factor 1.80 — Ratings 5900 / 11250 / 3280 — 13300 / 25300 / 7350

Cup No.	O.D. (in)	O.D. (mm)	No.
6320	5.3447	135.755	25

Page 158 — Cone 475

Cone No.	Bore (in)	Bore (mm)	No.	
475	2.1654	55.000	25	
476	2.3622	60.000	27	
476A	2.3622	60.000	27	
477	2.5000	63.500	29	
483	2.5000	63.500	29	
478	2.5591	65.000	30	
479	2.6250	66.675	30	
480	2.6875	68.262	31	
482	2.7500	69.850	32	
N4482	2.7500	69.850		
N4483SW	2.7559	70.000		38
484	2.7559	70.000	32	
N4484	2.7559	70.000		
48770	2.8375	72.072	17	38

Dim 59.8 — Factor 1.52 — Ratings 2640 / 5000 / 1735 — 5900 / 11300 / 3900

Cup No.	O.D. (in)	O.D. (mm)	No.
472	4.7244	120.000	27
472A	4.7244	120.000	25
472B	4.7244	120.000	64
4720	4.7244	120.000	
4720C	4.7244	120.000	

†Dimension shown is maximum value—see note at bottom of fitting practice table in Reference Tables.
*For "J" part tolerances—see metric tolerance and fitting practice in Reference Tables.

The following index of bearing series is listed by increasing bore size.

BEARING SELECTION INDEX

The bearing type and specific cone and cup dimensions are located on the page reference number indicated.

bore range min.	bore range max.	OD range min.	OD range max.	series number	rating lb (one-/two-row radial thrust)	daN	fac-tor K	fac-tor G	cone number	cone bore inch	cone bore metric	SS/SR	TS or TSL	cup number	cup OD inch	cup OD metric	TS or TSF	TDO and TDODC	dim. sheet page no.
2.2500		3.4375		L507900	2810 / 5350 / 1870	1250 / 2380 / 835	1.50	35.4	L507949	2.2500	57,150		25	L507910	3.4375	87,312	25		161
57,150		87,312												L507910B	3.4375	87,312	63		
2.2500	2.8750	4.6250	4.7244	33000	5950 / 11400 / 4450	2660 / 5050 / 1980	1.34	63.9	33225	2.2500	57,150		26	33462	4.6250	117,475	26		162
57,150	73,025	117,475	120,000						33251	2.5000	63,500		29	33462B	4.6250	117,475	64		
									33262	2.6250	66,675		30	33462D	4.6250	117,475		24	
									33269	2.6875	68,262		31	33462DC	4.6250	117,475		24	
									33275	2.7500	69,850		32	33472	4.7244	120,000	29		
									33281	2.8125	71,438		33	33472DC	4.7244	120,000		24	
									33287	2.8750	73,025		33						
2.2500	3.0000	5.8750	5.9055	6400	14700 / 28000 / 9100	6550 / 12450 / 4060	1.61	121.	6455	2.2500	57,150		26	6420	5.8750	149,225	26		163
57,150	76,200	149,225	150,000						6464	2.5575	64,960		29	6420B	5.8750	149,225	65		
									6454	2.7500	69,850		32	6424	5.9055	150,000	29		
									6459	2.7559	70,000		33						
									6460	2.8750	73,025		34						
									6461	3.0000	76,200		35						
									6461A	3.0000	76,200		35						
2.3622		3.7402		LM508700	4100 / 7800 / 2830	1820 / 3480 / 1260	1.45	41.3	JLM508748	*2.3622	*60,000	2	26	JLM508710	*3.7402	*95,000	26		165
60,000		95,000																	
2.3622	2.5000	4.1250	4.3330	39000	3880 / 7400 / 2570	1725 / 3280 / 1145	1.51	40.7	39236	†2.3622	60,000		26	39412	4.1250	104,775	26		164
60,000	63,500	104,775	110,058						39250	2.5000	63,500		28	39412B	4.1250	104,775	64		
														39422	4.2188	107,158	28		
														39433	4.3330	110,058	29		
2.3622	2.6250	4.2500	4.3307	29500	4650 / 8850 / 3670	2080 / 3940 / 1630	1.27	52.0	29582	2.3622	60,000		27	29520	4.2500	107,950	28		166
60,000	66,675	107,950	110,000						29585	2.5000	63,500		28	29520B	4.2500	107,950	64		
									29586	2.5000	63,500		28	29522	4.2500	107,950	27		
									29588	†2.5591	†65,000		30	29521	4.3307	110,000	28		
									29590	2.6250	66,675		30	29521B	4.3307	110,000	64		
2.3622	2.7500	5.7500		H913800	8900 / 17000 / 11900	3960 / 7550 / 5300	0.75	61.7	H913840	†2.3622	†60,000		27	H913810	5.7500	146,050	27		167
60,000	69,850	146,050							H913842	2.4375	61,912		28						
									H913843	2.4375	61,912		28						
									H913849	2.7500	69,850		32						
2.3750		6.0000		HH814500	14600 / 27800 / 12200	6500 / 12400 / 5400	1.20	104.	HH814542	2.3750	60,325		28	HH814510	6.0000	152,400	28		172
60,325		152,400																	
2.3750	2.4700	3.9370	4.0000	28900	4550 / 8650 / 3310	2020 / 3840 / 1470	1.37	46.2	28985	2.3750	60,325		27	28921	3.9370	100,000	27		168
60,325	62,738	100,000	101,600						28990	2.4400	61,976		28	28921B	3.9370	100,000	63		
									28995	2.4700	62,738		28	28921D	3.9370	100,000		24	
														28921DC	3.9370	100,000		24	
														28920	4.0000	101,600	28		

BEARING SELECTION INDEX

Index (summary)

Bore range, in	Bore range, mm	Part No.	OD range, in	OD range, mm	Factor	Factor
2.3750 — 3.0000	60.325 — 76.200	9200	6.3750 — 5.5000	161.925 — 139.700	0.82	79.9
2.3750 — 3.0625	60.325 — 77.788	H715300	5.3750 — 5.5000	136.525 — 139.700	1.24	109.
2.4375 — 2.6875	61.912 — 68.262	9100	6.0000	152.400	0.89	69.3
2.5000	63.500	LL510700	3.6250	92.075	1.44	27.1
2.5000	63.500	L610500	3.7188	94.458	1.38	42.8
2.5000 — 2.8125	63.500 — 71.438	H414200	5.3750	136.525	1.62	88.5
2.5000 — 2.9062	63.500 — 73.817	565	5.0000 — 5.1181	127.000 — 130.000	1.61	78.3
2.5000 — 3.3475	63.500 — 85.026	745	5.9055 — 6.1250	150.000 — 155.575	1.80	123.

Load ratings (as listed per family)

Part No.	Ratings
9200	5300 / 2360 — 5100 9700 6200 — 11500 21800 14000
H715300	5300 10100 4280 — 11900 22700 9600
9100	4850 9200 5450 — 10900 20700 12200
LL510700	750 1425 520 — 1680 3200 1170 — 3070 5850 2220
L610500	1365 2600 990 — 3070 5850 2220
H414200	4850 9250 3000 — 10900 20800 6750
565	3660 6950 2280 — 8250 15700 5100
745	5850 11200 3260 — 13200 25100 7350

Detail listing

Part No.	Bore, in	Bore, mm	OD, in	OD, mm	Width	Page
HM212047 / HM212049	2.5000 / 2.6250	63.500 / 66.675	6.3750	161.925	29 / 31	169
9275 / 9285	2.3750 / 3.0000	60.325 / 76.200	6.3750	161.925	28 / 35	170
9220 / 92200 / 92218B			6.3750	161.925	28 / 65	170
H715332	2.3750	60.325	5.3750	136.525	28	171
H715334	2.4375	61.912			28	171
H715336	2.5000	63.500			29	171
H715340	2.5625	65.088			30	171
H715341	2.6250	66.675			31	171
H715341A	2.6250	66.675			31	171
H715343	2.6875	68.262			31	171
H715344	2.7500	69.850			32	171
H715345	2.8125	71.438			33	171
H715348	3.0625	77.788			36	171
H715311 / H715310 / H715310B			5.3750 / 5.5000	136.525 / 139.700	28 / 65	171
9180 / 9185	2.4375 / 2.6875	61.912 / 68.262	6.0000	152.400	28	173
9121			6.0000	152.400	28	173
LL510749	2.5000	63.500	3.6250	92.075	28	174
LL510710			3.6250	92.075	28	174
L610549	2.5000	63.500	3.7188	94.458	28	175
L610510			3.7188	94.458	28	175
H414215	2.5000	63.500	5.3750	136.525	29	177
H414242	2.6250	66.675			31	177
H414245	2.6875	68.262			31	177
H414245X	2.6875	68.262			31	177
H414249	2.8125	71.438			33	177
H414210			5.3750	136.525	29	177
585	2.5000	63.500	5.0000	127.000	29	176
569	2.5576	64.963			29	176
570	2.6875	68.262			31	176
566	2.7500	69.850			32	176
5665	2.7500	69.850			32	176
567A	2.8125	71.438			33	176
567B	2.8125	71.438			33	176
567	2.8750	73.025			33	176
567X	2.8750	73.025			33	176
NA567	2.8750	73.025			33	176
568	2.9062	73.817			34	176
563			5.0000 / 5.1181	127.000 / 130.000	29 / 65	176
563B			5.0000	127.000		176
563D			5.0000	127.000		176
563DC			5.0000	127.000	29	176
563X			5.0000	127.000	29	176
562X			5.1181	130.000	31	176
743			5.9055	150.000	29	178
742			5.9090	150.089	32	178
742B			5.9090	150.089	65	178
742B			6.1250	155.575		178
742BC			6.1250	155.575		178
745S	2.5000	63.500	5.9055	150.000	29	178
745A	2.7500	69.850			32	178
744	3.0000	76.200			34	178
748S	3.0000	76.200			35	178
750	3.1250	79.375			36	178
740	3.1875	80.962			36	178
749M	3.2500	82.550			37	178
750A	3.2500	82.550			37	178
749	3.3475	85.026			38	178
748S	3.3475	85.026			38	178

†Dimension shown is maximum value—see note at bottom of fitting practice table in Reference Tables.
*For 'J' part tolerances—see metric tolerance and fitting practice in Reference Tables.

BEARING SELECTION INDEX

The following index of bearing series is listed by increasing bore size.

The bearing type and specific cone or cup dimensions are located on the page reference number indicated.

bore range min	max	outside diameter range min	max	series number	rating at 500 RPM for 3000 hours L10 — one-row radial thrust / two-row radial thrust lb	daN	factor K	factor G	cone number	cone bore inch	cone bore metric	TS or TSL	SS or SR	TBI or TDIT	TNA and TNADC	THASW or TNASWE	cup number	cup outside diameter inch	cup outside diameter metric	TS or TSF	TDO or TDODC	page ref. sheet no.
2.5591	65.000	4.1339	105.000	LM710900	4450 / 8500 / 3450	1980 / 3780 / 1535	1.29	43.2	JLM710949	*2.5591	*65.000	30	2				JLM710910	*4.1339	*105.000	30		179
2.5591	65.000	4.3307	110.000	M511900	5900 / 11200 / 4050	2620 / 5000 / 1800	1.45	57.8	JM511946	*2.5591	*65.000	30	2				JM511910	*4.3307	*110.000	30		180
2.5591	65.000	4.7244	120.000	H211700	9200 / 17500 / 5300	4100 / 7800 / 2360	1.73	73.7	JH211749 / JH211749A	*2.5591 / *2.5591	*65.000 / *65.000	30 / 30	2				JH211710	*4.7244	*120.000	30		181
2.6250	66.675	4.0635	103.213	L812100	2800 / 5350 / 2340	1245 / 2380 / 1040	1.20	33.9	L812148	2.6250	66.675	30					L812111	4.0635	103.213	30		182
2.6250	66.675	7.0000	177.800	HH914400	14800 / 28200 / 20300	6600 / 12550 / 9000	0.73	88.4	HH914449	2.6250	66.675	31					HH914412	7.0000	177.800	31		183
2.7500	69.850	3.8750	98.425	LL713000	1780 / 3400 / 1340	795 / 1510 / 595	1.33	31.6	LL713049	2.7500	69.850	31					LL713010	3.8750	98.425	31		184
2.7500	69.850	4.0000 — 4.0625	101.600 — 103.188	L713000	3110 / 5950 / 2450	1385 / 2640 / 1090	1.27	48.1	L713049	2.7500	69.850	31					L713010 / L713012	4.0000 / 4.0625	101.600 / 103.188	31 / 31		185
2.7500	69.850	4.4375	112.712	LM613400	4150 / 7900 / 2950	1840 / 3500 / 1315	1.40	47.1	LM613449	2.7500	69.850	32					LM613410	4.4375	112.712	32		186
2.7500 — 2.8125	69.850 — 71.438	4.7244	120.000	47400	7600 / 14500 / 4700	3380 / 6450 / 2080	1.62	75.5	47487 / 47490	2.7500 / 2.8125	69.850 / 71.438	32 / 33					47420 / 47420D / 47420DC	4.7244 / 4.7244 / 4.7244	120.000 / 120.000 / 120.000	32	25 / 25	189
2.7500 — 2.8125	69.850 — 71.438	5.7500	146.050	HM914500	6950 / 13300 / 11200	3100 / 5900 / 5000	0.62	56.0	HM914545 / HM914549	2.7500 / 2.8125	69.850 / 71.438	32 / 33					HM914510	5.7500	146.050	32		188
2.7500 — 2.9062	69.850 — 73.817	4.4375 — 4.7500	112.712 — 120.650	29600	4900 / 9350 / 4100	2180 / 4160 / 1820	1.20	58.8	29675 / 29680 / 29685 / 29688	2.7500 / 2.7810 / 2.8750 / 2.9062	69.850 / 70.637 / 73.025 / 73.817	32 / 33 / 33 / 34					29620 / 29620B / 29622D / 29622DC / 29630	4.4375 / 4.4375 / 4.4995 / 4.4995 / 4.7500	112.712 / 112.712 / 114.287 / 114.287 / 120.650	32 / 64 / / / 33	25 / 25	187
2.7500 — 3.3750	69.850 — 85.725	5.7500 — 6.0000	146.050 — 152.400	655	10300 / 19500 / 7150	4600 / 8650 / 3180	1.43	104.	655 / 658 / 659 / N4659 / 661 / 663 / 663A	2.7500 / 2.9375 / 3.0000 / 3.0000 / 3.1250 / 3.2500 / 3.2500	69.850 / 74.612 / 76.200 / 76.200 / 79.375 / 82.550 / 82.550	32 / 34 / 35 / 36 / 37 / 37			38		653 / 653X / 652 / 652B / 653B / 654D / 654DC	5.7500 / 5.9055 / 6.0000 / 6.0000 / 6.0000 / 6.0000 / 6.0000	146.050 / 150.000 / 152.400 / 152.400 / 152.400 / 152.400 / 152.400	32 / 34 / 35 / 65	25 / 25	190

Bore range (in / mm)	OD range (in / mm)	Cone	Cup	A (in)	A (mm)	W	Part no.	Bore (in)	Bore (mm)	W	Page
69.850 — 88.900	168.275		8328	6.6250	168.275	66	837 / 843 / 838 / 842 / 841 / 850	3.0000 / 3.0000 / 3.1875 / 3.2500 / 3.3750 / 3.5000	76.200 / 76.200 / 80.962 / 82.550 / 85.725 / 88.900	35 / 35 / 36 / 37 / 38 / 39	191
2.7540 — 3.0625 / 69.952 — 77.788	4.7812 — 5.0000 / 121.442 — 127.000	34000	34478	4.7812	121.442	32	34274	2.7540	69.952	32	192
			34478D	4.7812	121.442	25	34275	2.7559	70.000	32	
			34478DC	4.7812	121.442	25	34300	3.0000	76.200	34	
			34481B	4.8125	122.238	64	34301	3.0000	76.200	34	
			34492A	4.9233	125.052	32	34306	3.0625	77.788	35	
			34500	5.0000	127.000	34	34307	3.0625	77.788	35	
2.7559 / 70.000	4.3307 / 110.090	LM813000	ILM813010	*4.3307	*110.000	32	ILM813049	*2.7559	*70.000	32	193 (2)
2.7559 / 70.000	4.5276 / 115.000	M612900	JM612910	*4.5276	*115.000	32	JM612849	*2.7559	*70.000	32	194 (4)
2.7559 / 70.000	6.9375 / 176.212	H916800	H916610	6.9375	176.212	33	H916642	†2.7559	†70.000	33	195
2.8125 — 3.2500 / 71.438 — 82.550	5.2500 / 133.350	47600	47620	5.2500	133.350	34	47675	2.8125	71.438	33	197
			47620A	5.2500	133.350	33	47678	3.0000	76.200	34	
			47620B	5.2500	133.350	65	47679	3.0000	76.200	34	
							47680	3.0000	76.200	34	
							47681	3.1875	80.962	36	
							47685	3.2500	82.550	37	
							47686	3.2500	82.550	37	
							47687	3.2500	82.550	37	
2.8125 — 3.3750 / 71.438 — 85.725	5.2500 — 5.3750 / 133.350 — 136.525	495	492A	5.2500	133.350	33	495S	2.8125	71.438	33	196
			493	5.3750	136.525	35	495A	3.0000	76.200	24	
			493B	5.3750	136.525	65	495AX	3.0000	76.200	36	
			4930	5.3750	136.525	25	495AS	3.0625	77.788	36	
			4930C	5.3750	136.525	25	496	3.1875	80.962	36	
							4960	3.2500	82.550	36	
							495	3.3125	84.138	37	
							498	3.3750	85.725	38	
							497	3.3750	85.725		
						44	NA4975SW	3.3750	85.725	9	
2.8750 — 4.7500 / 117.475 — 120.650	4.6250 — 4.7500	LM814800	LM814810	4.6250	117.475	33	LM814845	2.8750	73.025	33	199
			LM814814	4.7500	120.650	35	LM814849	3.0625	77.788	35	
2.8750 — 3.0625 / 73.025 — 77.788	5.0000 / 127.000	42600	42620	5.0000	127.000	33	42683	2.8750	73.025	33	200
			42620B	5.0000	127.000	65	42687	3.0000	76.200	34	
							42688	3.0000	76.200	34	
							42690	3.0625	77.788	36	
2.8750 — 3.2813 / 73.025 — 83.345	4.9375 / 125.412	27600	27620	4.9375	125.412	33	27680	2.8750	73.025	33	198
			27620B	4.9375	125.412	65	27684	3.0000	76.200	34	
							27687	3.2500	82.550	36	
							27689	3.2813	83.345	37	
							27690	3.2813	83.345	37	
							27691	3.2813	83.345	37	1

Load ratings (lb): 32300 / 14350 / 8700 / 3860 · 4250 / 8100 / 3270 (1900 3600 1455, 1.30) · 4900 / 9400 / 4100 (2200 4180 1820, 1.20) · 6150 / 11700 / 4500 (2740 5200 2020, 1.36) · 14400 / 27500 / 17200 (6450 12250 7650, 0.84) · 7850 / 14900 / 5450 (3500 6550 2420, 1.44) · 6550 / 12500 / 5000 (2920 5550 2220, 1.31) · 5150 / 9800 / 4450 (2280 4360 1980, 1.15) · 6750 / 12900 / 4850 (3000 5750 2160, 1.39) · 5150 / 9850 / 3690 (2300 4380 1640, 1.40)

53.5 · 54.7 · 58.4 · 102. · 89.9 · 78.9 · 65.0 · 73.5 · 73.2

*For "†" part tolerances—see metric tolerance and fitting practice in Reference Tables.
†Dimension shown is maximum value—see note at bottom of fitting practice table in Reference Tables.

BEARING SELECTION INDEX

The following index of bearing series is listed by increasing bore size.

The bearing type and specific cone or cup dimensions are located on the page reference number indicated.

Series 575 — bore range 2.8750–3.3518 / 73.025–85.136; outside diameter range 5.5000–5.5115 / 139.700–139.992; rating at 500 RPM for 3000 hours L10: lb 8800 / 16800 / 6100, daN 3920 / 7500 / 2700; factor K 1.45; factor G 95.2; dimension sheet page 201

cone number	cone bore inch	cone bore metric	TS or TSL	SS or SR	TDI or TDIT	TNA and TNADC	TNASW or TNASWE
576	2.8750	73.025	33				
577	2.9375	74.612	34				
575	3.0000	76.200	35				
575S	3.0000	76.200	35				
581	3.1875	80.962	36				
581D	3.1875	80.962			9		
580	3.2500	82.550	37				
NA580SW	3.2500	82.550					44
582	3.2500	82.550	37				
579TD	3.3518	85.136			17		

cup number	cup outside diameter inch	cup outside diameter metric	TS or TSF	TDO or TDODC
572X	5.5000	139.700	33	
572	5.5115	139.992	34	
572B	5.5115	139.992	65	
5720	5.5115	139.992		25
5720C	5.5115	139.992		25

Series 755 — bore range 2.8750–3.5625 / 73.025–90.488; outside diameter range 6.3750–6.6250 / 161.925–168.275; rating at 500 RPM for 3000 hours L10: lb 13800 / 26200 / 6050, daN 6100 / 11650 / 3580; factor K 1.71; factor G 136.; dimension sheet page 202

cone number	cone bore inch	cone bore metric	TS or TSL	SS or SR	TDI or TDIT	TNA and TNADC	TNASW or TNASWE
782XA	2.8750	73.025	34				
755	3.0000	76.200	35				
756A	3.1250	79.375	36				
757	3.2500	82.550	37				
758	3.3750	85.725	38				
759	3.5000	88.900	39				
NA759	3.5000	88.900				38	
NA759SW	3.5000	88.900					44
766	3.5000	88.900	39				
7670	3.5000	88.900	39		10		
767X	3.5433	90.000	39				
760	3.5625	90.488	39				

cup number	cup outside diameter inch	cup outside diameter metric	TS or TSF	TDO or TDODC
752	6.3750	161.925	34	
752B	6.3750	161.925	65	
752D	6.3750	161.925		25
752DC	6.3750	161.925		25
753	6.6250	168.275	35	

Series LM714100 — bore range 2.9528–75.000; outside diameter range 4.5276–115.000; rating at 500 RPM for 3000 hours L10: lb 4950 / 9450 / 3900, daN 2200 / 4200 / 1735; factor K 1.27; factor G 57.1; dimension sheet page 203

cone number	cone bore inch	cone bore metric	SS or SR
LM714149	2.9528	*75.000 (TS/TSL 34)	4

cup number	cup outside diameter inch	cup outside diameter metric	TS or TSF
JLM714110	*4.5276	*115.000	34

Series M714200 — bore range 2.9528–75.000; outside diameter range 4.7244–120.000; rating at 500 RPM for 3000 hours L10: lb 6750 / 12900 / 5150, daN 3020 / 5750 / 2300; factor K 1.31; factor G 70.9; dimension sheet page 204

cone number	cone bore inch	cone bore metric	TS or TSL	SS or SR
JM714249	*2.9528	*75.000	34	4

cup number	cup outside diameter inch	cup outside diameter metric	TS or TSF
JM714210	*4.7244	*120.000	34

Series H415600 — bore range 2.9528–75.000; outside diameter range 5.7087–145.000; rating at 500 RPM for 3000 hours L10: lb 14700 / 28000 / 9100, daN 6550 / 12450 / 4060; factor K 1.61; factor G 121.; dimension sheet page 205

cone number	cone bore inch	cone bore metric	TS or TSL	SS or SR
JH415647	*2.9528	*75.000	34	4

cup number	cup outside diameter inch	cup outside diameter metric	TS or TSF
JH415610	*5.7087	*145.000	34

Series LL714600 — bore range 3.0000–76.200; outside diameter range 4.1563–105.570; rating at 500 RPM for 3000 hours L10: lb 1840 / 3510 / 1480, daN 820 / 1560 / 660; factor K 1.24; factor G 35.8; dimension sheet page 206

cone number	cone bore inch	cone bore metric	TS or TSL
LL714649	3.0000	76.200	34

cup number	cup outside diameter inch	cup outside diameter metric	TS or TSF
LL714610	4.1563	105.570	34

Series L814700 — bore range 3.0000–76.200; outside diameter range 4.3125–109.538; rating at 500 RPM for 3000 hours L10: lb 3270 / 6250 / 2820, daN 1455 / 2780 / 1255; factor K 1.16; factor G 56.0; dimension sheet page 207

cone number	cone bore inch	cone bore metric	TS or TSL
L814749	3.0000	76.200	34

cup number	cup outside diameter inch	cup outside diameter metric	TS or TSF
L814710	4.3125	109.538	34

Series 5700 — bore range 3.0000–3.0625 / 76.200–77.788; outside diameter range 5.3438–135.733; rating at 500 RPM for 3000 hours L10: lb 11200 / 21400 / 7800, daN 5000 / 9550 / 3480; factor K 1.44; factor G 109.; dimension sheet page 210

cone number	cone bore inch	cone bore metric	TS or TSL
5760	3.0000	76.200	35
5795	3.0625	77.788	36

cup number	cup outside diameter inch	cup outside diameter metric	TS or TSF
5735	5.3438	135.733	35

This is a Timken bearing selection index table. Bearings are grouped by reference page (shown at right). Within each group, cup and cone part numbers are listed with their bore/outside-diameter dimensions in inches and millimetres.

Part Number	Dim (in)	Dim (mm)	Code	Ref. Page
Group — bore range 133,350—136,525 / 76,200—82,550				**209**
HM516414B	5.3750	136,525	65	
HM516447	3.1875	80,962	36	
HM516448	3.2500	82,550	37	
HM516449	3.2500	82,550	37	
HM516410B				
Group — 171,450—177,800 / 76,200—82,550				**212**
H917810	7.1250	180,975	35	
H917840	3.0000	76,200	35	
H917849	3.2500	82,550	37	
H917800				
Group — 6.7500—7.0000 / 171,450—177,800				**211**
9321	6.7500	171,450	35	
9320	7.0000	177,800	35	
93200	7.0000	177,800	37	
9378	3.0000	76,200	35	
NA9378	3.0000	76,200	38	
9380	3.0000	76,200	35	
9385	3.3125	84,138	37	
9300				
Group — 6.2992—6.3750 / 160,000—161,925				**213**
6525X	6.2992	160,000	35	
6535	6.3750	161,925	35	
6535B	6.3750	161,925	65	
6536	6.3750	161,925	35	
6575	3.0000	76,200	35	
6576	3.0000	76,200	35	
6559	3.2500	82,550	37	
6560	3.5000	88,900	37	
6581X	3.5433	90,000	39	
6525				
6500				
Group — 5.8125—6.0000 / 147,638—152,400				**208**
592XE	5.8125	147,638	35	
592XS	5.9055	150,000	36	
593X	6.0000	152,400	37	
592A	6.0000	152,400	38	
592B	6.0000	152,400	65	
592D	6.0000	152,400		
592DC	6.0000	152,400		
590A	3.0000	76,200	35	
595A	3.1250	79,375	36	
595	3.2500	82,550	37	
596	3.3750	85,725	38	
593	3.5000	88,900	39	
593A	3.5000	88,900	39	
NA595SW	3.5000	88,900		
597X	3.5433	90,000	39	
598	3.6250	92,075	39	
598A	3.6250	92,075	39	
598X	3.6250	92,075	40	
597	3.6875	93,662	40	
594	3.7500	95,250	40	
594A	3.7500	95,250	40	
595			44	
Group — 7.5000 / 190,500 ; 3.0000—4.0000 / 76,200—101,600				**214**
HH221410	7.5000	190,500	35	
HH221410D	7.5000	190,500	36	
HH221410DC	7.5000	190,500	38	
HH221430	3.0000	76,200	35	
HH221431	3.1250	79,375	36	
HH221432	3.4375	87,312	38	
HH221434	3.5000	88,900	39	
HH221440	3.7500	95,250	41	
HH221442	3.8750	98,425	41	
HH221447	3.9363	99,982	41	
HH221449	4.0000	101,600	42	
HH221449TD	4.0000	101,600	17	
HH221400				
Group — 5.1181 / 130,000 ; 3.1496 / 80,000				**215**
JM515610	*5.1181	*130,000	35	
JM515649	3.1496	80,000	36	
M515600			4	
Group — 5.7874—6.0000 / 147,000—152,400 ; 3.1496—3.5433 / 80,000—90,000				**216**
HM218210	15.7874	†147,000	36	
HM218215	6.0000	152,400	39	
HM218238	3.1496	†80,000	36	
HM218248	3.5433	†90,000	39	
HM218200				
Group — 7.8740—7.8750 / 200,000—200,025 ; 3.1496—4.0000 / 80,000—101,600				**217**
98788	7.8740	200,000	36	
98789B	7.8740	200,000	38	
98790D	7.8750	200,025	39	
98790DC	7.8750	200,025	41	
98788B	7.8750	200,025	42	
98316	3.1496	80,000	36	
98335	3.3465	85,000	38	
98350	3.5000	88,900	39	
98394X	3.9370	100,000	41	
98400	4.0000	101,600	42	
98000				
Group — 4.5625 / 115,888 ; 3.2500 / 82,550				**218**
L116110	4.5625	115,888	36	
L116110B	4.5625	115,888	64	
L116149	3.2500	82,550	36	
L116100				

*For "J" part tolerances—see metric tolerance and fitting practice in Reference Tables.
†Dimension shown is maximum value—see note at bottom of fitting practice table in Reference Tables.

The following index of bearing series is listed by increasing bore size.

The bearing type and specific cone or cup dimensions are located on the page reference number indicated.

bore range min	bore range max	OD range min	OD range max	series number	500 RPM 3000h L10 one-row radial thrust lb	daN	two-row radial thrust lb	daN	factor K	factor G	cone number	cone bore inch	cone bore metric	TS or TSL	SS or SR	TDI or TDIT	TNA and TNADC	TNA and TNADC	TNASW or TNASWE	cup number	cup OD inch	cup OD metric	TS or TSF	TDO and TDODC	dim sheet page no.
3.3465	85,000	5.1181	130,000	M716600	7100	3160	13500 / 5400	6000 / 2400	1.31	87.1	JM716648	*3.3465	*85,000	37	4					JM716610	*5.1181	*130.000	37		219
											JM716649	*3.3465	*85,000	37											
3.3465	85,000	5.5118	140,000	HM516800	10300	4550	19500 / 7150	8700 / 3200	1.43	106.	JHM516849	*3.3465	*85,000	38	4					JHM516810	*5.5118	*140.000	38		220
3.3465	85,000	5.9055	150,000	H217200	13900	6200	26500 / 7900	11800 / 3520	1.76	129.	JH217249	*3.3465	*85,000	38	4					JH217210	*5.9055	*150.000	38		222
3.3465 / 85,000	3.8125 / 96,838	-7.4375	188,912	90000	12900	5750	24600 / 19200	10950 / 8550	0.67	113.	90334	3.3465	85,000	38						90744	7.4375	188.912	38		221
											90381	3.8125	96,838	41											
3.3750	85,725	5.5960	142,138	HM617000	11600	5150	22100 / 8600	9850 / 3820	1.35	121.	HM617049	3.3750	85,725	38						HM617010	5.5960	142.138	38		224
3.3750 / 85,725	4.0000 / 101,600	6.6250 / 168,275	6.6929 / 170,000	675	11500	5100	21900 / 9250	9700 / 4120	1.24	136.	677	3.3750	85,725	38						672	6.6250	168.275	38	25	223
											679	3.5000	88,900	39						672B	6.6250	168.275	39		
											681	3.6250	92,075	40						672D	6.6250	168.275	40		
											681A	3.6250	92,075	40						672DC	6.6250	168.275	40	25	
											683	3.7500	95,250	40						673X	6.6929	170.000	39		
											685	3.8750	98,425	40											
											686TD	3.9453	100,211	41		17									
											687	4.0000	101,600	41											
											NA691	4.0000	101,600				39								
											NA691SW	4.0000	101,600						44						
3.4375 / 87,312	4.0000 / 101,600	7.5000	190,500	855	19300	8600	36900 / 11100	16400 / 4950	1.74	200.	869	3.4375	87,312	38						854	7.5000	190.500	38	25	225
											855	3.5000	88,900	39						854B	7.5000	190.500	66		
											857	3.6250	92,075	40						854D	7.5000	190.500	40		
											864	3.7500	95,250	40						854DC	7.5000	190.500		25	
											866	3.8750	98,425	41											
											861	4.0000	101,600	42											
											868D	4.0000	101,600			10									
3.4630 / 87,960	3.8125 / 96,838	5.8437 / 148,430	5.8750 / 149,225	42000	7100	3160	13600 / 6000	6050 / 2660	1.19	96.7	42346	3.4630	87,960	38						42584	5.8437	148.430	38		226
											42350	3.5000	88,900	39						42587	5.8750	149.225	39		
											42362	3.6250	92,075	40						42587B	5.8750	149.225	65		
											42362D	3.6250	92,075			10				42587D	5.8750	149.225		25	
											42368	3.6875	93,662	40						42587DC	5.8750	149.225		25	
											42375	3.7500	95,250	40											
											42376	3.7500	95,250	40											
											42381	3.8125	96,838	41											
3.5000	88,900	4.7812	121,442	LL217800	2600	1160	4950 / SEE	2200	1.77	56.2	LL217849	3.5000	88,900	38						LL217810	4.7812	121.442	38		227

Bearing Selection Index — detail (cone/cup assemblies)

Page	Cone No.	Bore (in)	Bore (mm)	Cup No.	O.D. (in)	O.D. (mm)
228		3.5000	88,900	L217810D / L217810DC / L217813	4.8750 / 4.8750 / 5.0000	123,825 / 123,825 / 127,000
229	77350 / 77375	3.5000 / 3.7500	88,900 / 95,250	77675 / 77676X	6.7500	171,450
230	HM921343	3.5400	89,916	HM921310D / HM921310DC	7.4790	189,967
231	M919048 / M919049	3.5425	89,980	M919010D	6.3740	161,900
232	JM718149	*3.5433	*90,000	JM718110	*5.7087	*145,000
233	JHM318448	*3.5433	*90,000	JHM318410	*6.1024	*155,000
—	LM718947	†3.6220	†92,000	LM718910	5.6250	142,875
—	47890 / 47896	3.6250 / 3.7500	92,075 / 95,250	47625B / 47820	5.6250 / 5.7500	142,875 / 146,050
234	778	3.6250	92,075	773D	7.0866	180,000
234	776	3.7500	95,250	773DC	7.0866	180,000
234	NA776	3.7500	95,250	772	7.1250	180,975
234	779	3.8750	98,425	772B	7.1250	180,975
234	783	3.9370	100,000	774D	7.1250	180,975
234	780	4.0000	101,600	774DC	7.1250	180,975
234	NA780 / 782 / NA782 / 786 / 787	4.1250	104,775			
235	JM719149	*3.7402	*95,000	JM719113	*5.9055	*150,000
236	LL319349	3.7500	95,250	LL319310	5.0625	128,588
237	L319249	3.7500	95,250	L319210 / L319210D	5.1250	130,175
238	52375	3.7500	95,250	52618	6.1875	157,162
238	NA52375	3.7500	95,250	52630XB	6.2992	160,000
238	52387	3.8750	98,425	52637	6.3750	161,925
238	52393	3.9375	100,012	52637B	6.3750	161,925
238	52394TD	3.9453	100,211	52637D	6.3750	161,925
238	52400 / 52401	4.0000	101,600	52637DC	6.3750	161,925

Special dimension notes:
- "B"=1.4375 / 36,512 "R"=.14 / 3,5 "0b"=4.61 / 117,0
- "B"=1.1875 / 30,162 "R"=.34 / 3,5 "0b"=4.29 / 109,0
- "B"=1.1875 / 30,162 "R"=.08 / 2,0 "0b"=4.17 / 106,0

Bearing Selection Index — ratings summary (by cone)

Cone No.	Max O.D. (in / mm)	Rating	Rating	Factor	Factor
77000	6.7500 / 171,450	14300 / 27300 / 16800	6400 / 12150 / 4000	1.59	154
HM921300	7.4790 / 189,967	11200 / 21400 / 16800	5000 / 9500 / 7450	0.67	105
M919000	6.3740 / 161,900	7900 / 15000 / 9850	3500 / 6700 / 4380	0.80	77.9
M718100	5.7087 / 145,000	9450 / 18000 / 7200	4200 / 8000 / 3200	1.31	103
HM318400	6.1024 / 155,000	13800 / 26200 / 8050	6100 / 11650 / 3580	1.71	136
LM718900	5.6250 / 142,875	6950 / 13200 / 5700	3080 / 5850 / 2520	1.22	91.0
47800	5.6250 / 142,875	8750 / 16700 / 6750	3900 / 7400 / 3000	1.30	113
775	7.0866—7.1250 / 180,000—180,975	14900 / 28300 / 9850	6600 / 12600 / 4380	1.51	170
M719100	5.9055 / 150,000	9350 / 17900 / 7600	4160 / 7950 / 3160	1.32	113
LL319200	5.0625 / 128,588	2760 / 5250 / 1660	1225 / 2340 / 740	1.66	64.1
L319200	5.1250 / 130,175	4450 / 8500 / 2670	1980 / 3780 / 1190	1.67	91.6
52000	6.1875—6.3750 / 157,162—161,925	9900 / 18800 / 8050	4400 / 8400 / 3580	1.23	129

†Dimension shown is maximum value—see note at bottom of fitting practice table in Reference Tables.
*For "J" part tolerances—see metric tolerance and fitting practice in Reference Tables.

BEARING SELECTION INDEX

The following index of bearing series is listed by increasing bore size.

The bearing type and specific cone or cup dimensions are located on the page reference number indicated.

bore range (min. – max.)	outside diameter range (min. – max.)	series number	rating at 500 RPM for 3000 hours L10 one-row radial / two-row radial / thrust (lb; daN)	fac-tor K	fac-tor G	cone number	cone bore (inch; metric)	page ref. CONES TS or TSL	SS or SR	TDI or TDIT	TNA and TNADC	TNASW or TNASWE	cup number	cup outside diameter (inch; metric)	page ref. CUPS TS or TSF	TDO and TDODC	dimension sheet page no.
3.8750 / 98,425	7.2500 / 184,150	HH421200	23200; 44000; 14900 / 10350; 19600; 6600	1.56	222.	HH421246	3.8750 / 98,425	41					HH421210	7.2500 / 184,150	41		239
3.9060 / 99,212	6.7500 / 171,450	HM321200	14800; 28300; 8750 / 6600; 12600; 3880	1.70	168.	HM321245	3.9060 / 99,212	41					HM321210	6.7500 / 171,450	41		240
3.9362 / 99,979	5.9048 / 149,982	LM820000	7100; 13500; 6100 / 3160; 6000; 2720	1.16	98.8	LM820048	3.9362 / 99,979	41					LM820012	5.9048 / 149,982	41		241
3.9362 / 99,979	7.7500 / 196,850	HM821500	14600; 27800; 15200 / 6500; 12350; 6750	0.96	128.	HM821547	3.9362 / 99,979		"B"=1.8125 / 46,038	"R"=.14 / 3.5	"G"=4.84 / 123.0		HM821510D / HM821511D	7.7500 / 196,850		26	242
3.9370 / 100,000	*6.1024 / *155,000	M720200	10100; 19200; 8100 / 4480; 8550; 3620	1.24	127.	JM720249	*3.9370 / *100,000	41	6				JM720210	*6.1024 / *155,000	41		243
3.9370 / 100,000	*6.2992 / *160,000	HM720200	12200; 23300; 9850 / 5450; 10350; 4380	1.24	139.	JHM720249	*3.9370 / *100,000	41	6				JHM720210	*6.2992 / *160,000	41		243
4.0000 / 101,600	5.3125 / 134,938	LL420500	2800; 5350; 1770 / 1245; 2380; 790	1.58	69.4	LL420549	4.0000 / 101,600	41					LL420510	5.3125 / 134,938	41		244
4.0000 / 101,600	5.3750 / 136,525	L420400	4600; 8800; 2900 / 2060; 3920; 1290	1.59	101.	L420449	4.0000 / 101,600	41					L420410	5.3750 / 136,525	41		245
4.0000 / 101,600	7.0000 / 177,800	LM921800	6950; 13300; 13900 / 3100; 5900; 6200	0.50	85.2	LM921845	4.0000 / 101,600	42					LM921810	7.0000 / 177,800	42		247
4.0000 / 101,600	9.8750 / 250,825	HH923600	27900; 53000; 33200 / 12400; 23600; 14750	0.84	215.	HH923649	4.0000 / 101,600	42					HH923610 / HH923611	9.8750 / 250,825 / 9.8750 / 250,825	42 / 42		251
4.0000 — 4.2500 / 101,600 — 107,950	5.7500 / 146,050	L521900	4700; 8900; 3140 / 2080; 3960; 1400	1.49	111.	L521945 / L521949	4.0000 / 101,600 / 4.2500 / 107,950	41 / 42					L521910 / L521910D / L521910DC	5.7500 / 146,050	41	26 / 26	246
4.0000 — 4.3750 / 101,600 — 111,125	8.4375 / 214,312	H924000	19200; 36600; 22100 / 8550; 16250; 9800	0.87	183.	H924033 / H924045	4.0000 / 101,600 / 4.3750 / 111,125	42 / 43					H924010 / H924010D	8.4375 / 214,312	42	26	248
4.0000 — 4.5000 / 101,600 — 114,300	8.3750 / 212,725	935	24300; 46500; 13600 / 10800; 20600; 6050	1.79	256.	941 / 936 / 946D / 942 / 938 / NA938	4.0000 / 101,600; 4.2500 / 107,950; 4.2500 / 107,950; 4.3307 / 110,000; 4.5000 / 114,300; 4.5000 / 114,300	42 / 43 / 42 / 43 / 43	10			39	932 / 932B / 932D / 932DC	8.3750 / 212,725	42 / 66	26 / 26	249

DEARING SELECTION INDEX

Bore in.	Bore mm	Cone No.	Bore in. / mm	Basic Load Ratings	Factor	Page ref.	Cup No.	O.D. in. / mm	O.D. mm			Page
4.0000 — 4.5000	101.600 — 114.300	**HH224300**	8.3750 / 212.725	28300 / 54000 / 15800 — 12600 — 1.79		278.	**HH224310**	8.3750	212.725	101.600	42	253
		HH224335	4.0000 / 101.600				HH224310D	8.3750	212.725	107.950	42	26
		HH224340	4.2500 / 107.950				HH224310DC	8.3750	212.725	114.300	43	26
		HH224346	4.5000 / 114.300									
4.1250 — 4.5625	104.775 — 115.888	**71000**	7.5000 / 190.500	15900 / 30200 / 11300 — 7050 — 1.40		198.	**71750**	7.5000	190.500	104.775	42	254
		71412	4.1250 / 104.775	104.775	42		71750B	7.5000	190.500	107.950	66	
		71425	4.2500 / 107.950	107.950	43		71751D	7.5000	190.500	190.500		27
		71426D	4.2500 / 107.950	107.950	10		71751DC	7.5000	190.500	190.500		27
		71437	4.3750 / 111.125	111.125	43							
		71450	4.5000 / 114.300	114.300	43							
		71450D	4.5000 / 114.300	114.300	10							
		71453	4.5310 / 115.087	115.087	43							
		71455	4.5310 / 115.087	115.087	43							
		71457TD	4.5625 / 115.888	115.888	17							
4.1875 — 4.2500	106.362 — 107.950	**59000**	6.5000 / 165.100	10100 / 19300 / 8600 — 4500 / 8600 / 3820 — 1.18		140.	**56650**	6.5000	165.100	165.100	42	255
		56418	4.1875 / 106.362	106.362	42		56650B	6.5000	165.100	165.100	66	
		56425	4.2500 / 107.950	107.950	42		56650D	6.5000	165.100			
		M86425SW	4.2500 / 107.950		44		56650DC	6.5000	165.100			
4.2500	107.950	**48100**	6.3750 / 161.925	8700 / 16600 / 7500 — 3860 / 7350 / 3340 — 1.16		130.	**48120**	6.3750	161.925	161.925	42	258
		48190	4.2500 / 107.950	107.950	42							
4.2500	107.950	**67000**	6.7500 / 171.450	7950 / 15200 / 6450 — 3540 / 6750 / 2860 — 1.24		112.	**67675**	6.7500	171.450	171.450	42	257
		67425	4.2500 / 107.950	107.950	42		67675B	6.7500	171.450	171.450	66	
4.2500 — 4.3125	107.950 — 109.538	**37000**	6.2500 / 158.750	5050 / 9600 / 5250 — 2240 / 4260 / 2340 — 0.96		90.5	**37625**	6.2500	158.750	158.750	42	256
		37425	4.2500 / 107.950	107.950	42		37625B	6.2500	158.750	158.750	65	
		37431	4.3125 / 109.538	109.538	43		37626D	6.2500	158.750			27
							37626DC	6.2500	158.750			27
4.2500 — 4.3302	107.950 — 109.987	**LM522500**	6.2987 / 159.987	9350 / 17800 / 6450 — 4160 / 7900 / 2860 — 1.45		165.	**LM522510**	6.2987	159.987	159.987	42	259
		LM522546	4.2500 / 107.950	107.950	42		LM522510D	6.2987	159.987	159.987	43	27
		LM522548	4.3302 / 109.987	109.987	43		LM522510DC	6.2987	159.987	159.987	43	27
		LM522548	4.3302 / 109.987	109.987	43							
4.2500 — 4.5276	107.950 — 115.000	**64000**	7.0000 — 7.0866 / 177.800 — 180.000	12100 / 23100 / 10700 — 5400 / 10250 / 4750 — 1.13	"B"=2.8125 "R"=.25 "Ob"=-6.18 / 71,438 ... 6.4 / 157.0	160.	**64700**	7.0000	177.800	109.992	43	260
		64433	4.3304 / 109.992	109.992	43	6		64700B	7.0000	177.800	114.300	66	
		64450	4.5000 / 114.300	114.300	43		64700D	7.0000	177.800	177.800		27
		64452	†4.5276 / †115.000	†115.000	43		64700DC	7.0000	177.800	177.800		27
							64701X	7.0079	178.000	178.000	43	
							64708B	†7.0866	†180.000	*180.000	66	
4.3307	110.000	**M822000**	6.4961 / 165.000	10100 / 19300 / 8600 — 4500 / 8600 / 3820 — 1.18	6	140.	**JM822010**	*6.4961	*165.000	*165.000	43	261
		JM822049	*4.3307 / *110.000	*110.000	43							
4.3307	110.000	**HM522600**	7.0866 / 180.000	16200 / 30800 / 11200 — 7200 / 13700 / 5000 — 1.44		190.	**JHM522610**	*7.0866	*180.000	*180.000	43	262
		JHM522649	*4.3307 / *110.000	*110.000	43							
4.3750	111.125	**HH924300**	9.5000 / 241.300	27600 / 52500 / 34500 — 12250 / 23400 / 15350 — 0.80		229.	**HH924310D**	9.5000	241.300	241.300	43	263
		HH924349	4.3750 / 111.125	111.125	43		HH924310DC	9.5000	241.300	241.300		27
4.5000	114.300	**L623100**	6.0000 / 152.400	4900 / 9350 / 3480 — 2180 / 4160 / 1550 — 1.41		124.	**L623110**	6.0000	152.400	152.400	43	263
		L623149	4.5000 / 114.300	114.300	43							
4.5000 — 4.6250	114.300 — 117.475	**68000**	7.0866 — 7.1250 / 180.000 — 180.975	8200 / 15600 / 6950 — 3640 / 6960 / 3080 — 1.18		122.	**68709**	†7.0866	†180.000	*180.000	43	264
		68450	4.5000 / 114.300	114.300	43		68712	7.1250	180.975	180.975	44	
		68462	4.6250 / 117.475	117.475	44							

†Dimension shown is maximum value—see note at bottom of fitting practice table in Reference Tables.
*For "J" part tolerances—see metric tolerance and fitting practice in Reference Tables.

BEARING SELECTION INDEX

The following index of bearing series is listed by increasing bore size.

The bearing type and specific cone or cup dimensions are located on the page reference number indicated.

bore range (min – max) inch / metric	outside diameter range (min – max) inch / metric	series number	rating at 500 RPM for 3000 hours L10 — one-row radial / two-row radial / thrust (lb)	(daN)	factor K	factor G	cone number	cone bore (inch)	cone bore (metric)	page ref. CONES — TS or TSL	SS or SR	TDI or TDIT	TNA and TNADC	TNASW or TNASWE	cup number	cup OD (inch)	cup OD (metric)	page ref. CUPS — TS or TSF	TDO and TDODC	dimen-sion sheet page no.
4.5000 – 4.7500 / 114,300 – 120,650	10.7500 – 11.0000 / 273,050 – 279,400	HH926700	35900 / 68500 / 39100	16000 / 30400 / 17350	0.92	291.	HH926744	4.5000	114.300	43					HH926710	10.7500	273.050	43		267
							HH926749	4.7500	120.650	44					HH926716	11.0000	279.400	44		
4.5000 – 5.0312 / 114,300 – 127,792	9.0000 / 228,600	HM926700	20500 / 39000 / 25900	9100 / 17350 / 11550	0.79	217.	HM926740	4.5000	114.300	43					HM926710	9.0000	228.600	43		265
							HM926745	4.9330	125.298	44					HM926710D	9.0000	228.600		27	
							HM926747	5.0000	127.000	45					HM926710DC	9.0000	228.600		27	
							HM926749	5.0312	127.792	45										
4.7230 – 5.5118 / 119,964 – 140,000	8.4646 – 8.5000 / 215,000 – 215,900	74000	17200 / 32800 / 14300	7650 / 14600 / 6400	1.20	260.	74472	4.7230	119.964	44					74846X	8.4646	215.000	44		269
							74500	5.0000	127.000	45		10			74850	8.5000	215.900	45		
							74510D	5.1183	130.005	45					74850B	8.5000	215.900	67		
							74525	5.2500	133.350	45					74851D	8.5000	215.900		27	
							74537	5.3750	136.525	46					74851DC	8.5000	215.900		27	
							74539TD	5.3750	136.525			18								
							74550	5.5000	139.700	46										
							74550A	5.5000	139.700	46										
							74551X	5.5118	140.000	46										
4.7244 / 120,000	7.0866 / 180,000	M624600	10800 / 20600 / 7650	4800 / 9150 / 3420	1.41	166.	M624649	†4.7244	†120.000	44					M624610	†7.0866	†180.000	44		271
															M624610B	†7.0866	†180.000	66		
4.7244 – 4.7500 / 120,000 – 120,650	6.5625 – 6.6920 / 166,688 – 170,000	L724300	6500 / 12200 / 5100	2880 / 5500 / 2260	1.27	125.	L724348	†4.7244	†120.000	44					L724310	6.5625	166.688	44		270
							L724349	4.7500	120.650	44					L724314	6.6929	170.000	44		
4.7500 / 120,650	6.3125 – 6.3750 / 160,338 – 161,925	L624500	5150 / 9750 / 3830	2280 / 4340 / 1700	1.34	137.	L624549	4.7500	120.650	44					L624510	6.3125	160.338	44		272
															L624510B	6.3125	160.338	65		
															L624510D	6.3750	161.925		27	
4.7500 / 120,650	6.8750 / 174,625	M224700	11300 / 21400 / 6400	5000 / 9550 / 2840	1.76	203.	M224749	4.7500	120.650	44					M224710	6.8750	174.625	44		274
							M224749D	4.7500	120.650			10			M224710D	6.8750	174.625		27	
															M224710DC	6.8750	174.625		27	
4.7500 / 120,650	7.5000 / 190,500	HM624700	15900 / 30200 / 11600	7050 / 13450 / 5150	1.37	205.	HM624749	4.7500	120.650	44					HM624710	7.5000	190.500	44		276
4.7500 – 5.0000 / 120,650 – 127,000	6.6875 – 7.1250 / 169,862 – 180,975	L225800	7000 / 13400 / 3990	3120 / 5950 / 1775	1.76	181.	L225842	4.7500	120.650	44					L225810	6.6875	169.862	44		273
							L225849	5.0000	127.000	44					L225818	7.1250	180.975	44		
4.7500 – 5.0000 / 120,650 – 127,000	7.1875 / 182,562	48200	12900 / 24600 / 6750	5750 / 10950 / 3000	1.91	252.	48282	4.7500	120.650	44					48220	7.1875	182.562	44		275
							48286	4.8750	123.825	44					48220B	7.1875	182.562	66		
							48290	5.0000	127.000	44					48220D	7.1875	182.562		27	
							48290D	5.0000	127.000			10			48220DC	7.1875	182.562		27	
							48290TD	5.0000	127.000			18								
							48290SW	5.0000	127.000				39							
							NA48291	5.0000	127.000					44						
4.7500 – 5.0000 / 120,650 – 127,000	10.0000 / 254,000	HH228300	38200 / ... / 17000	...	1.82	398.	HH228340	4.7500	120.650	44					HH228310	10.0000	254.000	44		279
								5.0000	127.000											

BEARING SELECTION INDEX

Cone	Factor	Ratings (in-lb set 1)	Ratings (set 2)	Ref.	Cup (middle)	O.D. in	O.D. mm	code	Cup (right)	dim in	dim mm	code	Page
795	1.27	7450 / 14200 / 5900	16800 / 32000 / 13200	236.	795	4.7500	120,650	44	792	8.1250	206,375	44	277
					799	5.0625	128,588	45	792B	8.1250	206,375	66	
					797	5.1181	130,000	45	792D	8.1250	206,375	27	
					799A	5.1250	130,175	45	792DC	8.1250	206,375	27	
95000	1.58	12150 / 23200 / 7700	27300 / 52000 / 17300	333.	95475	4.7500	120,650	44	95925	9.2500	234,950	44	278
					95491	4.9190	124,943	44	95925D	9.2500	234,950	27	
					95500	5.0000	127,000	45	95925DC	9.2500	234,950	27	
					95525	5.2500	133,350	45					
					95528	5.2500	133,350	45					
LL225700	1.76	1840 / 3500 / 1045	4150 / 7900 / 2350	121.	LL225749	5.0000	127,000	44	LL225710	6.5313	165,895	44	281
L725300	1.23	3000 / 5700 / 2440	6750 / 12800 / 5450	136.	L725349	5.0000	127,000	44	L725311	6.7500	171,450	44	282
67300	1.70	7500 / 14350 / 4420	16900 / 32200 / 9950	277.	67388	5.0000	127,000	45	67322	7.7500	196,850	45	283
					67389	5.1250	130,175	45	67322B	7.7500	196,850	66	
					67390	5.2500	133,350	45	67322D	7.7500	196,850	27	
					67390D	5.2500	133,350	45	67322DC	7.7500	196,850	27	
					67390TD	5.2500	133,350	10/18	67323D	7.7500	196,850	27	
					67391	5.2500	133,350	45	67325D	7.8750	200,025	45	
									67320	8.0000	203,200	66	
									67320B	8.0000	203,200	45	
									67324	8.0000	203,200	45	
HH231600	1.83	19000 / 36400 / 10400	43000 / 81500 / 23400	458.	HH231637	5.0000	127,000	45	HH231610	11.3750	288,925	45	289
					HH231649	5.5000	139,700	46	HH231615	11.6250	295,275	46	
HH932100	0.80	17550 / 33400 / 22000	39400 / 75000 / 49500	376.	HH932132	5.0000	127,000	45	HH932110	12.0000	304,800	45	287
					HH932145	5.7500	146,050	47					
516000	0.80	15350 / 29200 / 19200	34500 / 66000 / 43000	358.	EE516050	5.0000	127,000	45	516120	12.0000	304,800	45	285
					EE516055	5.5000	139,700	46	516122	12.2500	311,150	46	
					EE516057	5.7500	146,050	47					
48000	0.89	3620 / 6900 / 4060	8150 / 15500 / 9150	155.	48506	5.0625	128,588	45	48750	7.5000	190,500	45	291
LL327000	1.68	1920 / 3660 / 1145	4300 / 8250 / 2570	134.	LL327049	5.2500	133,350	45	LL327010	6.8125	173,038	45	292
L327200	1.68	3220 / 6150 / 1920	7250 / 13800 / 4300	197.	L327249	5.2500	133,350	45	L327210	6.9688	177,008	45	293
									L327210D	6.9688	177,008	27	
									L327210DC	6.9688	177,008	27	
48300	1.82	6100 / 11600 / 3340	13700 / 26100 / 7500	285.	48385	5.2500	133,350	45	48320	7.5000	190,500	45	294
					48393	5.3750	136,525	46	48320B	7.5000	190,500	66	
					48393D	5.3750	136,525		48320D	7.5000	190,500	27	
									48320DC	7.5000	190,500	27	
H228600	1.76	13000 / 24800 / 7400	29200 / 55500 / 16600	389.	H228649D	5.3750	136,525	10	H228610	8.8750	225,425		294

"G"=2.0625 / 52.388
"r1"=.13 / 3.3
"Db"=7.99 / 203.0

†Dimension shown is maximum value—see note at bottom of fitting practice table in Reference Tables.

BEARING SELECTION INDEX

The bearing type and specific cone or cup dimensions are located on the page reference number indicated.

The following index of bearing series is listed by increasing bore size.

bore range (min — max)	outside diameter range (min — max)	series number	rating at 500 RPM for 3000 hours L10 one-row radial / two-row radial thrust (lb)	(daN)	factor K	factor G	cone number	cone bore inch	cone bore metric	TS or TSL	SS or SR	TDI or TDIT	TNA and TNADC	TMASW or TMASWE	cup number	cup outside diameter inch	cup outside diameter metric	TS or TSF	TDO and TODDC	dim. sheet page no.
5.3750 — 5.5000 / 136,525 — 139,700	7.3750 / 187.325	LM328400	9400 / 17900 / 5700	4180 / 7950 / 2540	1.65	237.	LM328644	5.3750	136.525	45					LM328410	7.3750	187.325	45		295
							LM328448	5.5000	139.700	46										
5.3750 — 5.5000 / 136,525 — 139,700	9.0000 / 228.600	895	23000 / 44000 / 16500	10250 / 19400 / 7350	1.39	312.	896	5.3750	136.525	46					892	9.0000	228.600	46		298
							898	5.5000	139.700	46					928	9.0000	228.600	67	28	
							898A	5.5000	139.700	46					892CD	9.0000	228.600		28	
															892C	9.0000	228.600			
5.3750 — 5.6250 / 136,525 — 142,875	7.6772 / 195.000	LM229100	12000 / 22900 / 6800	5350 / 10200 / 3040	1.76	260.	LM229139	5.3750	136.525	46					LM229110	7.6772	195.000	46		296
							LM229146	5.6250	142.875	46										
5.5000 / 139,700	7.1250 / 180.975	LL428300	5250 / 10000 / 3290	2340 / 4460 / 1465	1.60	163.	LL428349	5.5000	139.700	46					LL428310	7.1250	180.975	46		299
5.5000 / 139,700	8.7500 / 222.250	73000	10200 / 19400 / 7600	4550 / 8600 / 3380	1.34	182.	73551	5.5000	139.700	46	"B" = 1.2450 / 31.623	"A" = .14 / 3.5	"db" = 6.14 / 156.0		73780	8.7500	222.250		28	
															73780DC	8.7500	222.250		28	
5.5000 — 5.6250 / 139,700 — 142,875	7.8750 / 200.025	48600	13900 / 26600 / 8000	6200 / 11800 / 3560	1.74	306.	46680D	5.5000	139.700	46		10			48620	7.8750	200.025	46		300
							46584	5.6250	142.875	46					48620B	7.8750	200.025	66	28	
							46585	5.6250	142.875	46					48620D	7.8750	200.025		28	
							46584TD	5.6250	142.875			18			48620DC	7.8750	200.025		28	
							M348085SW	5.6250	142.875					45						
							M348086	5.6250	142.875											
5.5000 — 5.8125 / 139,700 — 147,638	9.3125 — 9.5000 / 236,538 — 241,300	82000	23000 / 44000 / 17400	10200 / 19400 / 7750	1.32	331.	82550	5.5000	139.700	46					82931	9.3125	236.538	46		301
							82576	5.7500	146.050	47			39		82950	9.5000	241.300	47		
							NA82576	5.7500	146.050						82950B	9.5000	241.300		28	
							82581TD	5.8125	147.638			18			82951D	9.5000	241.300		28	
															82951DC	9.5000	241.300		28	
5.5000 — 6.0000 / 139,700 — 152,400	9.8425 — 10.0000 / 250,000 — 254,000	99000	29200 / 55500 / 20400	12950 / 24800 / 9050	1.43	400.	99550	5.5000	139.700	46					9909BX	9.8425	250.000	46		297
							99575	5.7500	146.050	47					99100	10.0000	254.000	47		
							99587	5.8750	149.225	47					99100B	10.0000	254.000	67	28	
							99600	6.0000	152.400	47					99101D	10.0000	254.000		28	
							99600TD	6.0000	152.400			18			99101DC	10.0000	254.000		28	
							NA99600	6.0000	152.400				39		99102D	10.0000	254.000		28	
															99102DC	10.0000	254.000		28	
5.5000 — 6.0000 / 139,700 — 152,400	12.1250 / 307.975	HH234000	49500 / 94500 / 27800	22200 / 42200 / 12350	1.79	542.	HH234031	5.5000	139.700	46					HH234010	12.1250	307.975	46		303
							HH234048	6.0000	152.400	47					HH234011D	12.1250	307.975		28	
															HH234011DC	12.1250	307.975		28	
5.6250 — 5.7500 / 142,875 — 146,050	7.6250 — 8.0000 / 193,675 — 203,200	36600	9700 / 18500 / 6100	4320 / 8200 / 2720	1.59	256.	36686	5.6250	142.875	46					36820	7.6250	193.675	46		306
							36690	5.7500	146.050	47					36820B	7.6250	193.675	66	28	
							36691	5.7500	146.050	47					36820D	7.6250	193.675		28	
															36820DC	7.6250	193.675		28	
															36626	8.0000	203.200	47		

Series	d (in / mm)	Complete Bearing	Rating 5400	Rating 2400	1.53	1/6.	Cone No.	Cone d (in / mm)	Cup No.	Cup OD (in / mm)	46
305	5.7500 / 146.050	LL529700	10300, 3540	4600, 1575	1.53		LL529749	5.7500 / 146.050	LL529710	9.3125 / 236.538	47
307	5.7500 — 5.8750 / 146.050 — 149.225	HM231100	26300, 50000, 14400	11700, 22400, 6400	1.83	388.	HM231140 / HM231148 / HM231149	5.7500 / 146.050; 5.8750 / 149.225	HM231110 / HM231110D / HM231110DC / HM231115 / HM231116D / HM231116DC	9.3125 / 236.538; 9.5000 / 241.300	47; 28; 29
309	5.7500 — 6.0000 / 146.050 — 152.400	107000	34400, 65500, 22900	15300, 29200, 10150	1.51	441.	EE107057 / EE107060	5.7500 / 146.050; 6.0000 / 152.400	107105 / 107105D / 107105DC	10.5625 / 268.288	47; 29
311	6.0000 / 152.400	L630300	6950, 13200, 4950	3080, 5900, 2200	1.40	206.	L630349	6.0000 / 152.400	L630310	7.5625 / 192.088	47
312	6.0000 / 152.400	L730600	8850, 16800, 6950	3940, 7500, 3100	1.27	209.	L730649	6.0000 / 152.400	L730610	8.0000 / 203.200	47
313	6.0000 / 152.400	M231600	17400, 33200, 9900	7750, 14750, 4400	1.76	345.	M231649	6.0000 / 152.400	M231610 / M231610D / M231610DC	8.7500 / 222.250	47; 29
315	6.0000 / 152.400	450000	44000, 84000, 24600	19600, 37400, 10950	1.79	551.	EE450601	6.0000 / 152.400	451212 / 4512150 / 451215DC	12.1250 / 307.975	47; 29
317	6.1250 — 6.6250 / 155.575 — 168.275	H936300	42500, 81000, 59000	18800, 36000, 26200	0.72	457.	H936340 / H936349	6.1250 / 155.575; 6.6250 / 168.275	H936310 / H936316	13.0000 / 330.200; 13.5000 / 342.900	47; 48
317	6.2500 / 158.750	L432300	7000, 13300, 4450	3120, 5950, 1980	1.57	225.	L432348 / L432349	6.2500 / 158.750	L432310	8.0938 / 205.583	47; 47
318	6.2500 — 6.5000 / 158.750 — 165.100	48700	15100, 28800, 9950	6750, 12800, 4420	1.52	389.	48780 / 48780TD / 48790 / 48790D / NA46790SW	6.2500 / 158.750; 6.5000 / 165.100	48720 / 48720B / 48720D / 48720DC	8.8750 / 225.425	47; 48
319	6.3120 — 7.1250 / 160.325 — 180.975	HM237500	35500, 67500, 19400	15800, 30000, 8600	1.83	549.	HM237532 / HM237535 / HM237542 / HM237545 / HM237545NA / HM237545TD / HM237549TD	6.3120 / 160.325; 6.5000 / 165.100; 6.8750 / 174.625; 7.0000 / 177.800; 7.1250 / 180.975	HM237210 / HM237210B / HM237210D / HM237210DC	11.3750 / 288.925	47; 48; 49
320	6.5000 / 165.100	L433700	8400, 16000, 5250	3740, 7150, 2340	1.60	257.	L433749	6.5000 / 165.100	L433710 / L433710B	8.5000 / 215.900	48; 67
	6.5000 / 165.100	M235100	20700, 39400, 11300	9200, 17550, 5050	1.83	386.	M235145	6.5000 / 165.100	M235113D / M235113DC	10.0000 / 254.000	29
320	6.5000 / 165.100	H234600	41500, 79000, 23600	18400, 35200, 10500	1.76	596.	H234649TD	6.5000 / 165.100	H234610	10.6250 / 269.875	29

"C" = 2.4375 / 61.912 / 3.13
"B" = 1.8125 / 46.038
"R" = .19 / 4.8
"dp" = −7.28 / 185.0
"Dp" = 3.3 / 9.61 / 244.0

†Dimension shown is maximum value—see note at bottom of fitting practice table in Reference Tables.

BEARING SELECTION INDEX

The following index of bearing series is listed by increasing bore size.

The bearing type and specific cone or cup dimensions are located on the page reference number indicated.

bore range min.	bore range max.	outside diameter range min.	max.	series number	rating lb	rating daN	K	G	cone number	cone bore inch	cone bore metric	SS or SR	TDI or TDIT	TNA and TNADC	TNASW or TNASWE	TS or TSL	cup number	cup outside diameter inch	metric	TS or TSF	TDO or TDODC	dim. sheet page no.
6.5000 165,100		13.2500 336,550		HH437500	58000 / 111000 / 37100	25800 / 49500 / 16500	1.57	671.	HH437549	6.5000	165,100					48	HH437510	13.2500	336,550	48		321
6.5000 165,100	6.6929 170,000	10.0000 254,000		86000	18100 / 34500 / 11500	8050 / 15350 / 5100	1.58	338.	86650	6.5000	165,100					48	86100	10.0000	254,000	48		321
									86669	6.6929	170,000					48						
6.5000 165,100	6.8750 174,625	12.2500 311,150		H238100	46000 / 92000 / 25900	20400 / 40800 / 11550	1.77	666.	H238140	6.5000	165,100					48	H238110	12.2500	311,150	48		325
									H238148	6.8750	174,625					49						
6.5000 165,100	7.0000 177,800	9.7500 247,650		67700	19500 / 37100 / 14700	8650 / 16500 / 6500	1.33	428.	67780	6.5000	165,100					48	67720	9.7500	247,650	48		322
									67782	6.6250	168,275					48	67720B	9.7500	247,650	67		
									67786	6.8750	174,625					48	67720D	9.7500	247,650		29	
									67787	6.8750	174,625					48	67720DC	9.7500	247,650		29	
									NA67787	6.8750	174,625			40								
									67790	7.0000	177,800					49						
									67790D	7.0000	177,800		10									
									67791	7.0000	177,800					49						
									NA67791SW	7.0000	177,800				45							
6.5000 165,100	7.1250 180,975	11.3750 288,925	11.7500 298,450	94000	30000 / 57000 / 24000	13350 / 25400 / 10650	1.25	488.	94649	6.5000	165,100					48	94113	11.3750	288,925	48		323
									94675	6.7500	171,450					48	94113B	11.3750	288,925	67		
									94687	6.8750	174,625					49	94114D	11.3750	288,925		29	
									94700	7.0000	177,800					49	94114DC	11.3750	288,925		29	
									NA94700	7.0000	177,800			40			94118	11.7500	298,450	48		
									94706D	7.0000	177,800		10				94118D	11.7500	298,450		29	
									94713TD	7.1250	180,975		18									
6.5000 165,100	8.5000 215,900	14.1732 360,000	14.6250 371,475	420000	48500 / 97000 / 33500	21600 / 43200 / 14900	1.45	821.	EE420651	6.5000	165,100					48	421417	14.1732	360,000	48		327
									EE420701	7.0000	177,800					49	421427	14.3720	365,049	49		
									EE420750D	7.5000	190,500		11				421490	14.5000	368,300	50		
									EE420750TD	7.5000	190,500		18				421451D	14.5000	368,300		29	
									EE420751	7.5000	190,500					50	421451DC	14.5000	368,300		29	
									EE420800D	8.0000	203,200		11				421462XD	14.6250	371,475		29	
									EE420801	8.0000	203,200					51						
									EE420812X	8.1250	206,375					51						
									EE420850	8.5000	215,900					52						
6.6929 170,000		9.0551 230,000		HM534100	15500 / 29600 / 10200	6900 / 13150 / 4550	1.52	337.	JHM534149	*6.6929	*170,000	6				48	JHM534110	*9.0551	*230,000	48		327
6.6929 170,000		9.4488 240,000		M734400	19900 / 38000 / 14900	8850 / 16900 / 6600	1.34	384.	JM734449	*6.6929	*170,000	6				48	JM734410	*9.4488	*240,000	48		329
6.7500 171,450		8.7500 222,250		L435000	7850 / 14900 / 5050	3480 / 6650 / 2240	1.55	255.	L435049	6.7500	171,450					48	L435010	8.7500	222,250	48		331

BEARING SELECTION INDEX

Cone	Bore in	Bore mm	Ref.	K	Center Part	Rating (set 1)	Rating (set 2)	Cup(s)	Cup OD in	Cup OD mm	Class	Ref.
HM535349	6.7500	171,450	524.	1.45	HM535300	31000 / 59000 / 21400	13800 / 26400 / 9500	HM535310	10.2500	260,350	48	332
EE590075	6.7500	171,450	492.	1.18	590000	34500 / 69000 / 29200	15350 / 30700 / 13000	591350	13.5000	342,900	48	335
EE219068	6.8750	174,625	608.	1.55	219000	43500 / 82500 / 28000	19400 / 36800 / 12450	219117 / 219122	11.7500 / 12.2500	298,450 / 311,150	49 / 49	333
M236845 / M236848 / M236849	6.8750 – 7.0000	174,625 – 177,800	489.	1.76	M236800	24800 / 47500 / 14100	11050 / 21000 / 6300	M236810	10.2500	260,350	48	333
36990	7.0000	177,800	347.	1.33	36900	10600 / 20200 / 8000	4700 / 9000 / 3540	36920	8.9375	227,012	49	337
EE280700D	7.0000	177,800	435.	1.62	280000	24500 / 49000 / 15100	10900 / 21800 / 6750	281200	12.0000	304,800	11	—
EE807070	7.0000	177,800	586.	1.07	607000	41000 / 82000 / 38400	18200 / 36400 / 17100	607140	14.0000	355,600	49	338
M238840 / M238849 / M238849D	7.0000 – 7.3750	177,800 – 187,325	548.	1.76	M238800	24200 / 48400 / 13700	10750 / 21500 / 6100	M238810 / M238810D / M238810DC	10.6250	269,875	49 / 50	338
H239640 / H239649 / H239649D / H239649NA	7.0000 – 7.3750	177,800 – 187,325	666.	1.83	M239600	44500 / 89000 / 24300	19800 / 39600 / 10800	H239610 / H239612 / H239612D / H239612DC	12.5970 / 12.6250	319,964 / 320,675	49 / 50	341
EE670078X / EE670075	7.0000 – 7.5000	177,800 – 190,500	663.	1.60	470000	43500 / 87000 / 27200	19400 / 38800 / 12100	470128	12.8750	327,025	49 / 50	339
EE350701 / EE350760	7.0000 – 7.5000	177,800 – 190,500	608.	0.77	350000	51000 / 102000 / 66000	22600 / 45200 / 29400	351687	16.8750	428,625	49 / 50	—
NA87700 / NA87700SW / 87737 / 87750 / 87762	7.0000 – 7.6250	177,800 – 193,675	403.	1.41	87000	17200 / 34400 / 12200	7650 / 15300 / 5400	87111 / 87112D / 87112DC	11.1250	282,575	50	346
JM736149	7.0866	180,000	411.	1.22	M738100	20600 / 39200 / 16900	9150 / 17450 / 7500	JM736110	9.8425	250,000	49	344
67875 / 67883 / 67884 / 67886 / 67885 / NA67885SW / 67887	7.0866 – 7.5625	180,000 – 192,088	492.	1.22	67100	19200 / 38400 / 15800	8550 / 17100 / 7000	67820 / 67820B / 67820D / 67820DC / 67830 / 67835	10.5000 / 11.0236 / 11.4170	266,700 / 280,000 / 289,992	49 / 67 / 50	343

Note (for 280000 series):
$$"C" = 1.6875 = 42.862 \qquad "Db" = 10.98 = 279.0 \qquad \frac{1}{=} 1.3$$

*For "J" part tolerances—see metric tolerance and fitting practice in Reference Tables.

BEARING SELECTION INDEX

The following index of bearing series is listed by increasing bore size.

The bearing type and specific cone or cup dimensions reference number indicated are located on the page reference number indicated.

bore range (min / max)	outside diameter range (min / max)	series number	rating at 500 RPM for 3000 hours L10 — one-row radial / two-row radial / thrust (ib)	(daN)	fac-tor K	fac-tor G	cone number	cone bore inch	cone bore metric	cone page ref (TS/TSL, SS/SR, TDI/TDIT, TNA/TNADC, TNASW)	cup number	cup O.D. inch	cup O.D. metric	cup page ref (TS/TSF, TDO/TDODC)	dim. sheet page no.
7.0866 — 8.2500 / 180.000 — 209.550	12.5000 / 317.500	93000	32900 / 65800 / 29400	14650 / 29300 / 13050	1.12	637.	93708	17.0866	180.000	TS 49	93125	12.5000	317.500	TS 49	
							93750	7.5000	190.500	TS 50	93125B	12.5000	317.500	TS 67	
							93775	7.7500	196.850	TS 50	93126	12.5000	317.500	TS 50	
							93787	7.8750	200.025	TS 50	93127D	12.5000	317.500	TDO 29	
							93800	8.0000	203.200	TS 51	93127DC	12.5000	317.500	TDO 29	
							93800A	8.0000	203.200	TS 51					
							N493800	8.0000	203.200	TDI 11					
							93801D	8.0000	203.200	TNA 40					
							93806A	8.0625	204.788	TS 51					
							93812	8.1250	206.375	TS 51					
							93825	8.2500	209.550	TS 51					
							93825A	8.2500	209.550	TS 51					
							93826TD	8.2500	209.550	TDI 18					345
7.2500 / 184.150	9.2610 / 235.229	LM236700	13700 / 26100 / 7900	6100 / 11600 / 3500	1.74	388.	LM236749	7.2500	184.150	TS 49	LM236710A	9.2610	235.229	TS 49	
7.2500 / 184.150	9.5625 / 242.888	LM637300	15800 / 30000 / 11300	7000 / 13350 / 5050	1.39	452.	LM637349WW	7.2500	184.150	TNASW 45	LM637310D	9.5625	242.888		
7.4803 / 190.000	10.2362 / 260.000	M738200	19200 / 38400 / 15700	8550 / 17100 / 7000	1.22	445.	JM738249	*7.4803	*190.000	SS 6	JM738210	10.2362*	260.000*	TS 50	347
7.4896 / 190.236	11.3750 / 288.925	82700	26600 / 53200 / 16300	11850 / 23700 / 7250	1.63	568.	82785TD	7.4896	190.236	TDI 18	82720	11.3750	288.925		
7.5000 / 190.500	13.2500 / 336.550	HH840200	55000 / 110000 / 54500	24600 / 49200 / 24200	1.01	763.	HH840249	7.5000	190.500	TS 50	HH840210	13.2500	336.550	TS 50	349
7.7500 / 196.850	9.5000 / 241.300	LL639200	7550 / 15100 / 5400	3360 / 6720 / 2400	1.40	307.	LL639249	7.7500	196.850	TS 50	LL639210	9.5000	241.300	TS 50	351
7.7500 / 196.850	10.0000 / 254.000	L540000	8900 / 17800 / 6050	3960 / 7920 / 2700	1.47	341.	L540049	7.7500	196.850	TS 50	L540010	10.0000	254.000	TS 50	
											L540010D	10.0000	254.000	TDO 29	
											L540010DC	10.0000	254.000	TDO 29	352
7.7500 / 196.850	10.1250 / 257.175	LM739700	15600 / 31200 / 11900	6950 / 13900 / 5300	1.31	502.	LM739749	7.7500	196.850	TS 50	LM739710	10.1250	257.175	TS 50	
											LM739710D	10.1250	257.175	TDO 30	
											LM739710DC	10.1250	257.175	TDO 30	353

Note (82700 series): "C"=1.6875 / 42.862 ; "r"=.313 / 3.13 ; "Db"=10.43 / 265.0

BEARING SELECTION INDEX

Bore in. / mm	O.D. in. / mm	Cone	Cone ratings	Cup ratings	Factor	Ref.	Cone part No.	B in.	B mm	—	—	Cup part No.	C in.	C mm	—
7.8125 — 8.1250 / 198.438 — 206.375	11.1250 / 282.575	67900	19900 39800 17300	8850 17700 7700	1.15	547.	67790TD 67983 67985	7.8125 8.0000 8.1250	198.438 203.200 206.375	51 51	18	67928 67920 67920C 67920DC	11.1250 11.1250 11.1250 11.1250	282.575 282.575 282.575 282.575	51 67 30 30
7.8740 / 200.000	11.8110 / 300.000	HM840400	33200 66400 29700	14750 29500 13200	1.12	592.	HM840449	7.8740†	200.000	50 6		HM840410	11.8110†	300.000*	50 ... 355
7.8750 / 200.025	15.5000 / 393.700	HH144600	72500 145000 37000	32200 64400 16450	1.96	1068.	HH144642	7.8750	200.025	51		HH144614	15.5000	393.700	51
7.8750 — 8.2500 / 200.025 — 209.550	13.1250 / 333.375	HM743300	41000 82000 30700	18200 36400 13650	1.33	724.	HM743337 HM743345	7.8750 8.2500	200.025 209.550	51 51		HM743310 HM743310B HM743310BC	13.1250 13.1250 13.1250	333.375 333.375 333.375	51 30 30
7.8750 — 9.2500 / 200.025 — 234.950	15.1250 / 384.175	H247500	81500 163000 46500	36200 72400 20600	1.76	1369.	H247535 H247549	7.8750 9.2500	200.025 234.950	51 53		H247510 H247510B H247510DC	15.1250 15.1250 15.1250	384.175 384.175 384.175	51 30 30
8.0000 / 203.200	10.2812 / 261.142	LL641100	9000 18000 6300	4020 8040 2800	1.43	358.	LL641149	8.0000	203.200	51		LL641110	10.2812	261.142	51
8.0000 / 203.200	10.8750 / 276.225	LM241100	19100 38200 10400	8450 16900 4650	1.83	536.	LM241149 LM241149NW	8.0000 8.0000	203.200 203.200	51	45	LM241110 LM241110D LM241110DC	10.8750 10.8750 10.8750	276.225 276.225 276.225	51 30 30
8.0000 / 203.200	16.0000 / 406.400	114000	42500 85000 58000	18800 37600 25800	0.73	583.	EE114080	8.0000	203.200	"B" = 3.3750 "R" = .25 "db" = 9.69 / 85.725 6.4 246.0		114161B 114161DC	16.0000 16.0000	406.400 406.400	51 30
8.0000 — 8.0625 / 203.200 — 204.788	11.5000 / 292.100	M241500	28500 57000 16200	12700 25400 7200	1.76	663.	M241547 M241549	8.0000 8.0625	203.200 204.788	51 51		M241510 M241510B M241510DC	11.5000 11.5000 11.5000	292.100 292.100 292.100	51 51
8.0000 — 8.7500 / 203.200 — 222.250	19.0000 / 482.600	380000	58000 116000 86500	25800 51600 38600	0.67	799.	EE380080 EE380081 EE380875	8.0000 8.1250 8.7500	203.200 206.375 222.250	51 51 52		380190	19.0000	482.600	51
8.1250 / 206.375	12.5000 / 317.500	132000	23000 46000 12400	10250 20500 5500	1.86	576.	EE132084	8.1250	206.375	51		132125	12.5000	317.500	51
8.1250 — 9.2500 / 206.375 — 234.950	13.2500 / 336.550	H242600	61000 122000 34800	27200 54400 15500	1.76	989.	H242649 H242649D	8.1250 8.1250	206.375 206.375	51	11	H242610	13.2500	336.550	51
8.2500 — 9.2500 / 209.550 — 234.950	14.0000 / 355.600	96000	35300 70600 35600	15700 31400 15850	0.99	780.	96825 96900 96925	8.2500 9.0000 9.2500	209.550 228.600 234.950	51 52 53		96140 96140D 96140DC	14.0000 14.0000 14.0000	355.600 355.600 355.600	51 30 30
8.3750 — 8.5000 / 212.725 — 215.900	11.2500 — 11.3750 / 285.750 — 288.925	LM742710	20100 40200 16600	8950 17900 7400	1.21	579.	LM742745 LM742749	8.3750 8.5000	212.725 215.900	52 52		LM742710B LM742710B LM742710BC LM742714	11.2500 11.2500 11.2500 11.3750	285.750 285.750 285.750 288.925	52 67 52 30 30	
8.5000 / 215.900	16.0000 / 406.400	820000	61500 123000 41500	27200 54400 18400	1.48	951.	EE820085	8.5000	215.900	"B" = 3.6875 "R" = .25 "db" = 9.88 / 93.662 6.4 251.0		820016B 820016DC	16.0000 16.0000	406.400 406.400	52 31 31

†Dimension shown is maximum value—see note at bottom of fitting practice table in Reference Tables.
*For "J" part tolerances—see metric tolerance and fitting practice in Reference Tables.

BEARING SELECTION INDEX

The bearing type and specific cone or cup dimensions are located on the page reference number indicated.

bore range (inch / metric) min. – max.	outside diameter range (inch / metric) min. – max.	series number	rating at 500 RPM for 3000 hours L10 one-row radial thrust (lb / daN)	two-row radial (lb / daN)	factor K	factor G	cone number	cone bore (inch / metric)	page ref. to locate CONES (TS or TSL / SS or SR / TDI or TDIT)	cup number	cup outside diameter (inch / metric)	page ref. to locate CUPS (TS or TSF / TDO and TDODC)	dimension notes / sheet page no.
8.5000 – 8.6602 / 215.900 – 219.969	11.4177 / 290.009	543000	10300 / 4550	20600 / 9100; 6750 / 3000	1.52	414.	543085; 543086	8.5000 / 215.900; 8.6602 / 219.969	TS/TSL 52; 52	543114	11.4177 / 290.009	TSF 52	
8.5000 – 9.0000 / 215.900 – 228.600	14.0000 / 355.600	130000	36100 / 16050	72200 / 32100; 20400 / 9050	1.77	824.	EE130051; EE130089; EE130902	8.5000 / 215.900; 8.8750 / 225.425; 9.0000 / 228.600	TS/TSL 52; 52; 52	1314000; 131401D; 131401DC	14.0000 / 355.600	TSF 52; TDO 30, 30	
8.6250 / 219.075	14.1250 / 358.775	H244800	69500 / 31000	139000 / 62000; 39600 / 17600	1.76	1140.	H244849D	8.6250 / 219.075	TDI 11	H244810	14.1250 / 358.775		"C"=3.3750 / 85.725, "Y"=.64, "Db"=12.72 / 323.0
8.6875 / 220.662	12.3750 / 314.325	M244200	33700 / 15000	67400 / 30000; 19100 / 8500	1.76	790.	M244249	8.6875 / 220.662	TS/TSL 52	M244210; M244210D; M244210DC	12.3750 / 314.325	TSF 52; TDO 31, 31	
8.7500 – 9.0000 / 225.425 – 228.600	15.7500 / 400.050	430000	50500 / 22400	101000 / 44800; 38000 / 16900	1.33	946.	EE430888; EE430900	8.8750 / 225.425; 9.0000 / 228.600	TS/TSL 52; 52	431575; 431576D; 431576DC	15.7500 / 400.050	TSF 52; TDO 31, 31	
8.9920 – 8.9945 / 228.397 – 228.460	17.0000 / 431.800	113000	45500 / 20200	91000 / 40400; 69000 / 30800	0.66	699.	EE113089; EE113091	8.9920 / 228.397; 8.9945 / 228.460	TS/TSL 52; 52	113170; 113171D	17.0000 / 431.800	TSF 52; TDO 31	
9.0000 / 228.600	12.5000 / 311.150	LM245100	24900 / 11100	49800 / 22200; 14200 / 6300	1.76	684.	LM245149D	9.0000 / 228.600	TDI 11	LM245110	12.5000 / 311.150		"C"=1.5000 / 38.100, "Y"=.13, "Db"=11.54 / 293.0
9.0000 / 228.600	14.0000 / 355.600	HM746600	43500 / 19200	87000 / 38400; 34900 / 15550	1.24	833.	HM746646	9.0000 / 228.600 "B"=2.7500 69.850	"G"=10.16 258.0; 6.4	HM746610D; HM746610DC	14.0000 / 355.600	TDO 31, 31	
9.0000 / 228.600	15.7500 / 400.050	529000	48000 / 21200	96000 / 42400; 25300 / 11250	1.89	995.	EE529090D	9.0000 / 228.600	TDI 11	529157	15.7500 / 400.050		"C"=2.2500 / 57.150, "Y"=.13, "Db"=14.45 / 367.0
9.0000 / 228.600	19.2500 / 488.950	HH949500	74000 / 33000	148000 / 66000; 119000 / 53000	0.62	959.	HH949549	9.0000 / 228.600	TS/TSL 52	HH949510; HH949510D; HH949510DC	19.2500 / 488.950	TSF 52; TDO 31, 31	
9.0000 – 9.1250 / 228.600 – 231.775	11.6250 – 11.8125 / 295.275 – 300.038	544000	10600 / 4700	21200 / 9400; 7300 / 3240	1.45	448.	544090; 544091	9.0000 / 228.600; 9.1250 / 231.775	TS/TSL 52; 53	544116; 544118	11.6250 / 295.275; 11.8125 / 300.038	TSF 52, 53	
9.0000 – 9.2500 / 228.600 – 234.950	12.6250 – 12.8750 / 320.675 – 327.025	88000	19500 / 8650	39000 / 17300; 16200 / 7200	1.20	548.	88900; 88925	9.0000 / 228.600; 9.2500 / 234.950	TS/TSL 52; 53	88126; 88128	12.6250 / 320.675; 12.8750 / 327.025	TSF 52, 53	

9.0000 — 9.5000 228.600 — 241.300	8573 8573TD 8575 NA8575SW 8576D 8578	9.0000 9.0000 9.2500 9.2500 9.2500 9.5000	228.600 228.600 234.950 234.950 234.950 241.300	52 53 53	18		713.	1.44	11100 22200 7700	24900 49800 17300	8500	12.8750 327.025	9.0000 — 9.5000 228.600 — 241.300	8520 85208 85200 85200DC	12.8750 12.8750 12.8750 12.8750	327.025 327.025 327.025 327.025	52 67	45	31 31
9.0000 — 9.5000 228.600 — 241.300	EE390090 EE390095	9.0000 9.5000	228.600 241.300	52 53	11		900.	0.62	26300 53600 43200	60000 120000 97000	390000	20.0000 508.000	9.0000 — 9.5000 228.600 — 241.300	390200	20.0000	508.000	52		
9.0000 — 10.000 228.600 — 254.000	M249732 M249734 M249736 M249746TD M249748D M249749	9.0000 9.1250 9.3437 9.3375 10.0000 10.0000	228.600 231.775 237.330 237.412 254.000 254.000	52 53 53 54	18 11		1121.	1.76	20200 40400 11450	45000 90000 25700	M249700	14.1250 358.775	9.0000 — 10.000 228.600 — 254.000	M249710 M249710D M249710DC	14.1250 14.1250 14.1250	358.775 358.775 358.775	52		31 31
9.1250 231.775	LL244549	9.1250	231.775	53			459.	1.76	3180 6360 1800	7150 14300 4050	LL244500	10.5625 268.288	9.1250 231.775	LL244510	10.5625	268.288	53		
9.1250 — 9.3437 231.775 — 237.330	M246942 M246949	9.1250 9.3437	231.775 237.330	53 53			939.	1.76	17200 34400 9750	38700 77400 22000	M246900	13.2500 336.550	9.1250 — 9.3437 231.775 — 237.330	M246910	13.2500	336.550	53		
9.2500 234.950	LM446349	9.2500	234.950	53	"D_b"=9.92 252.0		680.	1.61	9300 18600 5750	20900 41800 13000	LM446300	12.2500 311.150	9.2500 234.950	LM446310D	12.2500	311.150		45	31
9.2500 234.950	LM446349WN	9.2500	234.950	53	"D_b"=.14 3.5														
9.2500 234.950	LM545849	9.2500	234.950	53			695.	1.47	11200 22400 7600	25200 50400 17100	LM545800	12.3750 — 12.5000 314.325 — 317.500	9.2500 234.950	LM545810 LM545812	12.3750 12.5000	314.325 317.500	53 53		
9.4970 — 9.5070 241.224 — 241.478	EE170900D EE170970D	9.4970 9.5070	241.224 241.478		11 11	"R"=1.8125 46.038	824.	1.65	13700 27400 8300	30800 61600 18700	127000	13.7460 — 13.9960 349.148 — 355.498	9.4970 — 9.5070 241.224 — 241.478	127135	13.7460	349.148			11 11
9.5000 241.300	H249148	9.5000	241.300	52 53			1218.	1.76	32200 64400 18400	72500 145000 41000	H249100	16.0000 406.400		127138	13.9960	355.498			
9.5000 241.300	EE810196D	9.5000	241.300	53	11	"B"=3.9375 "R"=.25 100.012 6.4	1055.	1.40	28600 57200 20400	64500 129000 46000	821000	16.5000 419.100	9.5000 241.300	H249111D H249111DC	16.0000 16.0000	406.400 406.400	53 53		31 31
9.5000 241.300	EE923095	9.5000	241.300	53			1172.	1.73	29600 59200 17100	66500 133000 38500	923000	17.5000 444.500	9.5000 241.300	821165	16.5000	419.100			
9.5000 — 10.0000 241.300 — 254.000	EE170950 NA170950 EE170975 EE171000D	9.5000 9.5000 9.7500 10.0000	241.300 241.300 247.650 254.000	53 53 53	41 11		753.	1.61	11350 22700 7050	25500 51000 15800	170000	14.3720 — 14.5000 365.049 — 368.300	9.5000 241.300	923175 923176D	17.5000 17.5000	444.500 444.500	53		31
													9.5000 — 10.0000 241.300 — 254.000	171436 171450 171451D 171451DC	14.3720 14.5000 14.5000 14.5000	365.049 368.300 368.300 368.300	53 53		31 31

BEARING SELECTION INDEX

The following index of bearing series is listed by increasing bore size.

The bearing type and specific cone and cup dimensions are located on the page reference number indicated.

bore range min. — max.	outside diameter range min. — max.	series number	rating at 500 RPM / 3000 hours L10 (lb)	(daN)	fac-tor K	fac-tor G	cone number	cone bore inch	metric	TS or TSL	SS or SR	TDI or TDIT	TNA and TNADC	TNASW or TNASWE	cup number	cup outside diameter inch	metric	TS or TSF	TDO and TODODC	di-mension sheet page no.
9.5000 — 10.8750 / 241,300 — 276,225	15.5000 / 393,700	275000	40000 / 80000 / 27600	17800 / 35600 / 12300	1.45	1014.	EE275095	9.5000	241,300	53					275155	15.5000	393,700	53		
							EE275100	10.0000	254,000		54				2751560	15.5000	393,700		31	
							EE275105	10.5000	266,700		55				2751560C	15.5000	393,700		31	
							EE275108	10.7500	273,050		55									
							EE275109D	10.8750	276,225			12								
9.5000 — 11.0000 / 241,300 — 279,400	19.2500 / 488,950	295000	90500 / 181000 / 48500	40200 / 80400 / 21400	1.87	1604.	EE295950	9.5000	241,300	53					295193	19.2500	488,950	53		
							EE295102	10.2500	260,350	54										
							EE295106D	10.5000	266,700			12								
							EE295110	11.0000	279,400	55										
9.6250 / 244,475	12.8750 / 327,025	LM247700	27000 / 54000 / 14800	12000 / 24000 / 6600	1.82	794.	LM247748D	9.6250	244,475			11			LM247710	12.8750	327,025			"C" = 1.5000 / 38.100 "y" = .13 / 3.3 "Db" = 12.20 / 310.0
9.6250 — 9.8130 / 244,475 — 249,250	15.0000 / 381,000	126000	43000 / 86000 / 38200	19200 / 38400 / 17000	1.13	916.	EE126096D	9.6250	244,475	53					126150	15.0000	381,000	53		
							EE126097	9.6250	244,475	53					126151D	15.0000	381,000		31	
							EE126098	9.8130	249,250	54		11			126151DC	15.0000	381,000		31	
9.7500 / 247,650	12.0000 / 304,800	28800	7600 / 15200 / 4250	3380 / 6760 / 1880	1.80	540.	28880	9.7500	247,650	53					28820	12.0000	304,800	53		
9.7500 / 247,650	13.6250 / 346,075	M348400	39600 / 79200 / 23300	17600 / 35200 / 10350	1.70	997.	M348449	9.7500	247,650	53					M348410	13.6250	346,075	53		
9.7500 / 247,650	16.0000 / 406,400	HH249900	96500 / 193000 / 55000	43000 / 86000 / 24400	1.76	1644.	HH249949	9.7500	247,650	53					HH249910	16.0000	406,400	53		
							HH249949D	9.7500	247,650			11								
10.0000 / 254,000	13.6875 / 347,662	LM249700	23600 / 47200 / 13400	10500 / 21000 / 5950	1.76	715.	LM249747NW	10.0000	254,000		"B" = 1.6875 "R" = .14 "Db" = 10.71		3.5	45 / 272.0	LM249710D	13.6875	347,662		31	
							LM249748	10.0000	254,000		42,862				LM249710DC	13.6875	347,662		31	
10.0000 / 254,000	17.5000 / 444,500	822000	46500 / 93000 / 27300	20600 / 41200 / 12150	1.71	979.	EE822100X	10.0000	254,000	54					822175	17.5000	444,500	54		
							EE822101D	10.0000	254,000			11			822176D	17.5000	444,500		32	
10.0000 / 254,000	21.0000 / 533,400	HH953700	90000 / 180000 / 145000	40000 / 80000 / 64500	0.62	1183.	HH953749	10.0000	254,000	54					HH953710	21.0000	533,400	54		
															HH953710D	21.0000	533,400		32	
															HH953710DC	21.0000	533,400		32	
10.0000 — 10.2500 / 254,000 — 260,350	14.3750 / 365,125	134000	32200 / 64400 / 20700	14350 / 28700 / 9200	1.56	919.	EE134100	10.0000	254,000	54					134143	14.3750	365,125	54		
							EE134102	10.2500	260,350	54					134144D	14.3750	365,125		32	
															134144DC	14.3750	365,125		32	

Dimensional note (upper right):

"C" = 2.6250 / 66.675
"r" = .13 / 3.3
"Db" = 14.80 / 376.0

Bore in / mm	Outer range in / mm	Assembly No.	Rating (3-stack)	Rating (3-stack)	K	Ref.	Cone(s) — bore in / mm / code	Cup(s) — O.D. in / mm / code
10.0000 — 10.2500 / 254.000 — 260.350	16.6250 — 16.9970 / 422.275 — 431.723	HM252300	54000 / 108000 / 30700	24000 / 48000 / 13650	1.76	1077.	HM252343 10.0000/254.000/54; HM252348 10.2500/260.350/54	HM252343 16.2500/422.275/54; HM252348 16.2500/422.275/32; HM252310D 16.6250/422.275/32; HM252310DC 16.6250/422.275/32; HM252310D 16.6250/422.275/32; HM252315D 16.9970/431.723/32; HM252315DC 16.9970/431.723/32
10.0000 — 10.2500 / 254.000 — 260.350	16.6250 — 16.9970 / 422.275 — 431.723	HM252300	56000 / 112000 / 31700	24800 / 49600 / 14100	1.76	1109.	HM252344NA 10.0000/254.000; HM252349 10.2500/260.350/54; HM252349NA 10.2500/260.350	HM252310 16.2500/422.275/54; HM252310D 16.2500/422.275/32; HM252310DC 16.6250/422.275/32; HM252310D 16.6250/422.275/32; HM252315D 16.9970/431.723/32; HM252315DC 16.9970/431.723/32
10.0000 — 10.5000 / 254.000 — 266.700		29800	7900 / 15800 / 4650	3500 / 7000 / 2080	1.69	602.	29875 10.0000/254.000/54; 29880 10.5000/266.700/54	29820 12.7500/323.850/54; 29820C 12.7500/323.850; 29820DC 12.7500/323.850
10.1250 / 257.175		M349500	33400 / 66800 / 19900	14850 / 29700 / 8850	1.68	964.	M349549 10.1250/257.175/54	M349510 13.5000/342.900/54; M349510B 13.5000/342.900/67
10.2500 / 260.350		220000	37100 / 74200 / 25100	16500 / 33000 / 11150	1.48	924.	EE2210250 10.2500/260.350; EE2210260 10.2500/260.350/54; NA2210260 10.2500/260.350; EE2210280 10.2500/260.350	221575 15.7500/400.050/54; 221576D 15.7500/400.050/32; 221576DC 15.7500/400.050/32
10.2500 / 260.350	16.0000 / 406.400	324000	53000 / 106000 / 30400	23600 / 47200 / 13500	1.75	1203.	EE3241030 10.2500/260.350	324160 16.0000/406.400
10.2500 — 10.5000 / 260.350 — 266.700	16.6250 — 16.9970 / 422.275 — 431.723	550000	51000 / 102000 / 29000	22600 / 45200 / 12900	1.76	1154.	EE551026 10.2500/260.350/54; EE551050 10.5000/266.700/55	551662 16.6250/422.275/54; 551700 16.9970/431.723/55
10.3750 — 10.5000 / 263.525 — 266.700	12.8125 / 325.438	38800	11500 / 23000 / 3180	5100 / 10200 / 3180	1.60	676.	38880 10.3750/263.525/54; 38885 10.5000/266.700/54	38820 12.8125/325.438/54
10.3750 — 10.5000 / 263.525 — 266.700	14.0000 / 355.600	LM451300	34700 / 69400 / 21400	15450 / 30900 / 9500	1.62	1042.	LM451345 10.3750/263.525/54; LM451349 10.5000/266.700/54; LM451349A 10.5000/266.700/54; LM451349D 10.5000/266.700; LM451349TD 10.5000/266.700	LM451310 14.0000/355.600/54; LM451310B 14.0000/355.600/67; LM451310D 14.0000/355.600; LM451310DC 14.0000/355.600/33
10.5000 / 266.700	13.8750 / 352.425	LM251600	27400 / 54800 / 15000	12150 / 24300 / 6650	1.83	950.	LM251649NW 10.5000/266.700	LM251610100 13.8750/352.425
10.5000 / 266.700	17.5000 / 444.500	H852800	91000 / 182000 / 90000	40400 / 80800 / 40000	1.01	1528.	H852849 10.5000/266.700/55	H852810 17.5000/444.500/55
10.6250 / 269.875	15.0000 / 381.000	M252300	50000 / 100000 / 28300	22200 / 44400 / 12600	1.76	1262.	M2523490 10.6250/269.875/55; M2523490 10.6250/269.875	M252310 15.0000/381.000/55
10.8750 / 276.225	13.7795 — 13.8750 / 350.000 — 352.425	L853000	15700 / 31400 / 14600	7000 / 14000 / 6500	1.08	685.	L853049 10.8750/276.225/55	L853011B† 13.7795/350.000/67; L853010 13.8750/352.425/55

†Dimension shown is maximum value—see note at bottom of fitting practice table in Reference Tables.

BEARING SELECTION INDEX

The bearing type and specific cone or cup dimensions are located on the page reference number indicated.

The following index of bearing series is listed by increasing bore size.

"O" = 4.1875 / 106,362
"r" = .25 / 6,4
"Db" = 16.22 / 412,0

bore range (min. – max.) inch/metric	outside diameter range (min. – max.)	series number	one-row radial	two-row radial	thrust (lb)	one-row radial	two-row radial	thrust (daN)	factor K	factor G	cone number	cone bore inch	cone bore metric	cones page ref (TS/TSL)	cones (SS/SR)	cones (TDI/TDIT)	cones (TNA/TNADC)	cones (THASW/THASWE)	cup number	outside diameter inch	outside diameter metric	cups page ref (TS/TSF)	cups (TDO/TDODC)	dim. sheet page no.
11.0000 / 279,400	12.5000 / 317,500	LL352100	8800	17600	5200	3920	7840	2320	1.69	713.	LL352149	11.0000	279,400	55					LL352110	12.5000	317,500	55		
11.0000 / 279,400	18.0000 / 457,200	HH255100	123000	246000	70000	54500	109000	31200	1.76	2168.	HH255149D	11.0000	279,400			12			HH255110	18.0000	457,200	55		
11.0000 — 11.5000 / 279,400 — 292,100	18.5000 / 469,900	722000	62500	125000	40000	27800	55600	17800	1.55	1330.	EE722110	11.0000	279,400	55					722185	18.5000	469,900		33	
											EE722115	11.5000	292,100	55					722186D	18.5000	469,900			
																			722186DC	18.5000	469,900		33	
11.0070 — 11.2500 / 279,578 — 285,750	14.9610 — 14.9960 / 380,009 — 380,898	LM654600	38800	77600	28800	17300	34600	12800	1.35	1267.	LM654644D	11.0070	279,578			12			LM654611	14.9610	380,009	55		
											LM654642	11.0229	279,981						LM654610	14.9960	380,898	55		
											LM654648D	11.2500	285,750			12			LM654610B	14.9960	380,898	67		
											LM654649	11.2500	285,750						LM654610D	14.9960	380,898		33	
																			LM654610DC	14.9960	380,898		33	
11.0236 — 11.0312 / 280,000 — 280,192	16.0000 / 406,400	128000	41000	82000	27200	18200	36400	12100	1.51	1119.	EE128113TD	11.0236	280,000			19			128160	16.0000	406,400	55		
											EE128111	11.0312	280,192	55					128160D	16.0000	406,400		33	
																			128160DC	16.0000	406,400		33	
11.0312 / 280,192	15.7500 — 16.0000 / 400,050 — 406,400	100000	28300	56600	19800	12600	25200	8800	1.43	953.	EE101103	11.0312	280,192	55					101579	15.7500	400,050	55		
																			101610	16.0000	406,400		33	
																			101610D	16.0000	406,400			
																			101610DC	16.0000	406,400		33	
11.2500 / 285,750	13.9375 — 14.1250 / 354,012 — 358,775	545000	12500	25000	10500	5550	11100	4650	1.19	664.	545112	11.2500	285,750	55					545139	13.9375	354,012	55		
																			545141	14.1250	358,775	55		
11.2500 / 285,750	19.7500 / 501,650	147000	57500	115000	82000	25400	50800	36400	0.70	1044.	EE147112	11.2500	285,750	"B" = 3.5000 / 88,900	"R" = .25 / 6,4	"b" = 12.95 / 329,0			147190	19.7500	501,650		33	
																			147190DC	19.7500	501,650		33	
11.3750 / 288,925	16.0000 / 406,400	M255400	59500	119000	34500	26600	53200	15300	1.73	1560.	M255449	11.3750	288,925	55					M255410	16.0000	406,400	55		
											M255449D	11.3750	288,925			12			M255410D	16.0000	406,400		33	
											M255449TD	11.3750	288,925			19			M255410DC	16.0000	406,400		33	
11.5000 / 292,100	14.7500 / 374,650	L555200	25500	51000	17600	11350	22700	7800	1.45	976.	L555249	11.5000	292,100	55					L555210	14.7500	374,650	55		
11.5000 / 292,100	15.5000 / 393,700	84000	21900	43800	22800	9750	19500	10150	0.96	799.	84115	11.5000	292,100	55					84155	15.5000	393,700	55		
11.5000 — 12.0000 / 292,100 — 304,800	22.0000 / 558,800	790000	115000	230000	78000	51000	102000	34600	1.48	1885.	EE790114	11.5000	292,100	55					790221	22.0000	558,800	55		
											EE790120	12.0000	304,800	56										

Bore (in) / (mm)	Series / OD (in) / (mm)	Ratings			Ratio	Ref.	Cone No.	(in) / (mm)			"B" etc.			Cup No.	(in) / (mm)	
11.6250 — 12.0000 / 295.275 — 304.800	LM737000	40500 / 61000 / 30700			1.32	1308.	LM737043TD / LM737049	11.6250 / 12.0000	295.275 / 304.800	56	19			LM737010	16.0000 / 406.400	56
11.7500 — 12.5000 / 298.450 — 317.500	280000	35200 / 70400 / 22700			1.55	1092.	EE281175 / EE281200D / EE281201 / EE281250	11.7500 / 12.0000 / 12.0000 / 12.5000 / 317.500	298.450 / 304.800 / 304.800 / 317.500	55 / 56 / 56	12			291749 / 291750 / 291750B / 291751D / 291751DC	17.5000 / 444.500 ×5	56 / 55 / 67 / 33 / 33
11.8125 / 300.038	HM258000	65000 / 130000 / 37600			1.73	1717.	HM258649 / HM258649D	11.8125 / 11.8125	300.038 / 300.038	55	12			HM256810 / HM258810D / HM258810DC	16.6250 / 422.275 ×3	55 / 33 / 33
11.9375 / 303.212	HH258200	144000 / 288000 / 82000			1.76	2619.	HH258249TD / HH258249NW	11.9375 / 303.212	303.212	55	19			HH258210	19.5000 / 495.300	"C" = 4.5000 / 14.300 "r" = .25 / 6.4 "Db" = 17.64 / 448.0
11.9940 / 304.647	M737400	50500 / 101000 / 40500			1.24	1255.	M737447D	11.9940 / 304.647	304.647		12			M737410	17.2460 / 438.048	"C" = 2.1250 / 53.975 "r" = .19 / 4.8 "Db" = 16.02 / 407.0
11.9940 — 12.0000 / 304.647 — 304.800	329000	50000 / 100000 / 28500			1.76	1411.	EE329119D / NA329120	11.9940 / 12.0000	304.647 / 304.800	55	12		41	329172	17.2460 / 438.048	"C" = 2.1250 / 53.975 "r" = .13 / 3.3 "Db" = 16.14 / 410.0
12.0000 / 304.800	L357000	29200 / 58400 / 17900			1.63	1164.	L357049 / L357049NW	12.0000 / 12.0000	304.800 / 304.800	55			45	329173D / 329173DC / L357010 / L357010D / L357010DC / L357010B	17.2460 / 17.2460 / 15.5000 / 15.5000 / 15.5000 / 15.5449	438.048 / 438.048 / 393.700 / 393.700 / 393.700 / 405.000 — 33 / 33 / 55 / 33 / 33 / 67
12.0000 / 304.800	109000	29400 / 58800 / 21400			1.37	1040.	EE109120	12.0000 / 304.800	304.800		12	"B" = 2.1250 / 53.975 "R" = .25 / 6.4 "db" = 12.99 / 330.0		1091630	16.2500 / 412.750	33
12.0000 / 304.800	M257100	50500 / 101000 / 28700			1.76	1458.	M257149D	12.0000 / 304.800	304.800		12			M257110	16.5000 / 419.100	56
12.0000 / 304.800	724000	66500 / 133000 / 46000			1.45	1515.	EE724120	12.0000 / 304.800	304.800	56				724195	19.5000 / 495.300	56
12.0000 / 304.800	724000	68000 / 136000 / 47000			1.45	1554.	EE724119	12.0000 / 304.800	304.800	56				724195	19.5000 / 495.300	56
12.0000 / 304.800	940000	54000 / 108000 / 37400			1.45	1245.	EE941205X	12.0000 / 304.800	304.800	56				941950 / 941953D	19.5000 / 19.5000	495.300 / 495.300 — 56 / 33

†Dimension shown is maximum value—see note at bottom of fitting practice table in Reference Tables.

The following index of bearing series is listed by increasing bore size.

BEARING SELECTION INDEX

The bearing type and specific cone or cup dimensions are located on the page reference number indicated.

bore range min.	bore range max.	outside diameter range min.	outside diameter range max.	series number	one-row radial thrust lb	two-row radial thrust lb/daN	K factor	cone number	cone bore inch	cone bore metric	G factor	cone page ref TS or TSL	SS or SR	TDI or TDIT	TNA and TNADC	TNASW or TNASWE	cup number	cup outside diameter inch	cup outside diameter metric	cup page ref TS or TSF	TDO and TDODC	dim. sheet page no.
12.0000	304.800	19.6850	500.000	M959400	51000 / 102000 / 102000 (daN 22800 / 45600 / 45600)		0.50	M959442	12.0000	304,800	1063.	56					M959410	19.6850†	500,000†	56	"C"=2.1250 / 53.975 "r"=.13 / 3.3 "Db"=15.28 / 388.0	
12.0040	304.901	16.2460	412.648	M257200	50000 / 100000 / 27200 (daN 22200 / 44400 / 12100)		1.83	M257240D	12.0040	304,901	1573.			12			M257210	16.2460	412,648	56		
12.3125	312.738	14.1250	358.775	LL957000	6450 / 12900 / 9100 (daN 2860 / 5720 / 4040)		0.71	LL957049	12.3125	312,738	569.	56					LL957010	14.1250	358,775	56		
12.5000	317.500	17.6250	447.675	HM255000	73500 / 147000 / 42500 (daN 32800 / 65600 / 18800)		1.74	HM255049	12.5000	317,500	1974.	56					HM255010	17.6250	447,675	56		
12.5000	317.500	24.5000	622.300	H961600	118000 / 236000 / 190000 (daN 52500 / 105000 / 84500)		0.62	H961649	12.5000	317,500	1812.	56					H961610	24.5000	622,300	56		
12.5000 — 12.8125	317.500 — 325.438	23.5000	596.900	720000	126000 / 252000 / 91000 (daN 56000 / 112000 / 40400)		1.38	EE720125 / EE720128	12.5000 / 12.8125	317,500 / 325,438	2204.	56 / 56					720236	23.5000	596,900	56		
12.7500	323.850	15.0000	381.000	LL758700	12800 / 25600 / 9600 (daN 5650 / 11300 / 4260)		1.33	LL758744	12.7500	323,850	931.	56					LL758715	15.0000	381,000	56		
13.0000	330.200	16.3750	415.925	L860000	24900 / 49800 / 21300 (daN 11100 / 22200 / 9500)		1.17	L860048 / L860049	13.0000 / 13.0000	330,200 / 330,200	1169.	56 / 56					L860010	16.3750	415,925	56		
13.0000	330.200	19.0000	482.600	526000	57000 / 114000 / 38400 (daN 25400 / 50800 / 17100)		1.49	EE526130 / EE526132	13.0000 / 13.0000	330,200 / 330,200	1553.	56 / 56					526190 / 526190B / 526191D / 526191DC	19.0000 / 19.0000 / 19.0000 / 19.0000	482,600 / 482,600 / 482,600 / 482,600	56 / 68	33 / 33	
13.0000 — 14.0000	330.200 — 355.600	18.5000 — 19.0000	469.900 — 482.600	160000	27300 / 54600 / 23300 (daN 12150 / 24300 / 10350)		1.17	EE161300 / EE161363 / EE161400	13.0000 / 13.6250 / 14.0000	330,200 / 346,075 / 355,600	1166.	56 / 57 / 57					161850 / 161900	18.5000 / 19.0000	469,900 / 482,600	56 / 56		
13.0040	330.301	17.2450	438.023	138000	36800 / 73600 / 29000 (daN 16400 / 32800 / 12900)		1.27	EE138131D	13.0040	330,301	1321.			13			138172	17.2450	483,023	56	"C"=1.8750 / 47.625 "r"=.13 / 3.3 "Db"=16.22 / 412.0	
13.1250	333.375	18.5000	469.900	HM261000	81000 / 162000 / 46500 (daN 36000 / 72000 / 20600)		1.74	HM261049 / HM261049D / HM261049TD	13.1250 / 13.1250 / 13.1250	333,375 / 333,375 / 333,375	2216.	56	13 / 19				HM261010 / HM261010D / HM261010DC	18.5000 / 18.5000 / 18.5000	469,900 / 469,900 / 469,900	56 / 56	33 / 33	

13,250 — 14,5000 333,375 — 368,300	20,6250 523,875	HM265010	102000 204000 57500	45000 90000 25600	1.76	2846.	HM265032TD HM265049 HM265049D HM265049TD HM265049XD	13,1250 14,4980 14,5000 14,5000 14,5000 333,375 368,249 368,300 368,300 368,300	333,375	57	19 13 19 13	HM285010 HM285010D	20,6250 20,6250 523,875 523,875	57	"C"=1,9375 / 49,212 "Y"=.13 / 3,3 "Db"=17,01 / 432,0 33
13,5000 342,900	17,7500 450,850	LM361600	51000 102000 30700	22600 45200 13650	1.66	1805.	LM361649	13,5000 342,900	342,900	56		LM361610	17,7500 450,850	56	
13,5000 342,900	17,9960 457,098	LM961500	43500 87000 53500	19400 38800 23800	0.82	1477.	LM961549	13,5000 342,900	342,900	57		LM961510	17,9960 457,098	57	
13,5000 342,900	21,0000 533,400	970000	62500 125000 35400	27800 55600 15750	1.76	1683.	E971354	13,5000 342,900	342,900	57		972100	21,0000 533,400	57	
13,5060 343,052	17,9960 457,098	LM761600	45000 90000 36400	20200 40400 16200	1.24	1469.	LM761649D	13,5060 343,052	343,052		13	LM761610	17,9960 457,098		
13,6250 346,075	17,9960 457,098	133000	36200 72400 29700	16100 32200 13200	1.22	1369.	EE1331370	13,6250 346,075	346,075		13	133180	17,9960 457,098		"C"=1,8750 / 47,625 "Y"=.13 / 3,3 "Db"=16,93 / 430,0 33
13,6250 346,075	19,0000 482,600	203000	42000 84000 29900	18600 37200 13300	1.40	1446.	EE203136 EE203137	13,6250 13,6250 346,075 346,075	346,075 346,075	57 57		203190	19,0000 482,600	57	
13,6250 346,075	19,2500 488,950	HM262700	88000 176000 50500	39200 78400 22600	1.74	2427.	HM262749 HM262749TD HM262749TD	13,6250 13,6250 13,6250 346,075 346,075 346,075	346,075 346,075 346,075	57	13 19	HM262710 HM262710D HM262710DC	19,2500 19,2500 19,2500 488,950 488,950 488,950	57	33 33
13,7500 349,250	18,0000 457,200	LM263100	49500 99000 27100	22000 44000 12050	1.83	2029.	LM263145TD	13,7500 349,250	349,250		19	LM263110	18,0000 457,200		"C"=2,0000 / 50,800 "Y"=.13 / 3,3 "Db"=17,09 / 434,0
13,7500 — 14,0000 349,250 — 355,600	19,7500 — 20,2500 501,650 — 514,350	333000	66500 133000 42000	29600 59200 18600	1.59	2030.	EE333137 EE333140	13,7500 14,0000 349,250 355,600	349,250 355,600	57 57		333197 3332030 3332030C	19,7500 20,2500 20,2500 501,650 514,350 514,350	57	33 33
14,0000 355,600	17,5000 444,500	L163100	42000 84000 22000	18600 37200 9800	1.90	2037.	L163149 L163149D	14,0000 14,0000 355,600 355,600	355,600 355,600	57	13	L163110 L163110D L163110DC	17,5000 17,5000 17,5000 444,500 444,500 444,500	57	33 33
14,0000 355,600	19,0000 482,600	LM763400	53000 106000 42500	23400 46800 19000	1.24	1663.	LM763449D	14,0000 355,600	355,600		13	LM763410	19,0000 482,600		
14,0000 — 14,6250 355,600 — 371,475	19,7500 — 20,2500 501,650 — 514,350	230000	43500 87000 32700	19400 38800 14550	1.33	1599.	EE231400 EE231401D EE231462	14,0000 14,0000 14,6250 355,600 355,600 371,475	355,600 355,600 371,475	57 57	13	231975 232025	19,7500 20,2500 501,650 514,350	57 57	"C"=2,0625 / 52,388 "Y"=.13 / 3,3 "Db"=17,83 / 453,0

†Dimension shown is maximum value—see note at bottom of fitting practice table in Reference Tables.

43

BEARING SELECTION INDEX

The following index of bearing series is listed by increasing bore size.

The bearing type and specific cone or cup dimensions are located on the page reference number indicated.

bore range (min. — max.)	outside diameter range (min. — max.)	series number	rating at 500 RPM for 3000 hours L10 one-row radial thrust / two-row radial thrust (lb)	(daN)	fac-tor K	fac-tor G	cone number	cone bore (inch)	cone bore (metric)	page ref. to locate CONES — TS or TSL	SS or SR	TDI or TDIT	TNA and TNADC	THASW or TNASWE	cup number	cup outside diameter (inch)	(metric)	page ref. to locate CUPS — TS or TSF	TDO and TDODC	dimension sheet page no.
14.2500 — 361.950	15.8125 — 401.638	LL762600	8900 / 17800 / 6750	3960 / 7920 / 3000	1.32	982.	LL762648	14.2500	361.950	57					LL762610	15.8125	401.638	57		
14.2500 — 361.950	16.0000 — 406.400	LL582700	10600 / 21200 / 7350	4700 / 9400 / 3260	1.45	1039.	LL582749	14.2500	361.950	57					LL582710	16.0000	406.400	57		
14.2500 — 361.950	18.8125 — 477.838	LM763800	50000 / 100000 / 40500	22200 / 44400 / 17950	1.24	1708.	LM763848	14.2500	361.950	57					LM763811B	18.8125	477.838	67		
14.7500 — 374.650	17.0000 — 431.800	LL264600	13800 / 27600 / 7850	6100 / 12200 / 3500	1.76	1322.	LL264648	14.7500	374.650	**57**					LL264610	17.0000	431.800	57		
15.0000 — 381.000	18.8750 — 479.425	L865500	29000 / 58000 / 24600	12900 / 25800 / 10950	1.18	1429.	L865547 / L865548	15.0000 / 15.0000	381.000 / 381.000	57 / 57					L865512	18.8750	479.425	57		
15.0000 — 381.000	20.0000 — 508.000	192000	33300 / 66600 / 30300	14800 / 29600 / 13450	1.10	1514.	EE192150	15.0000	381.000	57					192201D / 192201DC	20.0000 / 20.0000	508.000 / 508.000		34 / 34	
15.0000 — 381.000	20.5625 — 20.6250 / 522.288 — 523.875	LM565900	69500 / 139000 / 46000	31000 / 62000 / 20400	1.51	2239.	LM565949	15.0000	381.000	57					LM565910 / LM565910B / LM565912	20.5625 / 20.5625 / 20.6250	522.288 / 522.288 / 523.875	57 / 68 / 57		
15.0000 — 15.1250 / 381.000 — 384.175	21.5000 — 546.100	HM266400	110000 / 220000 / 63000	49000 / 98000 / 28000	1.76	3140.	HM266447 / HM266449 / HM266449TD / HM266449STD	15.0000 / 15.1250 / 16.3750 / 15.1250	381.000 / 384.175 / 415.925 / 384.175	57 / 58	13 / 19				HM266410 / HM266410D / HM266410DC	21.5000 / 21.5000 / 21.5000	546.100 / 546.100 / 546.100		34 / 34	
15.0000 — 16.3750 / 381.000 — 415.925	23.2500 — 590.550	M268700	130000 / 260000 / 73500	58000 / 116000 / 32600	1.76	3769.	M268730 / M268749 / M268749D / M268749TD	15.0000 / 16.3750 / 16.3750 / 16.3750	381.000 / 415.925 / 415.925 / 415.925	57 / 58	13 / 19				M268710 / M268710D / M268710DC	23.2500 / 23.2500 / 23.2500	590.550 / 590.550 / 590.550		34 / 34	
15.1250 — 384.175	17.3750 — 441.325	LL365300	13300 / 26600 / 7700	5900 / 11800 / 3440	1.72	1313.	LL365348	15.1250	384.175	57					LL365310	17.3750	441.325	57		
15.1875 — 385.762	20.2500 — 514.350	LM665900	72000 / 144000 / 51500	32000 / 64000 / 22800	1.40	2432.	LM665949	15.1875	385.762	58					LM665910	20.2500	514.350	58		
15.5000 — 16.0000 / 393.700 — 406.400	21.5000 — 546.100	LM767700	66000 / 132000 / 53500	29400 / 58800 / 23800	1.23	2223.	LM767745D / LM767749D	15.5000 / 16.0000	393.700 / 406.400	58	13 / 13				LM767710	21.5000	546.100	58		

Notes (192000): "B"=−2.3125 / 58.738 · "R"=−.25 · "db"=−16.14 / 6.4 / 410.0

Notes (LM767700): "C"=−2.1250 / 53.975 · "H"=−.25 / 6.4 · "Db"=−20.08 / 510.0

BEARING SELECTION INDEX

Bore (in / mm)	OD (in / mm)	Family	F	Ratings (small)	Ratings (large)	Detail No.	Value	Notes	Cup detail	OD detail (in)	OD detail (mm)	Code
15.6250 — 16.0000 / 396.875 — 406.400	21.2500 — 22.0000 / 539.750 — 558.800	234000	1.23	20400 / 40800 / 16600	46000 / 92000 / 37300	EE234156 / EE234160	1840.		234213D / 234213DC / 234215 / 234220	21.2500 / 21.2500 / 21.5000 / 22.0000	539.750 / 539.750 / 546.100 / 558.800	34 / 34
15.8750 / 403.225	18.1250 / 460.375	LL566800	1.45	5800 / 11600 / 4020	13100 / 26200 / 9050	LL566848	1413.	58 / 58	LL566810	18.1250	460.375	58 / 58
16.0000 / 406.400	20.0000 / 508.000	L467900	1.60	21200 / 42400 / 13300	48000 / 96000 / 29900	L467549	2377.	58	L467510 / L467510B	20.0000 / 20.0000	508.000 / 508.000	58 / 68
16.0000 / 406.400	21.5000 / 546.100	LM767700	1.23	31400 / 62800 / 25600	71000 / 142000 / 57500	LM767748D	2381.	13	LM767710	21.5000	546.100	
16.0000 / 406.400	21.6250 / 549.275	LM567900	1.43	32200 / 64400 / 22600	72500 / 145000 / 50500	LM567949	2480.	58	LM567910 / LM567910B	21.6250 / 21.6250	549.275 / 549.275	58 / 68
16.0000 / 406.400	22.6250 / 574.675	285000	1.17	21000 / 42000 / 18000	47500 / 95000 / 40500	N4285160	1994.	41	2852280 / 2852280C	22.6250 / 22.6250	574.675 / 574.675	58
16.0000 / 406.400	23.3500 / 590.550	833000	1.80	50500 / 101000 / 28200	114000 / 228000 / 63500	EE833160X / EE833161XD	3296.	13	833223 / 833223D	23.3500 / 23.3500	590.550 / 590.550	58
16.0000 / 406.400	24.0000 / 609.600	910000	1.52	31000 / 62000 / 20400	69500 / 139000 / 46000	EE911600	2206.		912400	24.0000	609.600	58
16.0000 / 406.400	30.0000 / 762.000	H969200	0.62	84000 / 168000 / 135500	189000 / 378000 / 304000	H969249	3127.	"B"=6.3750 161.925 "R"=.50 "db"=20.20 12.7 513.0	H969210D	30.0000	762.000	34
16.1250 / 409.575	21.5000 / 546.100	M667900	1.40	35000 / 70000 / 25000	79000 / 158000 / 56500	M667947D	2716.	13	M667911	21.5000	546.100	58
16.7500 — 17.0040 / 425.450 — 431.901	26.9960 / 685.698	328000	1.45	67000 / 134000 / 46000	151000 / 302000 / 104000	EE328167 / EE328172D	3744.	13	328269	26.9960	685.698	58
17.0000 / 431.800	21.0000 / 533.400	80300	1.91	14250 / 28500 / 7450	32000 / 64000 / 16800	80385	2087.	58	80325	21.0000	533.400	58
17.0000 / 431.800	22.5000 / 571.500	239000	1.52	27400 / 54800 / 18000	61500 / 123000 / 40500	EE239171D	2611.	13	239225	22.5000	571.500	58
17.0000 / 431.800	22.5000 / 571.500	LM869400	1.07	28000 / 56000 / 26200	63000 / 126000 / 59000	LM869448	2402.		LM869410 / LM869410D / LM869410DC	22.5000 / 22.5000 / 22.5000	571.500 / 571.500 / 571.500	34 / 34

Top (234000): $"C" = 2.1250$, 53.375; $"Y" = .25$, 6.4; $"Db" = 20.08$, 510.0

Top (LM869400): $"C" = 2.1250$, 53.375; $"Y" = .13$, 3.3; $"Db" = 21.26$, 540.0

BEARING SELECTION INDEX

The following index of bearing series is listed by increasing bore size.

The bearing type and specific cone or cup dimensions are located on the page reference number indicated.

bore range min. — max.	outside diameter range min. — max.	series number	rating at 500 RPM for 3000 hours L10 — one-row radial thrust / two-row radial thrust (lb)	(daN)	factor K	factor G	cone number	cone bore inch	cone bore metric	page reference no. to locate CONES in bearing tables TS or TSL	SS SR	TDI TDIT	TNA and THADC	TNASW or TMSWE	cup number	cup outside diameter inch	cup outside diameter metric	page ref. to locate CUPS in bearing tables TS or TSF	TDO and TDODC	dim. sheet page no.
17.0000 431.800	23.7500 603.250	240000	49000 98000 44000	21800 43600 19600	1.11	2183.	EE241701	17.0000	431.800	58					242375	23.7500	603.250	58		
17.0000 — 17.6250 431.800 — 447.675	21.7500 552.450	80000	32400 64800 17700	14400 28800 7900	1.83	2220.	80170 80178	17.0000 17.6250	431.800 447.675	58 58					80217	21.7500	552.450	58		
17.6250 447.675	25.0000 635.000	M270700	150000 300000 85000	66500 133000 37800	1.76	4459.	M270748D M270749 M270749D M270749TD	17.6250 17.6250 17.6250 17.6250	447.675 447.675 447.675 447.675	58		13 13 19			M270710 M270710D M270710DC	25.0000 25.0000 25.0000	635.000 635.000 635.000	58	34 34	
18.0000 457.200	22.5625 573.088	L570600	69000 138000 47500	30600 61200 21200	1.45	3161.	L570649	18.0000	457.200	58					L570610	22.5625	573.088	58		
18.0000 457.200	23.5000 596.900	244000	63500 127000 44000	28200 56400 19600	1.44	2852.	EE244180	18.0000	457.200	58					244235 2442360 2442360C	23.5000 23.5000 23.5000	596.900 596.900 596.900	58	34 34	
18.0000 457.200	23.5000 596.900	L770800	64500 129000 52000	28800 57600 23200	1.24	2517.	L770849D	18.0000	457.200	58		13			L770810	23.5000	596.900	58		
18.0000 457.200	23.7500 603.250	LM770900	77500 155000 60500	34600 69200 26800	1.29	3001.	LM770849	18.0000	457.200	58					LM770910 LM770910B	23.7500 23.7500	603.250 603.250	58	68	
18.0000 457.200	26.0000 660.400	M271600	116000 232000 63500	51500 103000 28200	1.83	3548.	M271648	18.0000	457.200	"B"=4.1875 "R"=25 "Db"=19.41 106.362 6.4 493.21		13			M271610D	26.0000	660.400		34	
18.0000 457.200	33.9960 863.498	480000	235000 470000 145000	104500 209000 64500	1.62	5017.	EE480181D	18.0000	457.200	58		13			480340	33.9960	863.498	"C"=5.7500 146.050 "r"=.25 "Db"=30.71 780.0 9.4		
18.7500 476.250	22.2500 565.150	LL771900	26000 52000 21000	11550 23100 9350	1.24	2340.	LL771948	18.7500	476.250	58					LL771911	22.2500	565.150	58		
18.8750 479.425	26.7500 679.450	M272700	172000 344000 98000	76500 153000 43600	1.76	5254.	M272749 M272749D M272749TD	18.8750 18.8750 18.8750	479.425 479.425 479.425	59		14 19			M272710 M272710D M272710DC	26.7500 26.7500 26.7500	679.450 679.450 679.450	59	35 35	
19.0000 482.600	24.2500 615.950	LM272200	91000 182000 51500	40400 80800 23000	1.76	3869.	LM272249	19.0000	482.600	59					LM272210 LM272210D LM272210DC	24.2500 24.2500 24.2500	615.950 615.950 615.950	59	35 35	

BEARING SELECTION INDEX

Bore (in)	Bore (mm)	Part	Ratings	factor	value	Part	in	mm	col	59	Part	in	mm	specs
19.0000	482,600	M272800	133000 / 266000 / 75500	1.76	4787.	M272847D	19.0000	482,600	14		M272810	25.5000	647,700	"C"=4.3750 85.725 6.4 "Db"=23.98 609.0
19.0000 — 19.6250	482,600 → 498,475	243000	79500 / 159000 / 47000	1.70	3855.	EE243190 / EE243192 / EE243193D / EE243196	19.0000 / 19.2530 / 19.2530 / 19.6250	482,600 / 489,026 / 489,026 / 498,475		59 / 59 / 59 / 59	243250	24.9950	634,873	59
19.2500	488,950	640000	104000 / 208000 / 55000	1.90	4112.	EE640192	19.2500	488,950		59	640260 / 640261D / 640261DC	26.0000 / 26.0000 / 26.0000	660,400 / 660,400 / 660,400	35 / 35
19.2500 — 19.2530	488,950 → 489,026	LM772700	86500 / 173000 / 69500	1.24	3470.	LM772748 / LM772749D	19.2500 / 19.2530	488,950 / 489,026	14	59	LM772710 / LM772710D / LM772710DC	24.9950 / 24.9950 / 24.9950	634,873 / 634,873 / 634,873	35 / 35
19.7500	501,650	M274100	188000 / 376000 / 107000	1.76	5836.	M274149TD	19.7500	501,650	19		M274110	28.0000	711,200	"C"=4.1875 106.362 6.4 "Db"=26.10 663.0
20.4375	519,112	M273300	202000 / 404000 / 115000	1.76	6325.	M273349D / M273349TD	20.4375 / 20.4375	519,112 / 519,112	14 / 19		M273310	29.0000	736,600	"C"=4.3750 111.125 6.4 "Db"=26.93 684.0
20.5000	520,700	980000	79500 / 159000 / 64500	1.23	3205.	EE982051	20.5000	520,700		59	982900	29.0000	736,600	59
21.0000 — 21.2500	533,400 → 539,750	LL575300	40500 / 81000 / 28200	1.44	3010.	LL575343 / LL575349	21.0000 / 21.2500	533,400 / 539,750		59 / 59	LL575310	25.0000	635,000	59
21.0000 — 21.5000	533,400 — 546,100	715000	450000 / 900000 / 243000	1.85	9336.	EE715210XD / EE715215XD	21.0000 / 21.5000	533,400 / 546,100	14 / 14		715380	38.0000	965,200	"C"=8.2500 209.550 / 190.550 12.7 34.25 870.0
21.1250	536,575	M276400	216000 / 432000 / 122000	1.76	6844.	M276448D / M276449	21.1250 / 21.1250	536,575 / 536,575	14	59	M276410 / M276410D / M276410DC	29.9950 / 29.9950 / 29.9950	761,873 / 761,873 / 761,873	35 / 35
21.6250	549,275	L476500	84500 / 169000 / 54500	1.55	4547.	L476549	21.6250	549,275		59	L476510	27.2500	692,150	59
21.9950	558,673	548000	410000 / 820000 / 257000	1.60	9371.	EE546230D	21.9950	558,673	14		548355	35.4950	901,573	"C"=7.5000 190.500 12.7 32.13 816.0
22.0000	558,800	LL876400	41500 / 83000 / 38900	1.07	2899.	LL876449D	22.0000	558,800	14		LL876410	26.0000	660,400	"C"=1.3750 34.925 3.3 "Db"=25.04 636.0
22.0000	558,800	647000	75000 / 150000 / 63500	1.18	3582.	EE647220	22.0000	558,800		59	647285	28.5000	723,900	59

BEARING SELECTION INDEX

The following index of bearing series is listed by increasing bore size.

The bearing type and specific cone or cup dimensions are located on the page reference number indicated.

bore range min. – max.	outside diameter range min. – max.	series number	rating at 500 RPM for 3000 hours L10 one-row radial / two-row radial thrust (lb)	(daN)	factor K	factor G	cone number	cone bore inch	cone bore metric	page ref. no. to locate CONES — TS/TSL	SS/SR	TDI/TDIT	TMA and TNADC	TMA and TNADC	TNASW / TNASWE	cup number	cup outside diameter inch	cup outside diameter metric	TS/TSF	TDO and TDODC	6-mension sheet page no.
22.0000 558.800	29.0000 736.600	LM377400	140000 / 280000 / 82500	62500 / 125000 / 36600	1.69	5907.	LM377449	22.0000	558.800	59						LM377410 / LM377410D / LM377410DC	29.0000	736.600	59	35 / 35	
22.0000 558.800	29.0000 736.600	542000	71000 / 142000 / 62000	31600 / 63200 / 27600	1.15	3653.	EE542220	22.0000	558.800		"B"=3.0000 76.200		6.4		"R"=.25 "db"=23.39 / 594.0	542291D / 542291DC	29.0000	736.600		35 / 35	
22.0000 558.800	29.0000 736.600	843000	103000 / 206000 / 60500	45500 / 91000 / 26800	1.70	4593.	EE843220	22.0000	558.800	59						843290 / 843291D / 843291DC	29.0000	736.600	59	35 / 35	
22.5000 571.500	32.0000 812.800	M278700	246000 / 492000 / 140000	109500 / 219000 / 62500	1.76	7956.	M278740TD / M278749D	22.5000 / 22.5000	571.500 / 571.500			19 / 14				M278710	32.0000	812.800		"C"=4.7500 120.650 "r"=.25 "Db"=29.54 756.0	
23.0000 584.200	27.0000 685.800	LL778100	43500 / 87000 / 32500	19400 / 38800 / 14450	1.34	3618.	LL778149	23.0000	584.200	59						LL778110	27.0000	685.800	59		
23.4375 595.312	33.2500 844.550	M280000	265000 / 530000 / 151000	118000 / 236000 / 67000	1.76	8708.	M280049D	23.4375	595.312			14				M280010	33.2500	844.550		"C"=4.9375 125.412 "r"=.25 "Db"=30.94 786.0	
23.5000 596.900	27.0000 685.800	LL379000	31700 / 63400 / 18500	14100 / 28200 / 8250	1.71	3570.	LL379049	23.5000	596.900	59						LL379010B	27.0000	685.800	68		
23.5000 596.900	27.0000 685.800	680000	18400 / 36800 / 16600	8200 / 16400 / 7400	1.11	2322.	680235	23.5000	596.900	59						680270	27.0000	685.800	59		
24.0000 609.600	30.0000 762.000	L879900	115000 / 230000 / 96000	51000 / 102000 / 42600	1.20	5876.	L879947	24.0000	609.600	59						L879910	30.0000	762.000	59		
24.0000 609.600	30.5000 774.700	L580000	101000 / 202000 / 69500	45000 / 90000 / 31000	1.45	4854.	L580049	24.0000	609.600	59						L580010	30.5000	774.700	59		
24.0000 609.600	31.0000 787.400	649000	121000 / 242000 / 76500	54000 / 108000 / 34000	1.58	5912.	EE649240 / EE649241D	24.0000 / 24.0000	609.600 / 609.600	59	"B"=3.2500 82.550	14			"R"=.25 "db"=25.39 / 645.0	649310 / 649311D / 649311DC	31.0000	787.400	59	35 / 35	
24.0000 609.600	32.0000 812.800	743000	91000 / 182000 / 51500	40400 / 80800 / 23000	1.77	4930.	EE743240	24.0000	609.600		"B"=3.2500 82.550		6.4		"R"=.25 "db"=25.39 / 645.0	743210 / 743321DC	32.0000	812.800		35 / 35	
24.5000 622.300	28.5625 725.488	LL780200	43500 / 87000 / 34700	19400 / 38800 / 15450	1.25	4121.	LL780249	24.5000	622.300							LL780210B	28.5625	725.488	68		

BEARING SELECTION INDEX

Bore	Cone No.	Factors	Factors	Ratio	Ref.	Assembly No.	O.D.	R	Cup No.	Width	R₂	Design Data
25.0000 / 635.000	M281000	302000 / 604000 / 171000	134000 / 268000 / 76500	1.76	10132.	M281049D	25.0000 / 635.000	14	M281010	35.5000 / 901.700	68	"C"=5.3750 136.525 "r"=.25 6.4 "Db"=33.19 843.0
25.5000 / 647.700	LL480700	33400 / 66800 / 21100	14850 / 29700 / 9400	1.58	4201.	LL480749	25.5000 / 647.700		LL4807108	29.0000 / 736.600		
25.8010 — 25.8750 / 655.345 — 657.225	M281800	324000 / 648000 / 184000	144000 / 288000 / 82000	1.76	10997.	M281647D / M281649D	25.8010 — 25.8750 / 655.345 — 657.225	14 / 14	M281610	36.7500 / 933.450		"C"=5.5625 141.288 "r"=.25 6.4 "Db"=34.25 870.0
									M281619	39.4410 / 1001.801		"C"=5.5625 141.288 "r"=.25 6.4 "Db"=35.43 900.0
26.7500 / 679.450	LM281800	245000 / 490000 / 139000	109000 / 218000 / 62000	1.76	10188.	LM281849	26.7500 / 679.450		LM281810	35.5000 / 901.700	59	
27.0000 / 685.800	895000	131000 / 262000 / 94000	58000 / 116000 / 41800	1.40	7310.	EE855270 / EE855271D	27.0000 / 685.800	14	655345	34.5000 / 876.300	35	
									655346D	34.5000 / 876.300	35	
									655346DC	34.5000 / 876.300		
27.9528 / 710.000	L882400	158000 / 316000 / 143000	70500 / 141000 / 63500	1.11	7890.	L882449D	27.9528 / 710.000 †	15	L882410	35.4331 / 900.000 †		"C"=3.0709 78.000 "r"=.25 6.4 "Db"=33.54 852.0
28.0000 — 28.5000 / 711.200 — 723.900	755000	108000 / 216000 / 70500	48000 / 96000 / 31400	1.54	6897.	EE755280 / EE755281D / EE755285	28.0000 / 28.0000 / 28.5000 / 711.200 / 711.200 / 723.900	15	755360	36.0000 / 914.400	59	
									755361D	36.0000 / 914.400	35	
									755361DC	36.0000 / 914.400	35	
29.0000 / 736.600	LL582900	25000 / 50000 / 17000	11100 / 22200 / 7550	1.47	4016.	LL582949	29.0000 / 736.600		LL582910B	32.5000 / 825.500	68	
29.5000 / 749.300	LM283600	299000 / 598000 / 170000	133000 / 266000 / 75500	1.76	12977.	LM283649	29.5000 / 749.300		LM283610	39.0000 / 990.600	60	
29.9213 — 30.0000 / 760.000 — 762.000	LL483400	83500 / 167000 / 54500	37200 / 74400 / 24200	1.54	7731.	LL483448 / LL483449	29.9213 / 30.0000 † / 760.000 / 762.000		LL483418	35.0000 / 889.000	60 / 60	
30.0000 / 762.000	752000	101000 / 202000 / 70000	45000 / 90000 / 31200	1.45	6900.	EE752300	30.0000 / 762.000		752380	38.0000 / 965.200	60	
30.0000 / 762.000	M284200	430000 / 860000 / 246000	192000 / 384000 / 109500	1.76	15448.	M284249D	30.0000 / 762.000	15	M284210	42.5000 / 1079.500	60	"C"=6.3750 161.925 "r"=.50 12.7 "Db"=39.57 1005.0
30.0000 / 762.000	433000	362000 / 724000 / 238000	161000 / 322000 / 106000	1.52	14027.	EE433301D	30.0000 / 762.000	15	433512	51.0000 / 1295.400	60	"C"=5.1250 130.175 "r"=.25 6.4 "Db"=47.64 1210.0

†Dimension shown is maximum value—see note at bottom of fitting practice table in Reference Tables.

BEARING SELECTION INDEX

The following index of bearing series is listed by increasing bore size.

The bearing type and specific cone or cup dimensions are located on the page reference number indicated.

bore range min. / max. (inch / metric)	outside diameter range min. / max.	series number	rating at 500 hours L10 / 3000 hours L10 one-row radial / two-row radial thrust — lb	— daN	factor K	factor G	cone number	cone bore inch	cone bore metric	TS or TSL	SS or SR	TDI or TDIT	TNA and TNADC	TNASW or TNASWE	cup number	cup outside diameter inch	metric	TS or TSF	TDO and TDODC	dimension sheet page nos.
30.5000 — 30.7087 / 774.700 — 780.000	48.0000 — 48.0315 / 1219.200 — 1220.000	631000	465000 / 930000 / 313000	208000 / 416000 / 139000	1.49	15320.	EE631305D EE631307D	30.5000 30.7087 †	774.700 780.000 †		15 15				631480	48.0000	1219.200			"C"=-6.5000 165,100 "r"=.50 12.7 "Db"=44.29 1125.0
															631484	48.0315 †	1220.000 †			"C"=-6.5954 165,524 "r"=.50 12.7 "Db"=44.29 1125.0
31.5625 / 801.688	36.0000 / 914.400	LL584400	65500 / 131000 / 44500	29200 / 58400 / 19800	1.47	7415.	LL584449	31.5625	801.688	60					LL584410	36.0000	914.400	60		
33.0000 / 838.200	41.0000 / 1041.400	763000	119000 / 238000 / 89500	53000 / 106000 / 39800	1.33	8880.	EE763330	33.0000	838.200	60					763410	41.0000	1041.400	60		
33.7500 / 857.250	43.0000 / 1092.200	157000	158000 / 316000 / 150000	70500 / 141000 / 66500	1.05	9770.	EE157337	33.7500	857.250	60					157430	43.0000	1092.200	60		
34.0000 / 863.600	38.5000 / 977.900	LL586000	46000 / 92000 / 31600	20400 / 40800 / 14050	1.45	8427.	LL586049	34.0000	863.600	68					LL586018B	38.5000	977.900	68		
34.0000 / 863.600	48.0000 / 1219.200	547000	555000 / 1110000 / 314000	246000 / 492000 / 140000	1.76	20552.	EE547341D	34.0000	863.600		15				547480	48.0000	1219.200			"C"=-7.3750 187,325 "r"=.50 12.7 "Db"=44.69 1135.0
34.5625 / 877.888	48.0315 / 1220.000	LM286700	510000 / 1020000 / 290000	228000 / 456000 / 129000	1.76	20364.	LM286749D	34.5625	877.888		15				LM286711	48.0315 †	1220.000 †			"C"=-6.6250 168,275 "r"=.50 12.7 "Db"=44.88 1140.0
35.5000 / 901.700	51.0000 / 1295.400	634000	620000 / 1240000 / 356000	276000 / 552000 / 158500	1.74	22304.	EE634356D	35.5000	901.700		15				634510	51.0000	1295.400			"C"=-7.6250 193,675 "r"=.50 12.7 "Db"=47.44 1205.0
36.0000 / 914.400	42.0000 / 1066.800	LL686900	93000 / 186000 / 65000	41400 / 82800 / 29000	1.43	10008.	LL686947	36.0000	914.400	"B"=2.5000 63.500	"R"=25	"db"=37.20 945.0 6.4			LL686910	42.0000	1066.800			35
36.9375 / 938.212	50.0000 / 1270.000	LM287600	535000 / 1070000 / 303000	238000 / 476000 / 135000	1.76	22915.	LM287690D	36.9375	938.212		15				LM287610	50.0000	1270.000			"C"=-6.6875 169,862 "r"=.50 12.7 "Db"=46.85 1190.0

BEARING SELECTION INDEX

This page is a dense two‑panel (mirror‑image) bearing index. The data below transcribes the canonical half of the table (the two halves carry identical data so they can be read from either edge).

C90 (a)	C90 (b)	CONE	K	CUP	Assembly	Bore / rating	aux	factor	Assembly	OD / rating
665000 / 1330000 / 377000	296000 / 592000 / 167500	LM287800	1.76	25382.	LM287810D	37.0000 / 939,800	60	15	LM287810	52.5000 / 1333,500
96500 / 193000 / 72000	43000 / 86000 / 32000	LL687900	1.34	11165.	LL687349	38.5000 / 977,901			LL687910	44.5000 / 1130,300
500000 / 1000000 / 283000	222000 / 444000 / 126000	LM288200	1.76	26146.	LM282249D	39.6250 / 1006,475	60	15	LM288210	51.0000 / 1295,400
159000 / 318000 / 134000	71000 / 142000 / 59500	168000	1.19	13427.	EE168400	40.0000 / 1016,000	60		168500	50.0000 / 1270,000
101000 / 202000 / 82500	45000 / 90000 / 36600	LL788300	1.23	12905.	LL788349	41.8750 / 1053,625 — 42.0000 / 1066,800	60 / 60		LL788310 / LL788310B	48.0000 / 1219,200 — 48.0000 / 1219,200
134000 / 268000 / 132000	59500 / 119000 / 58500	776000	1.02	13504.	EE776420	42.0000 / 1066,800	60		776520	52.0000 / 1320,800
244000 / 488000 / 151000	108500 / 217000 / 67000	277000	1.62	23806.	EE277455	45.5000 / 1155,700	60		277565	56.5000 / 1435,100
820000 / 1640000 / 465000	364000 / 728000 / 208000	LM288900	1.76	39897.	LM288849D	47.2500 / 1200,150		15	LM288910	62.7500 / 1593,850
113000 / 226000 / 111000	50500 / 101000 / 49500	LL889300	1.02	17711.	LL889049	50.0000 / 1270,000	60		LL889010 / LL889010B / LL889010C	56.5000 / 1435,100 (×3)
274000 / 548000 / 203000	121500 / 243000 / 90000	292000	1.35	32805.	EE292548 / EE292549 / EE292550	54.9450 / 1395,602 — 54.9750 / 1396,364 — 55.0000 / 1397,000		"B"=4.6250 "R"=.24 "db"=56.89 / 57.09 / 57.09 (117,475 / 6.0 / 1445,0–1450,0)	292668D	66.8125 / 1697,038
98500 / 197000 / 105000	43800 / 87600 / 46500	LL989300	0.94	19456.	LL889349	56.3750 / 1431,925		"B"=2.2500 "R"=.25 "db"=57.68 (57,150 / 6.4 / 1465,0)	LL989310XD6 / LL989310XD	62.3750 / 1584,324 (×2)
331000 / 662000 / 218000	147000 / 294000 / 97000	289000	1.52	49121.	EE289070	67.0000 / 1701,800	60		289815	81.5000 / 2070,099
195000 / 390000 / 158000	86500 / 173000 / 70500	LL789900	1.23	44471.	LL789949	72.0000 / 1828,800		"B"=3.1250 "R"=.25 "db"=73.43 (79,375 / 6.4 / 1865,0)	LL789910XD	79.0000 / 2006,599
715000 / 1430000 / 1070000	318000 / 636000 / 475000	LL980300	0.67	80682.	LL990349	82.0866 / 2085,000 †		"B"=7.0866 "R"=.50 "db"=85.43 (180,0 / 12.7 / 2170,0)	LL990310XD	96.8504 / 2460,000 †

Marginal note boxes:

- "C"=7.8750 / 200,025; "Y"=.50 / 12.7; "Db"=48.82 / 1240,0 — 60
- "C"=6.1417 / 156,000; "Y"=.50 / 12.7; "Db"=48.22 / 1225,0 — 60
- "C"=8.0000 / 203,200; "Y"=.50 / 12.7; "Db"=59.06 / 1500,0 — 60, 68

Right‑edge case width markers: 60, 68, 35 (as applicable per row).

†Dimension shown is maximum value—see note at bottom of fitting practice table in Reference Tables.

BEARING TABLES

Single-row and Thrust Assemblies

PAGE

Tolerances .... **I-III**

TS Type **1-60**

TSF Type **61-68**

TSL Type **69**

TTSP Type **71, 72**

TTC — TTCS Types **73, 74**

TTHD Type **75, 76**

**SINGLE-ROW AND
THRUST BEARINGS**

Note: The ratings shown in these tables are in pounds and decanewtons. The unit for force —newton—within the International System of Units (SI) was adopted in March, 1968 by the International Organization for Standardization (ISO) as the official unit for bearing rating in the metric system. Specifically, the newton is the **force** required to give a mass of 1 kilogram an acceleration of 1 meter per second per second. Comparing a decanewton unit with a kilogram or pound technically requires a comparison of a unit of force (newton) with a unit of mass (kilogram or pound). The **newton** was introduced as a unit of **force** to avoid the confusion of using the same name for units of both force and mass.

Despite this difference, the user of this journal will want to know the conversion factors that apply. They are as follows:

1 decanewton = 10 newtons = 1.02 kilograms = 2.25 pounds

1 kilogram = 9.81 newtons = .98 decanewtons = 2.20 pounds

INCH SYSTEM
BEARING TOLERANCES

SEE REFERENCE TABLES FOR ADDITIONAL BEARING TOLERANCES.

CONE BORE TOLERANCE †

BEARING TYPES	CONE BORE OVER	CONE BORE INCL.	CUP O.D. OVER	CUP O.D. INCL.	CLASS 4 All Sizes HIGH	LOW	CLASS 2 24.0000 609,600 Max. Cone Bore HIGH	LOW	CLASS 3 All Sizes HIGH	LOW	CLASS 0 12.0000 304,800 Max. Cup O.D. HIGH	LOW	CLASS 00 10.5000 266,700 Max. Cup O.D. HIGH	LOW
					DEVIATION IN .0001 INCH AND MICROMETERS									
	——	3.0000 76,200			+ 5▲ +13	0 0	+ 5 +13	0 0	+ 5 +13	0 0	+ 5 +13	0 0	+3 +8	0 0
TS TSF TSL	3.0000 76,200	12.0000 304,800			+ 10 + 25	0 0	+10 +25	0 0	+ 5 +13	0 0	+ 5 +13	0 0	+3 +8	0 0
	12.0000 304,800	24.0000 609,600			+ 20 + 51	0 0	+20 +51	0 0	+10 +25	0 0	—	—	—	—
	24.0000 609,600	36.0000 914,400			+ 30 + 76	0 0	—	—	+15 +38	0 0	—	—	—	—
	36.0000 914,400	48.0000 1219,200			+ 40 +102	0 0	—	—	+20 +51	0 0	—	—	—	—
	48.0000 1219,200				+ 50 +127	0 0	—	—	+30 +76	0 0	—	—	—	—

▲Cone bore deviation = 8 High, 0 Low (20 High, 0 Low) for cones in series LM11700, LM11900, M12600, M12700, L44600, L45400, LM48500, LM67000 and L68100.

†Inch system bearings in the dimension tables with this sign (†) are shown with maximum cone bore; the tolerance is minus by the same magnitude as shown.

CUP O.D. TOLERANCE †

BEARING TYPES	CONE BORE OVER	CONE BORE INCL.	CUP O.D. OVER	CUP O.D. INCL.	HIGH	LOW	HIGH	LOW	HIGH	LOW	HIGH	LOW	HIGH	LOW
			——	12.0000 304,800	+ 10 + 25	0 0	+10 +25	0 0	+ 5 +13	0 0	+ 5 +13	0 0	+3 +8	0 0
TS TSF TSL			12.0000 304,800	24.0000 609,600	+ 20 + 51	0 0	+20 +51	0 0	+10 +25	0 0	—	—	—	—
			24.0000 609,600	36.0000 914,400	+ 30 + 76	0 0	+30 +76	0 0	+15 +38	0 0	—	—	—	—
			36.0000 914,400	48.0000 1219,200	+ 40 +102	0 0	—	—	+20 +51	0 0	—	—	—	—
			48.0000 1219,200	——	+ 50 +127	0 0	—	—	+30 +76	0 0	—	—	—	—

†Inch system bearings in the dimension tables with this sign (†) are shown with maximum cup O.D.; the tolerance is minus by the same magnitude as shown.

OVERALL BEARING WIDTH TOLERANCE

BEARING TYPES	CONE BORE OVER	CONE BORE INCL.	CUP O.D. OVER	CUP O.D. INCL.	HIGH	LOW	HIGH	LOW	HIGH	LOW	HIGH	LOW	HIGH	LOW
	——	4.0000 101,600			+ 80▲ +203	0 0	+ 80 +203	0 0	+ 80 +203	— 80 −203	+ 80 +203	− 80 −203	+ 80 +203	− 80 −203
TS TSF TSL (1)	4.0000 101,600	12.0000 304,800			+140 +356	−100 −254	+ 80 +203	0 0	+ 80 +203	− 80 −203	+ 80 +203	− 80 −203	+ 80 +203	− 80 −203
	12.0000 304,800	24.0000 609,600	——	20.0000 508,000	+150 +381	−150 −381	+150 +381	−150 −381	+ 80 +203	− 80 −203	—	—	—	—
	12.0000 304,800	24.0000 609,600	20.0000 508,000	——	+150 +381	−150 −381	+150 +381	−150 −381	+150 +381	−150 −381	—	—	—	—
	24.0000 609,600				+150 +381	−150 −381	—	—	+150 +381	−150 −381	—	—	—	—

▲Overall bearing width deviation = 140 High, 0 Low (356 High, 0 Low) for series LM11700, LM11900, M12600, M12700, L44600, L45400, LM48500, LM67000 and L68100.

(1) For TSF type bearings, the tolerance applies to the dimension from the backface of the flange to the backface of the cone.

ASSEMBLED BEARING MAXIMUM RADIAL RUNOUT

BEARING TYPES	CONE BORE OVER	CONE BORE INCL.	CUP O.D. OVER	CUP O.D. INCL.					
			——	12.0000 304,800	20 51	15 38	3 8	1.5 4	0.75 2
TS TSF TSL			12.0000 304,800	24.0000 609,600	20 51	15 38	7 18	—	—
			24.0000 609,600	36.0000 914,400	30 76	20 51	20 51	—	—
			36.0000 914,400	——	30 76	—	30 76	—	—

METRIC SYSTEM BEARING TOLERANCES (FOR "J" PREFIX PARTS)

SEE REFERENCE TABLES FOR ADDITIONAL BEARING TOLERANCES.

CONE BORE TOLERANCE

BEARING TYPES	CONE BORE OVER	CONE BORE INCL.	K ALL SIZES HIGH	K LOW	N 19.6850 / 500 Max. Cone Bore & Max. Cup O.D. HIGH	N LOW	C 62.9921 / 1600 Max. Cone Bore & Max. Cup O.D. HIGH	C LOW	B 12.4016 / 315 Max. Cone Bore & Max. Cup O.D. HIGH	B LOW
	0.3937 10	0.7087 18	0	− 5	0	− 5	0	− 4	0	− 3
			0	− 13	0	−13	0	−10	0	− 8
	0.7087 18	1.1811 30	0	− 5	0	− 5	0	− 4	0	− 3
			0	− 13	0	−13	0	−10	0	− 8
	1.1811 30	1.9685 50	0	− 5	0	− 5	0	− 4	0	− 4
			0	− 13	0	−13	0	−10	0	−10
	1.9685 50	3.1496 80	0	− 6	0	− 6	0	− 5	0	− 4
			0	− 15	0	−15	0	−13	0	−10
	3.1496 80	4.7244 120	0	− 8	0	− 8	0	− 5	0	− 4
			0	− 20	0	−20	0	−13	0	−10
	4.7244 120	7.0866 180	0	− 10	0	−10	0	− 5	0	− 4
			0	− 25	0	−25	0	−13	0	−10
	7.0866 180	9.8425 250	0	− 12	0	−12	0	− 6	0	− 5
			0	− 30	0	−30	0	−15	0	−13
	9.8425 250	12.4016 315	0	− 14	0	−14	0	− 7	0	− 5
			0	− 35	0	−35	0	−18	0	−13
TS	12.4016 315	15.7480 400	0	− 16	0	−16	0	− 8	−	−
			0	− 40	0	−40	0	−20	−	−
	15.7480 400	19.6850 500	0	− 18	0	−18	0	−10	−	−
			0	− 45	0	−45	0	−25	−	−
	19.6850 500	24.8031 630	0	− 20	−	−	0	−12	−	−
			0	− 50	−	−	0	−30	−	−
	24.8031 630	31.4961 800	0	− 31	−	−	0	−16	−	−
			0	− 80	−	−	0	−40	−	−
	31.4961 800	39.3700 1000	0	− 39	−	−	0	−20	−	−
			0	−100	−	−	0	−50	−	−
	39.3700 1000	47.2441 1200	0	− 51	−	−	0	−24	−	−
			0	−130	−	−	0	−60	−	−
	47.2441 1200	62.9921 1600	0	− 59	−	−	0	−31	−	−
			0	−150	−	−	0	−80	−	−
	62.9921 1600	78.7402 2000	0	− 79	−	−	−	−	−	−
			0	−200	−	−	−	−	−	−
	78.7402 2000		0	− 98	−	−	−	−	−	−
			0	−250	−	−	−	−	−	−

CUP O.D. TOLERANCE

BEARING TYPES	CUP O.D. OVER	CUP O.D. INCL.	HIGH	LOW	HIGH	LOW	HIGH	LOW	HIGH	LOW
	0.7087 18	1.1811 30	0	− 8	0	− 8	0	− 3	0	− 3
			0	− 20	0	−20	0	− 8	0	− 8
	1.1811 30	1.9685 50	0	− 8	0	− 8	0	− 4	0	− 3
			0	− 20	0	−20	0	−10	0	− 8
	1.9685 50	3.1496 80	0	− 8	0	− 8	0	− 4	0	−3.5
			0	− 20	0	−20	0	−10	0	− 9
	3.1496 80	4.7244 120	0	− 8	0	− 8	0	− 5	0	− 4
			0	− 20	0	−20	0	−13	0	−10
	4.7244 120	5.9055 150	0	− 10	0	−10	0	− 5	0	− 4
			0	− 25	0	−25	0	−13	0	−10
	5.9055 150	7.0866 180	0	− 10	0	−10	0	− 5	0	− 4
			0	− 25	0	−25	0	−13	0	−10
	7.0866 180	9.8425 250	0	− 12	0	−12	0	− 6	0	− 5
			0	− 30	0	−30	0	−15	0	−13
	9.8425 250	12.4016 315	0	− 16	0	−16	0	− 8	0	− 6
			0	− 40	0	−40	0	−20	0	−15
TS	12.4016 315	15.7480 400	0	− 16	0	−16	0	− 8	−	−
			0	− 40	0	−40	0	−20	−	−
	15.7480 400	19.6850 500	0	− 20	0	−20	0	−10	−	−
			0	− 50	0	−50	0	−25	−	−
	19.6850 500	24.8031 630	0	− 20	−	−	0	−10	−	−
			0	− 50	−	−	0	−25	−	−
	24.8031 630	31.4961 800	0	− 31	−	−	0	−16	−	−
			0	− 80	−	−	0	−40	−	−
	31.4961 800	39.3700 1000	0	− 39	−	−	0	−20	−	−
			0	−100	−	−	0	−50	−	−
	39.3700 1000	47.2441 1200	0	− 51	−	−	0	−24	−	−
			0	−130	−	−	0	−60	−	−
	47.2441 1200	62.9921 1600	0	− 65	−	−	0	−31	−	−
			0	−165	−	−	0	−80	−	−
	62.9921 1600	78.7402 2000	0	− 79	−	−	−	−	−	−
			0	−200	−	−	−	−	−	−
	78.7402 2000		0	− 98	−	−	−	−	−	−
			0	−250	−	−	−	−	−	−

METRIC SYSTEM BEARING TOLERANCES (FOR "J" PREFIX PARTS)

SEE REFERENCE TABLES FOR ADDITIONAL BEARING TOLERANCES.

OVERALL BEARING WIDTH TOLERANCE

BEARING TYPES	CONE BORE OVER	CONE BORE INCL.	K ALL SIZES HIGH	K LOW	N 19.6850/500 Max. Cone Bore & Max. Cup O.D. HIGH	N LOW	C 62.9921/1600 Max. Cone Bore & Max. Cup O.D. HIGH	C LOW	B 12.4016/315 Max. Cone Bore & Max. Cup O.D. HIGH	B LOW
						DEVIATION—In .0001 Inch and Micrometers				
	0.3937 / 10	0.7087 / 18	+79 / +200	0 / 0	+39 / +100	0 / 0	+79 / +200	−79 / −200	+79 / +200	−79 / −200
	0.7087 / 18	1.1811 / 30	+79 / +200	0 / 0	+39 / +100	0 / 0	+79 / +200	−79 / −200	+79 / +200	−79 / −200
	1.1811 / 30	1.9685 / 50	+79 / +200	0 / 0	+39 / +100	0 / 0	+79 / +200	−79 / −200	+79 / +200	−79 / −200
	1.9685 / 50	3.1496 / 80	+79 / +200	0 / 0	+39 / +100	0 / 0	+79 / +200	−79 / −200	+79 / +200	−79 / −200
	3.1496 / 80	4.7244 / 120	+79 / +200	−79 / −200	+39 / +100	0 / 0	+79 / +200	−79 / −200	+79 / +200	−79 / −200
	4.7244 / 120	7.0866 / 180	+79 / +200	−79 / −200	+59 / +150	0 / 0	+79 / +200	−98 / −250	+79 / +200	−98 / −250
	7.0866 / 180	9.8425 / 250	+79 / +200	−79 / −200	+59 / +150	0 / 0	+79 / +200	−118 / −300	+79 / +200	−118 / −300
	9.8425 / 250	12.4016 / 315	+79 / +200	−79 / −200	+79 / +200	0 / 0	+79 / +200	−118 / −300	+79 / +200	−118 / −300
TS	12.4016 / 315	15.7480 / 400	+79 / +200	−79 / −200	+79 / +200	0 / 0	+98 / +250	−118 / −300	−	−
	15.7480 / 400	19.6850 / 500	+98 / +250	−118 / −300	+79 / +200	0 / 0	+118 / +300	−118 / −300	−	−
	19.6850 / 500	24.8031 / 630	+98 / +250	−118 / −300	−	−	+118 / +300	−157 / −400	−	−
	24.8031 / 630	31.4961 / 800	+98 / +250	−118 / −300	−	−	+118 / +300	−157 / −400	−	−
	31.4961 / 800	39.3700 / 1000	+118 / +300	−118 / −300	−	−	+138 / +350	−157 / −400	−	−
	39.3700 / 1000	47.2441 / 1200	+118 / +300	−138 / −350	−	−	+138 / +350	−177 / −450	−	−
	47.2441 / 1200	62.9921 / 1600	+138 / +350	−157 / −400	−	−	+138 / +350	−197 / −500	−	−
	62.9921 / 1600	78.7402 / 2000	+138 / +350	−157 / −400	−	−	−	−	−	−
	78.7402 / 2000	————	+138 / +350	−157 / −400	−	−	−	−	−	−

ASSEMBLED BEARING MAXIMUM RADIAL RUNOUT

BEARING TYPES	CUP O.D. OVER	CUP O.D. INCL.	K	N	C	B
	0.7087 / 18	1.1811 / 30	12 / 30	12 / 30	2 / 5	1 / 2.5
	1.1811 / 30	1.9685 / 50	12 / 30	12 / 30	2.4 / 6	1 / 2.5
	1.9685 / 50	3.1496 / 80	12 / 30	12 / 30	2.4 / 6	1.4 / 3.5
	3.1496 / 80	4.7244 / 120	16 / 40	16 / 40	2.4 / 6	1.4 / 3.5
	4.7244 / 120	5.9055 / 150	16 / 40	16 / 40	2.8 / 7	1.4 / 3.5
	5.9055 / 150	7.0866 / 180	16 / 40	16 / 40	3 / 8	1.5 / 4
	7.0866 / 180	9.8425 / 250	20 / 50	20 / 50	4 / 10	2 / 5
	9.8425 / 250	12.4016 / 315	20 / 50	20 / 50	4.3 / 11	2 / 5
TS	12.4016 / 315	15.7480 / 400	20 / 50	20 / 50	5 / 13	−
	15.7480 / 400	19.6850 / 500	25 / 65	25 / 65	7 / 18	−
	19.6850 / 500	24.8031 / 630	25 / 65	−	10 / 25	−
	24.8031 / 630	31.4961 / 800	25 / 65	−	14 / 35	−
	31.4961 / 800	39.3700 / 1000	35 / 90	−	20 / 50	−
	39.3700 / 1000	47.2441 / 1200	35 / 90	−	24 / 60	−
	47.2441 / 1200	62.9921 / 1600	35 / 90	−	31 / 80	−
	62.9921 / 1600	78.7402 / 2000	35 / 90	−	−	−
	78.7402 / 2000	————	35 / 90	−	−	−

SINGLE-ROW STRAIGHT BORE

TS

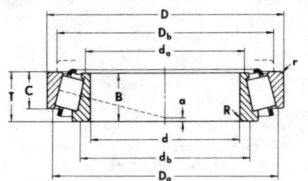

bore	outside diameter	width	rating at 500 RPM for 3000 hours L10		factor	eff. load center	part numbers		cone		backing shoulder diameters		cup		backing shoulder	
			one row radial	thrust					max. shaft fillet radius	width			max. housing fillet radius	width		
d	**D**	**T**	lb daN	lb daN	**K**	**a①**	cone	cup	**R①**	**B**	**d_b**	**d_a**	**r①**	**C**	**D_b**	**D_a**
0.3750 9.525	1.2595 31,991	0.3940 10,008	435 192	301 134	1.44	−0.12 −3,0	A2037	A2126	0.05 1,3	0.4246 10,785	0.59 15,0	0.53 13,5	0.05 1,3	0.3125 7,938	1.02 26,0	1.14 29,0
†0.4724 †12,000	1.2595 31,991	0.3940 10,008	435 192	301 134	1.44	−0.12 −3,0	A2047	A2126	0.03 0,8	0.4246 10,785	0.65 16,5	0.61 15,5	0.05 1,3	0.3125 7,938	1.02 26,0	1.14 29,0
0.4992 12,680	1.3775 34,988	0.4330 10,998	500 222	387 172	1.29	−0.10 −2,5	A4049	A4138	0.03 0,8	0.4326 10,988	0.69 17,5	0.69 17,5	0.05 1,3	0.3437 8,730	1.14 29,0	1.26 32,0
0.5000 12,700	1.3775 34,988	0.4330 10,998	500 222	387 172	1.29	−0.10 −2,5	A4050	A4138	0.05 1,3	0.4326 10,988	0.73 18,5	0.67 17,0	0.05 1,3	0.3437 8,730	1.14 29,0	1.26 32,0
0.5000 12,700	1.5000 38,100	0.5313 13,495	760 338	358 159	2.12	−0.20 −5,1	00050	00150	0.06 1,5	0.5540 14,072	0.75 19,0	0.65 16,5	0.03 0,8	0.4375 11,112	1.30 33,0	1.34 34,0
†0.5906 †15,000	1.3775 34,988	0.4330 10,998	500 222	387 172	1.29	−0.10 −2,5	A4059	A4138	0.03 0,8	0.4326 10,988	0.75 19,5	0.75 19,0	0.05 1,3	0.3437 8,730	1.14 29,0	1.26 32,0
0.6250 15,875	1.3775 34,988	0.4330 10,998	575 256	314 140	1.83	−0.13 −3,3	L21549	L21511	0.05 1,3	0.4330 10,998	0.85 21,5	0.77 19,5	0.05 1,3	0.3430 8,712	1.14 29,0	1.28 32,5
0.6250 15,875	1.5745 39,992	0.4730 12,014	530 236	480 212	1.11	−0.06 −1,5	A6062	A6157	0.05 1,3	0.4391 11,153	0.87 22,0	0.81 20,5	0.05 1,3	0.3750 9,525	1.34 34,0	1.46 37,0
0.6250 15,875	1.6250 41,275	0.5625 14,288	890 396	475 210	1.88	−0.20 −5,2	03062	03162	0.05 1,3	0.5780 14,681	0.85 21,5	0.79 20,0	0.08 2,0	0.4375 11,112	1.34 34,0	1.48 37,5
0.6250 15,875	1.6875 42,862	0.5625 14,288	725 324	875 390	0.83	−0.05 −1,1	11590	11520	0.06 1,5	0.5625 14,288	0.96 24,5	0.89 22,5	0.06 1,5	0.3750 9,525	1.36 34,5	1.56 39,5
0.6250 15,875	1.6875 42,862	0.6563 16,670	1150 515	655 292	1.76	−0.23 −6,0	17580	17520	0.06 1,5	0.6563 16,670	0.91 23,0	0.83 21,0	0.06 1,5	0.5313 13,495	1.44 36,5	1.54 39,0
0.6250 15,875	1.7500 44,450	0.6100 15,494	1020 450	620 276	1.64	−0.15 −3,9	05062	05175	0.06 1,5	0.5662 14,381	0.93 23,5	0.83 21,0	0.06 1,5	0.4500 11,430	1.50 38,0	1.65 42,0
0.6250 15,875	1.9380 49,225	0.7813 19,845	1600 715	730 324	2.20	−0.36 −9,1	09062	09195	0.03 0,8	0.8480 21,539	0.87 22,0	0.85 21,5	0.05 1,3	0.5625 14,288	1.65 42,0	1.75 44,5
0.6250 15,875	2.1250 53,975	0.8750 22,225	1710 760	1730 770	0.99	−0.23 −5,8	21063	21212	0.03 0,8	0.8598 21,839	1.14 29,0	1.04 26,4	0.09 2,3	0.6250 15,875	1.69 43,0	1.97 50,0
†0.6299 †16,000	1.8504 47,000	0.8268 21,000	1560 695	1460 650	1.07	−0.24 −6,0	HM81649	HM81610	0.04 1,0	0.8268 21,000	1.08 27,5	0.91 23,0	0.08 2,0	0.6299 16,000	1.48 37,5	1.69 43,0
0.6690 16,993	1.6250 41,275	0.4687 11,905	530 236	480 212	1.11	−0.06 −1,5	A6067	A6162	0.03 0,8	0.4391 11,153	0.87 22,0	0.83 21,0	0.05 1,3	0.3437 8,730	1.36 34,5	1.46 37,0
0.6872 17,455	1.4380 36,525	0.4375 11,112	500 224	420 186	1.20	−0.08 −2,0	A5069	A5144	0.06 1,5	0.4375 11,112	0.93 23,5	0.84 21,3	0.06 1,5	0.3125 7,938	1.18 30,0	1.32 33,5
0.6875 17,462	1.5700 39,878	0.5450 13,843	935 416	460 204	2.04	−0.20 −5,2	▲LM11749	LM11710	0.05 1,3	0.5750 14,605	0.91 23,0	0.85 21,5	0.05 1,3	0.4200 10,668	1.34 34,0	1.46 37,0
0.6875 17,462	1.8504 47,000	0.5662 14,381	1020 450	620 276	1.64	−0.15 −3,9	05068	05185	0.03 0,8	0.5662 14,381	0.91 23,0	0.89 22,5	0.05 1,3	0.4375 11,112	1.59 40,5	1.67 42,5

①These maximum fillet radii will be cleared by the bearing corners.
②Minus value indicates center is inside cone backface.
†Dimension shown is maximum value—see note at bottom of fitting practice table page 4 in Reference Tables.
▲Non-standard tolerances, see Inch System bearing tolerance page 18 in Reference Tables.

SINGLE-ROW STRAIGHT BORE—TS

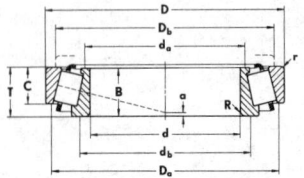

bore	outside diameter	width	rating at 500 RPM for 3000 hours L10 one row radial	thrust	fac-tor	eff. lead center	part numbers cone	cup	cone max. shaft fillet radius	width	backing shoulder diameters		cup max. housing fillet radius	width	backing shoulder	
d	D	T	lb daN	lb daN	K	a	cone	cup	R	B	d_b	d_a	r	C	D_b	D_a
0.7500 19,050	1.5745 39,992	0.4730 12,014	530 236	480 212	1.11	−0.06 −1,5	A6075	A6157	0.04 1,0	0.4391 11,153	0.94 24,0	0.91 23,0	0.05 1,3	0.3750 9,525	1.34 34,0	1.46 37,0
0.7500 19,050	1.7500 44,450	0.5000 12,700	815 364	670 298	1.22	−0.07 −1,9	4A	6	0.06 1,5	0.4688 11,908	1.00 25,5	0.93 23,5	0.06 1,5	0.3750 9,525	1.50 38,0	1.61 41,0
0.7500 19,050	1.7500 44,450	0.6100 15,494	1020 450	620 276	1.64	−0.15 −3,9	05075X	05175	0.06 1,5	0.5662 14,381	1.00 25,5	0.93 23,5	0.06 1,5	0.4500 11,430	1.50 38,0	1.65 42,0
0.7500 19,050	1.7810 45,237	0.6100 15,494	1230 545	635 282	1.94	−0.22 −5,6	▲LM11949	LM11910	0.05 1,3	0.6550 16,637	0.98 25,0	0.93 23,5	0.05 1,3	0.4750 12,065	1.56 39,5	1.63 41,5
0.7500 19,050	1.8504 47,000	0.5662 14,381	1020 450	620 276	1.64	−0.15 −3,9	05075	05185S	0.05 1,3	0.5662 14,381	0.98 25,0	0.93 23,5	0.06 1,5	0.4375 11,112	1.59 40,5	1.67 42,5
0.7500 19,050	1.9380 49,225	0.7813 19,845	1600 715	730 324	2.20	−0.36 −9,1	09078	09195	0.05 1,3	0.8480 21,539	1.00 25,5	0.94 24,0	0.05 1,3	0.5625 14,288	1.65 42,0	1.75 44,5
0.7500 19,050	1.9380 49,225	0.8350 21,209	1600 715	730 324	2.20	−0.29 −7,3	09067	09196	0.05 1,3	0.7500 19,050	1.00 25,5	0.94 24,0	0.06 1,5	0.6875 17,462	1.63 41,5	1.75 44,5
0.7500 19,050	1.9380 49,225	0.9063 23,020	1600 715	730 324	2.20	−0.36 −9,1	09074	09194	Spec.	0.8480 21,539	1.02 26,0	0.94 24,0	0.14 3,5	0.6875 17,462	1.54 39,0	1.75 44,5
0.7500 19,050	2.1250 53,975	0.7625 19,368	1740 775	915 408	1.90	−0.27 −6,8	1775	1730	0.06 1,5	0.7810 19,837	1.06 27,0	0.98 25,0	0.03 0,8	0.6250 15,875	1.91 48,5	1.97 50,0
0.7500 19,050	2.1250 53,975	0.8750 22,225	1710 760	1730 770	0.99	−0.23 −5,8	21075	21212	0.06 1,5	0.8598 21,839	1.24 31,5	1.04 26,4	0.09 2,3	0.6250 15,875	1.69 43,0	1.97 50,0
†0.7874 †20,000	1.7500 44,450	0.6100 15,494	1020 450	620 276	1.64	−0.15 −3,9	05079	05175	0.06 1,5	0.5662 14,381	1.04 26,5	0.94 24,0	0.06 1,5	0.4500 11,430	1.50 38,0	1.65 42,0
0.7874 20,000	1.9687 50,005	0.5313 13,495	1130 500	780 346	1.45	−0.11 −2,9	07079	07196	0.06 1,5	0.5614 14,260	1.08 27,5	1.02 26,0	0.04 1,0	0.3750 9,525	1.75 44,5	1.85 47,0
0.8115 20,612	1.9380 49,225	0.7813 19,845	1600 715	730 324	2.20	−0.36 −9,1	09081S	09195	Spec.	0.8480 21,539	1.08 27,5	1.00 25,5	0.05 1,3	0.5625 14,288	1.65 42,0	1.75 44,5
0.8125 20,638	1.9380 49,225	0.7813 19,845	1660 740	915 408	1.81	−0.28 −7,1	12580	12520	0.06 1,5	0.7813 19,845	1.12 28,5	1.02 26,0	0.06 1,5	0.6250 15,875	1.67 42,5	1.79 45,5
0.8437 21,430	1.9687 50,005	0.6900 17,526	1660 740	790 352	2.10	−0.25 −6,4	▲M12649	M12610	0.05 1,3	0.7200 18,288	1.08 27,5	1.00 25,5	0.05 1,3	0.5500 13,970	1.73 44,0	1.81 46,0
†0.8661 †22,000	†1.8110 †46,000	0.6100 15,494	1280 570	670 298	1.91	−0.21 −5,4	▲LM12749	LM12711	0.05 1,3	0.6550 16,637	1.08 27,5	1.02 26,0	0.05 1,3	0.4750 12,065	1.57 40,0	1.67 42,5
0.8750 22,225	1.6563 42,070	0.4400 11,176	670 298	455 202	1.47	−0.07 −1,8	LL52549	LL52510	0.05 1,3	0.4400 11,176	1.08 27,5	1.02 26,0	0.05 1,3	0.3400 8,636	1.44 36,5	1.54 39,0
0.8750 22,225	1.9687 50,005	0.6900 17,526	1660 740	790 352	2.10	−0.25 −6,4	▲M12648	M12610	0.05 1,3	0.7200 18,288	1.12 28,5	1.04 26,5	0.05 1,3	0.5500 13,970	1.73 44,0	1.81 46,0
0.8750 22,225	2.0000 50,800	0.5910 15,011	1130 500	780 346	1.45	−0.11 −2,9	07087	07210X	0.05 1,3	0.5614 14,260	1.12 28,5	1.06 27,0	0.06 1,5	0.5000 12,700	1.75 44,5	1.87 47,5
0.8750 22,225	2.0470 51,994	0.5910 15,011	1130 500	780 346	1.45	−0.11 −2,9	07087X	07204	0.06 1,5	0.5614 14,260	1.14 29,0	1.06 27,0	0.05 1,3	0.5000 12,700	1.77 45,0	1.89 48,0
0.8750 22,225	2.0625 52,388	0.7625 19,368	1820 810	910 404	2.00	−0.30 −7,6	1380	1328	0.06 1,5	0.7940 20,168	1.16 29,5	1.17 29,7	0.06 1,5	0.5625 14,288	1.77 45,0	1.91 48,5

| bore | outside diameter | width | rating at 500 RPM for 3000 hours L10 one row radial | thrust | factor | eff. load center | part numbers cone | cup | cone max. shaft fillet radius | width | backing shoulder diameters | | cup max. housing fillet radius | width | backing shoulder | |
d	D	T	lb daN	lb daN	K	a[1]	cone	cup	R[1]	B	db	da	r[1]	C	Db	Da
0.8750 22,225	2.1250 53,975	0.7625 19,368	1820 810	910 404	2.00	−0.30 −7,6	1380	1329	0.06 1,5	0.7940 20,168	1.16 29,5	1.17 29,7	0.06 1,5	0.5625 14,288	1.81 46,0	1.93 49,0
0.8750 22,225	2.2400 56,896	0.7625 19,368	1740 775	915 408	1.90	−0.27 −6,8	1755	1729	0.05 1,3	0.7810 19,837	1.14 29,0	1.08 27,5	0.05 1,3	0.6250 15,875	1.93 49,0	2.01 51,0
0.8750 22,225	2.2500 57,150	0.7813 19,845	1850 825	1050 465	1.77	−0.23 −5,8	1975	1922	0.03 0,8	0.7620 19,355	1.14 29,0	1.10 28,0	0.06 1,5	0.6250 15,875	2.01 51,0	2.11 53,5
0.8750 22,225	2.2500 57,150	0.8750 22,225	2100 935	1240 555	1.69	−0.27 −7,0	1280	1220	0.03 0,8	0.8750 22,225	1.16 29,5	1.14 29,0	0.06 1,5	0.6875 17,462	1.93 49,0	2.05 52,0
0.8750 22,225	2.6150 66,421	0.9375 23,812	2970 1320	1290 575	2.30	−0.37 −9,4	2684	2631	0.06 1,5	1.0013 25,433	1.24 31,5	1.14 29,0	0.05 1,3	0.7500 19,050	2.28 58,0	2.36 60,0
0.8900 22,606	1.8504 47,000	0.6102 15,500	1210 535	970 432	1.24	−0.12 −3,0	LM72849	LM72810	0.06 1,5	0.6102 15,500	1.18 30,0	1.10 28,0	0.04 1,0	0.4724 12,000	1.59 40,5	1.73 44,0
0.9375 23,812	1.9800 50,292	0.5600 14,224	1200 535	770 342	1.56	−0.13 −3,3	▲L44640	L44610	0.06 1,5	0.5800 14,732	1.20 30,5	1.12 28,5	0.05 1,3	0.4200 10,668	1.75 44,5	1.85 47,0
0.9375 23,812	2.0472 52,000	0.5910 15,011	1130 500	780 346	1.45	−0.11 −2,9	07093	07205	0.06 1,5	0.5614 14,260	1.20 30,5	1.12 28,5	0.08 2,0	0.5000 12,700	1.75 44,5	1.89 48,0
0.9375 23,812	2.2500 57,150	0.7960 20,218	1740 775	915 408	1.90	−0.27 −6,8	1779	1738X	0.03 0,8	0.7810 19,837	1.16 29,5	1.12 28,5	0.09 2,3	0.6910 17,551	1.91 48,5	2.01 51,0
0.9375 23,812	2.4375 61,912	1.1250 28,575	3360 1495	1630 725	2.07	−0.47 −11,9	3659	3620	0.09 2,3	1.1975 30,416	1.40 35,5	1.24 31,5	0.13 3,3	0.9375 23,812	2.05 52,0	2.27 57,5
0.9375 23,812	2.5625 65,088	0.8750 22,225	2050 910	2560 1140	0.80	−0.09 −2,2	23092	23256	0.06 1,5	0.8450 21,463	1.52 38,5	1.36 34,6	0.06 1,5	0.6250 15,875	2.09 53,0	2.48 61,0
0.9600 24,384	3.0000 76,200	0.9688 24,608	2880 1285	3320 1475	0.87	−0.08 −2,0	43096	43300	0.03 0,8	0.9478 24,074	1.59 40,5	1.56 39,5	Spec.	0.6563 16,670	2.52 64,0	2.87 73,0
0.9835 24,981	1.9687 50,005	0.5313 13,495	1130 500	780 346	1.45	−0.11 −2,9	07098	07196	0.06 1,5	0.5614 14,260	1.22 31,0	1.14 29,0	0.04 1,0	0.3750 9,525	1.75 44,5	1.85 47,0
0.9835 24,981	2.4409 62,000	0.6300 16,002	1620 720	1060 470	1.53	−0.14 −3,5	17098	17244	0.06 1,5	0.6522 16,566	1.30 33,0	1.20 30,5	0.06 1,5	0.5625 14,288	2.13 54,0	2.24 57,0
0.9843 25,000	1.9687 50,005	0.5313 13,495	1130 500	780 346	1.45	−0.11 −2,9	07097	07196	0.06 1,5	0.5614 14,260	1.22 31,0	1.14 29,0	0.04 1,0	0.3750 9,525	1.75 44,5	1.85 47,0
1.0000 25,400	1.9687 50,005	0.5313 13,495	1130 500	780 346	1.45	−0.11 −2,9	07100	07196	0.04 1,0	0.5614 14,260	1.20 30,5	1.16 29,5	0.04 1,0	0.3750 9,525	1.75 44,5	1.85 47,0
1.0000 25,400	1.9687 50,005	0.5313 13,495	1130 500	780 346	1.45	−0.11 −2,9	07100S	07196	0.06 1,5	0.5614 14,260	1.24 31,5	1.16 29,5	0.04 1,0	0.3750 9,525	1.75 44,5	1.85 47,0
1.0000 25,400	1.9687 50,005	0.5313 13,495	1130 500	780 346	1.45	−0.11 −2,9	07100SA	07196	0.13 3,3	0.5614 14,260	1.38 35,0	1.16 29,5	0.04 1,0	0.3750 9,525	1.75 44,5	1.85 47,0
1.0000 25,400	1.9800 50,292	0.5600 14,224	1200 535	770 342	1.56	−0.13 −3,3	▲L44643	L44610	0.05 1,3	0.5800 14,732	1.24 31,5	1.16 29,5	0.05 1,3	0.4200 10,668	1.75 44,5	1.85 47,0
1.0000 25,400	2.1250 53,975	0.7625 19,368	1740 775	915 408	1.90	−0.27 −6,8	1780	1730	0.03 0,8	0.7810 19,837	1.20 30,5	1.18 30,0	0.03 0,8	0.6250 15,875	1.91 48,5	1.97 50,0
1.0000 25,400	2.2500 57,150	0.6875 17,462	1800 800	1070 475	1.69	−0.20 −5,1	15578	15520	0.05 1,3	0.6875 17,462	1.28 32,5	1.20 30,5	0.06 1,5	0.5313 13,495	2.01 51,0	2.09 53,0
1.0000 25,400	2.2500 57,150	0.7650 19,431	1900 845	1780 790	1.07	−0.12 −3,1	M84548	M84510	0.06 1,5	0.7650 19,431	1.42 36,0	1.31 33,2	0.06 1,5	0.5800 14,732	1.91 48,5	2.13 54,0
1.0000 25,400	2.3125 58,738	0.7500 19,050	1850 825	1050 465	1.77	−0.23 −5,8	1986	1932	0.05 1,3	0.7620 19,355	1.28 32,5	1.20 30,5	0.05 1,3	0.5937 15,080	2.05 52,0	2.13 54,0

① These maximum fillet radii will be cleared by the backing corners.
② Minus value indicates center is inside cone backface.
† Dimension shown is maximum value—see note at bottom of fitting practice table page 4 in Reference Tables.
▲ Non-standard tolerances, see Inch System bearing tolerance page 18 in Reference Tables.

SINGLE-ROW STRAIGHT BORE—TS

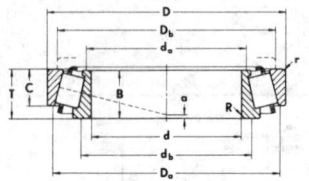

bore	outside diameter	width	rating at 500 RPM for 3000 hours L10 one row radial	thrust	factor K	eff. load center a②	part numbers cone	cup	cone max shaft fillet radius R①	width B	backing shoulder diameters db	da	cup max housing fillet radius r①	width C	backing shoulder Db	Da
d	D	T	lb daN	lb daN	K	a②	cone	cup	R①	B	db	da	r①	C	Db	Da
1.0000 25,400	2.3437 59,530	0.9200 23,368	2320 1035	2170 965	1.07	−0.20 −5,1	M84249	M84210	0.03 0,8	0.9100 23,114	1.42 36,0	1.28 32,5	0.06 1,5	0.7200 18,288	1.95 49,5	2.20 56,0
1.0000 25,400	2.3750 60,325	0.7813 19,845	1850 825	1050 465	1.77	−0.23 −5,8	1994X	1931	0.14 3,5	0.7620 19,355	1.46 37,0	1.20 30,5	0.05 1,3	0.6250 15,875	2.05 52,0	2.17 55,0
1.0000 25,400	2.4409 62,000	0.7150 18,161	1990 885	1190 530	1.67	−0.19 −5,0	15100SR	15245	0.05 1,3	0.7500 19,050	1.32 33,5	1.28 32,5	0.05 1,3	0.5625 14,288	2.17 55,0	2.28 58,0
1.0000 25,400	2.4409 62,000	0.7500 19,050	1990 885	1190 530	1.67	−0.23 −5,8	15100	15245	0.14 3,5	0.8125 20,638	1.50 38,0	1.24 31,5	0.05 1,3	0.5625 14,288	2.17 55,0	2.28 58,0
1.0000 25,400	2.5000 63,500	0.7500 19,050	1990 885	1190 530	1.67	−0.23 −5,8	15101	15250R	0.03 0,8	0.8125 20,638	1.28 32,5	1.24 31,5	0.05 1,3	0.5625 14,288	2.17 55,0	2.32 59,0
1.0000 25,400	2.5000 63,500	0.8125 20,638	1990 885	1190 530	1.67	−0.23 −5,8	15100S	15250	0.05 1,3	0.8125 20,638	1.32 33,5	1.24 31,5	0.05 1,3	0.6250 15,875	2.20 56,0	2.32 59,0
1.0000 25,400	2.5000 63,500	0.8125 20,638	1990 885	1190 530	1.67	−0.23 −5,8	15102	15250X	0.06 1,5	0.8125 20,638	1.34 34,0	1.24 31,5	0.06 1,5	0.6250 15,875	2.17 55,0	2.32 59,0
1.0000 25,400	2.5312 64,292	0.8438 21,433	2450 1090	2290 1020	1.07	−0.13 −3,3	M86643	M86610	0.06 1,5	0.8438 21,433	1.50 38,0	1.44 36,5	0.06 1,5	0.6563 16,675	2.13 54,0	2.40 61,0
1.0000 25,400	2.5625 65,088	0.8750 22,225	2050 910	2560 1140	0.80	−0.09 −2,2	23100	23256	0.06 1,5	0.8450 21,463	1.54 39,0	1.36 34,6	0.06 1,5	0.6250 15,875	2.09 53,0	2.48 61,0
1.0000 25,400	2.6150 66,421	0.9375 23,812	2970 1320	1290 575	2.30	−0.37 −9,4	2687	2631	0.05 1,3	1.0013 25,433	1.32 33,5	1.24 31,5	0.05 1,3	0.7500 19,050	2.28 58,0	2.36 60,0
1.0000 25,400	2.6875 68,262	0.8750 22,225	2640 1175	1540 685	1.72	−0.26 −6,6	2473X	2420	0.09 2,3	0.9375 23,812	1.44 36,5	1.28 32,5	0.06 1,5	0.6875 17,462	2.36 60,0	2.48 63,0
1.0000 25,400	2.6875 68,262	0.8750 22,225	2490 1110	1780 790	1.40	−0.20 −5,1	02473	02420	0.03 0,8	0.8750 22,225	1.36 34,5	1.32 33,5	0.06 1,5	0.6875 17,462	2.32 59,0	2.48 63,0
1.0000 25,400	2.8346 72,000	0.7480 19,000	2210 985	1370 605	1.62	−0.16 −4,2	26100	26283	0.06 1,5	0.7450 18,923	1.36 34,5	1.28 32,5	0.06 1,5	0.6250 15,875	2.44 62,0	2.56 65,0
1.0000 25,400	2.8438 72,233	1.0000 25,400	3190 1415	2980 1325	1.07	−0.18 −4,6	HM88630	HM88610	0.03 0,8	1.0000 25,400	1.56 39,5	1.56 39,5	0.09 2,3	0.7812 19,842	2.36 60,0	2.72 69,0
1.0000 25,400	2.8593 72,626	0.9688 24,608	2550 1130	2620 1165	0.97	−0.16 −4,0	41100	41286	0.09 2,3	0.9550 24,257	1.61 41,0	1.45 36,7	0.06 1,5	0.6875 17,462	2.40 61,0	2.68 68,0
1.0000 25,400	2.8593 72,626	1.1875 30,162	3700 1645	2100 935	1.76	−0.40 −10,1	3189	3130	0.03 0,8	1.1810 29,997	1.40 35,5	1.38 35,0	0.03 0,8	0.9375 23,812	2.48 63,0	2.64 67,0
1.0300 26,162	2.6150 66,421	0.9375 23,812	2970 1320	1290 575	2.30	−0.37 −9,4	2682	2631	0.06 1,5	1.0013 25,433	1.36 34,5	1.26 32,0	0.05 1,3	0.7500 19,050	2.28 58,0	2.36 60,0
1.0620 26,975	2.2500 57,150	0.7813 19,845	1850 825	1050 465	1.77	−0.23 −5,8	1987	1922	0.03 0,8	0.7620 19,355	1.28 32,5	1.24 31,5	0.06 1,5	0.6250 15,875	2.01 51,0	2.11 53,5
1.0625 26,988	1.9800 50,292	0.5600 14,224	1200 535	770 342	1.56	−0.13 −3,3	▲L44649	L44610	0.14 3,5	0.5800 14,732	1.48 37,5	1.22 31,0	0.05 1,3	0.4200 10,668	1.75 44,5	1.85 47,0
1.0625 26,988	2.2500 57,150	0.7813 19,845	1850 825	1050 465	1.77	−0.23 −5,8	1997X	1922	0.13 3,3	0.7620 19,355	1.48 37,5	1.24 31,5	0.06 1,5	0.6250 15,875	2.01 51,0	2.11 53,5
1.0625 26,988	2.3750 60,325	0.7812 19,842	1800 800	1070 475	1.69	−0.20 −5,1	15580	15523	0.14 3,5	0.6875 17,462	1.52 38,5	1.26 32,0	0.06 1,5	0.6250 15,875	2.01 51,0	2.13 54,0

bore	outside diameter	width	rating at 500 RPM for 3000 hours L10 one row radial	thrust	factor	eff. load center	part numbers cone	cup	cone max shaft fillet radius	width	backing shoulder diameters		cup max housing fillet radius	width	backing shoulder	
d	D	T	lb daN	lb daN	K	a[①]	cone	cup	R[①]	B	d_b	d_a	r[①]	C	D_b	D_a
1.0625 26,988	2.4409 62,000	0.7500 19,050	1990 885	1190 530	1.67	−0.23 −5,8	15106	15245	0.03 0,8	0.8125 20,638	1.32 33,5	1.30 33,0	0.05 1,3	0.5625 14,288	2.17 55,0	2.28 58,0
1.0625 26,988	2.6150 66,421	0.9375 23,812	2970 1320	1290 575	2.30	−0.37 −9,4	2888	2631	0.06 1,5	1.0013 25,433	1.38 35,0	1.30 33,0	0.05 1,3	0.7500 19,050	2.28 58,0	2.36 60,0
1.0625 26,988	2.8593 72,626	0.9688 24,608	2550 1130	2620 1165	0.97	−0.16 −4,0	41106	41286	0.09 2,3	0.9550 24,257	1.65 42,0	1.45 36,7	0.06 1,5	0.6875 17,462	2.40 61,0	2.68 68,0
1.1250 28,575	2.2500 57,150	0.6875 17,462	1800 800	1070 475	1.69	−0.20 −5,1	15590	15520	0.14 3,5	0.6875 17,462	1.56 39,5	1.32 33,5	0.06 1,5	0.5313 13,495	2.01 51,0	2.09 53,0
1.1250 28,575	2.2500 57,150	0.7813 19,845	1850 825	1050 465	1.77	−0.23 −5,8	1985	1922	0.03 0,8	0.7620 19,355	1.34 34,0	1.32 33,5	0.06 1,5	0.6250 15,875	2.01 51,0	2.11 53,5
1.1250 28,575	2.2500 57,150	0.7813 19,845	1850 825	1050 465	1.77	−0.23 −5,8	1988	1922	0.14 3,5	0.7620 19,355	1.56 39,5	1.32 33,5	0.06 1,5	0.6250 15,875	2.01 51,0	2.11 53,5
1.1250 28,575	2.4409 62,000	0.7500 19,050	1990 885	1190 530	1.67	−0.23 −5,8	15112	15245	0.14 3,5	0.8125 20,638	1.34 40,0	1.34 34,0	0.05 1,3	0.5625 14,288	2.17 55,0	2.28 58,0
1.1250 28,575	2.4409 62,000	0.7500 19,050	1990 885	1190 530	1.67	−0.23 −5,8	15113	15245	0.03 0,8	0.8125 20,638	1.36 34,5	1.34 34,0	0.05 1,3	0.5625 14,288	2.17 55,0	2.28 58,0
1.1250 28,575	2.5312 64,292	0.8438 21,433	2450 1090	2290 1020	1.07	−0.13 −3,3	M86647	M86610	0.06 1,5	0.8438 21,433	1.57 40,0	1.50 38,0	0.06 1,5	0.6563 16,670	2.13 54,0	2.40 61,0
1.1250 28,575	2.6150 66,421	0.9375 23,812	2970 1320	1290 575	2.30	−0.37 −9,4	2689	2631	0.05 1,3	1.0013 25,433	1.42 36,0	1.34 34,0	0.06 1,3	0.7500 19,050	2.28 58,0	2.36 60,0
1.1250 28,575	2.6150 66,421	1.0000 25,400	3280 1460	1530 685	2.14	−0.34 −8,6	2578	2520	0.09 2,3	0.9983 25,357	1.54 39,0	1.38 35,0	0.13 3,3	0.8125 20,638	2.24 57,0	2.46 62,4
1.1250 28,575	2.6875 68,262	0.8750 22,225	2640 1175	1540 685	1.72	−0.26 −6,6	2474	2420	0.03 0,8	0.9375 23,812	1.42 36,0	1.38 35,0	0.06 1,5	0.6875 17,462	2.36 60,0	2.48 63,0
1.1250 28,575	2.6875 68,262	0.8750 22,225	2490 1110	1780 790	1.40	−0.20 −5,1	02474	02420	0.03 0,8	0.8750 22,225	1.44 36,5	1.42 36,0	0.06 1,5	0.6875 17,462	2.32 59,0	2.48 63,0
1.1250 28,575	2.6875 68,262	0.8750 22,225	2620 1165	2450 1090	1.07	−0.11 −2,8	M88040	M88010	0.09 2,3	0.8750 22,225	1.65 42,0	1.54 39,0	0.06 1,5	0.6875 17,462	2.28 58,0	2.56 65,0
1.1250 28,575	2.8346 72,000	0.7480 19,000	2210 985	1370 605	1.62	−0.16 −4,2	26112	26283	0.06 1,5	0.7450 18,923	1.46 37,0	1.38 35,0	0.06 1,5	0.6250 15,875	2.44 62,0	2.56 65,0
1.1250 28,575	2.8593 72,626	0.9688 24,608	2550 1130	2620 1165	0.97	−0.16 −4,0	41125	41286	0.19 4,8	0.9550 24,257	1.89 48,0	1.45 36,7	0.06 1,5	0.6875 17,462	2.40 61,0	2.68 68,0
1.1250 28,575	2.8593 72,626	0.9688 24,608	2550 1130	2620 1165	0.97	−0.16 −4,0	41126	41286	0.06 1,5	0.9550 24,257	1.63 41,5	1.45 36,7	0.06 1,5	0.6875 17,462	2.40 61,0	2.68 68,0
1.1250 28,575	2.8593 72,626	1.1875 30,162	3700 1645	2100 935	1.76	−0.40 −10,1	3198	3120	0.05 1,3	1.1810 29,997	1.54 39,0	1.46 37,0	0.13 3,3	0.9375 23,812	2.40 61,0	2.64 67,0
1.1250 28,575	2.8750 73,025	0.8750 22,225	2620 1165	2030 900	1.29	−0.15 −3,8	02872	02820	0.03 0,8	0.8750 22,225	1.48 37,5	1.46 37,0	0.13 3,3	0.6875 17,462	2.44 62,0	2.68 68,0
1.1250 28,575	3.1250 79,375	1.0000 25,400	2880 1285	3320 1475	0.87	−0.08 −2,0	43112	43312	0.03 0,8	0.9478 24,074	1.67 42,5	1.63 41,5	0.06 1,5	0.6875 17,462	2.64 67,0	2.91 74,0
1.1417 29,000	1.9800 50,292	0.5600 14,224	1250 560	795 352	1.58	−0.13 −3,2	▲L45449	L45410	0.14 3,5	0.5800 14,732	1.54 39,5	1.30 33,0	0.05 1,3	0.4200 10,668	1.75 44,5	1.89 48,0
1.1562 29,367	2.6150 66,421	0.9375 23,812	2970 1320	1290 575	2.30	−0.37 −9,4	2690	2631	0.14 3,5	1.0013 25,433	1.61 41,0	1.38 35,0	0.05 1,3	0.7500 19,050	2.28 58,0	2.36 60,0
1.1562 29,367	2.6150 66,421	0.9375 23,812	2970 1320	1290 575	2.30	−0.37 −9,4	2691	2631	0.03 0,8	1.0013 25,433	1.40 35,5	1.38 35,0	0.05 1,3	0.7500 19,050	2.28 58,0	2.36 60,0

① These maximum fillet radii will be cleared by the bearing corners.
② Minus value indicates center is inside cone backface.
▲ Non-standard tolerances, see Inch System bearing tolerance page 18 in Reference Tables.

SINGLE-ROW STRAIGHT BORE—TS

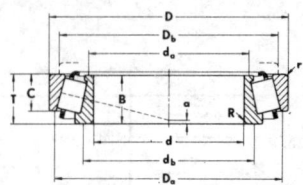

| bore | outside diameter | width | rating at 500 RPM for 3000 hours L10 | | factor | eff. load center | part numbers | | cone max. shaft fillet radius | width | backing shoulder diameters | | cup max. housing fillet radius | width | backing shoulder | |
| | | | one row radial | thrust | | | | | | | | | | | | |
d	D	T	lb daN	lb daN	K	a②	cone	cup	R①	B	d_b	d_a	r①	C	D_b	D_a
1.1811 30,000	2.4409 62,000	0.6300 16,002	1620 720	1060 470	1.53	−0.14 −3,5	17118S	17244	0.06 1,5	0.6522 16,566	1.46 37,0	1.36 34,5	0.06 1,5	0.5625 14,288	2.13 54,0	2.24 57,0
†1.1811 †30,000	2.4409 62,000	0.7500 19,050	1990 885	1190 530	1.67	−0.23 −5,8	15117	15245	0.05 1,3	0.8125 20,638	1.44 36,5	1.38 35,0	0.05 1,3	0.5625 14,288	2.17 55,0	2.28 58,0
1.1811 30,000	2.7148 68,956	0.7813 19,845	2180 970	1420 635	1.53	−0.17 −4,3	14118	14274A	0.03 0,8	0.7560 19,202	1.46 37,0	1.44 36,5	0.13 3,3	0.6250 15,875	2.32 59,0	2.48 63,0
1.1811 30,000	2.7170 69,012	0.7813 19,845	2180 970	1420 635	1.53	−0.17 −4,3	14117A	14276	0.14 3,5	0.7710 19,583	1.67 42,5	1.56 39,5	0.05 1,3	0.6250 15,875	2.36 60,0	2.48 63,0
†1.1811 †30,000	2.8346 72,000	0.7480 19,000	2210 985	1370 605	1.62	−0.16 −4,2	26118	26283	0.06 1,5	0.7450 18,923	1.50 38,0	1.42 36,0	0.06 1,5	0.6250 15,875	2.44 62,0	2.56 65,0
1.1855 30,112	2.4409 62,000	0.7500 19,050	1990 885	1190 530	1.67	−0.23 −5,8	15116	15245	0.03 0,8	0.8125 20,638	1.42 36,0	1.40 35,5	0.05 1,3	0.5625 14,288	2.17 55,0	2.28 58,0
1.1875 30,162	2.3125 58,738	0.5781 14,684	1280 570	1040 465	1.23	−0.05 −1,2	08118	08231	0.14 3,5	0.5937 15,080	1.63 41,5	1.38 35,0	0.04 1,0	0.4219 10,716	2.05 52,0	2.17 55,0
1.1875 30,162	2.4409 62,000	0.6300 16,002	1620 720	1060 470	1.53	−0.14 −3,5	17119	17244	0.06 1,5	0.6522 16,566	1.46 37,0	1.36 34,5	0.06 1,5	0.5625 14,288	2.13 54,0	2.24 57,0
1.1875 30,162	2.5312 64,292	0.8438 21,433	2450 1090	2290 1020	1.07	−0.13 −3,3	M86649	M86610	0.06 1,5	0.8438 21,433	1.61 41,0	1.50 38,2	0.06 1,5	0.6563 16,670	2.13 54,0	2.40 61,0
1.1875 30,162	2.6875 68,262	0.8750 22,225	2620 1165	2450 1090	1.07	−0.11 −2,8	M88043	M88010	0.09 2,3	0.8750 22,225	1.71 43,5	1.56 39,5	0.06 1,5	0.6875 17,462	2.28 58,0	2.56 65,0
1.1875 30,162	2.7500 69,850	0.9375 23,812	3280 1460	1530 685	2.14	−0.34 −8,6	2558	2523S	0.09 2,3	0.9983 25,357	1.57 40,0	1.44 36,5	0.06 1,5	0.7500 19,050	2.40 61,0	2.52 64,0
1.1875 30,162	2.7500 69,850	0.9375 23,812	3280 1460	1530 685	2.14	−0.34 −8,6	2559	2523	0.03 0,8	0.9983 25,357	1.46 37,0	1.56 36,5	0.05 1,3	0.7500 19,050	2.40 61,0	2.52 64,0
1.1875 30,162	2.8593 72,626	1.1875 30,162	3700 1645	2100 935	1.76	−0.40 −10,1	3187	3130	0.03 0,8	1.1810 29,997	1.54 39,0	1.52 38,5	0.03 0,8	0.9375 23,812	2.48 63,0	2.64 67,0
1.1875 30,162	3.0000 76,200	0.8120 20,625	2440 1085	1680 750	1.45	−0.19 −4,7	28118	28300X	0.06 1,5	0.8244 20,940	1.57 40,0	1.48 37,5	0.06 1,5	0.6100 15,494	2.68 68,0	2.80 71,0
1.1875 30,162	3.0000 76,200	0.9688 24,608	2880 1285	3320 1475	0.87	−0.08 −2,0	43118	43300	0.06 1,5	0.9478 24,074	1.77 45,0	1.66 42,1	Spec.	0.6563 16,670	2.52 64,0	2.87 73,0
1.1875 30,162	3.1250 79,375	1.1563 29,370	4150 1840	2590 1155	1.60	−0.34 −8,7	3474	3420	0.03 0,8	1.1721 29,771	1.61 41,0	1.57 40,0	0.13 3,3	0.9375 23,812	2.64 67,0	2.91 74,0
1.1895 30,213	2.4409 62,000	0.7500 19,050	1990 885	1190 530	1.67	−0.23 −5,8	15118	15245	0.14 3,5	0.8125 20,638	1.63 41,5	1.40 35,5	0.05 1,3	0.5625 14,288	2.17 55,0	2.28 58,0
1.1895 30,213	2.4409 62,000	0.7500 19,050	1990 885	1190 530	1.67	−0.23 −5,8	15119	15245	0.06 1,5	0.8125 20,638	1.48 37,5	1.40 35,5	0.05 1,3	0.5625 14,288	2.17 55,0	2.28 58,0
1.1895 30,213	2.4409 62,000	0.7500 19,050	1990 885	1190 530	1.67	−0.23 −5,8	15120	15245	0.03 0,8	0.8125 20,638	1.42 36,0	1.40 35,5	0.05 1,3	0.5625 14,288	2.17 55,0	2.28 58,0
1.1900 30,226	2.7170 69,012	0.7813 19,845	2180 970	1420 635	1.53	−0.17 −4,3	14116	14274	0.03 0,8	0.7710 19,583	1.46 37,0	1.44 36,5	0.13 3,3	0.6250 15,875	2.32 59,0	2.48 63,0
1.2187 30,955	2.5312 64,292	0.8438 21,433	2450 1090	2290 1020	1.07	−0.13 −3,3	M86648A	M86610	0.06 1,5	0.8438 21,433	1.65 42,0	1.50 38,2	0.06 1,5	0.6563 16,670	2.13 54,0	2.40 61,0

bore	outside diameter	width	rating at 500 RPM for 3000 hours L10		fac-tor	eff. load center	part numbers		cone max. shaft fillet radius	width	backing shoulder diameters		cup max. hous-ing fillet radius	width	backing shoulder	
			one row radial	thrust			cone	cup								
d	D	T	lb daN	lb daN	K	a[2]			R[1]	B	d_b	d_a	r[1]	C	D_b	D_a
1.2500 31.750	2.3125 58.738	0.5781 14.684	1280 570	1040 465	1.23	-0.05 -1,2	08125	08231	0.04 1,0	0.5937 15,080	1.48 37,5	1.42 36,0	0.04 1,0	0.4219 10,716	2.05 52,0	2.17 55,0
1.2500 31.750	2.3280 59,131	0.6250 15.875	1580 700	1110 495	1.42	-0.12 -2,9	▲LM67048	LM67010	Spec. —	0.6600 16,764	1.67 42,5	1.42 36,0	0.05 1,3	0.4650 11,811	2.05 52,0	2.20 56,0
1.2500 31.750	2.4404 61.986	0.6250 15.875	1580 700	1110 495	1.42	-0.12 -2,9	▲LM67049A	LM67014	0.03 0,8	0.6600 16,764	1.46 37,0	1.42 36,0	0.05 1,3	0.4650 11,811	2.13 54,0	2.24 57,0
1.2500 31.750	2.4409 62.000	0.7150 18,161	1990 885	1190 530	1.67	-0.19 -5,0	15123	15245	Spec. —	0.7500 19,050	1.67 42,5	1.44 36,5	0.05 1,3	0.5625 14,288	2.17 55,0	2.28 58,0
1.2500 31.750	2.4409 62.000	0.7500 19,050	1990 885	1190 530	1.67	-0.23 -5,8	15125	15245	0.14 3,5	0.8125 20,638	1.67 42,5	1.44 36,5	0.05 1,3	0.5625 14,288	2.17 55,0	2.28 58,0
1.2500 31.750	2.4409 62.000	0.7500 19,050	1990 885	1190 530	1.67	-0.23 -5,8	15126	15245	0.03 0,8	0.8125 20,638	1.46 37,0	1.44 36,5	0.05 1,3	0.5625 14,288	2.17 55,0	2.28 58,0
1.2500 31.750	2.6150 66,421	1.0000 25.400	3280 1460	1530 685	2.14	-0.34 -8,6	2580	2520	0.03 0,8	0.9983 25,357	1.52 38,5	1.48 37,5	0.13 3,3	0.8125 20,638	2.24 57,0	2.46 62,4
1.2500 31.750	2.6150 66,421	1.0000 25.400	3280 1460	1530 685	2.14	-0.34 -8,6	2582	2520	0.14 3,5	0.9983 25,357	1.73 44,0	1.48 37,5	0.13 3,3	0.8125 20,638	2.24 57,0	2.46 62,4
1.2500 31.750	2.6875 68.262	0.8750 22.225	2640 1175	1540 685	1.72	-0.26 -6,6	2475	2420	0.14 3,5	0.9375 23,812	1.73 44,0	1.48 37,5	0.06 1,5	0.6875 17,462	2.36 60,0	2.48 63,0
1.2500 31.750	2.6875 68.262	0.8750 22.225	2490 1110	1780 790	1.40	-0.20 -5,1	02475	02420	0.14 3,5	0.8750 22,225	1.75 44,5	1.52 38,5	0.06 1,5	0.6875 17,462	2.32 59,0	2.48 63,0
1.2500 31.750	2.6875 68.262	0.8750 22.225	2490 1110	1780 790	1.40	-0.20 -5,1	02476	02420	0.03 0,8	0.8750 22,225	1.54 39,0	1.52 38,5	0.06 1,5	0.6875 17,462	2.32 59,0	2.48 63,0
1.2500 31.750	2.6875 68.262	0.8750 22.225	2620 1165	2450 1090	1.07	-0.11 -2,8	M88046	M88010	0.06 1,5	0.8750 22,225	1.69 43,0	1.59 40,5	0.06 1,5	0.6875 17,462	2.28 58,0	2.56 65,0
1.2500 31.750	2.6875 68.262	1.0625 26,988	3210 1430	1940 860	1.66	-0.34 -8,7	23491	23420	0.06 1,5	1.0625 26,988	1.61 41,0	1.54 39,0	0.06 1,5	0.8750 22,225	2.32 59,0	2.52 64,0
1.2500 31.750	2.7148 68.956	0.7813 19.845	2180 970	1420 635	1.53	-0.17 -4,3	14125A	14274A	0.14 3,5	0.7710 19,583	1.73 44,0	1.48 37,5	0.13 3,3	0.6250 15,875	2.32 59,0	2.48 63,0
1.2500 31.750	2.8380 72.085	0.8813 22.385	2180 970	1420 635	1.53	-0.17 -4,3	14124	14283	0.03 0,8	0.7710 19,583	1.52 38,5	1.48 37,5	0.09 2,3	0.7250 18,415	2.36 60,0	2.56 65,0
1.2500 31.750	2.8593 72.626	1.1875 30,162	3700 1645	2100 935	1.76	-0.40 -10,1	3188	3130	0.03 0,8	1.1810 29,997	1.57 40,0	1.56 39,5	0.03 0,8	0.9375 23,812	2.48 63,0	2.64 67,0
1.2500 31.750	2.8593 72.626	1.1875 30,162	3700 1645	2100 935	1.76	-0.40 -10,1	3188S	3130	0.06 1,5	1.1810 29,997	1.63 41,5	1.56 39,5	0.03 0,8	0.9375 23,812	2.48 63,0	2.64 67,0
1.2500 31.750	2.8593 72.626	1.1875 30,162	3700 1645	2100 935	1.76	-0.40 -10,1	3193	3130	0.14 3,5	1.1810 29,997	1.79 45,5	1.56 39,5	0.03 0,8	0.9375 23,812	2.48 63,0	2.64 67,0
1.2500 31.750	2.8750 73.025	0.8750 22.225	2620 1165	2030 900	1.29	-0.15 -3,8	02875	02820	0.14 3,5	0.8750 22,225	1.79 45,5	1.56 39,5	0.13 3,3	0.6875 17,462	2.44 62,0	2.68 68,0
1.2500 31.750	2.8750 73.025	0.8750 22.225	2620 1165	2030 900	1.29	-0.15 -3,8	02876	02820	0.03 0,8	0.8750 22,225	1.57 40,0	1.56 39,5	0.13 3,3	0.6875 17,462	2.44 62,0	2.68 68,0
1.2500 31.750	2.8750 73.025	1.1563 29,370	3640 1620	3400 1515	1.07	-0.22 -5,6	HM88542	HM88510	0.05 1,3	1.0938 27,783	1.79 45,5	1.68 42,6	0.13 3,3	0.9063 23,020	2.32 59,0	2.76 70,0
1.2500 31.750	3.0000 76.200	0.9688 24,608	3280 1285	3320 1475	0.87	-0.08 -2,0	43125	43300	0.06 1,5	0.9478 24,074	1.73 44,0	1.63 41,5	Spec. —	0.6563 16,670	2.52 64,0	2.87 73,0
1.2500 31.750	3.0000 76.200	1.1563 29,370	3880 1725	3630 1615	1.07	-0.22 -5,6	HM89440	HM89411	0.03 0,8	1.1250 28,575	1.79 45,5	1.75 44,6	0.03 0,8	0.9063 23,020	2.56 65,0	2.87 73,0

[1] These maximum fillet radii will be cleared by the bearing corners.
[2] Minus value indicates center is inside cone backface.
†Dimension shown is maximum value—see note at bottom of fitting practice table page 4 in Reference Tables.
▲Non-standard tolerances, see Inch System bearing tolerance page 18 in Reference Tables.

SINGLE-ROW STRAIGHT BORE—TS

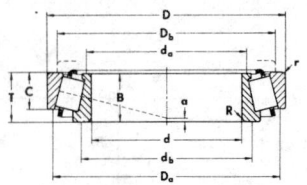

| bore | outside diameter | width | rating at 500 RPM for 3000 hours L10 | | fac-tor | eff. load center | part numbers | | cone | | | | cup | | | |
| | | | one row radial | thrust | | | cone | cup | max. shaft fillet radius | width | backing shoulder diameters | | max. hous-ing fillet radius | width | backing shoulder | |
d	D	T	lb daN	lb daN	K	a[①]			R[①]	B	d_b	d_a	r[①]	C	D_b	D_a
1.2500 31,750	3.1496 80,000	0.8268 21,000	3000 1335	1400 625	2.14	−0.25 −6,2	346	332	0.03 0,8	0.8820 22,403	1.57 40,0	1.56 39,5	0.05 1,3	0.7018 17,826	2.87 73,0	2.95 75,0
1.2500 31,750	3.1562 80,167	1.1563 29,370	4150 1840	2590 1155	1.60	−0.34 −8,7	3476	3422	0.05 1,3	1.1721 29,771	1.69 43,0	1.61 41,0	0.13 3,3	0.9375 23,812	2.68 68,0	2.91 74,0
1.2500 31,750	3.7500 95,250	1.0938 27,783	4950 2200	2410 1070	2.05	−0.36 −9,2	443	432A	0.03 0,8	1.1772 29,901	1.65 42,0	1.61 41,0	0.03 0,8	0.8750 22,225	3.31 84,0	3.43 87,0
†1.2598 †32,000	2.6875 68,262	0.8750 22,225	2490 1110	1780 790	1.40	−0.20 −5,1	02476X	02420	0.03 0.8	0.8071 20,500	1.56 39,5	1.52 38,5	0.06 1,5	0.6875 17,462	2.32 59,0	2.48 63,0
†1.2598 †32,000	2.8438 72,233	1.0000 25,400	3190 1415	2980 1325	1.07	−0.18 −4,6	HM88638	HM88610	0.13 3,3	1.0000 25,400	1.91 48,5	1.67 42,5	0.09 2,3	0.7812 19,842	2.36 60,0	2.72 69,0
1.2600 32,004	2.8346 72,000	0.7480 19,000	2210 985	1370 605	1.62	−0.16 −4,2	26126	26283	0.06 1,5	0.7450 18,923	1.56 39,5	1.48 37,5	0.06 1,5	0.6250 15,875	2.44 62,0	2.56 65,0
1.3125 33,338	2.6150 66,421	1.0000 25,400	3280 1460	1530 685	2.14	−0.34 −8,6	2581	2520	0.03 0,8	0.9983 25,357	1.56 39,5	1.54 39,0	0.13 3,3	0.8125 20,638	2.24 57,0	2.46 62,4
1.3125 33,338	2.6150 66,421	1.0000 25,400	3280 1460	1530 685	2.14	−0.34 −8,6	2585	2520	0.14 3,5	0.9983 25,357	1.77 45,0	1.54 39,0	0.13 3,3	0.8125 20,638	2.24 57,0	2.46 62,4
1.3125 33,338	2.6250 66,675	0.8125 20,638	2090 930	1330 590	1.57	−0.21 −5,3	1680	1620	0.14 3,5	0.8125 20,638	1.75 44,5	1.52 38,5	0.06 1,5	0.6250 15,875	2.28 58,0	2.40 61,0
1.3125 33,338	2.6875 68,262	0.8750 22,225	2620 1165	2450 1090	1.07	−0.11 −2,8	M88048	M88010	0.03 0,8	0.8750 22,225	1.67 42,5	1.62 41,2	0.06 1,5	0.6875 17,462	2.28 58,0	2.56 65,0
1.3125 33,338	2.6875 68,262	0.8750 22,225	2620 1165	2450 1090	1.07	−0.11 −2,8	M88048A	M88010	0.05 1,3	0.8750 22,225	1.71 43,5	1.62 41,2	0.06 1,5	0.6875 17,462	2.28 58,0	2.56 65,0
1.3125 33,338	2.7148 68,956	0.7813 19,845	2180 970	1420 635	1.53	−0.17 −4,3	14130	14274A	0.14 3,5	0.7710 19,583	1.77 45,0	1.52 38,5	0.13 3,3	0.6250 15,875	2.32 59,0	2.48 63,0
1.3125 33,338	2.7148 68,956	0.7813 19,845	2180 970	1420 635	1.53	−0.17 −4,3	14131	14274A	0.03 0,8	0.7710 19,583	1.56 39,5	1.52 38,5	0.13 3,3	0.6250 15,875	2.32 59,0	2.48 63,0
1.3125 33,338	2.8346 72,000	0.7480 19,000	2210 985	1370 605	1.62	−0.16 −4,2	26131	26283	0.14 3,5	0.7450 18,923	1.75 44,5	1.52 38,5	0.06 1,5	0.6250 15,875	2.44 62,0	2.56 65,0
1.3125 33,338	2.8593 72,626	1.1875 30,162	3700 1645	2100 935	1.76	−0.40 −10,1	3196	3130	0.14 3,5	1.1810 29,997	1.85 47,0	1.59 40,5	0.03 0,8	0.9375 23,812	2.60 63,0	2.64 67,0
1.3125 33,338	2.8593 72,626	1.1875 30,162	3700 1645	2100 935	1.76	−0.40 −10,1	3197	3130	0.03 0,8	1.1810 29,997	1.63 41,5	1.59 40,5	0.03 0,8	0.9375 23,812	2.60 63,0	2.64 67,0
1.3125 33,338	2.8750 73,025	0.8750 22,225	2910 1295	1830 815	1.59	−0.22 −5,6	2876	2821	0.14 3,5	0.9375 23,812	1.81 46,0	1.57 40,0	0.03 0,8	0.6875 17,462	2.56 65,0	2.68 68,0
1.3125 33,338	2.8750 73,025	0.9375 23,812	3460 1540	1790 800	1.93	−0.31 −8,0	2790	2735X	0.06 1,5	1.0100 25,654	1.65 42,0	1.57 40,0	0.03 0,8	0.7500 19,050	2.60 66,0	2.72 69,0
1.3125 33,338	2.8750 73,025	1.1563 29,370	3640 1620	3400 1515	1.07	−0.22 −5,6	HM88547	HM88510	0.03 0,8	1.0938 27,783	1.79 45,5	1.68 42,6	0.13 3,3	0.9063 23,020	2.32 59,0	2.76 70,0
1.3125 33,338	3.0000 76,200	0.9375 23,812	3460 1540	1790 800	1.93	−0.31 −8,0	2785	2729	0.14 3,5	1.0100 25,654	1.81 46,0	1.57 40,0	0.03 0,8	0.7500 19,050	2.68 68,0	2.76 70,0
1.3125 33,338	3.0000 76,200	0.9688 24,608	2880 1285	3320 1475	0.87	−0.08 −2,0	43131	43300	0.14 3,5	0.9478 24,074	2.01 51,0	1.66 42,1	Spec.	0.6563 16,670	2.52 64,0	2.87 73,0

bore d	outside diameter D	width T	rating one row radial	rating thrust	factor K	eff. load center a[2]	part number cone	part number cup	max shaft fillet radius R[1]	width B	db	da	max housing fillet radius r[1]	width C	Db	Da
1.3125	3.0000	0.9688	2880	3320	0.87	−0.08	43132	43300	0.08	0.9478	1.89		Spec.	0.6563	2.52	2.87
33,338	76,200	24,608	1285	1475		−2,0			2,0	24,074	48,0	42,1		16,670	64,0	73,0
1.3125	3.0000	1.1563	3770	2600	1.45	−0.30	31590	31521	0.03	1.1250	1.69	1.67	0.05	0.9375	2.60	2.83
33,338	76,200	29,370	1680	1155		−7,7			0,8	28,575	43,0	42,5	1,3	23,812	66,0	72,0
1.3125	3.0000	1.1563	3880	3630	1.07	−0.22	HM89443	HM89410	0.03	1.1250	1.83	1.75	0.13	0.9063	2.44	2.87
33,338	76,200	29,370	1725	1615		−5,6			0,8	28,575	46,5	44,6	3,3	23,020	62,0	73,0
1.3125	3.0000	1.1563	3880	3630	1.07	−0.22	HM89444	HM89411	0.15	1.1250	2.09	1.75	0.03	0.9063	2.56	2.87
33,338	76,200	29,370	1725	1615		−5,6			3,8	28,575	53,0	44,6	0,8	23,020	65,0	73,0
1.3125	3.4843	1.0000	3180	4250	0.75	0.09	44131	44348	0.08	0.9330	2.01	1.89	0.06	0.6875	2.95	3.31
33,338	88,501	25,400	1410	1880		2,3			2,0	23,698	51,0	48,0	1,5	17,462	75,0	84,0
1.3750	2.5625	0.7100	2140	1380	1.55	−0.15	▲LM48548	LM48510	Spec.	0.7200	1.81	1.57	0.05	0.5500	2.28	2.40
34,925	65,088	18,034	950	615		−3,7				18,288	46,0	40,0	1,3	13,970	58,0	61,0
1.3750	2.5625	0.8300	2140	1380	1.55	−0.15	▲LM48548A	LM48511A	0.03	0.7200	1.59	1.66	0.06	0.6700	2.28	2.40
34,925	65,088	21,082	950	615		−3,7			0,8	18,288	40,5	42,2	1,5	17,018	58,0	61,0
1.3750	2.6250	0.8125	2520	1520	1.66	−0.22	M38549	M38510	0.14	0.8125	1.83	1.57	0.09	0.6563	2.28	2.44
34,925	66,675	20,638	1120	675		−5,6			3,5	20,638	46,5	40,0	2,3	16,670	58,0	62,0
1.3750	2.6875	0.8125	2330	1410	1.66	−0.23	14585	14525	0.14	0.8125	1.81	1.57	0.09	0.6250	2.32	2.48
34,925	68,262	20,638	1040	625		−5,7			3,5	20,638	46,0	40,0	2,3	15,875	59,0	63,0
1.3750	2.7148	0.7813	2180	1420	1.53	−0.17	14137A	14274A	0.06	0.7710	1.65	1.57	0.13	0.6250	2.32	2.48
34,925	68,956	19,845	970	635		−4,3			1,5	19,583	42,0	40,0	3,3	15,875	59,0	63,0
1.3750	2.7148	0.7813	2180	1420	1.53	−0.17	14138A	14274A	0.14	0.7710	1.81	1.57	0.13	0.6250	2.32	2.48
34,925	68,956	19,845	970	635		−4,3			3,5	19,583	46,0	40,0	3,3	15,875	59,0	63,0
1.3750	2.8438	1.0000	3190	2980	1.07	−0.18	HM88649	HM88610	0.09	1.0000	1.91	1.69	0.09	0.7812	2.36	2.72
34,925	72,233	25,400	1415	1325		−4,6			2,3	25,400	48,5	42,8	2,3	19,842	60,0	69,0
1.3750	2.8750	0.8750	2620	2030	1.29	−0.15	02877	02820	0.14	0.8750	1.91	1.65	0.13	0.6875	2.44	2.68
34,925	73,025	22,225	1165	900		−3,8			3,5	22,225	48,5	42,0	3,3	17,462	62,0	68,0
1.3750	2.8750	0.8750	2620	2030	1.29	−0.15	02878	02820	0.03	0.8750	1.67	1.65	0.13	0.6875	2.44	2.68
34,925	73,025	22,225	1165	900		−3,8			0,8	22,225	42,5	42,0	3,3	17,462	62,0	68,0
1.3750	2.8750	0.9375	3460	1790	1.93	−0.31	2786	2735X	0.20	1.0100	2.01	1.61	0.03	0.7500	2.60	2.72
34,925	73,025	23,812	1540	800		−8,0			5,0	25,654	51,0	41,0	0,8	19,050	66,0	69,0
1.3750	2.8750	0.9375	3340	1660	2.01	−0.32	25877	25821	0.06	0.9688	1.69	1.59	0.03	0.7500	2.56	2.68
34,925	73,025	23,812	1485	740		−8,1			1,5	24,608	43,0	40,5	0,8	19,050	65,0	68,0
1.3750	2.8750	0.9375	3340	1660	2.01	−0.32	25878	25820	0.14	0.9688	1.85	1.59	0.09	0.7500	2.52	2.68
34,925	73,025	23,812	1485	740		−8,1			3,5	24,608	47,0	40,5	2,3	19,050	64,0	68,0
1.3750	3.0000	0.8125	2440	1680	1.45	−0.19	28137	28300	0.06	0.8244	1.71	1.61	0.05	0.6105	2.68	2.80
34,925	76,200	20,638	1085	750		−4,7			1,5	20,940	43,5	41,0	1,3	15,507	68,0	71,0
1.3750	3.0000	0.9375	3460	1790	1.93	−0.31	2793	2729X	0.03	1.0100	1.65	1.61	0.06	0.7500	2.64	2.76
34,925	76,200	23,812	1540	800		−8,0			0,8	25,654	42,0	41,0	1,5	19,050	67,0	70,0
1.3750	3.0000	0.9375	3460	1790	1.93	−0.31	2796	2720	0.14	1.0100	1.87	1.61	0.13	0.7500	2.60	2.76
34,925	76,200	23,812	1540	800		−8,0			3,5	25,654	47,5	41,0	3,3	19,050	66,0	70,0
1.3750	3.0000	1.1563	3770	2600	1.45	−0.30	31593	31521	0.14	1.1250	1.97	1.71	0.05	0.9375	2.60	2.83
34,925	76,200	29,370	1680	1155		−7,7			3,5	28,575	50,0	43,5	1,3	23,812	66,0	72,0
1.3750	3.0000	1.1563	3770	2600	1.45	−0.30	31594	31520	0.06	1.1250	1.81	1.71	0.13	0.9375	2.52	2.83
34,925	76,200	29,370	1680	1155		−7,7			1,5	28,575	46,0	43,5	3,3	23,812	64,0	72,0
1.3750	3.0000	1.1563	3930	2350	1.67	−0.36	36137	36300	0.06	1.1750	1.77	1.67	0.13	0.9375	2.60	2.80
34,925	76,200	29,370	1750	1045		−9,3			1,5	29,845	45,0	42,5	3,3	23,812	66,0	71,0

① These maximum fillet radii will be cleared by the bearing corners.
② Minus value indicates center is inside cone backface.
† Dimension shown is maximum value—see note at bottom of fitting practice table page 4 in Reference Tables.
▲ Non-standard tolerances, see Inch System bearing tolerance page 18 in Reference Tables.

SINGLE-ROW STRAIGHT BORE—TS

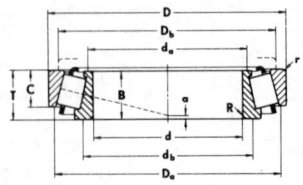

bore	outside diameter	width	rating at 500 RPM for 3000 hours L10		fac-tor	eff. load center	part numbers		cone max. shaft fillet radius	backing shoulder width	backing shoulder diameters		cup max. housing fillet radius	width	backing shoulder	
			one row radial	thrust			cone	cup								
d	D	T	lb daN	lb daN	K	a③	cone	cup	R①	B	d_b	d_a	r①	C	D_b	D_a
1.3750 34,925	3.0000 76,200	1.1563 29,370	3880 1725	3630 1615	1.07	−0.22 −5,6	HM89446	HM89411	0.14 3,5	1.1250 28,575	2.09 53,0	1.75 44,6	0.03 0,8	0.9063 23,020	2.56 65,0	2.87 73,0
1.3750 34,925	3.0000 76,200	1.1563 29,370	3880 1725	3630 1615	1.07	−0.22 −5,6	HM89446A	HM89411	0.03 0,8	1.1250 28,575	1.87 47,5	1.75 44,6	0.03 0,8	0.9063 23,020	2.56 65,0	2.87 73,0
1.3750 34,925	3.1250 79,375	1.1563 29,370	4150 1840	2590 1155	1.60	−0.34 −8,7	3478	3420	0.14 3,5	1.1721 29,771	1.97 50,0	1.71 43,5	0.13 3,3	0.9375 23,812	2.64 67,0	2.91 74,0
1.3750 34,925	3.1250 79,375	1.1563 29,370	4150 1840	2590 1155	1.60	−0.34 −8,7	3482	3420	0.03 0,8	1.1721 29,771	1.73 44,0	1.71 43,5	0.13 3,3	0.9375 23,812	2.64 67,0	2.91 74,0
1.3750 34,925	3.1496 80,000	0.8268 21,000	3000 1335	1400 625	2.14	−0.25 −6,2	335	332US	0.03 0,8	0.8820 22,403	1.67 42,5	1.63 41,5	0.08 2,0	0.7018 17,826	2.83 72,0	2.95 75,0
1.3750 34,925	†3.1496 †80,000	1.1563 29,370	4300 1900	2000 890	2.14	−0.43 −10,9	3379	3325	0.14 3,5	1.1965 30,391	1.89 48,0	1.63 41,5	0.13 3,3	0.9375 23,812	2.76 70,0	2.94 74,8
1.3750 34,925	3.1510 80,035	0.9688 24,608	3080 1370	2960 1315	1.04	−0.10 −2,5	27875	27820	0.03 0,8	0.9330 23,698	1.79 45,5	1.75 44,5	0.06 1,5	0.7288 18,512	2.68 68,0	2.95 75,0
1.3750 34,925	3.3750 85,725	1.1875 30,162	5000 2220	3450 1535	1.45	−0.32 −8,2	3872	3821	0.14 3,5	1.1875 30,162	2.09 53,0	1.81 46,0	0.05 1,3	0.9375 23,812	2.95 75,0	3.19 81,0
1.3750 34,925	3.4843 88,501	1.0625 26,988	4450 1980	2000 890	2.22	−0.38 −9,7	417	414	0.03 0,8	1.1450 29,083	1.67 42,5	1.65 42,0	0.06 1,5	0.8750 22,225	3.03 77,0	3.15 80,0
1.3750 34,925	3.7500 95,250	1.0938 27,783	4950 2200	2410 1070	2.05	−0.36 −9,2	449	432	0.03 0,8	1.1772 29,901	1.73 44,0	1.71 43,5	0.09 2,3	0.8750 22,225	3.27 83,0	3.43 87,0
1.3770 34,976	2.6875 68,262	0.6250 15,875	2000 890	1530 680	1.31	−0.06 −1,5	19138	19268	0.06 1,5	0.6504 16,520	1.67 42,5	1.59 40,5	0.06 1,5	0.4688 11,908	2.40 61,0	2.56 65,0
1.3770 34,976	2.7148 68,956	0.7813 19,845	2180 970	1420 635	1.53	−0.17 −4,3	14139	14274A	0.05 1,3	0.7710 19,583	1.63 41,5	1.57 40,0	0.13 3,3	0.6250 15,875	2.32 59,0	2.48 63,0
1.3770 34,976	3.1496 80,000	0.8270 21,006	2440 1085	1680 750	1.45	−0.19 −4,7	28138	28315	0.06 1,5	0.8244 20,940	1.71 43,5	1.61 41,0	0.06 1,5	0.6250 15,875	2.72 69,0	2.87 73,0
†1.3780 †35,000	†2.3622 †60,000	0.6250 15,875	1610 715	1150 510	1.40	−0.10 −2,5	▲L68149	L68111	Spec.	0.6600 16,764	1.79 45,5	1.54 39,0	0.05 1,3	0.4700 11,938	2.09 53,0	2.20 56,0
†1.3780 †35,000	†2.4409 †62,000	0.6575 16,700	1780 790	1360 605	1.31	−0.10 −2,5	LM78349	LM78310A	Spec.	0.6693 17,000	1.81 46,0	1.57 40,0	0.06 1,5	0.5354 13,599	2.13 54,0	2.32 59,0
1.3780 35,000	2.8750 73,025	1.0625 26,988	3540 1575	2240 995	1.58	−0.32 −8,1	23691	23621	0.14 3,5	1.0620 26,975	1.93 49,0	1.66 42,1	0.03 0,8	0.8750 22,225	2.48 63,0	2.68 68,0
1.3780 35,000	3.0000 76,200	1.0000 25,400	3660 1630	2000 890	1.83	−0.29 −7,5	26883	26823	0.03 0,8	1.0000 25,400	1.67 42,5	1.65 42,0	0.06 1,5	0.8125 20,638	2.72 69,0	2.87 73,0
1.3780 35,000	3.1496 80,000	0.8268 21,000	3000 1335	1400 625	2.14	−0.25 −6,2	339	333	0.03 0,8	0.8820 22,403	1.67 42,5	1.63 41,5	0.08 2,0	0.8268 21,000	2.83 72,0	2.99 75,0
1.4062 35,717	2.8438 72,233	1.0000 25,400	3190 1415	2980 1325	1.07	−0.18 −4,6	HM88648	HM88610	0.14 3,5	1.0000 25,400	2.05 52,0	1.69 42,8	0.09 2,3	0.7812 19,842	2.36 60,0	2.72 69,0
1.4365 36,487	2.8750 73,025	0.9375 23,812	3460 1540	1790 800	1.93	−0.31 −8,0	2780	2735X	0.06 1,5	1.0100 25,654	1.75 44,5	1.67 42,5	0.03 0,8	0.7500 19,050	2.60 66,0	2.72 69,0
1.4365 36,487	2.8750 73,025	0.9375 23,812	3460 1540	1790 800	1.93	−0.31 −8,0	2794	2735X	0.14 3,5	1.0100 25,654	1.93 49,0	1.67 42,5	0.03 0,8	0.7500 19,050	2.60 66,0	2.72 69,0

| | | | rating at 500 RPM for 3000 hours L10 | | fac-tor | eff. load center | part numbers | | cone max shaft fillet radius | cone width | backing shoulder diameters | | cup max housing fillet radius | cup width | backing shoulder | |
| bore | outside diameter | width | one row radial | thrust | | | cone | cup | | | | | | | | |
d	D	T	lb daN	lb daN	K	a②			R①	B	d_b	d_a	r①	C	D_b	D_a
1.4365 36,487	2.8750 73,025	0.9375 23,812	3340 1485	1660 740	2.01	−0.32 −8,1	25880	25821	0.06 1,5	0.9688 24,608	1.73 44,0	1.65 42,0	0.03 0,8	0.7500 19,050	2.56 65,0	2.68 68,0
1.4375 36,512	2.7170 69,012	0.7500 19,050	2230 990	1540 685	1.45	−0.12 −3,0	13682	13620	0.14 3,5	0.7500 19,050	1.89 48,0	1.63 41,5	0.03 0,8	0.5938 15,083	2.44 62,0	2.56 65,0
1.4375 36,512	3.0000 76,200	1.1563 29,370	3770 1680	2600 1155	1.45	−0.30 −7,7	31597	31521	0.14 3,5	1.1250 28,575	2.01 51,0	1.75 44,4	0.05 1,3	0.9375 23,812	2.60 66,0	2.83 72,0
1.4375 36,512	3.0000 76,200	1.1563 29,370	3880 1725	3630 1615	1.07	−0.22 −5,6	HM89448	HM89411	0.03 0,8	1.1250 28,575	1.91 48,5	1.75 44,6	0.03 0,8	0.9063 23,020	2.56 65,0	2.87 73,0
1.4375 36,512	3.0000 76,200	1.1563 29,370	3880 1725	3630 1615	1.07	−0.22 −5,6	HM89449	HM89411	0.14 3,5	1.1250 28,575	2.13 54,0	1.75 44,6	0.03 0,8	0.9063 23,020	2.56 65,0	2.87 73,0
1.4375 36,512	3.1250 79,375	0.9375 23,812	3660 1630	2000 890	1.83	−0.29 −7,5	26877	26822	0.03 0,8	1.0000 25,400	1.73 44,0	1.69 43,0	0.03 0,8	0.7500 19,050	2.80 71,0	2.91 74,0
1.4375 36,512	3.1250 79,375	1.1563 29,370	4150 1840	2590 1155	1.60	−0.34 −8,7	3479	3420	0.03 0,8	1.1721 29,771	1.79 45,5	1.75 44,5	0.13 3,3	0.9375 23,812	2.64 67,0	2.91 74,0
1.4375 36,512	3.2500 82,550	0.9375 23,812	3680 1635	2110 940	1.74	−0.25 −6,2	25570	25519	0.14 3,5	1.0000 25,400	2.01 51,0	1.77 45,0	0.08 2,0	0.7500 19,050	2.87 73,0	3.03 77,0
1.4375 36,512	3.3750 85,725	1.1875 30,162	5000 2220	3450 1535	1.45	−0.32 −8,2	3878	3820	0.03 0,8	1.1875 30,162	1.89 48,0	1.85 47,0	0.13 3,3	0.9375 23,812	2.87 73,0	3.19 81,0
1.4375 36,512	3.4843 88,501	1.0000 25,400	3180 1410	4250 1880	0.75	0.09 2,3	44143	44348	0.09 2,3	0.9330 23,698	2.13 54,0	1.97 50,0	0.06 1,5	0.6875 17,462	2.95 75,0	3.31 84,0
1.5000 38,100	2.5000 63,500	0.5000 12,700	1140 510	675 300	1.69	−0.03 −0,8	13889	13830	0.06 1,5	0.4688 11,908	1.77 45,0	1.67 42,5	0.03 0,8	0.3750 9,525	2.32 59,0	2.36 60,0
1.5000 38,100	2.5625 65,088	0.5000 12,700	1140 510	675 300	1.69	−0.03 −0,8	13889	13836	0.06 1,5	0.4688 11,908	1.77 45,0	1.67 42,5	0.03 0,8	0.3750 9,525	2.32 59,0	2.40 61,0
1.5000 38,100	2.5625 65,088	0.7100 18,034	2020 900	1150 510	1.76	−0.16 −4,2	LM29748	LM29710	Spec.	0.7200 18,288	1.93 49,0	1.67 42,5	0.05 1,3	0.5500 13,970	2.32 59,0	2.44 62,0
1.5000 38,100	2.5625 65,088	0.7800 19,812	2020 900	1150 510	1.76	−0.16 −4,2	LM29749	LM29711	0.09 2,3	0.7200 18,288	1.81 46,0	1.67 42,5	0.05 1,3	0.6200 15,748	2.28 58,0	2.44 62,0
1.5000 38,100	2.7170 69,012	0.7500 19,050	2230 990	1540 685	1.45	−0.12 −3,0	13685	13620	0.14 3,5	0.7500 19,050	1.95 49,5	1.69 43,0	0.03 0,8	0.5938 15,083	2.44 62,0	2.56 65,0
1.5000 38,100	2.7170 69,012	0.7500 19,050	2230 990	1540 685	1.45	−0.12 −3,0	13687	13621	0.08 2,0	0.7500 19,050	1.83 46,5	1.69 43,0	0.09 2,3	0.5938 15,083	2.40 61,0	2.56 65,0
1.5000 38,100	2.8125 71,438	0.6250 15,875	2000 890	1530 680	1.31	−0.06 −1,5	19150	19281	0.06 1,5	0.6504 16,520	1.77 45,0	1.69 43,0	0.04 1,0	0.4688 11,908	2.48 63,0	2.60 66,0
1.5000 38,100	2.8346 72,000	0.6700 17,018	2000 890	1530 680	1.31	−0.06 −1,5	19150	19283	0.06 1,5	0.6504 16,520	1.77 45,0	1.69 43,0	0.06 1,5	0.5625 14,288	2.48 63,0	2.60 66,0
1.5000 38,100	2.8346 72,000	0.6700 17,018	2000 890	1530 680	1.31	−0.06 −1,5	19150	19283X	0.06 1,5	0.6504 16,520	1.77 45,0	1.69 43,0	0.08 2,0	0.5625 14,288	2.44 62,0	2.60 66,0
1.5000 38,100	2.8346 72,000	0.7480 19,000	2280 1015	1570 700	1.45	−0.16 −4,0	16150	16282	0.14 3,5	0.8125 20,638	1.95 49,5	1.69 43,0	0.06 1,5	0.5605 14,237	2.48 63,0	2.64 67,0
1.5000 38,100	2.8440 72,238	0.8125 20,638	2280 1015	1570 700	1.45	−0.16 −4,0	16150	16284	0.14 3,5	0.8125 20,638	1.95 49,5	1.69 43,0	0.05 1,3	0.6250 15,875	2.48 63,0	2.64 67,0
1.5000 38,100	2.8440 72,238	0.9375 23,812	2280 1015	1570 700	1.45	−0.16 −4,0	16150	16283	0.14 3,5	0.8125 20,638	1.95 49,5	1.69 43,0	0.09 2,3	0.7500 19,050	2.40 61,0	2.64 67,0
1.5000 38,100	2.8750 73,025	0.9375 23,812	3460 1540	1790 800	1.93	−0.31 −8,0	2776	2735X	0.17 4,3	1.0100 25,654	2.05 52,0	1.71 43,5	0.03 0,8	0.7500 19,050	2.60 66,0	2.72 69,0

① These maximum fillet radii will be cleared by the bearing corners.
② Minus value indicates center is inside cone backface.
† Dimension shown is maximum value—see note at bottom of fitting practice table page 4 in Reference Tables.
▲ Non-standard tolerances, see Inch System bearing tolerance page 18 in Reference Tables.

SINGLE-ROW STRAIGHT BORE—TS

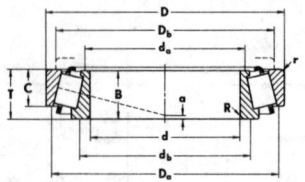

bore	outside diameter	width	rating at 500 RPM for 3000 hours L10		fac-tor	eff. lead center	part numbers		cone				cup			
			one row radial	thrust			cone	cup	max. shaft fillet radius	width	backing shoulder diameters		max. housing fillet radius	width	backing shoulder	
d	D	T	lb daN	lb daN	K	a①			R①	B	d_b	d_a	r①	C	D_b	D_a
1.5000 38,100	2.8750 73,025	0.9375 23,812	3460 1540	1790 800	1.93	−0.31 −8,0	2788	2735X	0.14 3,5	1.0100 25,654	1.97 50,0	1.71 43,5	0.03 0,8	0.7500 19,050	2.60 66,0	2.72 69,0
1.5000 38,100	2.8750 73,025	0.9375 23,812	3460 1540	1790 800	1.93	−0.31 −8,0	2788A	2735X	0.06 1,5	1.0100 25,654	1.81 46,0	1.71 43,5	0.03 0,8	0.7500 19,050	2.60 66,0	2.72 69,0
1.5000 38,100	3.1250 79,375	0.9375 23,812	3660 1630	2000 890	1.83	−0.29 −7,5	26878	26822A	0.03 0,8	1.0000 25,400	1.77 45,0	1.75 44,5	0.09 2,3	0.7500 19,050	2.72 69,0	2.91 74,0
1.5000 38,100	3.1250 79,375	1.1563 29,370	4150 1840	2590 1155	1.60	−0.34 −8,7	3490	3420	0.14 3,5	1.1721 29,771	2.05 52,0	1.81 45,9	0.13 3,3	0.9375 23,812	2.64 67,0	2.91 74,0
1.5000 38,100	3.1496 80,000	0.9518 24,176	3000 1335	1400 625	2.14	−0.25 −6,2	337	332A	0.03 0,8	0.8820 22,403	1.75 44,5	1.73 44,0	0.09 2,3	0.8268 21,000	2.80 71,0	2.95 75,0
1.5000 38,100	3.1510 80,035	0.8438 21,433	2440 1085	1680 750	1.45	−0.19 −4,7	28150	28317	0.06 1,5	0.8244 20,940	1.79 45,5	1.71 43,5	0.06 1,5	0.6250 15,875	2.72 69,0	2.87 73,0
1.5000 38,100	3.1510 80,035	0.9688 24,608	3080 1370	2960 1315	1.04	−0.10 −2,5	27880	27820	0.03 0,8	0.9330 23,698	1.89 48,0	1.85 47,0	0.06 1,5	0.7288 18,512	2.68 68,0	2.95 75,0
1.5000 38,100	3.1510 80,035	0.9688 24,608	3080 1370	2960 1315	1.04	−0.10 −2,5	27881	27820	0.14 3,5	0.9330 23,698	2.09 53,0	1.85 47,0	0.06 1,5	0.7288 18,512	2.68 68,0	2.95 75,0
1.5000 38,100	3.1510 80,035	1.1563 29,370	4300 1900	2000 890	2.14	−0.43 −10,9	3387	3339	0.03 0,8	1.1965 30,391	1.77 45,0	1.75 44,5	0.06 1,5	0.9375 23,812	2.80 71,0	2.94 74,8
1.5000 38,100	3.1562 80,167	1.1563 29,370	4300 1900	2000 890	2.14	−0.43 −10,9	3381	3331	0.14 3,5	1.1965 30,391	2.01 51,0	1.75 44,5	0.03 0,8	0.9375 23,812	2.83 72,0	2.94 74,8
1.5000 38,100	3.2500 82,550	1.1563 29,370	4300 1900	4000 1780	1.07	−0.19 −4,8	HM801346	HM801310	0.03 0,8	1.1250 28,575	2.01 51,0	1.93 49,1	0.13 3,3	0.9063 23,020	2.68 68,0	3.07 78,0
1.5000 38,100	3.2500 82,550	1.1563 29,370	4300 1900	4000 1780	1.07	−0.19 −4,8	HM801346X	HM801310	0.09 2,3	1.1250 28,575	2.13 54,0	1.93 49,1	0.13 3,3	0.9063 23,020	2.68 68,0	3.07 78,0
1.5000 38,100	3.2650 82,931	0.9375 23,812	3680 1635	2110 940	1.74	−0.25 −6,2	25572	25520	0.03 0,8	1.0000 25,400	1.81 46,0	1.81 46,0	0.03 0,8	0.7500 19,050	2.91 74,0	3.03 77,0
1.5000 38,100	3.3125 84,138	1.1875 30,162	4550 2020	2380 1060	1.91	−0.40 −10,2	3580	3520	0.06 1,5	1.2160 30,886	1.89 48,0	1.79 45,5	0.13 3,3	0.9375 23,812	2.91 74,0	3.13 79,5
1.5000 38,100	3.3475 85,026	1.1875 30,162	4550 2020	2380 1060	1.91	−0.40 −10,2	3583	3526	0.14 3,5	1.2160 30,886	2.05 52,0	1.79 45,5	0.03 0,8	0.9375 23,812	2.99 76,0	3.15 80,0
1.5000 38,100	3.3750 85,725	1.1875 30,162	5000 2220	3450 1535	1.45	−0.32 −8,2	3875	3821	0.03 0,8	1.1875 30,162	1.95 49,5	1.91 48,5	0.05 1,3	0.9375 23,812	2.95 75,0	3.19 81,0
1.5000 38,100	3.3750 85,725	1.1875 30,162	5000 2220	3450 1535	1.45	−0.32 −8,2	3876	3821	0.14 3,5	1.1875 30,162	2.17 55,0	1.91 48,5	0.05 1,3	0.9375 23,812	2.95 75,0	3.19 81,0
1.5000 38,100	3.4843 88,501	1.0000 25,400	3180 1410	4250 1880	0.75	0.09 2,3	44150	44348	0.09 2,3	0.9330 23,698	2.17 55,0	2.00 50,8	0.06 1,5	0.6875 17,462	2.95 75,0	3.31 84,0
1.5000 38,100	3.4843 88,501	1.0625 26,988	4450 1980	2000 890	2.22	−0.38 −9,7	415	414	0.03 0,8	1.1450 29,083	1.77 45,0	1.75 44,5	0.06 1,5	0.8750 22,225	3.03 77,0	3.15 80,0
1.5000 38,100	3.4843 88,501	1.0625 26,988	4450 1980	2000 890	2.22	−0.38 −9,7	418	414	0.14 3,5	1.1450 29,083	2.01 51,0	1.75 44,5	0.06 1,5	0.8750 22,225	3.03 77,0	3.15 80,0
1.5000 38,100	3.5625 90,488	1.5625 39,688	6850 3060	3350 1490	2.05	−0.59 −14,9	4375	4335	0.06 1,5	1.5900 40,386	2.01 51,0	1.91 48,5	0.13 3,3	1.3125 33,338	3.03 77,0	3.35 85,0

SINGLE-ROW STRAIGHT BORE   TS

										cone					cup			
bore	outside diameter	width	rating at 500 RPM for 3000 hours L10		fac-tor	eff. load center	part numbers			max. shaft fillet radius	width	backing shoulder diameters		max. hous-ing fillet radius	width	backing shoulder	
			one row radial	thrust			cone	cup									
d	D	T	lb / daN	lb / daN	K	a②			R①	B	d_b	d_a	r①	C	D_b	D_a
1.5000 / 38.100	3.7500 / 95.250	1.0938 / 27.783	4950 / 2200	2410 / 1070	2.05	−0.36 / −9,2	440	432A	0.03 / 0,8	1.1772 / 29.901	1.83 / 46,5	1.79 / 45,5	0.03 / 0,8	0.8750 / 22.225	3.31 / 84,0	3.43 / 87,0
1.5000 / 38.100	3.7500 / 95.250	1.0938 / 27.783	4950 / 2200	2410 / 1070	2.05	−0.36 / −9,2	444	432A	0.14 / 3,5	1.1772 / 29.901	2.05 / 52,0	1.79 / 45,5	0.03 / 0,8	0.8750 / 22.225	3.31 / 84,0	3.43 / 87,0
1.5000 / 38.100	3.7500 / 95.250	1.0938 / 27.783	5250 / 2320	2960 / 1315	1.77	−0.30 / −7,6	33880	33822	0.14 / 3,5	1.1250 / 28.575	2.13 / 54,0	1.89 / 48,0	0.03 / 0,8	0.8750 / 22.225	3.39 / 86,0	3.54 / 90,0
1.5000 / 38.100	3.7500 / 95.250	1.2188 / 30.958	3850 / 1715	4900 / 2160	0.79	−0.01 / −0,3	53150	53375	0.06 / 1,5	1.1142 / 28.301	2.17 / 55,0	2.08 / 52,7	0.03 / 0,8	0.8125 / 20.638	3.19 / 81,0	3.50 / 89,0
1.5000 / 38.100	3.7500 / 95.250	1.2188 / 30.958	4500 / 2000	5700 / 2540	0.79	0.03 / 0,6	HM903241	HM903210	0.14 / 3,5	1.1250 / 28.575	2.40 / 61,0	2.12 / 54,0	0.03 / 0,8	0.8750 / 22.225	3.19 / 81,0	3.58 / 91,0
1.5000 / 38.100	4.0000 / 101.600	1.3750 / 34.925	6550 / 2920	3200 / 1425	2.05	−0.50 / −12,7	525	522	0.14 / 3,5	1.4200 / 36.068	2.13 / 54,0	1.89 / 48,0	0.13 / 3,3	1.0625 / 26.988	3.50 / 89,0	3.74 / 95,0
1.5625 / 39.688	2.8750 / 73.025	0.9375 / 23.812	3460 / 1540	1790 / 800	1.93	−0.31 / −8,0	2789	2735X	0.14 / 3,5	1.0100 / 25.654	2.05 / 52,0	1.77 / 45,0	0.03 / 0,8	0.7500 / 19.050	2.60 / 66,0	2.72 / 69,0
1.5625 / 39.688	2.8750 / 73.025	1.0100 / 25.654	2980 / 1325	1690 / 750	1.76	−0.23 / −5,9	M201047	M201011	0.03 / 0,8	0.8700 / 22.098	1.79 / 45,5	1.88 / 47,8	0.09 / 2,3	0.8400 / 21.336	2.52 / 64,0	2.72 / 69,0
1.5625 / 39.688	3.1496 / 80.000	0.9375 / 23.812	3660 / 1630	2000 / 890	1.83	−0.29 / −7,5	26880	26824	0.06 / 1,5	1.0000 / 25.400	1.89 / 48,0	1.79 / 45,5	0.05 / 1,3	0.7500 / 19.050	2.76 / 70,0	2.91 / 74,0
1.5625 / 39.688	3.1562 / 80.167	1.0000 / 25.400	3660 / 1630	2000 / 890	1.83	−0.29 / −7,5	26881	26830	0.14 / 3,5	1.0000 / 25.400	2.05 / 52,0	1.79 / 45,5	0.03 / 0,8	0.8125 / 20.638	2.80 / 71,0	2.91 / 74,0
1.5625 / 39.688	3.1562 / 80.167	1.1563 / 29.370	4300 / 1900	2000 / 890	2.14	−0.43 / −10,9	3386	3320	0.03 / 0,8	1.1965 / 30.391	1.83 / 46,5	1.79 / 45,5	0.13 / 3,3	0.9375 / 23.812	2.76 / 70,0	2.94 / 74,8
1.5625 / 39.688	3.2187 / 81.755	1.1563 / 29.370	4300 / 1900	2000 / 890	2.14	−0.43 / −10,9	3382	3329	0.14 / 3,5	1.1965 / 30.391	2.05 / 52,0	1.79 / 45,5	0.13 / 3,3	0.9375 / 23.812	2.80 / 71,0	2.95 / 75,0
1.5625 / 39.688	3.3125 / 84.138	1.1563 / 29.370	4300 / 1900	2000 / 890	2.14	−0.43 / −10,9	3382	3328	0.14 / 3,5	1.1965 / 30.391	2.05 / 52,0	1.79 / 45,5	0.13 / 3,3	0.9375 / 23.812	2.99 / 72,0	2.99 / 76,0
1.5625 / 39.688	3.4843 / 88.501	1.0000 / 25.400	3180 / 1410	4250 / 1880	0.75	0.09 / 2,3	44158	44348	0.14 / 3,5	0.9330 / 23.698	2.28 / 58,0	2.00 / 50,8	0.06 / 1,5	0.6875 / 17.462	2.95 / 75,0	3.31 / 84,0
1.5740 / 39.980	3.0000 / 76.200	0.8120 / 20.625	2440 / 1085	1680 / 750	1.45	−0.19 / −4,7	28159	28300X	0.14 / 3,5	0.8244 / 20.940	2.05 / 52,0	1.77 / 45,0	0.06 / 1,5	0.6100 / 15.494	2.68 / 68,0	2.80 / 71,0
1.5748 / 40.000	3.0000 / 76.200	0.8120 / 20.625	2440 / 1085	1680 / 750	1.45	−0.19 / −4,7	28158	28300X	0.06 / 1,5	0.8244 / 20.940	1.87 / 47,5	1.77 / 45,0	0.06 / 1,5	0.6100 / 15.494	2.68 / 68,0	2.80 / 71,0
1.5748 / 40.000	3.1496 / 80.000	0.8268 / 21.000	3000 / 1335	1400 / 625	2.14	−0.25 / −6,2	344	332	0.14 / 3,5	0.8820 / 22.403	2.05 / 52,0	1.79 / 45,5	0.05 / 1,3	0.7018 / 17.826	2.87 / 73,0	2.95 / 75,0
1.5748 / 40.000	3.1496 / 80.000	0.8268 / 21.000	3000 / 1335	1400 / 625	2.14	−0.25 / −6,2	344A	332	0.03 / 0,8	0.8820 / 22.403	1.81 / 46,0	1.79 / 45,5	0.05 / 1,3	0.7018 / 17.826	2.87 / 73,0	2.95 / 75,0
1.5748 / 40.000	3.3465 / 85.000	0.8125 / 20.638	3140 / 1395	1640 / 730	1.91	−0.19 / −4,9	350A	354A	0.03 / 0,8	0.8540 / 21.692	1.87 / 47,5	1.83 / 46,5	0.05 / 1,3	0.6875 / 17.462	3.03 / 77,0	3.15 / 80,0
1.5748 / 40.000	3.3465 / 85.000	0.8125 / 20.638	3140 / 1395	1640 / 730	1.91	−0.19 / −4,9	357	354X	0.09 / 2,3	0.8540 / 21.692	2.01 / 51,0	1.83 / 46,5	0.06 / 1,5	0.6875 / 17.462	3.05 / 77,0	3.15 / 80,0
1.5748 / 40.000	3.3750 / 85.725	1.1875 / 30.162	5000 / 2220	3450 / 1535	1.45	−0.32 / −8,2	3879	3821	0.03 / 0,8	1.1875 / 30.162	2.01 / 51,0	1.97 / 50,0	0.05 / 1,3	0.9375 / 23.812	2.95 / 75,0	3.19 / 81,0
1.5748 / 40.000	3.4843 / 88.501	0.9750 / 24.765	3180 / 1410	4250 / 1880	0.75	0.12 / 3,0	44157X	44348	0.09 / 2,3	0.9080 / 23.063	2.20 / 56,0	2.00 / 50,8	0.06 / 1,5	0.6875 / 17.462	2.95 / 75,0	3.31 / 84,0
1.5748 / 40.000	3.4843 / 88.501	1.0000 / 25.400	3180 / 1410	4250 / 1880	0.75	0.09 / 2,3	44157	44348	0.09 / 2,3	0.9330 / 23.698	2.20 / 56,0	2.00 / 50,8	0.06 / 1,5	0.6875 / 17.462	2.95 / 75,0	3.31 / 84,0

① These maximum fillet radii will be cleared by the bearing corners.
② Minus value indicates center is inside cone backface.

SINGLE-ROW STRAIGHT BORE—TS

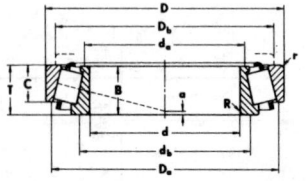

| bore | outside diameter | width | rating at 500 RPM for 3000 hours L10 | | fac-tor | eff. load center | part numbers | | cone | | | | cup | | | |
| | | | one row radial | thrust | | | cone | cup | max. shaft fillet radius | width | backing shoulder diameters | | max. housing fillet radius | width | backing shoulder | |
d	D	T	lb daN	lb daN	K	a			R	B	d_b	d_a	r	C	D_b	D_a
1.5748 40,000	3.4843 88,501	1.0625 26,988	4450 1980	2000 890	2.22	−0.38 −9,7	420	414	0.14 3,5	1.1450 29,083	2.05 52,0	1.81 46,0	0.06 1,5	0.8750 22,225	3.03 77,0	3.15 80,0
1.5748 40,000	3.5480 90,119	0.9055 23,000	3140 1395	1640 730	1.91	−0.19 −4,9	350	352	0.16 4,0	0.8540 21,692	2.13 54,0	1.83 46,5	0.09 2,3	0.8586 21,808	3.07 78,0	3.23 82,0
1.5748 40,000	4.2500 107,950	1.4375 36,512	6900 3060	3500 1560	1.97	−0.48 −12,2	543	632X	0.14 3,5	1.4550 36,957	2.24 57,0	1.97 50,0	0.13 3,3	1.1250 28,575	3.70 94,0	3.94 100,0
1.5938 40,483	3.2500 82,550	1.1563 29,370	4300 1900	4000 1780	1.07	−0.03 −4,8	HM801349	HM801310	0.14 3,5	1.1250 28,575	2.28 58,0	1.93 49,1	0.13 3,3	0.9063 23,020	2.68 68,0	3.07 78,0
†1.6142 †41,000	†2.6772 †68,000	0.6890 17,500	2090 930	1240 555	1.68	−0.14 −3,6	LM300849	LM300811	Spec.	0.7087 18,000	2.05 52,0	1.77 45,0	0.06 1,5	0.5315 13,500	2.40 61,0	2.56 65,0
1.6250 41,275	2.8750 73,025	0.6562 16,667	2020 895	1210 535	1.67	−0.11 −2,8	18590	18520	0.14 3,5	0.6875 17,462	2.09 53,0	1.81 46,0	0.06 1,5	0.5000 12,700	2.60 66,0	2.72 69,0
1.6250 41,275	2.8910 73,431	0.7700 19,558	2520 1120	1720 765	1.46	−0.13 −3,4	LM501349	LM501310	0.14 3,5	0.7800 19,812	2.09 53,0	1.83 46,5	0.03 0,8	0.5800 14,732	2.64 67,0	2.76 70,0
1.6250 41,275	2.8910 73,431	0.8437 21,430	2520 1120	1720 765	1.46	−0.13 −3,4	LM501349	LM501314	0.14 3,5	0.7800 19,812	2.09 53,0	1.83 46,5	0.03 0,8	0.6537 16,604	2.60 66,0	2.76 70,0
1.6250 41,275	2.8910 73,431	0.9060 23,012	2520 1120	1720 765	1.46	−0.13 −3,4	LM501349	LM501311	0.14 3,5	0.7800 19,812	2.09 53,0	1.83 46,5	0.09 2,3	0.7160 18,186	2.52 64,0	2.76 70,0
1.6250 41,275	3.0000 76,200	0.7090 18,009	1930 860	1610 715	1.20	−0.03 −0,7	11162	11300	0.06 1,5	0.6844 17,384	1.93 49,0	1.83 46,5	0.06 1,5	0.5625 14,288	2.64 67,0	2.80 71,0
1.6250 41,275	3.0000 76,200	0.7090 18,009	1930 860	1610 715	1.20	−0.03 −0,7	11163	11300	0.03 0,8	0.6844 17,384	1.85 47,0	1.83 46,5	0.06 1,5	0.5625 14,288	2.64 67,0	2.80 71,0
1.6250 41,275	3.0000 76,200	0.8750 22,225	3040 1355	2040 910	1.49	−0.19 −4,8	24780	24720	0.14 3,5	0.9063 23,020	2.13 54,0	1.85 47,0	0.03 0,8	0.6875 17,462	2.68 68,0	2.83 72,0
1.6250 41,275	3.0000 76,200	1.0000 25,400	3040 1355	2040 910	1.49	−0.19 −4,8	24780	24721	0.14 3,5	0.9063 23,020	2.13 54,0	1.85 47,0	0.09 2,3	0.8125 20,638	2.60 66,0	2.83 72,0
1.6250 41,275	3.1496 80,000	0.8268 21,000	3000 1335	1400 625	2.14	−0.25 −6,2	336	332	0.03 0,8	0.8820 22,403	1.85 47,0	1.81 46,0	0.05 1,3	0.7018 17,826	2.87 73,0	2.95 75,0
1.6250 41,275	3.1496 80,000	0.8268 21,000	3000 1335	1400 625	2.14	−0.25 −6,2	342	332	0.14 3,5	0.8820 22,403	2.09 53,0	1.81 46,0	0.05 1,3	0.7018 17,826	2.87 73,0	2.95 75,0
1.6250 41,275	3.1562 80,167	1.0000 25,400	3660 1630	2000 890	1.83	−0.29 −7,5	26885	26820	0.03 0,8	1.0000 25,400	1.89 48,0	1.85 47,0	0.13 3,3	0.8125 20,638	2.72 69,0	2.91 74,0
1.6250 41,275	3.1562 80,167	1.1563 29,370	3660 1630	2000 890	1.83	−0.29 −7,5	26882	26821	0.14 3,5	1.0000 25,400	2.13 54,0	1.85 47,0	0.13 3,3	0.9688 24,608	2.68 68,0	2.91 74,0
1.6250 41,275	3.2500 82,550	1.0313 26,195	3810 1695	2630 1170	1.45	−0.25 −6,4	22778	22721	0.14 3,5	1.0625 26,988	2.17 55,0	1.93 49,0	0.03 0,8	0.8125 20,638	2.87 73,0	3.03 77,0
1.6250 41,275	3.2500 82,550	1.0450 26,543	3740 1665	3500 1555	1.07	−0.12 −3,0	M802048	M802011	0.14 3,5	1.0100 25,654	2.24 57,0	1.99 50,6	0.13 3,3	0.7950 20,193	2.76 70,0	3.11 79,0
1.6250 41,275	3.3125 84,138	1.1875 30,162	4550 2020	2380 1060	1.91	−0.40 −10,2	3577	3520	0.14 3,5	1.2160 30,886	2.13 54,0	1.89 48,0	0.13 3,3	0.9375 23,812	2.91 74,0	3.13 79,5
1.6250 41,275	3.3125 84,138	1.1875 30,162	4550 2020	2380 1060	1.91	−0.40 −10,2	3585	3520	0.06 1,5	1.2160 30,886	1.97 50,0	1.89 48,0	0.13 3,3	0.9375 23,812	2.91 74,0	3.13 79,5

| bore | outside diameter | width | rating at 500 RPM for 3000 hours L10 | | fac-tor | eff. load center | part numbers | | cone max. shaft fillet radius | width | backing shoulder diameters | | cup max. hous-ing fillet radius | width | backing shoulder | |
| | | | one row radial | thrust | | | cone | cup | | | | | | | | |
d	D	T	lb daN	lb daN	K	a②			R①	B	d_b	d_a	r①	C	D_b	D_a
1.6250 41,275	3.3750 85,725	1.1875 30,162	5000 2220	3450 1535	1.45	−0.32 −8,2	3877	3821	0.14 3,5	1.1875 30,162	2.24 57,0	1.98 50,3	0.05 1,3	0.9375 23,812	2.95 75,0	3.19 81,0
1.6250 41,275	3.3750 85,725	1.1875 30,162	5000 2220	3450 1535	1.45	−0.32 −8,2	3877A	3821	0.09 2,3	1.1875 30,162	2.17 55,0	1.98 50,3	0.05 1,3	0.9375 23,812	2.95 75,0	3.19 81,0
1.6250 41,275	3.3750 85,725	1.1875 30,162	5000 2220	3450 1535	1.45	−0.32 −8,2	3880	3821	0.03 0,8	1.1875 30,162	2.05 52,0	1.98 50,3	0.05 1,3	0.9375 23,812	2.95 75,0	3.19 81,0
1.6250 41,275	3.4375 87,312	1.1875 30,162	4550 2020	2380 1060	1.91	−0.40 −10,2	3576	3525	0.03 0,8	1.2160 30,886	1.93 49,0	1.89 48,0	0.13 3,3	0.9375 23,812	2.95 75,0	3.19 81,0
1.6250 41,275	3.4843 88,501	1.0000 25,400	3180 1410	4250 1880	0.75	0.09 2,3	44162	44348	0.09 2,3	0.9330 23,698	2.24 57,0	2.00 50,8	0.06 1,5	0.6875 17,462	2.95 75,0	3.31 84,0
1.6250 41,275	3.4843 88,501	1.0625 26,988	4450 1980	2000 890	2.22	−0.38 −9,7	419	414	0.14 3,5	1.1450 29,083	2.13 54,0	1.85 47,0	0.06 1,5	0.8750 22,225	3.03 77,0	3.15 80,0
1.6250 41,275	3.5000 88,900	0.8125 20,638	3310 1475	1810 805	1.83	−0.17 −4,2	365A	362A	0.14 3,5	0.8750 22,225	2.17 55,0	1.91 48,5	0.05 1,3	0.6501 16,513	3.19 81,0	3.31 84,0
1.6250 41,275	3.5000 88,900	1.1875 30,162	4700 2100	4400 1960	1.07	−0.17 −4,3	HM803145	HM803110	0.03 0,8	1.1563 29,370	2.13 54,0	2.09 53,0	0.13 3,3	0.9063 23,020	2.91 74,0	3.35 85,0
1.6250 41,275	3.5000 88,900	1.1875 30,162	4700 2100	4400 1960	1.07	−0.17 −4,3	HM803146	HM803110	0.14 3,5	1.1563 29,370	2.36 60,0	2.09 53,0	0.13 3,3	0.9063 23,020	2.91 74,0	3.35 85,0
1.6250 41,275	3.5625 90,488	1.5625 39,688	6850 3060	3350 1490	2.05	−0.59 −14,9	4388	4335	0.14 3,5	1.5900 40,386	2.24 57,0	2.01 51,0	0.13 3,3	1.3125 33,338	3.03 77,0	3.35 85,0
1.6250 41,275	3.6250 92,075	1.0313 26,195	3300 1470	4700 2100	0.70	0.14 3,6	M903345	M903310	0.14 3,5	0.9375 23,812	2.36 60,0	2.13 54,0	0.06 1,5	0.6563 16,670	3.07 78,0	3.46 88,0
1.6250 41,275	3.6875 93,662	1.2500 31,750	5250 2320	3610 1605	1.45	−0.31 −7,8	46162	46368	0.03 0,8	1.2500 31,750	2.05 52,0	2.01 51,0	0.13 3,3	1.0313 26,195	3.11 79,0	3.43 87,0
1.6250 41,275	3.7500 95,250	1.0938 27,783	4950 2200	2410 1070	2.05	−0.36 −9,2	447	432A	0.14 3,5	1.1772 29,901	2.17 55,0	1.91 48,5	0.03 0,8	0.8750 22,225	3.31 84,0	3.43 87,0
1.6250 41,275	3.7500 95,250	1.1875 30,162	5150 2280	4800 2140	1.07	−0.15 −3,8	HM804840	HM804810	0.14 3,5	1.1563 29,370	2.40 61,0	2.13 54,0	0.13 3,3	0.9063 23,020	3.19 81,0	3.58 91,0
1.6250 41,275	3.7500 95,250	1.2188 30,958	4500 2000	5700 2540	0.79	0.03 0,6	HM903245	HM903210	0.14 3,5	1.1250 28,575	2.48 63,0	2.12 54,0	0.03 0,8	0.8750 22,225	3.19 81,0	3.58 91,0
1.6250 41,275	3.8750 98,425	1.2188 30,958	3850 1715	4900 2160	0.79	−0.01 −0,3	53162	53387	0.06 1,5	1.1142 28,301	2.24 57,0	2.08 52,7	0.03 0,8	0.8125 20,638	3.23 82,0	3.58 91,0
1.6250 41,275	3.8750 98,425	1.2188 30,958	4500 2000	5700 2540	0.79	0.03 0,6	HM903244	HM903216	0.06 1,5	1.1142 28,301	2.32 59,0	2.12 54,0	0.03 0,8	0.8750 22,225	3.23 82,0	3.62 92,0
1.6250 41,275	4.0000 101,600	1.3750 34,925	6550 2920	3200 1425	2.05	−0.50 −12,7	526	522	0.14 3,5	1.4200 36,068	2.24 57,0	1.97 50,0	0.13 3,3	1.0625 26,988	3.50 89,0	3.74 95,0
1.6250 41,275	4.1250 104,775	1.1875 30,162	5400 2400	3090 1375	1.74	−0.28 −7,0	464A	453X	0.06 1,5	1.1542 29,317	2.13 54,0	2.05 52,0	0.13 3,3	0.9687 24,605	3.62 92,0	3.86 98,0
1.6250 41,275	4.1250 104,775	1.4375 36,512	7150 3180	5950 2660	1.20	−0.29 −7,4	HM807035	HM807011	0.06 1,5	1.4375 36,512	2.36 60,0	2.24 57,0	0.03 0,8	1.1250 28,575	3.58 91,0	3.94 100,0
1.6563 42,070	3.5625 90,488	1.5625 39,688	6850 3060	3350 1490	2.05	−0.59 −14,9	4395	4335	0.14 3,5	1.5900 40,386	2.28 58,0	2.01 51,0	0.13 3,3	1.3125 33,338	3.03 77,0	3.35 85,0
1.6875 42,862	3.0312 76,992	0.6875 17,462	2000 890	1740 775	1.15	0.0 0,0	12168	12303	0.06 1,5	0.6750 17,145	2.01 51,0	1.91 48,5	0.06 1,5	0.4688 11,908	2.68 68,0	2.87 73,0
1.6875 42,862	3.2500 82,550	0.7812 19,842	2550 1135	1870 835	1.36	−0.10 −2,4	22168	22325	0.09 2,3	0.7810 19,837	2.05 52,0	1.91 48,5	0.06 1,5	0.5937 15,080	2.87 73,0	2.99 76,0

① These maximum fillet radii will be cleared by the bearing corners.
③ Minus value indicates center is inside cone backface.
† Dimension shown is maximum value—see note at bottom of fitting practice table page 4 in Reference Tables.

SINGLE-ROW STRAIGHT BORE—TS

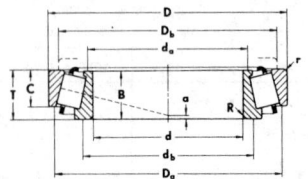

| bore | outside diameter | width | rating at 500 RPM for 3000 hours L10 | | fac-tor | eff. load center | part numbers | | cone | | | | cup | | | |
| | | | one row radial | thrust | | | cone | cup | max. shaft fillet radius | width | backing shoulder diameters | | max. housing fillet radius | width | backing shoulder | |
d	D	T	lb daN	lb daN	K	a[2]			R[1]	B	d_b	d_a	r[1]	C	D_b	D_a
1.6875 42,862	3.2650 82,931	1.0625 26,988	3680 1635	2110 940	1.74	−0.25 −6,2	25578	25523	0.09 2,3	1.0000 25,400	2.09 53,0	1.95 49,5	0.09 2,3	0.8750 22,225	2.83 72,0	3.03 77,0
1.6875 42,862	3.3125 84,138	1.1875 30,162	4550 2020	2380 1060	1.91	−0.40 −10,2	3579	3520	0.14 3,5	1.2160 30,886	2.20 56,0	1.95 49,5	0.13 3,3	0.9375 23,812	2.91 74,0	3.13 79,5
1.6880 42,875	3.0000 76,200	1.0000 25,400	3660 1630	2000 890	1.83	−0.29 −7,5	26884	26823	0.14 3,5	1.0000 25,400	2.17 55,0	1.91 48,5	0.06 1,5	0.8125 20,638	2.72 69,0	2.87 73,0
1.6880 42,875	3.0000 76,200	1.0000 25,400	3660 1630	2000 890	1.83	−0.29 −7,5	26886	26823	0.06 1,5	1.0000 25,400	2.01 51,0	1.91 48,5	0.06 1,5	0.8125 20,638	2.72 69,0	2.87 73,0
1.6880 42,875	3.1496 80,000	0.8268 21,000	3000 1335	1400 625	2.14	−0.25 −6,2	342S	332	0.14 3,5	0.8820 22,403	2.13 54,0	1.87 47,5	0.05 1,3	0.7018 17,826	2.87 73,0	2.95 75,0
1.6880 42,875	3.2700 83,058	0.9375 23,812	3680 1635	2110 940	1.74	−0.25 −6,2	25577	25521	0.14 3,5	1.0000 25,400	2.17 55,0	1.93 49,0	0.13 3,3	0.7500 19,050	2.83 72,0	3.03 77,0
1.7500 44,450	2.8125 71,438	0.5000 12,700	1420 630	740 330	1.91	−0.05 −1,3	LL103049	LL103010	0.06 1,5	0.5000 12,700	2.01 51,0	1.93 49,0	0.06 1,5	0.3750 9,525	2.56 65,0	2.68 68,0
1.7500 44,450	2.8750 73,025	0.7188 18,258	2470 1095	1350 600	1.83	−0.15 −3,8	L102849	L102810	0.06 1,5	0.7188 18,258	2.01 51,0	1.93 49,0	0.06 1,5	0.5938 15,083	2.60 66,0	2.72 69,0
1.7500 44,450	3.0312 76,992	0.6875 17,462	2000 890	1740 775	1.15	0.0 0,0	12175	12303	0.06 1,5	0.6750 17,145	2.05 52,0	1.95 49,5	0.06 1,5	0.4688 11,908	2.68 68,0	2.87 73,0
1.7500 44,450	3.1250 79,375	0.6875 17,462	2090 930	1340 595	1.56	−0.08 −2,0	18685	18620	0.11 2,8	0.6875 17,462	2.13 54,0	1.95 49,5	0.06 1,5	0.5313 13,495	2.80 71,0	2.91 74,0
1.7500 44,450	3.1875 80,962	0.7500 19,050	2070 920	1860 830	1.11	0.03 0,9	13175	13318	0.00 0,0	0.6875 17,462	1.97 50,0	1.97 50,0	0.06 1,5	0.5625 14,288	2.83 72,0	2.99 76,0
1.7500 44,450	3.2650 82,931	0.8750 22,225	3150 1400	1610 715	1.96	−0.24 −6,1	35176	35326	0.03 0,8	0.9060 23,012	1.97 50,0	1.95 49,5	0.03 0,8	0.6875 17,462	2.99 76,0	3.07 78,0
1.7500 44,450	3.2700 83,058	0.9400 23,876	3680 1635	2110 940	1.74	−0.24 −6,2	25581	25522	0.02 0,5	1.0000 25,400	2.01 51,0	1.97 50,0	0.08 2,0	0.7525 19,114	2.87 73,0	3.03 77,0
1.7500 44,450	3.3125 84,138	1.1875 30,162	4550 2020	2380 1060	1.91	−0.40 −10,2	3578	3520	0.14 3,5	1.2160 30,886	2.24 57,0	2.01 51,0	0.13 3,3	0.9375 23,812	2.91 74,0	3.13 79,5
1.7500 44,450	3.3465 85,000	0.8125 20,638	3140 1395	1640 730	1.91	−0.19 −4,9	355	354A	0.09 2,3	0.8540 21,692	2.13 54,0	1.97 50,0	0.05 1,3	0.6875 17,462	3.03 77,0	3.15 80,0
1.7500 44,450	3.3465 85,000	0.8125 20,638	3140 1395	1640 730	1.91	−0.19 −4,9	355A	354A	0.03 0,8	0.8540 21,692	2.01 51,0	1.97 50,0	0.05 1,3	0.6875 17,462	3.03 77,0	3.15 80,0
1.7500 44,450	3.3465 85,000	0.8125 20,638	3140 1395	1640 730	1.91	−0.19 −4,9	355X	354A	0.14 3,5	0.8540 21,692	2.20 56,0	1.97 50,0	0.05 1,3	0.6875 17,462	3.03 77,0	3.15 80,0
1.7500 44,450	3.3465 85,000	0.9375 23,812	3680 1635	2110 940	1.74	−0.25 −6,2	25580	25526	0.14 3,5	1.0000 25,400	2.24 57,0	1.97 50,0	0.09 2,3	0.7500 19,050	2.91 74,0	3.07 78,0
1.7500 44,450	3.5000 88,900	1.1875 30,162	4700 2100	4400 1960	1.07	−0.17 −4,3	HM803149	HM803110	0.14 3,5	1.1563 29,370	2.44 62,0	2.10 53,4	0.13 3,3	0.9063 23,020	2.91 74,0	3.35 85,0
1.7500 44,450	3.6718 93,264	1.1875 30,162	5000 2220	2890 1285	1.73	−0.32 −8,2	3782	3730	0.14 3,5	1.1930 30,302	2.28 58,0	2.05 52,0	0.03 0,8	0.9375 23,812	3.31 84,0	3.46 88,0
1.7500 44,450	3.6875 93,662	1.2500 31,750	5250 2320	3610 1605	1.45	−0.31 −7,8	46175	46368	0.03 0,8	1.2500 31,750	2.17 55,0	2.13 54,0	0.13 3,3	1.0313 26,195	3.11 79,0	3.43 87,0

| bore | outside diameter | width | rating at 500 RPM for 3000 hours L10 | | factor | eff. load center | part numbers | | cone | | | | cup | | | |
| | | | one row radial | thrust | | | | | max. shaft fillet radius | width | backing shoulder diameters | | max. housing fillet radius | width | backing shoulder | |
d	D	T	lb daN	lb daN	K	a②	cone	cup	R①	B	d_b	d_a	r①	C	D_b	D_a
1.7500 / 44,450	3.6875 / 93,662	1.2500 / 31,750	5250 / 2320	3610 / 1605	1.45	−0.31 / −7,8	46176	46368	0.14 / 3,5	1.2500 / 31,750	2.36 / 60,0	2.13 / 54,0	0.13 / 3,3	1.0313 / 26,195	3.11 / 79,0	3.43 / 87,0
1.7500 / 44,450	3.6875 / 93,662	1.2500 / 31,750	5250 / 2340	3230 / 1440	1.62	−0.36 / −9,1	49175	49368	0.14 / 3,5	1.2500 / 31,750	2.32 / 59,0	2.09 / 53,0	0.13 / 3,3	1.0000 / 25,400	3.23 / 82,0	3.43 / 87,0
1.7500 / 44,450	3.6875 / 93,662	1.2500 / 31,750	5250 / 2340	3230 / 1440	1.62	−0.36 / −9,1	49176	49368	0.03 / 0,8	1.2500 / 31,750	2.13 / 54,0	2.09 / 53,0	0.13 / 3,3	1.0000 / 25,400	3.23 / 82,0	3.43 / 87,0
1.7500 / 44,450	3.7500 / 95,250	1.0938 / 27,783	4950 / 2200	2410 / 1070	2.05	−0.36 / −9,2	438	432A	0.14 / 3,5	1.1772 / 29,901	2.24 / 57,0	2.01 / 51,0	0.03 / 0,8	0.8750 / 22,225	3.31 / 84,0	3.43 / 87,0
1.7500 / 44,450	3.7500 / 95,250	1.0938 / 27,783	5250 / 2320	2960 / 1315	1.77	−0.30 / −7,6	33885	33821	0.03 / 0,8	1.1250 / 28,575	2.09 / 53,0	2.09 / 53,0	0.09 / 2,3	0.8750 / 22,225	3.35 / 85,0	3.54 / 90,0
1.7500 / 44,450	3.7500 / 95,250	1.1875 / 30,162	5150 / 2280	4800 / 2140	1.07	−0.15 / −3,8	HM804842	HM804810	0.03 / 0,8	1.1563 / 29,370	2.24 / 57,0	2.24 / 57,0	0.13 / 3,3	0.9063 / 23,020	3.19 / 81,0	3.58 / 91,0
1.7500 / 44,450	3.7500 / 95,250	1.1875 / 30,162	5150 / 2280	4800 / 2140	1.07	−0.15 / −3,8	HM804843	HM804810	0.14 / 3,5	1.1563 / 29,370	2.48 / 63,0	2.24 / 57,0	0.13 / 3,3	0.9063 / 23,020	3.19 / 81,0	3.58 / 91,0
1.7500 / 44,450	3.7500 / 95,250	1.2188 / 30,958	3850 / 1715	4900 / 2160	0.79	−0.01 / −0,3	53177	53375	0.14 / 3,5	1.1142 / 28,301	2.48 / 63,0	2.08 / 52,7	0.03 / 0,8	0.8125 / 20,638	3.19 / 81,0	3.50 / 89,0
1.7500 / 44,450	3.7500 / 95,250	1.2188 / 30,958	3850 / 1715	4900 / 2160	0.79	−0.01 / −0,3	53178	53375	0.08 / 2,0	1.1142 / 28,301	2.36 / 60,0	2.08 / 52,7	0.03 / 0,8	0.8125 / 20,638	3.19 / 81,0	3.50 / 89,0
1.7500 / 44,450	3.7500 / 95,250	1.2188 / 30,958	4500 / 2000	5700 / 2540	0.79	0.03 / 0,6	HM903247	HM903210	0.05 / 1,3	1.1142 / 28,301	2.40 / 61,0	2.12 / 54,0	0.03 / 0,8	0.8750 / 22,225	3.19 / 81,0	3.58 / 91,0
1.7500 / 44,450	3.7500 / 95,250	1.2188 / 30,958	4500 / 2000	5700 / 2540	0.79	0.03 / 0,6	HM903249	HM903210	0.14 / 3,5	1.1250 / 28,575	2.56 / 65,0	2.12 / 54,0	0.03 / 0,8	0.8750 / 22,225	3.19 / 81,0	3.58 / 91,0
1.7500 / 44,450	3.7500 / 95,250	1.2188 / 30,958	4500 / 2000	5700 / 2540	0.79	0.03 / 0,6	HM903249A	HM903210	0.14 / 3,5	1.1142 / 28,301	2.56 / 65,0	2.12 / 54,0	0.03 / 0,8	0.8750 / 22,225	3.19 / 81,0	3.58 / 91,0
1.7500 / 44,450	3.8750 / 98,425	1.2188 / 30,958	3850 / 1715	4900 / 2160	0.79	−0.01 / −0,3	53176	53387X	0.05 / 1,3	1.1142 / 28,301	2.32 / 59,0	2.08 / 52,7	0.06 / 1,5	0.8125 / 20,638	3.23 / 82,0	3.58 / 91,0
1.7500 / 44,450	4.0000 / 101,600	1.2500 / 31,750	5300 / 2360	3630 / 1615	1.46	−0.28 / −7,1	49576	49522	0.03 / 0,8	1.2500 / 31,750	2.17 / 55,0	2.13 / 54,0	0.03 / 1,0	1.0000 / 25,400	3.54 / 90,0	3.78 / 96,0
1.7500 / 44,450	4.0000 / 101,600	1.3750 / 34,925	6550 / 2920	3200 / 1425	2.05	−0.50 / −12,7	527	522	0.14 / 3,5	1.4200 / 36,068	2.32 / 59,0	2.09 / 53,0	0.13 / 3,3	1.0625 / 26,988	3.50 / 89,0	3.74 / 95,0
1.7500 / 44,450	4.0625 / 103,188	1.7188 / 43,658	8800 / 3900	4450 / 1980	1.97	−0.63 / −16,1	5356	5335	0.05 / 1,3	1.7510 / 44,475	2.28 / 58,0	2.20 / 56,0	0.13 / 3,3	1.4375 / 36,512	3.50 / 89,0	3.82 / 97,0
1.7500 / 44,450	4.1250 / 104,775	1.1875 / 30,162	6200 / 2760	3520 / 1565	1.76	−0.32 / −8,1	45280	45221	0.03 / 0,8	1.2188 / 30,958	2.17 / 55,0	2.13 / 54,0	0.03 / 0,8	0.9375 / 23,812	3.74 / 95,0	3.90 / 99,0
1.7500 / 44,450	4.1250 / 104,775	1.4375 / 36,512	6800 / 3020	4700 / 2080	1.45	−0.38 / −9,7	59176	59412	0.03 / 0,8	1.4375 / 36,512	2.24 / 57,0	2.20 / 56,0	0.13 / 3,3	1.1250 / 28,575	3.62 / 92,0	3.90 / 99,0
1.7500 / 44,450	4.1250 / 104,775	1.4375 / 36,512	7150 / 3180	5950 / 2660	1.20	−0.29 / −7,4	HM807040	HM807010	0.14 / 3,5	1.4375 / 36,512	2.60 / 66,0	2.32 / 59,0	0.13 / 3,3	1.1250 / 28,575	3.50 / 89,0	3.94 / 100,0
1.7500 / 44,450	4.2500 / 107,950	1.0938 / 27,783	5400 / 2400	3090 / 1375	1.74	−0.28 / −7,0	460	453A	0.14 / 3,5	1.1542 / 29,317	2.36 / 60,0	2.13 / 54,0	0.03 / 0,8	0.8750 / 22,225	3.82 / 97,0	3.94 / 100,0
1.7500 / 44,450	4.2500 / 107,950	1.4375 / 36,512	6800 / 3020	4700 / 2080	1.45	−0.38 / −9,7	59175	59425	0.14 / 3,5	1.4375 / 36,512	2.48 / 63,0	2.20 / 56,0	0.13 / 3,3	1.1250 / 28,575	3.66 / 93,0	3.98 / 101,0
1.7500 / 44,450	4.3750 / 111,125	1.1875 / 30,162	4150 / 1840	6300 / 2800	0.66	0.28 / 7,1	55176	55437	0.03 / 0,8	1.0594 / 26,909	2.40 / 61,0	2.44 / 62,0	0.13 / 3,3	0.8125 / 20,638	3.62 / 92,0	4.13 / 105,0

① These maximum fillet radii will be cleared by the bearing corners.
② Minus value indicates center is inside cone backface.

SINGLE-ROW STRAIGHT BORE—TS

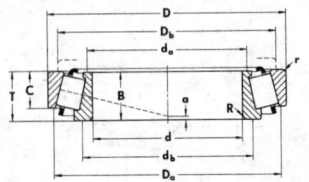

bore	outside diameter	width	rating at 500 RPM for 3000 hours L10 one row radial	thrust	fac-tor	eff. load center	part numbers cone	cup	cone max. shaft fillet radius R[①]	width B	db	da	cup max. hous-ing fillet radius r[①]	width C	Db	Da
d	D	T	lb daN	lb daN	K	a[②]	cone	cup	R[①]	B	db	da	r[①]	C	Db	Da
1.7500 44,450	4.3750 111,125	1.1875 30,162	5000 2220	7550 3360	0.66	0.30 7,5	HM907635	HM907614	0.03 0,8	1.1250 28,575	2.52 64,0	2.57 65,3	0.13 3,3	0.8125 20,638	3.58 91,0	4.13 105,0
1.7500 44,450	4.3750 111,125	1.5000 38,100	6900 3060	3500 1560	1.97	-0.48 -12,2	535	532A	0.14 3,5	1.4550 36,957	2.36 60,0	2.13 54,0	0.13 3,3	1.1875 30,162	3.74 95,0	3.94 100,0
1.7500 44,450	4.4375 112,712	1.1875 30,162	4150 1840	6300 2800	0.66	0.28 7,1	55175	55443	0.14 3,5	1.0594 26,909	2.64 67,0	2.36 60,0	0.13 3,3	0.8125 20,638	3.62 92,0	4.17 106,0
1.7500 44,450	4.5276 115,000	1.6150 41,021	8300 3700	4450 1980	1.86	-0.55 -14,0	615	614X	0.14 3,5	1.6250 41,275	2.44 62,0	2.20 56,0	0.12 3,0	1.2400 31,496	3.98 101,0	4.25 108,0
1.7500 44,450	5.0000 127,000	2.0000 50,800	12400 5550	6350 2820	1.96	-0.77 -19,5	6277	6220	0.14 3,5	2.0625 52,388	2.64 67,0	2.36 60,0	0.13 3,3	1.6250 41,275	4.25 108,0	4.61 117,0
1.7665 44,869	3.6250 92,075	0.9688 24,608	4100 1840	2660 1185	1.55	-0.19 -4,7	28576	28521	0.14 3,5	1.0000 25,400	2.32 59,0	2.09 53,0	0.03 0,8	0.7813 19,845	3.27 83,0	3.43 87,0
1.7710 44,983	3.3465 85,000	1.0625 26,988	3680 1635	2110 940	1.74	-0.25 -6,2	25584	25527	0.06 1,5	1.0000 25,400	2.09 53,0	2.01 51,0	0.09 2,3	0.8750 22,225	2.87 73,0	3.07 78,0
1.7710 44,983	3.6718 93,264	1.1875 30,162	5000 2220	2890 1285	1.73	-0.32 -8,2	3776	3720	0.14 3,5	1.1930 30,302	2.32 59,0	2.09 53,0	0.13 3,3	0.9375 23,812	3.23 82,0	3.46 88,0
1.7710 44,983	4.0000 101,600	1.3750 34,925	6550 2920	3200 1425	2.05	-0.50 -12,7	527S	522	0.17 4,3	1.4200 36,068	2.40 61,0	2.09 53,0	0.13 3,3	1.0625 26,988	3.50 89,0	3.74 95,0
1.7717 45,000	3.5433 90,000	0.7874 20,000	3310 1475	1810 805	1.83	-0.17 -4,2	367	362	0.08 2,0	0.8750 22,225	2.17 55,0	2.01 51,0	0.08 2,0	0.6250 15,875	3.19 81,0	3.31 84,0
†1.7717 †45,000	4.1333 104,986	1.2800 32,512	5550 2460	7400 3280	0.75	-0.07 1,8	HM905843	HM905810	0.10 2,5	1.2500 31,750	2.68 68,0	2.39 60,6	0.10 2,5	0.9200 23,368	3.39 86,0	3.94 100,0
1.7810 45,237	3.3125 84,138	1.1875 30,162	4550 2020	2380 1060	1.91	-0.40 -10,2	3586	3520	0.14 3,5	1.2160 30,886	2.28 58,0	2.05 52,0	0.13 3,3	0.9375 23,812	2.91 74,0	3.13 79,5
1.7812 45,242	2.8910 73,431	0.7700 19,558	2580 1150	1350 600	1.91	-0.18 -4,7	LM102949	LM102910	0.14 3,5	0.7800 19,812	2.20 56,0	1.97 50,0	0.03 0,8	0.6200 15,748	2.68 68,0	2.76 70,0
1.7812 45,242	2.8910 73,431	0.8437 21,430	2580 1150	1350 600	1.91	-0.18 -4,7	LM102949	LM102911	0.14 3,5	0.7800 19,812	2.20 56,0	1.97 50,0	0.03 0,8	0.6937 17,620	2.64 67,0	2.76 70,0
1.7812 45,242	3.0625 77,788	0.7812 19,842	2610 1160	1910 850	1.37	-0.09 -2,3	LM603049	LM603011	0.14 3,5	0.7812 19,842	2.24 57,0	1.97 50,0	0.03 0,8	0.5937 15,080	2.80 71,0	2.91 74,0
1.7812 45,242	3.0625 77,788	0.8437 21,430	2610 1160	1910 850	1.37	-0.09 -2,3	LM603049	LM603012	0.14 3,5	0.7812 19,842	2.24 57,0	1.97 50,0	0.03 0,8	0.6562 16,667	2.76 70,0	2.91 74,0
1.7812 45,242	†3.1496 †80,000	0.7812 19,842	2610 1160	1910 850	1.37	-0.09 -2,3	LM603049	LM603014	0.14 3,5	0.7812 19,842	2.24 57,0	1.97 50,0	0.03 0,8	0.5937 15,080	2.80 71,0	2.95 75,0
1.7960 45,618	3.9050 99,187	0.9375 23,812	3680 1635	2110 940	1.74	-0.25 -6,2	25590	25545	0.14 3,5	1.0000 25,400	2.28 58,0	2.01 51,0	0.03 0,8	0.7500 19,050	3.19 81,0	3.15 80,0
†1.8110 †46,000	†2.9528 †75,000	0.7087 18,000	2400 1070	1660 740	1.45	-0.07 -1,9	LM503349	LM503310	0.09 2,3	0.7087 18,000	2.17 55,0	2.01 51,0	0.06 1,5	0.5512 14,000	2.64 67,0	2.80 71,0
†1.8110 †46,000	†2.9528 †75,000	0.7657 19,449	2400 1070	1660 740	1.45	-0.07 -1,9	LM503349	LM503310A	0.09 2,3	0.7087 18,000	2.17 55,0	2.01 51,0	0.03 0,8	0.6082 15,448	2.68 68,0	2.83 72,0

bore d	outside diameter D	width T	rating radial (one row) lb daN	rating thrust lb daN	fac-tor K	eff. load center a①	part no. cone	part no. cup	cone max. shaft fillet radius R①	cone width B	cone d_b	cone d_a	cup max. housing fillet radius r①	cup width C	cup D_b	cup D_a
1.8125 / 46,038	3.1250 / 79,375	0.6875 / 17,462	2090 / 930	1340 / 595	1.56	-0.08 / -2,0	18690	18620	0.11 / 2,8	0.6875 / 17,462	2.20 / 56,0	2.01 / 51,0	0.06 / 1,5	0.5313 / 13,495	2.80 / 71,0	2.91 / 74,0
1.8125 / 46,038	3.3465 / 85,000	0.6875 / 17,462	2240 / 995	1550 / 690	1.44	-0.03 / -0,7	18780	18720	0.09 / 2,3	0.6875 / 17,462	2.20 / 56,0	2.05 / 52,0	0.06 / 1,5	0.5313 / 13,495	3.03 / 77,0	3.15 / 80,0
1.8125 / 46,038	3.3465 / 85,000	0.8125 / 20,638	3140 / 1395	1640 / 730	1.91	-0.19 / -4,9	359A	354A	0.14 / 3,5	0.8540 / 21,692	2.24 / 57,0	2.01 / 51,0	0.05 / 1,3	0.6875 / 17,462	3.03 / 77,0	3.15 / 80,0
1.8125 / 46,038	3.3465 / 85,000	0.8125 / 20,638	3140 / 1395	1640 / 730	1.91	-0.19 / -4,9	359S	354A	0.09 / 2,3	0.8540 / 21,692	2.17 / 55,0	2.01 / 51,0	0.05 / 1,3	0.6875 / 17,462	3.03 / 77,0	3.15 / 80,0
1.8125 / 46,038	3.3465 / 85,000	1.0000 / 25,400	3830 / 1705	2270 / 1010	1.69	-0.25 / -6,4	2984	2924	0.14 / 3,5	1.0082 / 25,608	2.28 / 58,0	2.05 / 52,0	0.05 / 1,3	0.8125 / 20,638	2.99 / 76,0	3.15 / 80,0
1.8125 / 46,038	3.3465 / 85,000	1.0000 / 25,400	3830 / 1705	2270 / 1010	1.69	-0.25 / -6,4	2984A	2924	0.03 / 0,8	1.0082 / 25,608	2.09 / 53,0	2.05 / 52,0	0.05 / 1,3	0.8125 / 20,638	2.99 / 76,0	3.15 / 80,0
1.8125 / 46,038	3.7500 / 95,250	1.0938 / 27,783	4950 / 2200	2410 / 1070	2.05	-0.36 / -9,2	436	432A	0.14 / 3,5	1.1772 / 29,901	2.32 / 59,0	2.05 / 52,0	0.03 / 0,8	0.8750 / 22,225	3.31 / 84,0	3.43 / 87,0
1.8125 / 46,038	3.7500 / 95,250	1.1875 / 30,162	5000 / 2220	2890 / 1285	1.73	-0.32 / -8,2	3777	3726	0.14 / 3,5	1.1930 / 30,302	2.36 / 60,0	2.09 / 53,0	0.13 / 3,3	0.9375 / 23,812	3.27 / 83,0	3.50 / 89,0
1.8750 / 47,625	3.5000 / 88,900	0.8125 / 20,638	3310 / 1475	1810 / 805	1.83	-0.17 / -4,2	369A	362A	0.14 / 3,5	0.8750 / 22,225	2.36 / 60,0	2.09 / 53,0	0.05 / 1,3	0.6501 / 16,513	3.19 / 81,0	3.31 / 84,0
1.8750 / 47,625	3.5000 / 88,900	1.0000 / 25,400	3930 / 1745	3670 / 1635	1.07	-0.07 / -1,7	M804049	M804010	0.14 / 3,5	1.0000 / 25,400	2.48 / 63,0	2.19 / 55,7	0.13 / 3,3	0.7500 / 19,050	3.03 / 77,0	3.35 / 85,0
1.8750 / 47,625	3.5433 / 90,000	0.7874 / 20,000	3310 / 1475	1810 / 805	1.83	-0.17 / -4,2	369S	363	0.09 / 2,3	0.8750 / 22,225	2.24 / 57,0	2.09 / 53,0	0.03 / 0,8	0.7874 / 20,000	3.23 / 82,0	3.34 / 84,7
1.8750 / 47,625	3.6718 / 93,264	1.1875 / 30,162	5000 / 2220	2890 / 1285	1.73	-0.32 / -8,2	3778	3730	0.25 / 6,4	1.1930 / 30,302	2.64 / 67,0	2.17 / 55,0	0.03 / 0,8	0.9375 / 23,812	3.31 / 84,0	3.46 / 88,0
1.8750 / 47,625	3.7500 / 95,250	1.1875 / 30,162	5150 / 2280	4800 / 2140	1.07	-0.15 / -3,8	HM804846	HM804810	0.14 / 3,5	1.1563 / 29,370	2.60 / 66,0	2.27 / 57,6	0.13 / 3,3	0.9063 / 23,020	3.19 / 81,0	3.58 / 91,0
1.8750 / 47,625	3.8125 / 96,838	0.8268 / 21,000	3590 / 1595	2180 / 970	1.65	-0.12 / -3,0	386A	382A	0.03 / 0,8	0.8640 / 21,946	2.20 / 56,0	2.17 / 55,0	0.03 / 0,8	0.6250 / 15,875	3.50 / 89,0	3.62 / 92,0
1.8750 / 47,625	3.8750 / 98,425	1.1875 / 30,162	5000 / 2220	2890 / 1285	1.73	-0.32 / -8,2	3779	3732	0.14 / 3,5	1.1930 / 30,302	2.40 / 61,0	2.17 / 55,0	0.13 / 3,3	0.9375 / 23,812	3.31 / 84,0	3.54 / 90,0
1.8750 / 47,625	4.0000 / 101,600	1.3750 / 34,925	6550 / 2920	3200 / 1425	2.05	-0.50 / -12,7	528	522	0.14 / 3,5	1.4200 / 36,068	2.44 / 62,0	2.17 / 55,0	0.13 / 3,3	1.0625 / 26,988	3.50 / 89,0	3.74 / 95,0
1.8750 / 47,625	4.0000 / 101,600	1.3750 / 34,925	6550 / 2920	3200 / 1425	2.05	-0.50 / -12,7	528A	522	0.06 / 1,5	1.4200 / 36,068	2.28 / 58,0	2.17 / 55,0	0.13 / 3,3	1.0625 / 26,988	3.50 / 89,0	3.74 / 95,0
1.8750 / 47,625	4.0625 / 103,188	1.7188 / 43,658	8800 / 3900	4450 / 1980	1.97	-0.63 / -16,1	5358	5335	0.05 / 1,3	1.7510 / 44,475	2.36 / 60,0	2.28 / 58,0	0.13 / 3,3	1.4375 / 36,512	3.50 / 89,0	3.82 / 97,0
1.8750 / 47,625	4.0625 / 103,188	1.7188 / 43,658	8800 / 3900	4450 / 1980	1.97	-0.63 / -16,1	5361	5335	0.14 / 3,5	1.7510 / 44,475	2.56 / 65,0	2.28 / 58,0	0.13 / 3,3	1.4375 / 36,512	3.50 / 89,0	3.82 / 97,0
1.8750 / 47,625	4.1250 / 104,775	1.4375 / 36,512	6800 / 3020	4700 / 2080	1.45	-0.38 / -9,7	59187	59412	0.14 / 3,5	1.4375 / 36,512	2.56 / 65,0	2.32 / 59,0	0.13 / 3,3	1.1250 / 28,575	3.62 / 92,0	3.90 / 99,0
1.8750 / 47,625	4.2500 / 107,950	1.0938 / 27,783	5400 / 2400	3090 / 1375	1.74	-0.28 / -7,0	487	453AS	0.03 / 0,8	1.1542 / 29,317	2.24 / 57,0	2.20 / 56,0	0.09 / 2,3	0.8750 / 22,225	3.74 / 95,0	3.94 / 100,0
1.8750 / 47,625	4.2500 / 107,950	1.4375 / 36,512	6900 / 3060	3500 / 1560	1.97	-0.48 / -12,2	536	532X	0.14 / 3,5	1.4550 / 36,957	2.44 / 62,0	2.20 / 56,0	0.13 / 3,3	1.1250 / 28,575	3.70 / 94,0	3.94 / 100,0
1.8750 / 47,625	4.3750 / 111,125	1.1875 / 30,162	4150 / 1840	6300 / 2800	0.66	0.28 / 7,1	55187	55437	0.14 / 3,5	1.0594 / 26,909	2.72 / 69,0	2.44 / 62,0	0.13 / 3,3	0.8125 / 20,638	3.62 / 92,0	4.13 / 105,0

① These maximum fillet radii will be cleared by the bearing corners.
Ⓜ Minus value indicates center is inside cone backface.
† Dimension shown is maximum value—see note at bottom of fitting practice table page 4 in Reference Tables.

SINGLE-ROW STRAIGHT BORE—TS

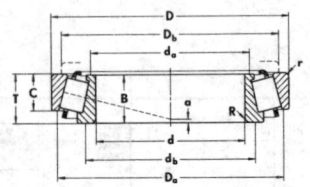

			rating at 500 RPM for 3000 hours L10		fac-tor	eff. load center	part numbers		cone				cup			
bore	outside diameter	width	one row radial	thrust			cone	cup	max. shaft fillet radius	width	backing shoulder diameters		max. housing fillet radius	width	backing shoulder	
d	D	T	lb daN	lb daN	K	a②			R①	B	d_b	d_a	r①	C	D_b	D_a
1.8750 47,625	4.4375 112,712	1.1875 30,162	5000 2220	7550 3360	0.66	0.30 7,5	HM907639	HM907616	0.14 3,5	1.1250 28,575	2.83 72,0	2.57 65,3	0.13 3,3	0.8125 20,638	3.58 91,0	4.17 106,0
1.8750 47,625	4.8750 123,825	1.4375 36,512	6250 2780	7900 3520	0.79	0.05 1,3	72187	72487	0.14 3,5	1.2910 32,791	2.83 72,0	2.59 65,9	0.13 3,3	1.0000 25,400	4.02 102,0	4.57 116,0
1.9060 48,412	3.7500 95,250	1.1875 30,162	5150 2280	4800 2140	1.07	-0.15 -3,8	HM804848	HM804810	0.09 2,3	1.1563 29,370	2.48 63,0	2.27 57,6	0.13 3,3	0.9063 23,020	3.19 81,0	3.58 91,0
1.9060 48,412	3.7500 95,250	1.1875 30,162	5150 2280	4800 2140	1.07	-0.15 -3,8	HM804849	HM804810	0.14 3,5	1.1563 29,370	2.60 66,0	2.27 57,6	0.13 3,3	0.9063 23,020	3.19 81,0	3.58 91,0
1.9375 49,212	3.5000 88,900	0.8125 20,638	3310 1475	1810 805	1.83	-0.17 -4,2	365S	362A	0.03 0,8	0.8750 22,225	2.17 55,0	2.13 54,0	0.05 1,3	0.6501 16,513	3.19 81,0	3.31 84,0
1.9375 49,212	3.6718 93,264	1.1875 30,162	5000 2220	2890 1285	1.73	-0.32 -8,2	3781	3730	0.14 3,5	1.1930 30,302	2.44 62,0	2.20 56,0	0.03 0,8	0.9375 23,812	3.31 84,0	3.46 88,0
1.9375 49,212	4.0625 103,188	1.7188 43,658	8800 3900	4450 1980	1.97	-0.63 -16,1	5395	5335	0.14 3,5	1.7510 44,475	2.60 66,0	2.36 60,0	0.13 3,3	1.4375 36,512	3.50 89,0	3.82 97,0
1.9375 49,212	4.1250 104,775	1.4375 36,512	7150 3180	5950 2660	1.20	-0.29 -7,4	HM807044	HM807011	0.14 3,5	1.4375 36,512	2.72 69,0	2.48 63,0	0.03 0,8	1.1250 28,575	3.58 91,0	3.94 100,0
1.9375 49,212	4.5000 114,300	1.7500 44,450	8850 3940	6500 2900	1.36	-0.49 -12,4	65390	65320	0.14 3,5	1.7500 44,450	2.76 70,0	2.36 60,0	0.13 3,3	1.3750 34,925	3.82 97,0	4.21 107,0
1.9375 49,212	4.5000 114,300	1.7500 44,450	9900 4400	6800 3040	1.45	-0.53 -13,5	HH506348	HH506310	0.14 3,5	1.7500 44,450	2.80 71,0	2.40 61,0	0.13 3,3	1.4200 36,068	3.82 97,0	4.21 107,0
1.9375 49,212	4.5000 114,300	1.7500 44,450	9900 4400	6800 3040	1.45	-0.53 -13,5	HH506348	HH506311	0.14 3,5	1.7500 44,450	2.80 71,0	2.40 61,0	0.03 0,8	1.4200 36,068	3.90 99,0	4.21 107,0
1.9675 49,974	4.3750 111,125	1.1875 30,162	4150 1840	6300 2800	0.66	0.28 7,1	55196	55437	0.14 3,5	1.0594 26,909	2.80 71,0	2.52 63,9	0.13 3,3	0.8125 20,638	3.62 92,0	4.13 105,0
1.9675 49,974	4.3750 111,125	1.1875 30,162	4150 1840	6300 2800	0.66	0.28 7,1	55197	55437	0.08 2,0	1.0594 26,909	2.68 68,0	2.52 63,9	0.13 3,3	0.8125 20,638	3.62 92,0	4.13 105,0
*1.9685 *50,000	*3.2283 *82,000	0.8465 21,500	3370 1500	1760 785	1.91	-0.21 -5,4	JLM104948	JLM104910	0.12 3,0	0.8465 21,500	2.36 60,0	2.17 55,0	0.02 0,5	0.6693 17,000	2.99 76,0	3.07 78,0
†1.9685 †50,000	3.2500 82,550	0.8500 21,590	3370 1500	1760 785	1.91	-0.23 -5,9	LM104947A	LM104911	0.02 0,5	0.8750 22,225	2.17 55,0	2.17 55,0	0.05 1,3	0.6500 16,510	2.95 75,0	3.07 78,0
1.9685 50,000	3.5000 88,900	0.8125 20,638	3310 1475	1810 805	1.83	-0.17 -4,2	365	362A	0.08 2,0	0.8750 22,225	2.28 58,0	2.17 55,0	0.05 1,3	0.6501 16,513	3.19 81,0	3.31 84,0
1.9685 50,000	3.5000 88,900	0.8125 20,638	3310 1475	1810 805	1.83	-0.17 -4,2	366	362A	0.09 2,3	0.8750 22,225	2.32 59,0	2.17 55,0	0.05 1,3	0.6501 16,513	3.19 81,0	3.31 84,0
*1.9685 *50,000	*3.5433 *90,000	1.1024 28,000	5000 2220	2800 1245	1.78	-0.30 -7,6	JM205149	JM205110	0.12 3,0	1.1024 28,000	2.44 62,0	2.24 57,0	0.10 2,5	0.9055 23,000	3.15 80,0	3.35 85,0
†1.9685 †50,000	3.6250 92,075	0.9688 24,608	4100 1840	2660 1185	1.55	-0.19 -4,7	28579	28521	0.09 2,3	1.0000 25,400	2.36 60,0	2.20 56,0	0.03 0,8	0.7813 19,845	3.27 83,0	3.43 87,0

COPYRIGHT 1972 BY THE TIMKEN COMPANY • PRINTED IN U.S.A.

20

| bore | outside diameter | width | rating at 500 RPM for 3000 hours L10 | | factor | eff. load center | part numbers | | cone | | | | cup | | | |
| | | | one row radial | thrust | | | | | max. shaft fillet radius | width | backing shoulder diameters | | max. housing fillet radius | width | backing shoulder | |
d	D	T	lb daN	lb daN	K	a[2]	cone	cup	R[1]	B	d_b	d_a	r[1]	C	D_b	D_a
*1.9685 / *50,000	*4.1339 / *105,000	1.4567 / 37,000	7150 / 3180	5950 / 2660	1.20	-0.29 / -7,5	JHM807045	JHM807012	0.12 / 3,0	1.4173 / 36,000	2.72 / 69,0	2.48 / 63,0	0.10 / 2,5	1.1417 / 29,000	3.54 / 90,0	3.94 / 100,0
1.9685 / 50,000	4.3307 / 110,000	0.8661 / 22,000	4000 / 1790	2770 / 1235	1.45	-0.03 / -0,8	396	394A	0.03 / 0,8	0.8660 / 21,996	2.40 / 61,0	2.36 / 60,0	0.05 / 1,3	0.7411 / 18,824	3.98 / 101,0	4.11 / 104,5
2.0000 / 50,800	3.0625 / 77,788	0.5000 / 12,700	1500 / 665	860 / 382	1.74	0.0 / -0,1	LL205449	LL205410	0.06 / 1,5	0.5000 / 12,700	2.24 / 57,0	2.17 / 55,0	0.06 / 1,5	0.3750 / 9,525	2.80 / 71,0	2.91 / 74,0
2.0000 / 50,800	3.1875 / 80,962	0.7188 / 18,258	2680 / 1190	1630 / 725	1.64	-0.09 / -2,4	L305649	L305610	0.06 / 1,5	0.7188 / 18,258	2.28 / 58,0	2.20 / 56,0	0.06 / 1,5	0.5625 / 14,288	2.87 / 73,0	3.03 / 77,0
2.0000 / 50,800	3.2500 / 82,550	0.9300 / 23,622	3370 / 1500	1760 / 785	1.91	-0.23 / -5,9	LM104949	LM104911A	0.14 / 3,5	0.8750 / 22,225	2.44 / 62,0	2.17 / 55,0	0.03 / 0,8	0.7300 / 18,542	2.95 / 75,0	3.07 / 78,0
2.0000 / 50,800	3.2650 / 82,931	0.8500 / 21,590	3370 / 1500	1760 / 785	1.91	-0.23 / -5,9	LM104949	LM104912	0.14 / 3,5	0.8750 / 22,225	2.44 / 62,0	2.17 / 55,0	0.05 / 1,3	0.6500 / 16,510	2.95 / 75,0	3.06 / 77,8
2.0000 / 50,800	3.3750 / 85,725	0.7500 / 19,050	2120 / 945	2060 / 915	1.03	0.08 / 1,9	18200	18337	0.06 / 1,5	0.7190 / 18,263	2.32 / 59,0	2.20 / 56,0	0.06 / 1,5	0.5000 / 12,700	2.99 / 76,0	3.19 / 81,0
2.0000 / 50,800	3.5000 / 88,900	0.6875 / 17,462	2240 / 995	1550 / 690	1.44	-0.03 / -0,7	18790	18724	0.14 / 3,5	0.6875 / 17,462	2.44 / 62,0	2.20 / 56,0	0.05 / 1,3	0.5313 / 13,495	3.07 / 78,0	3.23 / 82,0
2.0000 / 50,800	3.5000 / 88,900	0.8125 / 20,638	3310 / 1475	1810 / 805	1.83	-0.17 / -4,2	368	362A	0.06 / 1,5	0.8750 / 22,225	2.28 / 58,0	2.20 / 56,0	0.05 / 1,3	0.6501 / 16,513	3.19 / 81,0	3.31 / 84,0
2.0000 / 50,800	3.5000 / 88,900	0.8125 / 20,638	3310 / 1475	1810 / 805	1.83	-0.17 / -4,2	368A	362A	0.14 / 3,5	0.8750 / 22,225	2.44 / 62,0	2.20 / 56,0	0.05 / 1,3	0.6501 / 16,513	3.19 / 81,0	3.31 / 84,0
2.0000 / 50,800	3.5000 / 88,900	0.8125 / 20,638	3310 / 1475	1810 / 805	1.83	-0.17 / -4,2	370A	362A	0.20 / 5,0	0.8750 / 22,225	2.56 / 65,0	2.20 / 56,0	0.05 / 1,3	0.6501 / 16,513	3.19 / 81,0	3.31 / 84,0
2.0000 / 50,800	3.6250 / 92,075	0.9688 / 24,608	4100 / 1840	2660 / 1185	1.55	-0.19 / -4,7	28580	28521	0.14 / 3,5	1.0000 / 25,400	2.48 / 63,0	2.24 / 57,0	0.03 / 0,8	0.7813 / 19,845	3.27 / 83,0	3.43 / 87,0
2.0000 / 50,800	3.6718 / 93,264	0.8125 / 20,638	3430 / 1525	1980 / 880	1.73	-0.15 / -3,8	375	374	0.09 / 2,3	0.8750 / 22,225	2.36 / 60,0	2.24 / 57,0	0.05 / 1,3	0.5938 / 15,083	3.35 / 85,0	3.46 / 88,0
2.0000 / 50,800	3.6718 / 93,264	1.1875 / 30,162	5000 / 2220	2890 / 1285	1.73	-0.32 / -8,2	3775	3730	0.03 / 0,8	1.1930 / 30,302	2.28 / 58,0	2.28 / 58,0	0.03 / 0,8	0.9375 / 23,812	3.31 / 84,0	3.46 / 88,0
2.0000 / 50,800	3.6718 / 93,264	1.1875 / 30,162	5000 / 2220	2890 / 1285	1.73	-0.32 / -8,2	3780	3730	0.14 / 3,5	1.1930 / 30,302	2.52 / 64,0	2.28 / 58,0	0.03 / 0,8	0.9375 / 23,812	3.31 / 84,0	3.46 / 88,0
2.0000 / 50,800	3.6718 / 93,264	1.1875 / 30,162	5000 / 2220	2890 / 1285	1.73	-0.32 / -8,2	3784	3730	0.25 / 6,4	1.1930 / 30,302	2.76 / 70,0	2.28 / 58,0	0.03 / 0,8	0.9375 / 23,812	3.31 / 84,0	3.46 / 88,0
2.0000 / 50,800	3.7500 / 95,250	1.0938 / 27,783	5250 / 2320	2960 / 1315	1.77	-0.30 / -7,6	33889	33822	0.14 / 3,5	1.1250 / 28,575	2.52 / 64,0	2.28 / 58,0	0.03 / 0,8	0.8750 / 22,225	3.39 / 86,0	3.54 / 90,0
2.0000 / 50,800	3.8125 / 96,838	0.8750 / 22,225	3430 / 1525	1980 / 880	1.73	-0.15 / -3,8	375S	372A	0.14 / 3,5	0.8750 / 22,225	2.48 / 63,0	2.24 / 57,0	0.06 / 1,5	0.7500 / 19,050	3.39 / 86,0	3.54 / 90,0
2.0000 / 50,800	3.8125 / 96,838	0.9688 / 24,608	4400 / 1960	3040 / 1350	1.45	-0.13 / -3,4	28678	28621	0.14 / 3,5	0.9688 / 24,608	2.56 / 65,0	2.28 / 58,0	0.03 / 0,8	0.7656 / 19,446	3.46 / 88,0	3.62 / 92,0
2.0000 / 50,800	3.8125 / 96,838	1.0000 / 25,400	3590 / 1595	2180 / 970	1.65	-0.12 / -3,0	385A	382S	0.09 / 2,3	0.8640 / 21,946	2.40 / 61,0	2.36 / 60,0	0.09 / 2,3	0.7982 / 20,274	3.43 / 87,0	3.58 / 91,0
2.0000 / 50,800	4.0000 / 101,600	1.2500 / 31,750	5300 / 2360	3630 / 1615	1.46	-0.28 / -7,1	49585	49520	0.14 / 3,5	1.2500 / 31,750	2.60 / 66,0	2.32 / 59,0	0.13 / 3,3	1.0000 / 25,400	3.46 / 88,0	3.78 / 96,0
2.0000 / 50,800	4.0000 / 101,600	1.3750 / 34,925	6550 / 2920	3200 / 1425	2.05	-0.50 / -12,7	529	522	0.03 / 0,8	1.4200 / 36,068	2.32 / 59,0	2.28 / 58,0	0.13 / 3,3	1.0625 / 26,988	3.50 / 89,0	3.74 / 95,0
2.0000 / 50,800	4.0000 / 101,600	1.3750 / 34,925	6550 / 2920	3200 / 1425	2.05	-0.50 / -12,7	529X	522	0.14 / 3,5	1.4200 / 36,068	2.56 / 65,0	2.28 / 58,0	0.13 / 3,3	1.0625 / 26,988	3.50 / 89,0	3.74 / 95,0

① These maximum fillet radii will be cleared by the bearing corners.
② Minus value indicates center is inside cone backface.
† Dimension shown is maximum value—see note at bottom of fitting practice table page 4 in Reference Tables.
*For "J" part tolerances see metric tolerance, page 20 and fitting practice page 6 in Reference Tables.

SINGLE-ROW STRAIGHT BORE—TS

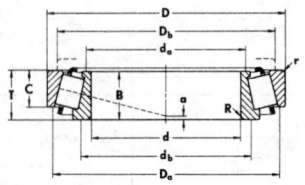

								cone					cup			
bore	outside diameter	width	rating at 500 RPM for 3000 hours L10		factor	eff. load center	part numbers		max. shaft fillet radius	width	backing shoulder diameters		max. housing fillet radius	width	backing shoulder	
			one row radial	thrust			cone	cup								
d	D	T	lb daN	lb daN	K	a[③]	cone	cup	R[①]	B	d_b	d_a	r[①]	C	D_b	D_a
2.0000 50,800	4.1250 104,775	1.1875 30,162	6200 2760	3520 1565	1.76	−0.32 −8,1	45284	45221	0.25 6,4	1.2188 30,958	2.80 71,0	2.32 59,0	0.03 0,8	0.9375 23,812	3.74 95,0	3.90 99,0
2.0000 50,800	4.1250 104,775	1.1875 30,162	6200 2760	3520 1565	1.76	−0.32 −8,1	45285	45221	0.09 2,3	1.2188 30,958	2.48 63,0	2.32 59,0	0.03 0,8	0.9375 23,812	3.74 95,0	3.90 99,0
2.0000 50,800	4.1250 104,775	1.1875 30,162	6200 2760	3520 1565	1.76	−0.32 −8,1	45285A	45220	0.03 0,8	1.2188 30,958	2.36 60,0	2.32 59,0	0.13 3,3	0.9375 23,812	3.66 93,0	3.90 99,0
2.0000 50,800	4.1250 104,775	1.4375 36,512	6800 3020	4700 2080	1.45	−0.38 −9,7	59200	59412	0.14 3,5	1.4375 36,512	2.68 68,0	2.40 61,0	0.13 3,3	1.1250 28,575	3.62 92,0	3.90 99,0
2.0000 50,800	4.1250 104,775	1.4375 36,512	6800 3020	4700 2080	1.45	−0.38 −9,7	59201	59412	0.03 0,8	1.4375 36,512	2.44 62,0	2.40 61,0	0.13 3,3	1.1250 28,575	3.62 92,0	3.90 99,0
2.0000 50,800	4.1250 104,775	1.4375 36,512	7150 3180	5950 2660	1.20	−0.29 −7,4	HM807046	HM807011	0.14 3,5	1.4375 36,512	2.76 70,0	2.48 63,1	0.13 3,3	1.1250 28,575	3.58 91,0	3.94 100,0
2.0000 50,800	4.1250 104,775	1.5625 39,688	7650 3400	4400 1960	1.74	−0.49 −12,3	4580	4535	0.14 3,5	1.5810 40,157	2.64 67,0	2.40 61,0	0.13 3,3	1.3125 33,338	3.54 90,0	3.90 99,0
2.0000 50,800	4.2500 107,950	1.2818 32,558	5400 2400	3090 1375	1.74	−0.28 −7,0	455	452	0.03 0,8	1.1542 29,317	2.36 60,0	2.32 59,0	0.03 0,8	1.0630 27,000	3.90 99,0	3.94 100,0
2.0000 50,800	4.2500 107,950	1.4375 36,512	6900 3060	3500 1560	1.97	−0.48 −12,2	537	532X	0.14 3,5	1.4550 36,957	2.56 65,0	2.32 59,0	0.13 3,3	1.1250 28,575	3.70 94,0	3.94 100,0
2.0000 50,800	4.3307 110,000	0.8661 22,000	4000 1790	2770 1235	1.45	−0.03 −0,8	398	394AS	0.03 0,8	0.8660 21,996	2.44 62,0	2.40 61,0	0.13 3,3	0.7411 18,824	3.90 99,0	4.11 104,5
2.0000 50,800	4.3307 110,000	1.0943 27,795	5400 2400	3090 1375	1.74	−0.28 −7,0	455S	454	0.14 3,5	1.1542 29,317	2.56 65,0	2.32 59,0	0.08 2,0	1.0630 27,000	3.78 96,0	3.94 100,0
2.0000 50,800	4.3750 111,125	1.1875 30,162	4150 1840	6300 2800	0.66	0.28 7,1	55200	55437	0.14 3,5	1.0594 26,909	2.80 71,0	2.52 63,9	0.13 3,3	0.8125 20,638	3.62 92,0	4.13 105,0
2.0000 50,800	4.3750 111,125	1.1875 30,162	5000 2220	7550 3360	0.66	0.30 7,5	HM907643	HM907614	0.14 3,5	1.1250 28,575	2.91 74,0	2.57 65,3	0.13 3,3	0.8125 20,638	3.58 91,0	4.13 105,0
2.0000 50,800	4.4375 112,712	1.1875 30,162	5900 2620	4050 1800	1.45	−0.18 −4,6	3975	3925	0.14 3,5	1.1830 30,048	2.68 68,0	2.40 61,0	0.03 0,8	0.9375 23,812	4.06 101,0	4.17 106,0
2.0000 50,800	4.4375 112,712	1.1875 30,162	7000 3100	4050 1800	1.72	−0.26 −6,6	39573	39521	0.03 0,8	1.1875 30,162	2.44 62,0	2.40 61,0	0.13 3,3	0.9375 23,812	4.06 103,0	4.21 107,0
2.0000 50,800	4.4375 112,712	1.1875 30,162	7000 3100	4050 1800	1.72	−0.26 −6,6	39575	39520	0.14 3,5	1.1875 30,162	2.68 68,0	2.40 61,0	0.13 3,3	0.9375 23,812	3.98 101,0	4.21 107,0
2.0000 50,800	4.6250 117,475	1.3125 33,338	5750 2560	6200 2760	0.93	−0.01 −0,3	66200	66461	0.14 3,5	1.2500 31,750	2.80 71,0	2.56 65,0	0.03 0,8	0.9375 23,812	4.02 102,0	4.37 111,0
2.0000 50,800	4.7244 120,000	1.5757 40,023	8300 3700	4450 1980	1.86	−0.55 −14,0	619	613X	0.14 3,5	1.6250 41,275	2.64 67,0	2.40 61,0	0.12 3,0	1.2200 30,988	4.09 104,0	4.33 110,0
2.0000 50,800	4.8125 122,238	1.5000 38,100	7900 3520	4700 2080	1.69	−0.37 −9,4	555	553X	0.09 2,3	1.4440 36,678	2.60 66,0	2.44 62,0	0.13 3,3	1.1875 30,162	4.25 108,0	4.53 115,0
2.0000 50,800	4.8125 122,238	1.7188 43,658	10200 4500	6250 2780	1.63	−0.48 −12,1	5565	5535	0.05 1,3	1.7230 43,764	2.64 67,0	2.56 65,0	0.13 3,3	1.4375 36,512	4.17 106,0	4.57 116,0

SINGLE-ROW STRAIGHT BORE   TS

| bore | outside diameter | width | rating at 500 RPM for 3000 hours L10 | | fac-tor | eff. load center | part numbers | | cone max. shaft fillet radius | width | backing shoulder diameters | | cup max. housing fillet radius | width | backing shoulder | |
| | | | one row radial | thrust | | | cone | cup | | | | | | | | |
d	D	T	lb daN	lb daN	K	a②	cone	cup	R①	B	db	da	r①	C	Db	Da
2.0000 50,800	4.8750 123,825	1.4375 36,512	6250 2780	7900 3520	0.79	0.05 1,3	72200	72487	0.14 3,5	1.2910 32,791	2.91 74,0	2.59 65,9	0.13 3,3	1.0000 25,400	4.02 102,0	4.57 116,0
2.0000 50,800	5.0000 127,000	1.4375 36,512	8050 3580	6950 3080	1.16	−0.15 −3,8	HM813836	HM813811	0.14 3,5	1.4375 36,512	2.83 72,0	2.60 66,0	0.06 1,5	1.0625 26,988	4.45 113,0	4.76 121,0
2.0000 50,800	5.0000 127,000	1.7500 44,450	9850 4380	8200 3660	1.20	−0.37 −9,4	65200	65500	0.14 3,5	1.7500 44,450	2.95 75,0	2.72 69,0	0.13 3,3	1.3750 34,925	4.21 107,0	4.69 119,0
2.0000 50,800	5.0000 127,000	2.0000 50,800	12400 5550	6350 2820	1.96	−0.77 −19,5	6279	6220	0.14 3,5	2.0625 52,388	2.80 71,0	2.56 65,0	0.13 3,3	1.6250 41,275	4.25 108,0	4.61 117,0
2.0312 51,592	3.5000 88,900	0.8125 20,638	3310 1475	1810 805	1.83	−0.17 −4,2	368S	362A	0.08 2,0	0.8750 22,225	2.32 59,0	2.20 56,0	0.05 1,3	0.6501 16,513	3.19 81,0	3.31 84,0
2.0625 52,388	3.6250 92,075	0.9688 24,608	4100 1840	2660 1185	1.55	−0.19 −4,7	28584	28521	0.14 3,5	1.0000 25,400	2.56 65,0	2.28 58,0	0.03 0,8	0.7813 19,845	3.27 83,0	3.43 87,0
2.0625 52,388	3.6718 93,264	1.1875 30,162	5000 2220	2890 1285	1.73	−0.32 −8,2	3767	3730	0.09 2,3	1.1930 30,302	2.48 63,0	2.32 59,0	0.03 0,8	0.9375 23,812	3.31 84,0	3.46 88,0
2.0625 52,388	3.7500 95,250	1.0938 27,783	5250 2320	2960 1315	1.77	−0.30 −7,6	33890	33822	0.06 1,5	1.1250 28,575	2.41 61,0	2.32 59,0	0.03 0,8	0.8750 22,225	3.39 86,0	3.54 90,0
2.0625 52,388	3.7500 95,250	1.0938 27,783	5250 2320	2960 1315	1.77	−0.30 −7,6	33891	33822	0.14 3,5	1.1250 28,575	2.60 66,0	2.32 59,0	0.03 0,8	0.8750 22,225	3.39 86,0	3.54 90,0
2.0625 52,388	3.9370 100,000	0.9842 24,999	3430 1525	1980 880	1.73	−0.15 −3,8	377	372	0.09 2,3	0.8750 22,225	2.44 62,0	2.28 58,0	0.08 2,0	0.8592 21,824	3.39 86,0	3.54 90,0
2.0625 52,388	3.9370 100,000	0.9842 24,999	3430 1525	1980 880	1.73	−0.15 −3,8	377	373	0.09 2,3	0.8750 22,225	2.44 62,0	2.28 58,0	0.08 2,0	0.9842 24,999	3.39 86,0	3.54 90,0
2.0625 52,388	4.1250 104,775	1.1875 30,162	5400 2400	3090 1375	1.74	−0.28 −7,0	468	453X	0.06 1,5	1.1542 29,317	2.44 62,0	2.36 60,0	0.13 3,3	0.9687 24,605	3.62 92,0	3.86 98,0
2.0625 52,388	4.3750 111,125	1.1875 30,162	4150 1840	6300 2800	0.66	0.28 7,1	55206	55437	0.14 3,5	1.0594 26,909	2.83 72,0	2.52 63,9	0.13 3,3	0.8125 20,638	3.62 92,0	4.13 105,0
2.1250 53,975	3.5000 88,900	0.7500 19,050	2690 1200	2520 1120	1.07	0.09 2,3	LM806649	LM806610	0.09 2,3	0.7500 19,050	2.48 63,0	2.36 60,0	0.08 2,0	0.5312 13,492	3.15 80,0	3.35 85,0
2.1250 53,975	3.7500 95,250	1.0938 27,783	5250 2320	2960 1315	1.77	−0.30 −7,6	33895	33822	0.06 1,5	1.1250 28,575	2.48 63,0	2.36 60,0	0.03 0,8	0.8750 22,225	3.39 86,0	3.54 90,0
2.1250 53,975	3.8750 98,425	0.8268 21,000	3590 1595	2180 970	1.65	−0.12 −3,0	389A	382	0.03 0,8	0.8640 21,946	2.40 61,0	2.36 60,0	0.03 0,8	0.7018 17,826	3.54 90,0	3.62 92,0
2.1250 53,975	3.9370 100,000	0.8268 21,000	3590 1595	2180 970	1.65	−0.12 −3,0	389AS	383A	0.06 1,5	0.8640 21,946	2.44 62,0	2.36 60,0	0.08 2,0	0.7018 17,826	3.50 89,0	3.66 93,0
2.1250 53,975	4.1250 104,775	1.1875 30,162	5400 2400	3090 1375	1.74	−0.28 −7,0	456	453X	0.14 3,5	1.1542 29,317	2.68 68,0	2.40 61,0	0.13 3,3	0.9687 24,605	3.62 92,0	3.86 98,0
2.1250 53,975	4.1250 104,775	1.1875 30,162	6200 2760	3520 1565	1.76	−0.32 −8,1	45287	45221	0.03 0,8	1.2188 30,958	2.44 62,0	2.44 62,0	0.03 0,8	0.9375 23,812	3.74 95,0	3.90 99,0
2.1250 53,975	4.1250 104,775	1.4375 36,512	7150 3180	5950 2660	1.20	−0.29 −7,4	HM807049	HM807011	0.14 3,5	1.4375 36,512	2.87 73,0	2.48 63,1	0.03 0,8	1.1250 28,575	3.58 91,0	3.94 100,0
2.1250 53,975	4.1250 104,775	1.5625 39,688	7650 3400	4400 1960	1.74	−0.49 −12,3	4595	4535	0.14 3,5	1.5810 40,157	2.76 70,0	2.48 63,0	0.13 3,3	1.3125 33,338	3.54 90,0	3.90 99,0

①These maximum fillet radii will be cleared by the bearing corners.
②Minus value indicates center is inside cone backface.

SINGLE-ROW STRAIGHT BORE—TS

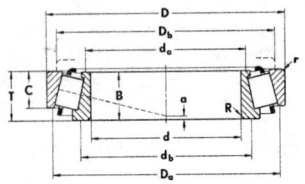

| bore | outside diameter | width | rating at 500 RPM for 3000 hours L10 | | fac-tor | eff. load center | part numbers | | cone | | | | cup | | | |
| | | | one row radial | thrust | | | cone | cup | max. shaft fillet radius | width | backing shoulder diameters | | max. hous-ing fillet radius | width | backing shoulder | |
d	D	T	lb daN	lb daN	K	a⊕			R①	B	d_b	d_a	r①	C	D_b	D_a
2.1250 53,975	4.2500 107,950	1.4375 36,512	6900 3060	3500 1560	1.97	−0.48 −12,2	539	532X	0.14 3,5	1.4550 36,957	2.68 68,0	2.40 61,0	0.13 3,3	1.1250 28,575	3.70 94,0	3.94 100,0
2.1250 53,975	4.2500 107,950	1.4375 36,512	6900 3060	3500 1560	1.97	−0.48 −12,2	539A	532X	0.22 5,5	1.4550 36,957	2.83 72,0	2.40 61,0	0.13 3,3	1.1250 28,575	3.70 94,0	3.94 100,0
2.1250 53,975	4.6250 117,475	1.3125 33,338	5750 2560	6200 2760	0.93	−0.01 −0,3	66212	66462	0.14 3,5	1.2500 31,750	2.87 73,0	2.64 67,0	0.13 3,3	0.9375 23,812	3.94 100,0	4.37 111,0
2.1250 53,975	4.7238 119,985	1.2894 32,751	7000 3100	4050 1800	1.72	−0.26 −6,6	39578	39528	0.14 3,5	1.1875 30,162	2.76 70,0	2.52 64,0	0.03 0,8	1.0610 26,949	4.21 107,0	4.33 110,0
2.1250 53,975	4.7500 120,650	1.6250 41,275	8300 3700	4450 1980	1.86	−0.55 −14,0	621	612	0.14 3,5	1.6250 41,275	2.76 70,0	2.48 63,0	0.13 3,3	1.2500 31,750	4.13 105,0	4.33 110,0
2.1250 53,975	4.7500 120,650	1.6250 41,275	8300 3700	4450 1980	1.86	−0.55 −14,0	624	612S	0.03 0,8	1.6250 41,275	2.52 64,0	2.48 63,0	0.03 0,8	1.2500 31,750	4.21 107,0	4.33 110,0
2.1250 53,975	4.8125 122,238	1.3125 33,338	6000 2680	6850 3040	0.88	0.08 2,0	66584	66520	0.14 3,5	1.2500 31,750	2.95 75,0	2.68 68,0	0.13 3,3	0.9375 23,812	4.13 105,0	4.57 116,0
2.1250 53,975	4.8125 122,238	1.7188 43,658	10200 4500	6250 2780	1.63	−0.48 −12,1	5578	5535	0.14 3,5	1.7230 43,764	2.87 73,0	2.64 67,0	0.13 3,3	1.4375 36,512	4.17 106,0	4.57 116,0
2.1250 53,975	4.8750 123,825	1.4375 36,512	6250 2780	7900 3520	0.79	0.05 1,3	72212	72487	0.14 3,5	1.2910 32,791	3.03 77,0	2.59 65,9	0.13 3,3	1.0000 25,400	4.02 102,0	4.57 116,0
2.1250 53,975	4.8750 123,825	1.5000 38,100	7900 3520	4700 2080	1.69	−0.37 −9,4	557S	552A	0.14 3,5	1.4440 36,678	2.80 71,0	2.56 65,0	0.13 3,3	1.1875 30,162	4.29 109,0	4.57 116,0
2.1250 53,975	5.0000 127,000	1.7500 44,450	9850 4380	8200 3660	1.20	−0.37 −9,4	65212	65500	0.14 3,5	1.7500 44,450	3.03 77,0	2.80 71,0	0.13 3,3	1.3750 34,925	4.21 107,0	4.69 119,0
2.1250 53,975	5.0000 127,000	2.0000 50,800	12400 5550	6350 2820	1.96	−0.77 −19,5	6280	6220	0.14 3,5	2.0625 52,388	2.91 74,0	2.64 67,0	0.13 3,3	1.6250 41,275	4.25 108,0	4.61 117,0
2.1250 53,975	5.1250 130,175	1.4375 36,512	6500 2900	9200 4080	0.71	0.21 5,3	HM911242	HM911210	0.14 3,5	1.3125 33,338	3.11 79,0	2.91 74,0	0.13 3,3	0.9375 23,812	4.29 109,0	4.87 123,6
2.1250 53,975	5.1250 130,175	1.6250 41,275	9600 4260	5950 2640	1.61	−0.44 −11,2	636	633	0.14 3,5	1.6250 41,275	2.87 73,0	2.64 67,0	0.13 3,3	1.2500 31,750	4.57 116,0	4.88 124,0
2.1250 53,975	5.3750 136,525	1.4375 36,512	6750 3000	10100 4480	0.67	0.31 8,0	78214	78537	0.03 0,8	1.3085 33,236	2.95 75,0	3.03 77,0	0.13 3,3	0.9260 23,520	4.53 115,0	5.12 130,0
2.1250 53,975	5.5130 140,030	1.4375 36,512	6750 3000	10100 4480	0.67	0.31 8,0	78215	78551	0.14 3,5	1.3085 33,236	3.19 81,0	2.95 75,0	0.09 2,3	0.9260 23,520	4.61 117,0	5.20 132,0
*2.1654 *55,000	*3.5433 *90,000	0.9055 23,000	3790 1685	2610 1165	1.45	−0.11 −2,8	JLM506849	JLM506810	0.06 1,5	0.9055 23,000	2.48 63,0	2.40 61,0	0.02 0,5	0.7283 18,500	3.23 82,0	3.39 86,0
*2.1654 *55,000	*3.7402 *95,000	1.1417 29,000	5400 2400	3110 1380	1.74	−0.30 −7,6	JM207049	JM207010	0.06 1,5	1.1417 29,000	2.52 64,0	2.44 62,0	0.10 2,5	0.9252 23,500	3.35 85,0	3.58 91,0
2.1654 55,000	3.8125 96,838	0.8268 21,000	3590 1595	2180 970	1.65	−0.12 −3,0	385	382A	0.09 2,3	0.8640 21,946	2.56 65,0	2.40 61,0	0.03 0,8	0.6250 15,875	3.50 89,0	3.62 92,0

bore	outside diameter	width	rating at 500 RPM for 3000 hours L10		fac-tor	eff. load center	part numbers		cone				cup			
			one row radial	thrust			cone	cup	max. shaft fillet radius	width	backing shoulder diameters		max. hous-ing fillet radius	width	backing shoulder	
d	D	T	lb daN	lb daN	K	a②			R①	B	d_b	d_a	r①	C	D_b	D_a
2.1654 55,000	3.8125 96,838	0.8268 21,000	3590 1595	2180 970	1.65	-0.12 -3,0	385X	382A	0.14 3,5	0.8640 21,946	2.64 67,0	2.40 61,0	0.03 0,8	0.6250 15,875	3.50 89,0	3.62 92,0
*2.1654 *55,000	*4.3307 *110,000	1.5354 39,000	8500 3780	5050 2240	1.69	-0.46 -11,7	JH307749	JH307710	0.12 3,0	1.5354 39,000	2.80 71,0	2.52 64,1	0.10 2,5	1.2598 32,000	3.82 97,0	4.09 104,0
2.1654 55,000	4.5276 115,000	1.6150 41,021	8300 3700	4450 1980	1.86	-0.55 -14,0	622X	614X	0.12 3,0	1.6250 41,275	2.76 70,0	2.52 64,0	0.12 3,0	1.2400 31,496	3.98 101,0	4.25 108,0
2.1654 55,000	4.7244 120,000	1.1418 29,002	5900 2640	3900 1735	1.52	-0.16 -4,1	475	472A	0.03 0,8	1.1420 29,007	2.64 67,0	2.60 66,0	0.13 3,3	0.9230 23,444	4.17 106,0	4.49 114,0
†2.1654 †55,000	5.3447 135,755	2.1250 53,975	13300 5900	7350 3280	1.80	-0.76 -19,2	6381	6320	0.14 3,5	2.2050 56,007	2.99 76,0	2.76 70,0	0.13 3,3	1.7500 44,450	4.61 117,0	4.96 126,0
2.1875 55,562	3.8437 97,630	0.9688 24,608	4400 1960	3040 1350	1.45	-0.13 -3,4	28680	28622	0.14 3,5	0.9688 24,608	2.68 68,0	2.44 62,0	0.03 0,8	0.7656 19,446	3.46 88,0	3.62 92,0
2.1875 55,562	4.8125 122,238	1.7188 43,658	10200 4500	6250 2780	1.63	-0.48 -12,1	5566	5535	0.05 1,3	1.7230 43,764	2.76 70,0	2.68 68,0	0.13 3,3	1.4375 36,512	4.17 106,0	4.57 116,0
2.1875 55,562	4.8750 123,825	1.4375 36,512	6250 2780	7900 3520	0.79	0.05 1,3	72218	72487	0.14 3,5	1.2910 32,791	3.07 78,0	2.59 65,9	0.13 3,3	1.0000 25,400	4.02 102,0	4.57 116,0
2.1875 55,562	5.0000 127,000	1.4375 36,512	8050 3580	6950 3080	1.16	-0.15 -3,8	HM813840	HM813810	0.14 3,5	1.4375 36,512	2.99 76,0	2.76 70,0	0.13 3,3	1.0625 26,988	4.37 111,0	4.76 121,0
2.1880 55,575	3.8125 96,838	0.8268 21,000	3590 1595	2180 970	1.65	-0.12 -3,0	389	382A	0.09 2,3	0.8640 21,946	2.56 65,0	2.40 61,0	0.03 0,8	0.6250 15,875	3.50 89,0	3.62 92,0
2.2500 57,150	3.4375 87,312	0.7188 18,258	2810 1250	1870 835	1.50	-0.03 -0,9	L507949	L507910	0.06 1,5	0.7188 18,258	2.56 65,0	2.44 62,0	0.06 1,5	0.5625 14,288	3.11 79,0	3.27 83,0
2.2500 57,150	3.8125 96,838	0.8268 21,000	3590 1595	2180 970	1.65	-0.12 -3,0	387	382A	0.09 2,3	0.8640 21,946	2.60 66,0	2.44 62,0	0.03 0,8	0.6250 15,875	3.50 89,0	3.62 92,0
2.2500 57,150	3.8125 96,838	0.8268 21,000	3590 1595	2180 970	1.65	-0.12 -3,0	387A	382A	0.14 3,5	0.8640 21,946	2.72 69,0	2.44 62,0	0.03 0,8	0.6250 15,875	3.50 89,0	3.62 92,0
2.2500 57,150	3.8125 96,838	0.8268 21,000	3590 1595	2180 970	1.65	-0.12 -3,0	387AS	382A	0.20 5,0	0.8640 21,946	2.83 72,0	2.44 62,0	0.03 0,8	0.6250 15,875	3.50 89,0	3.62 92,0
2.2500 57,150	3.8125 96,838	0.8268 21,000	3590 1595	2180 970	1.65	-0.12 -3,0	387S	382A	0.03 0,8	0.8640 21,946	2.48 63,0	2.44 62,0	0.03 0,8	0.6250 15,875	3.50 89,0	3.62 92,0
2.2500 57,150	3.8750 98,425	0.9688 24,608	4400 1960	3040 1350	1.45	-0.13 -3,4	28682	28623	0.14 3,5	0.9688 24,608	2.76 70,0	2.48 63,0	0.03 0,8	0.7656 19,446	3.46 88,0	3.62 93,0
2.2500 57,150	4.1250 104,775	1.1875 30,162	5400 2400	3090 1375	1.74	-0.28 -7,0	462	453X	0.09 2,3	1.1542 29,317	2.64 67,0	2.48 63,0	0.13 3,3	0.9687 24,605	3.62 92,0	3.86 98,0
2.2500 57,150	4.1250 104,775	1.1875 30,162	5400 2400	3090 1375	1.74	-0.28 -7,0	462A	453X	0.09 2,3	1.1542 29,317	2.64 67,0	2.66 67,6	0.13 3,3	0.9687 24,605	3.62 92,0	3.86 98,0
2.2500 57,150	4.1250 104,775	1.1875 30,162	5400 2400	3090 1375	1.74	-0.28 -7,0	469	453X	0.14 3,5	1.1542 29,317	2.76 70,0	2.48 63,0	0.13 3,3	0.9687 24,605	3.62 92,0	3.86 98,0
2.2500 57,150	4.1250 104,775	1.1875 30,162	6200 2760	3520 1565	1.76	-0.32 -8,1	45289	45221	0.03 0,8	1.2188 30,958	2.56 65,0	2.56 65,0	0.03 0,8	0.9375 23,812	3.74 95,0	3.90 99,0
2.2500 57,150	4.1250 104,775	1.1875 30,162	6200 2760	3520 1565	1.76	-0.32 -8,1	45290	45221	0.09 2,3	1.2188 30,958	2.68 68,0	2.56 65,0	0.03 0,8	0.9375 23,812	3.74 95,0	3.90 99,0
2.2500 57,150	4.1250 104,775	1.1875 30,162	6200 2760	3520 1565	1.76	-0.32 -8,1	45291	45221	0.25 6,4	1.2188 30,958	2.99 76,0	2.56 65,0	0.03 0,8	0.9375 23,812	3.74 95,0	3.90 99,0
2.2500 57,150	4.3750 111,125	0.8661 22,000	4000 1790	2770 1235	1.45	-0.03 -0,8	390	393AS	0.09 2,3	0.8660 21,996	2.76 70,0	2.60 66,0	0.05 1,3	0.7411 18,824	3.98 101,0	4.13 105,0

① These maximum fillet radii will be cleared by the bearing corners.
② Minus value indicates center is inside cone backface.
† Dimension shown is maximum value—see note at bottom of fitting practice table page 4 in Reference Tables.
* For "J" part tolerances see metric tolerance, page 20 and fitting practice page 6 in Reference Tables.

SINGLE-ROW STRAIGHT BORE—TS

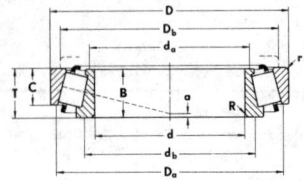

									cone				cup			
bore	outside diameter	width	rating at 500 RPM for 3000 hours L10		factor	eff. load center	part numbers		max. shaft fillet radius	width	backing shoulder diameters		max. housing fillet radius	width	backing shoulder	
			one row radial	thrust			cone	cup								
			lb daN	lb daN												
d	D	T			K	a②			R①	B	d_b	d_a	r①	C	D_b	D_a
2.2500 57,150	4.4375 112,712	1.1875 30,162	5900 2620	4050 1800	1.45	−0.18 −4,6	3979	3920	0.14 3,5	1.1830 30,048	2.83 72,0	2.60 66,0	0.13 3,3	0.9375 23,812	3.90 99,0	4.17 106,0
2.2500 57,150	4.4375 112,712	1.1875 30,162	7000 3100	4050 1800	1.72	−0.26 −6,6	39580	39521	0.14 3,5	1.1875 30,162	2.83 72,0	2.60 66,0	0.03 0,8	0.9375 23,812	4.06 103,0	4.21 107,0
2.2500 57,150	4.4375 112,712	1.1875 30,162	7000 3100	4050 1800	1.72	−0.26 −6,6	39581	39521	0.31 8,0	1.1875 30,162	3.19 81,0	2.60 66,0	0.03 0,8	0.9375 23,812	4.06 103,0	4.21 107,0
2.2500 57,150	4.5276 115,000	1.6150 41,021	8300 3700	4450 1980	1.86	−0.55 −14,0	623	614X	0.14 3,5	1.6250 41,275	2.83 72,0	2.60 66,0	0.12 3,3	1.2400 31,496	3.98 101,0	4.25 108,0
2.2500 57,150	4.6250 117,475	1.1875 30,162	5950 2660	4450 1980	1.34	−0.11 −2,8	33225	33462	0.14 3,5	1.1875 30,162	2.91 74,0	2.68 68,0	0.13 3,3	0.9375 23,812	4.09 104,0	4.41 112,0
2.2500 57,150	4.6250 117,475	1.3125 33,338	5750 2560	6200 2760	0.93	−0.01 −0,3	66225	66461	0.14 3,5	1.2500 31,750	2.99 76,0	2.71 68,9	0.13 3,3	0.9375 23,812	4.02 102,0	4.37 111,0
2.2500 57,150	4.8125 122,238	1.3125 33,338	6000 2680	6850 3040	0.88	0.08 2,0	66587	66520	0.14 3,5	1.2500 31,750	3.03 77,0	2.80 71,0	0.13 3,3	0.9375 23,812	4.13 105,0	4.57 116,0
2.2500 57,150	4.8125 122,238	1.5000 38,100	7900 3520	4700 2080	1.69	−0.37 −9,4	555S	553X	0.14 3,5	1.4440 36,678	2.87 73,0	2.64 67,0	0.13 3,3	1.1875 30,162	4.25 108,0	4.53 115,0
2.2500 57,150	5.0000 127,000	1.7500 44,450	9850 4380	8200 3660	1.20	−0.37 −9,4	65225	65500	0.14 3,5	1.7500 44,450	3.15 80,0	2.80 71,0	0.13 3,3	1.3750 34,925	4.21 107,0	4.69 119,0
2.2500 57,150	5.3750 136,525	1.6250 41,275	9600 4260	5950 2640	1.61	−0.44 −11,2	635	632	0.14 3,5	1.6250 41,275	2.95 75,0	2.72 69,0	0.13 3,3	1.2500 31,750	4.65 118,0	4.92 125,0
2.2500 57,150	5.7080 144,983	1.4173 36,000	6750 3000	10100 4480	0.67	0.31 8,0	78225	78571	0.14 3,5	1.3085 33,236	3.27 83,0	3.03 77,0	0.14 3,5	0.9058 23,007	4.65 118,0	5.20 132,0
2.2500 57,150	5.8750 149,225	2.1250 53,975	14700 6550	9100 4060	1.61	−0.59 −15,1	6455	6420	0.14 3,5	2.1350 54,229	3.19 81,0	2.95 75,0	0.13 3,3	1.7500 44,450	5.08 129,0	5.51 140,0
2.2650 57,531	3.8125 96,838	0.8268 21,000	3590 1595	2180 970	1.65	−0.12 −3,0	388A	382A	0.14 3,5	0.8640 21,946	2.72 69,0	2.48 63,0	0.03 0,8	0.6250 15,875	3.50 89,0	3.62 92,0
2.3125 58,738	4.4375 112,712	1.3125 33,338	5900 2620	4050 1800	1.45	−0.18 −4,6	3981	3926	0.14 3,5	1.1830 30,048	2.87 73,0	2.60 67,0	0.13 3,3	1.0625 26,988	3.86 98,0	4.17 106,0
2.3125 58,738	5.0000 127,000	1.7500 44,450	9850 4380	8200 3660	1.20	−0.37 −9,4	65231	65500	0.14 3,5	1.7500 44,450	3.19 81,0	2.80 71,0	0.13 3,3	1.3750 34,925	4.21 107,0	4.69 119,0
2.3575 59,880	5.0000 127,000	1.7500 44,450	9850 4380	8200 3660	1.20	−0.37 −9,4	65235	65500	0.14 3,5	1.7500 44,450	3.23 82,0	2.80 71,0	0.13 3,3	1.3750 34,925	4.21 107,0	4.69 119,0
2.3611 59,972	4.8125 122,238	1.3125 33,338	6000 2680	6850 3040	0.88	0.08 2,0	66589	66520	0.03 0,8	1.2500 31,750	2.91 74,0	2.87 73,0	0.13 3,3	0.9375 23,812	4.13 105,0	4.57 116,0
*2.3622 *60,000	*3.7402 *95,000	0.9449 24,000	4100 1820	2830 1260	1.45	−0.11 −2,7	JLM508748	JLM508710	0.20 5,0	0.9449 24,000	2.95 75,0	2.60 66,0	0.10 2,5	0.7480 19,000	3.35 85,0	3.58 91,0
†2.3622 †60,000	4.1250 104,775	0.8438 21,433	3880 1725	2570 1145	1.51	−0.06 −1,6	39236	39412	0.09 2,3	0.8661 22,000	2.80 71,0	2.64 67,0	0.08 2,0	0.6250 15,875	3.78 96,0	3.94 100,0

SINGLE-ROW STRAIGHT BORE

TS

bore d	outside diameter D	width T	rating at 500 RPM for 3000 hours L10 — one row radial (lb daN)	thrust (lb daN)	factor K	eff. load center a[2]	cone	cup	cone max shaft fillet radius R[1]	width B	db	da	cup max housing fillet radius r[1]	width C	Db	Da
2.3622 / 60,000	4.2500 / 107,950	1.0000 / 25,400	4650 / 2080	3670 / 1630	1.27	−0.03 / −0,8	29582	29522	0.03 / 0,8	1.0000 / 25,400	2.72 / 69,0	2.68 / 68,0	0.03 / 0,8	0.7500 / 19,050	3.86 / 98,0	4.06 / 103,0
2.3622 / 60,000	4.3307 / 110,000	0.8661 / 22,000	4000 / 1790	2770 / 1235	1.45	−0.03 / −0,8	397	394A	0.03 / 0,8	0.8660 / 21,996	2.72 / 69,0	2.68 / 68,0	0.05 / 1,3	0.7411 / 18,824	3.98 / 101,0	4.11 / 104,5
2.3622 / 60,000	4.4375 / 112,712	1.1875 / 30,162	5900 / 2620	4050 / 1800	1.45	−0.18 / −4,6	3977	3925	0.14 / 3,5	1.1830 / 30,048	2.91 / 74,0	2.68 / 68,0	0.03 / 0,8	0.9375 / 23,812	3.98 / 101,0	4.17 / 106,0
2.3622 / 60,000	4.7244 / 120,000	1.1418 / 29,002	5900 / 2640	3900 / 1735	1.52	−0.16 / −4,1	476	472A	0.08 / 2,0	1.1420 / 29,007	2.87 / 73,0	2.72 / 69,0	0.13 / 3,3	0.9230 / 23,444	4.17 / 106,0	4.49 / 114,0
2.3622 / 60,000	4.7244 / 120,000	1.1730 / 29,794	5900 / 2640	3900 / 1735	1.52	−0.16 / −4,1	476A	472	0.06 / 1,5	1.1420 / 29,007	2.83 / 72,0	2.72 / 69,0	0.08 / 2,0	0.9542 / 24,237	4.21 / 107,0	4.49 / 114,0
2.3622 / 60,000	4.8125 / 122,238	1.3125 / 33,338	6000 / 2680	6850 / 3040	0.88	0.08 / 2,0	66585	66520	0.14 / 3,5	1.2500 / 31,750	3.11 / 79,0	2.87 / 73,0	0.13 / 3,3	0.9375 / 23,812	4.13 / 105,0	4.57 / 116,0
†2.3622 / †60,000	4.8125 / 122,238	1.5000 / 38,100	7900 / 3520	4700 / 2080	1.69	−0.37 / −9,4	558S	553X	0.14 / 3,5	1.4440 / 36,678	2.95 / 75,0	2.72 / 69,0	0.13 / 3,3	1.1875 / 30,162	4.25 / 108,0	4.53 / 115,0
†2.3622 / †60,000	5.3143 / 134,983	1.3169 / 33,449	6500 / 2900	9200 / 4080	0.71	0.31 / 7,7	HM911244	HM911216	0.14 / 3,5	1.2175 / 30,924	3.31 / 84,0	2.93 / 74,4	0.14 / 3,5	0.8641 / 21,948	4.41 / 112,0	4.84 / 123,0
2.3622 / 60,000	5.3447 / 135,755	2.1250 / 53,975	13300 / 5900	7350 / 3280	1.80	−0.76 / −19,2	6361	6320	0.12 / 3,0	2.2050 / 56,007	3.11 / 79,0	2.91 / 74,0	0.13 / 3,3	1.7500 / 44,450	4.61 / 117,0	4.96 / 126,0
†2.3622 / †60,000	5.7500 / 146,050	1.6250 / 41,275	8900 / 3960	11900 / 5300	0.75	0.17 / 4,3	H913840	H913810	0.14 / 3,5	1.5625 / 39,688	3.46 / 88,0	3.24 / 82,4	0.13 / 3,3	1.0000 / 25,400	4.88 / 124,0	5.43 / 138,0
2.3750 / 60,325	3.9370 / 100,000	1.0000 / 25,400	4550 / 2020	3310 / 1470	1.37	−0.10 / −2,5	28985	28921	0.14 / 3,5	1.0000 / 25,400	2.87 / 73,0	2.64 / 67,0	0.13 / 3,3	0.7813 / 19,845	3.50 / 89,0	3.78 / 96,0
2.3750 / 60,325	4.4375 / 112,712	1.1875 / 30,162	5900 / 2620	4050 / 1800	1.45	−0.18 / −4,6	3980	3925	0.14 / 3,5	1.1830 / 30,048	2.95 / 75,0	2.68 / 68,0	0.03 / 0,8	0.9375 / 23,812	3.98 / 101,0	4.17 / 106,0
2.3750 / 60,325	4.8125 / 122,238	1.5000 / 38,100	7900 / 3520	4700 / 2080	1.69	−0.37 / −9,4	557A	553X	0.31 / 8,0	1.4440 / 36,678	3.31 / 84,0	2.72 / 69,0	0.13 / 3,3	1.1875 / 30,162	4.25 / 108,0	4.53 / 115,0
2.3750 / 60,325	4.8125 / 122,238	1.5000 / 38,100	7900 / 3520	4700 / 2080	1.69	−0.37 / −9,4	558	553X	0.09 / 2,3	1.4440 / 36,678	2.87 / 73,0	2.72 / 69,0	0.13 / 3,3	1.1875 / 30,162	4.25 / 108,0	4.53 / 115,0
2.3750 / 60,325	4.8125 / 122,238	1.5000 / 38,100	7900 / 3520	4700 / 2080	1.69	−0.37 / −9,4	558A	553X	0.14 / 3,5	1.4440 / 36,678	2.99 / 76,0	2.72 / 69,0	0.13 / 3,3	1.1875 / 30,162	4.25 / 108,0	4.53 / 115,0
2.3750 / 60,325	4.8125 / 122,238	1.5000 / 38,100	9150 / 4080	5300 / 2360	1.73	−0.43 / −10,9	HM212044	HM212010	0.31 / 8,0	1.5100 / 38,354	3.35 / 85,0	2.76 / 70,0	0.06 / 1,5	1.1700 / 29,718	4.33 / 110,0	4.57 / 116,0
2.3750 / 60,325	4.8125 / 122,238	1.7188 / 43,658	10200 / 4500	6250 / 2780	1.63	−0.48 / −12,1	5582	5535	0.03 / 0,8	1.7230 / 43,764	2.87 / 73,0	2.83 / 72,0	0.13 / 3,3	1.4375 / 36,512	4.17 / 106,0	4.57 / 116,0
2.3750 / 60,325	4.8125 / 122,238	1.7188 / 43,658	10200 / 4500	6250 / 2780	1.63	−0.48 / −12,1	5583	5535	0.14 / 3,5	1.7230 / 43,764	3.07 / 78,0	2.83 / 72,0	0.13 / 3,3	1.4375 / 36,512	4.17 / 106,0	4.57 / 116,0
2.3750 / 60,325	5.0000 / 127,000	1.4375 / 36,512	8050 / 3580	6950 / 3080	1.16	−0.15 / −3,8	HM813841	HM813811	0.14 / 3,5	1.4375 / 36,512	3.15 / 80,0	2.87 / 73,0	0.06 / 1,5	1.0625 / 26,988	4.45 / 113,0	4.76 / 121,0
2.3750 / 60,325	5.0000 / 127,000	1.7500 / 44,450	9850 / 4380	8200 / 3660	1.20	−0.37 / −9,4	65237	65500	0.14 / 3,5	1.7500 / 44,450	3.23 / 82,0	2.80 / 71,0	0.13 / 3,3	1.3750 / 34,925	4.21 / 107,0	4.69 / 119,0
2.3750 / 60,325	5.0000 / 127,000	1.7500 / 44,450	9850 / 4380	8200 / 3660	1.20	−0.37 / −9,4	65237A	65500	0.06 / 1,5	1.7500 / 44,450	3.07 / 78,0	2.80 / 71,0	0.13 / 3,3	1.3750 / 34,925	4.21 / 107,0	4.69 / 119,0
2.3750 / 60,325	5.1250 / 130,175	1.4375 / 36,512	6500 / 2900	9200 / 4080	0.71	0.21 / 5,0	HM911245	HM911210	0.20 / 5,0	1.3125 / 33,338	3.43 / 87,0	2.93 / 74,4	0.13 / 3,3	0.9375 / 23,812	4.29 / 109,0	4.87 / 123,6
2.3750 / 60,325	5.1250 / 130,175	1.6250 / 41,275	9600 / 4260	5950 / 2640	1.61	−0.44 / −11,2	637	633	0.14 / 3,5	1.6250 / 41,275	3.07 / 78,0	2.83 / 72,0	0.13 / 3,3	1.2500 / 31,750	4.57 / 116,0	4.88 / 124,0

① These maximum fillet radii will be cleared by the bearing corners.
② Minus value indicates center is inside cone backface.
†Dimension shown is maximum value—see note at bottom of fitting practice table page 4 in Reference Tables.
*For "J" part tolerances see metric tolerance, page 20 and fitting practice page 6 in Reference Tables.

SINGLE-ROW STRAIGHT BORE—TS

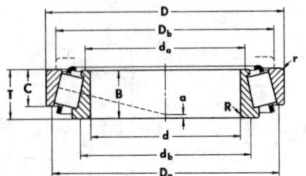

			rating at 500 RPM for 3000 hours L10		fac-tor	eff. load center	part numbers		cone				cup			
bore	outside diameter	width	one row radial	thrust			cone	cup	max. shaft fillet radius	width	backing shoulder diameters		max. housing fillet radius	width	backing shoulder	
d	D	T	lb daN	lb daN	K	a①			R①	B	d_b	d_a	r①	C	D_b	D_a
2.3750 / 60,325	5.3447 / 135,755	2.1250 / 53,975	13300 / 5900	7350 / 3280	1.80	-0.76 / -19,2	6376	6320	0.14 / 3,5	2.2050 / 56,007	3.19 / 81,0	2.91 / 74,0	0.13 / 3,3	1.7500 / 44,450	4.61 / 117,0	4.96 / 126,0
2.3750 / 60,325	5.3750 / 136,525	1.8125 / 46,038	11900 / 5300	9600 / 4280	1.24	-0.33 / -8,5	H715332	H715311	0.14 / 3,5	1.8125 / 46,038	3.31 / 84,0	3.07 / 78,0	0.13 / 3,3	1.4375 / 36,512	4.65 / 118,0	5.20 / 132,0
2.3750 / 60,325	6.0000 / 152,400	2.0750 / 52,705	14600 / 6500	12200 / 5400	1.20	-0.43 / -10,9	HH814542	HH814510	0.14 / 3,5	2.0750 / 52,705	3.50 / 89,0	3.27 / 83,0	0.13 / 3,3	1.6250 / 41,275	5.12 / 130,0	5.63 / 143,0
2.3750 / 60,325	6.3750 / 161,925	1.8750 / 47,625	11500 / 5100	14000 / 6200	0.82	0.07 / 1,7	9275	9220	0.14 / 3,5	1.8125 / 46,038	3.62 / 92,0	3.39 / 86,0	0.13 / 3,3	1.2500 / 31,750	5.43 / 138,0	6.03 / 153,0
2.4375 / 61,912	4.3307 / 110,000	0.8661 / 22,000	4000 / 1790	2770 / 1235	1.45	-0.03 / -0,8	392	394A	0.03 / 0,8	0.8660 / 21,996	2.76 / 70,0	2.72 / 69,0	0.05 / 1,3	0.7411 / 18,824	3.98 / 101,0	4.11 / 104,5
2.4375 / 61,912	4.8125 / 122,238	1.5000 / 38,100	7900 / 3520	4700 / 2080	1.69	-0.37 / -9,4	554	553X	0.14 / 3,5	1.4440 / 36,678	3.03 / 77,0	2.80 / 71,0	0.13 / 3,3	1.1875 / 30,162	4.25 / 108,0	4.53 / 115,0
2.4375 / 61,912	5.0000 / 127,000	1.4375 / 36,512	8050 / 3580	6950 / 3080	1.16	-0.15 / -3,8	HM813843	HM813811	0.14 / 3,5	1.4375 / 36,512	3.19 / 81,0	2.95 / 75,0	0.06 / 1,5	1.0625 / 26,988	4.45 / 113,0	4.76 / 121,0
2.4375 / 61,912	5.5000 / 139,700	1.8125 / 46,038	11900 / 5300	9600 / 4280	1.24	-0.33 / -8,5	H715334	H715310	0.14 / 3,5	1.8125 / 46,038	3.39 / 86,0	3.11 / 79,0	0.13 / 3,3	1.4375 / 36,512	4.72 / 120,0	5.24 / 133,0
2.4375 / 61,912	5.7500 / 146,050	1.6250 / 41,275	8900 / 3960	11900 / 5300	0.75	0.17 / 4,3	H913842	H913810	0.14 / 3,5	1.5625 / 39,688	3.54 / 90,0	3.24 / 82,4	0.13 / 3,3	1.0000 / 25,400	4.88 / 124,0	5.43 / 138,0
2.4375 / 61,912	5.7500 / 146,050	1.6250 / 41,275	8900 / 3960	11900 / 5300	0.75	0.17 / 4,3	H913843	H913810	0.28 / 7,0	1.5625 / 39,688	3.82 / 97,0	3.24 / 82,4	0.13 / 3,3	1.0000 / 25,400	4.88 / 124,0	5.43 / 138,0
2.4375 / 61,912	6.0000 / 152,400	1.8750 / 47,625	10900 / 4850	12200 / 5450	0.89	-0.15 / -3,7	9180	9121	0.14 / 3,5	1.8125 / 46,038	3.54 / 90,0	3.20 / 81,3	0.13 / 3,3	1.2500 / 31,750	5.43 / 138,0	5.71 / 145,0
2.4400 / 61,976	4.0000 / 101,600	0.9688 / 24,608	4550 / 2020	3310 / 1470	1.37	-0.07 / -1,7	28990	28920	0.08 / 2,0	0.9688 / 24,608	2.83 / 72,0	2.68 / 68,0	0.13 / 3,3	0.7813 / 19,845	3.54 / 90,0	3.82 / 97,0
2.4700 / 62,738	3.9370 / 100,000	1.0000 / 25,400	4550 / 2020	3310 / 1470	1.37	-0.10 / -2,5	28995	28921	0.14 / 3,5	1.0000 / 25,400	2.95 / 75,0	2.72 / 69,0	0.13 / 3,3	0.7813 / 19,845	3.50 / 89,0	3.78 / 96,0
2.5000 / 63,500	3.6250 / 92,075	0.5313 / 13,495	1680 / 750	1170 / 520	1.44	0.12 / 3,0	LL510749	LL510710	0.06 / 1,5	0.5000 / 12,700	2.76 / 70,0	2.68 / 68,0	0.06 / 1,5	0.3750 / 9,525	3.39 / 86,0	3.46 / 88,0
2.5000 / 63,500	3.7188 / 94,458	0.7500 / 19,050	3070 / 1365	2220 / 990	1.38	0.02 / 0,6	L610549	L610510	0.06 / 1,5	0.7500 / 19,050	2.80 / 71,0	2.72 / 69,0	0.06 / 1,5	0.5938 / 15,083	3.39 / 86,0	3.58 / 91,0
2.5000 / 63,500	4.2188 / 107,158	0.8661 / 22,000	3880 / 1725	2570 / 1145	1.51	-0.06 / -1,6	39250	39422	0.08 / 2,0	0.8661 / 22,000	2.87 / 73,0	2.72 / 69,0	0.09 / 2,3	0.8348 / 21,204	3.82 / 97,0	4.02 / 102,0
2.5000 / 63,500	4.2500 / 107,950	1.0000 / 25,400	4650 / 2080	3670 / 1630	1.27	-0.03 / -0,8	29586	29520	0.06 / 1,5	1.0000 / 25,400	2.87 / 73,0	2.80 / 71,0	0.13 / 3,3	0.7500 / 19,050	3.78 / 96,0	4.06 / 103,0
2.5000 / 63,500	4.3307 / 110,000	0.8661 / 22,000	4000 / 1790	2770 / 1235	1.45	-0.03 / -0,8	390A	394A	0.06 / 1,5	0.8660 / 21,996	2.87 / 73,0	2.76 / 70,0	0.05 / 1,3	0.7411 / 18,824	3.98 / 101,0	4.11 / 104,5
2.5000 / 63,500	4.3307 / 110,000	0.8661 / 22,000	4000 / 1790	2770 / 1235	1.45	-0.03 / -0,8	395	394A	0.14 / 3,5	0.8660 / 21,996	3.03 / 77,0	2.76 / 70,0	0.05 / 1,3	0.7411 / 18,824	3.98 / 101,0	4.11 / 104,5
2.5000 / 63,500	4.3307 / 110,000	1.0000 / 25,400	4650 / 2080	3670 / 1630	1.27	-0.03 / -0,8	29585	29521	0.14 / 3,5	1.0000 / 25,400	3.03 / 77,0	2.80 / 71,0	0.05 / 1,3	0.7500 / 19,050	3.90 / 99,0	4.09 / 104,0

bore	outside diameter	width	rating at 500 RPM for 3000 hours L10		fac-tor	eff. load center	part numbers		cone				cup			
			one row radial	thrust					max. shaft fillet radius	width	backing shoulder diameters		max. housing fillet radius	width	backing shoulder	
d	D	T	lb daN	lb daN	K	a	cone	cup	R	B	d_b	d_a	r	C	D_b	D_a
2.5000 63,500	4.3330 110,058	0.8661 22,000	3880 1725	2570 1145	1.51	−0.06 −1,6	39250	39433	0.08 2,0	0.8661 22,000	2.87 73,0	2.72 69,0	0.09 2,3	0.6786 17,236	3.86 98,0	4.06 103,0
2.5000 63,500	4.4375 112,712	1.1875 30,162	5900 2620	4050 1800	1.45	−0.18 −4,6	3982	3925	0.14 3,5	1.1830 30,048	3.03 77,0	2.80 71,0	0.03 0,8	0.9375 23,812	3.98 101,0	4.17 106,0
2.5000 63,500	4.4375 112,712	1.1875 30,162	7000 3100	4050 1800	1.72	−0.26 −6,6	39585	39521	0.14 3,5	1.1875 30,162	3.03 77,0	2.80 71,0	0.03 0,8	0.9375 23,812	4.06 103,0	4.21 107,0
2.5000 63,500	4.4375 112,712	1.1875 30,162	7000 3100	4050 1800	1.72	−0.26 −6,6	39585A	39521	0.03 0,8	1.1875 30,162	2.83 72,0	2.80 71,0	0.03 0,8	0.9375 23,812	4.06 103,0	4.21 107,0
2.5000 63,500	4.7244 120,000	1.1418 29,002	5900 2640	3900 1735	1.52	−0.16 −4,1	477	472A	0.03 0,8	1.1420 29,007	2.87 73,0	2.83 72,0	0.13 3,3	0.9230 23,444	4.17 106,0	4.49 114,0
2.5000 63,500	4.7244 120,000	1.1418 29,002	5900 2640	3900 1735	1.52	−0.16 −4,1	483	472A	0.14 3,5	1.1420 29,007	3.07 78,0	2.83 72,0	0.13 3,3	0.9230 23,444	4.17 106,0	4.49 114,0
2.5000 63,500	4.7244 120,000	1.1730 29,794	5950 2660	4450 1980	1.34	−0.11 −2,8	33251	33472	0.03 0,8	1.1875 30,162	2.87 73,0	2.83 72,0	0.03 0,8	0.9230 23,444	4.21 107,0	4.45 113,0
2.5000 63,500	4.8125 122,238	1.5000 38,100	7900 3520	4700 2080	1.69	−0.37 −9,4	559	553X	0.14 3,5	1.4440 36,678	3.07 78,0	2.83 72,0	0.13 3,3	1.1875 30,162	4.25 108,0	4.53 115,0
2.5000 63,500	4.8125 122,238	1.5000 38,100	9150 4080	5300 2360	1.73	−0.43 −10,9	HM212046	HM212011	0.14 3,5	1.5100 38,354	3.15 80,0	2.87 73,0	0.13 3,3	1.1700 29,718	4.25 108,0	4.57 116,0
2.5000 63,500	4.8125 122,238	1.5000 38,100	9150 4080	5300 2360	1.73	−0.43 −10,9	HM212047	HM212010	0.28 7,0	1.5100 38,354	3.43 87,0	2.87 73,0	0.06 1,5	1.1700 29,718	4.33 110,0	4.57 116,0
2.5000 63,500	4.8125 122,238	1.7188 43,658	10200 4500	6250 2780	1.63	−0.48 −12,1	5584	5535	0.14 3,5	1.7230 43,764	3.19 81,0	2.95 75,0	0.13 3,3	1.4375 36,512	4.17 106,0	4.57 116,0
2.5000 63,500	5.0000 127,000	1.4375 36,512	8250 3660	5100 2280	1.61	−0.32 −8,1	565	563X	0.14 3,5	1.4240 36,170	3.15 80,0	2.87 73,0	0.03 0,8	1.1250 28,575	4.49 114,0	4.72 120,0
2.5000 63,500	5.0000 127,000	1.4375 36,512	8050 3580	6950 3080	1.16	−0.15 −3,8	HM813842	HM813811	0.14 3,5	1.4375 36,512	3.23 82,0	2.99 76,0	0.06 1,5	1.0625 26,988	4.45 113,0	4.76 121,0
2.5000 63,500	5.0000 127,000	1.4375 36,512	8050 3580	6950 3080	1.16	−0.15 −3,8	HM813842A	HM813811	0.03 0,8	1.4375 36,512	3.03 77,0	2.99 76,0	0.06 1,5	1.0625 26,988	4.45 113,0	4.76 121,0
2.5000 63,500	5.1250 130,175	1.6250 41,275	9600 4260	5950 2640	1.61	−0.44 −11,2	639	633	0.14 3,5	1.6250 41,275	3.19 81,0	2.91 74,0	0.13 3,3	1.2500 31,750	4.57 116,0	4.88 124,0
2.5000 63,500	5.3447 135,755	2.1250 53,975	13300 5900	7350 3280	1.80	−0.76 −19,2	6382	6320	0.17 4,3	2.2050 56,007	3.31 84,0	3.03 77,0	0.13 3,3	1.7500 44,450	4.61 117,0	4.96 126,0
2.5000 63,500	5.3750 136,525	1.4375 36,512	6750 3000	10100 4480	0.67	0.31 8,0	78250	78537	0.09 2,3	1.3085 33,236	3.35 85,0	3.11 78,9	0.13 3,3	0.9260 23,520	4.53 115,0	5.12 130,0
2.5000 63,500	5.3750 136,525	1.6250 41,275	10900 4850	6750 3000	1.62	−0.43 −10,9	H414235	H414210	0.14 3,5	1.6250 41,275	3.23 82,0	3.07 78,0	0.13 3,3	1.2500 31,750	4.76 121,0	5.08 129,0
2.5000 63,500	5.3750 136,525	1.8125 46,038	11900 5300	9600 4280	1.24	−0.33 −8,5	H715336	H715311	0.14 3,5	1.8125 46,038	3.43 87,0	3.15 80,0	0.13 3,3	1.4375 36,512	4.65 118,0	5.20 132,0
2.5000 63,500	5.9055 150,000	1.7502 44,455	13200 5850	7350 3260	1.80	−0.47 −11,9	745S	743	0.14 3,5	1.8375 46,672	3.31 84,0	3.03 77,0	0.13 3,3	1.3780 35,000	5.28 134,0	5.59 142,0
2.5575 64,960	5.9055 150,000	2.1260 54,000	14700 6550	9100 4060	1.61	−0.59 −15,1	6464	6424	0.14 3,5	2.1350 54,229	3.43 87,0	3.19 81,0	0.12 3,0	1.7717 45,000	5.08 129,0	5.51 140,0
2.5576 64,963	5.0000 127,000	1.4375 36,512	8250 3660	5100 2280	1.61	−0.32 −8,1	569	563	0.14 3,5	1.4240 36,170	3.19 81,0	2.91 74,0	0.13 3,3	1.1250 28,575	4.41 112,0	4.72 120,0

① These maximum fillet radii will be cleared by the bearing corners.
② Minus value indicates center is inside cone backface.

SINGLE-ROW STRAIGHT BORE—TS

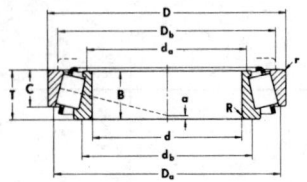

			rating at 500 RPM for 3000 hours L10		fac-tor	eff. load center	part numbers		cone				cup			
bore	outside diameter	width	one row radial	thrust					max. shaft fillet radius	width	backing shoulder diameters		max. hous-ing fillet radius	width	backing shoulder	
d	D	T	lb daN	lb daN	K	a③	cone	cup	R①	B	d_b	d_a	r①	C	D_b	D_a
*2.5591 *65,000	*4.1339 *105,000	0.9449 24,000	4450 1980	3450 1535	1.29	−0.01 −0,3	JLM710949	JLM710910	0.12 3,0	0.9055 23,000	3.03 77,0	2.80 71,0	0.04 1,0	0.7283 18,500	3.78 96,0	3.96 100,5
†2.5591 †65,000	4.2500 107,950	1.0000 25,400	4650 2080	3670 1630	1.27	−0.03 −0,8	29588	29522	0.14 3,5	1.0000 25,400	3.07 78,0	2.83 72,0	0.03 0,8	0.7500 19,050	3.86 98,0	4.06 103,0
*2.5591 *65,000	*4.3307 *110,000	1.1024 28,000	5900 2620	4050 1800	1.45	−0.13 −3,4	JM511946	JM511910	0.12 3,0	1.1024 28,000	3.07 78,0	2.83 72,0	0.10 2,5	0.8858 22,500	3.90 99,0	4.13 105,0
†2.5591 †65,000	4.4375 112,712	1.1875 30,162	7000 3100	4050 1800	1.72	−0.26 −6,6	39586	39521	0.09 2,3	1.2175 30,924	2.99 76,0	2.83 72,0	0.03 0,8	0.9375 23,812	4.06 103,0	4.21 107,0
2.5591 65,000	4.7244 120,000	1.1418 29,002	5900 2640	3900 1735	1.52	−0.16 −4,1	478	472A	0.09 2,3	1.1420 29,007	3.03 77,0	2.87 73,0	0.13 3,3	0.9230 23,444	4.17 106,0	4.49 114,0
*2.5591 *65,000	*4.7244 *120,000	1.5354 39,000	9200 4100	5300 2360	1.73	−0.42 −10,8	JH211749	JH211710	0.12 3,0	1.5157 38,500	3.15 80,0	2.91 74,0	0.10 2,5	1.2598 32,000	4.21 107,0	4.49 114,0
*2.5591 *65,000	*4.7244 *120,000	1.5354 39,000	9200 4100	5300 2360	1.73	−0.42 −10,8	JH211749A	JH211710	0.28 7,0	1.5157 38,500	3.46 88,0	2.91 74,0	0.10 2,5	1.2598 32,000	4.21 107,0	4.49 114,0
†2.5591 †65,000	5.3750 136,525	1.4375 36,512	6750 3000	10100 4480	0.67	0.31 8,0	78255X	78537	0.14 3,5	1.2962 32,923	3.50 89,0	3.11 78,9	0.13 3,3	0.9260 23,520	4.53 115,0	5.12 130,0
2.5625 65,088	5.3447 135,755	2.1250 53,975	13300 5900	7350 3280	1.80	−0.76 −19,2	6379	6320	0.14 3,5	2.2050 56,007	3.31 84,0	3.05 77,4	0.13 3,3	1.7500 44,450	4.61 117,0	4.96 126,0
2.5625 65,088	5.3750 136,525	1.8125 46,038	11900 5300	9600 4280	1.24	−0.33 −8,5	H715340	H715311	0.14 3,5	1.8125 46,038	3.46 88,0	3.23 82,0	0.13 3,3	1.4375 36,512	4.65 118,0	5.20 132,0
2.5938 65,883	4.8125 122,238	1.7188 43,658	10200 4500	6250 2780	1.63	−0.48 −12,1	5595	5535	0.14 3,5	1.7230 43,764	3.27 83,0	3.03 77,0	0.13 3,3	1.4375 36,512	4.17 106,0	4.57 116,0
2.6250 66,675	4.0635 103,213	0.6930 17,602	2800 1245	2340 1040	1.20	0.15 3,7	L812148	L812111	0.06 1,5	0.6930 17,602	2.91 74,0	2.83 72,0	0.03 0,8	0.4720 11,989	3.78 96,0	3.90 99,0
2.6250 66,675	4.2500 107,950	1.0000 25,400	4650 2080	3670 1630	1.27	−0.03 −0,8	29590	29522	0.14 3,5	1.0000 25,400	3.15 80,0	2.87 73,0	0.03 0,8	0.7500 19,050	3.86 98,0	4.06 103,0
2.6250 66,675	4.3307 110,000	0.8661 22,000	4000 1790	2770 1235	1.45	−0.03 −0,8	395A	394A	0.03 0,8	0.8660 21,996	2.87 73,0	2.87 73,0	0.05 1,3	0.7411 18,824	3.98 101,0	4.11 104,5
2.6250 66,675	4.3307 110,000	0.8661 22,000	4000 1790	2770 1235	1.45	−0.03 −0,8	395S	394A	0.14 3,5	0.8660 21,996	3.11 79,0	2.87 73,0	0.05 1,3	0.7411 18,824	3.98 101,0	4.11 104,5
2.6250 66,675	4.4375 112,712	1.1875 30,162	5900 2620	4050 1800	1.45	−0.18 −4,6	3984	3925	0.14 3,5	1.1830 30,048	3.15 80,0	2.91 74,0	0.03 0,8	0.9375 23,812	3.98 101,0	4.17 106,0
2.6250 66,675	4.4375 112,712	1.1875 30,162	5900 2620	4050 1800	1.45	−0.18 −4,6	3994	3925	0.22 5,5	1.1830 30,048	3.31 84,0	2.91 74,0	0.03 0,8	0.9375 23,812	3.98 101,0	4.17 106,0
2.6250 66,675	4.4375 112,712	1.1875 30,162	7000 3100	4050 1800	1.72	−0.26 −6,6	39590	39521	0.14 3,5	1.1875 30,162	3.15 80,0	2.91 74,0	0.03 0,8	0.9375 23,812	4.06 103,0	4.21 107,0
2.6250 66,675	4.4375 112,712	1.1875 30,162	7000 3100	4050 1800	1.72	−0.26 −6,6	39591	39521	0.22 5,5	1.1875 30,162	3.31 84,0	2.91 74,0	0.03 0,8	0.9375 23,812	4.06 103,0	4.21 107,0
2.6250 66,675	4.6250 117,475	1.1875 30,162	5950 2660	4450 1980	1.34	−0.11 −2,8	33262	33462	0.14 3,5	1.1875 30,162	3.19 81,0	2.95 75,0	0.13 3,3	0.9375 23,812	4.09 104,0	4.41 112,0
2.6250 66,675	4.7244 120,000	1.1418 29,002	5900 2640	3900 1735	1.52	−0.16 −4,1	479	472A	0.09 2,3	1.1420 29,007	3.07 78,0	2.91 74,0	0.13 3,3	0.9230 23,444	4.17 106,0	4.49 114,0

			rating at 500 RPM for 3000 hours L10		fac-tor	eff. load center	part numbers		cone				cup			
bore	outside diameter	width	one row radial	thrust			cone	cup	max. shaft fillet radius	width	backing shoulder diameters		max. housing fillet radius	width	backing shoulder	
d	D	T	lb daN	lb daN	K	a②			R①	B	d_b	d_a	r①	C	D_b	D_a
2.6250 / 66,675	4.8125 / 122,238	1.5000 / 38,100	7900 / 3520	4700 / 2080	1.69	-0.37 / -9,4	560	553X	0.14 / 3,5	1.4440 / 36,678	3.19 / 81,0	2.95 / 75,0	0.13 / 3,3	1.1875 / 30,162	4.25 / 108,0	4.53 / 115,0
2.6250 / 66,675	4.8125 / 122,238	1.5000 / 38,100	9150 / 4080	5300 / 2360	1.73	-0.43 / -10,9	HM212049	HM212010	0.14 / 3,5	1.5100 / 38,354	3.23 / 82,0	2.97 / 75,5	0.06 / 1,5	1.1700 / 29,718	4.33 / 110,0	4.57 / 116,0
2.6250 / 66,675	5.0000 / 127,000	1.4375 / 36,512	8050 / 3580	6950 / 3080	1.16	-0.15 / -3,8	HM813844	HM813811	0.14 / 3,5	1.4375 / 36,512	3.35 / 85,0	3.07 / 78,0	0.06 / 1,5	1.0625 / 26,988	4.45 / 113,0	4.76 / 121,0
2.6250 / 66,675	5.1250 / 130,175	1.6250 / 41,275	9600 / 4260	5950 / 2640	1.61	-0.44 / -11,2	641	633	0.14 / 3,5	1.6250 / 41,275	3.27 / 83,0	3.03 / 77,0	0.13 / 3,3	1.2500 / 31,750	4.57 / 116,0	4.88 / 124,0
2.6250 / 66,675	5.3447 / 135,755	2.1250 / 53,975	13300 / 5900	7350 / 3280	1.80	-0.76 / -19,2	6386	6320	0.17 / 4,3	2.2050 / 56,007	3.43 / 87,0	3.05 / 77,4	0.13 / 3,3	1.7500 / 44,450	4.61 / 117,0	4.96 / 126,0
2.6250 / 66,675	5.3447 / 135,755	2.1250 / 53,975	13300 / 5900	7350 / 3280	1.80	-0.76 / -19,2	6389	6320	0.25 / 6,4	2.2050 / 56,007	3.58 / 91,0	3.05 / 77,4	0.13 / 3,3	1.7500 / 44,450	4.61 / 117,0	4.96 / 126,0
2.6250 / 66,675	5.3750 / 136,525	1.6250 / 41,275	10900 / 4850	6750 / 3000	1.62	-0.43 / -10,9	H414242	H414210	0.14 / 3,5	1.6250 / 41,275	3.35 / 85,0	3.19 / 81,0	0.13 / 3,3	1.2500 / 31,750	4.76 / 121,0	5.08 / 129,0
2.6250 / 66,675	5.3750 / 136,525	1.8125 / 46,038	11900 / 5300	9600 / 4280	1.24	-0.33 / -8,5	H715341	H715311	0.14 / 3,5	1.8125 / 46,038	3.50 / 89,0	3.27 / 83,0	0.13 / 3,3	1.4375 / 36,512	4.65 / 118,0	5.20 / 132,0
2.6250 / 66,675	5.3750 / 136,525	1.8125 / 46,038	11900 / 5300	9600 / 4280	1.24	-0.33 / -8,5	H715341A	H715311	0.28 / 7,0	1.8125 / 46,038	3.78 / 96,0	3.27 / 83,0	0.13 / 3,3	1.4375 / 36,512	4.65 / 118,0	5.20 / 132,0
2.6250 / 66,675	7.0000 / 177,800	2.2500 / 57,150	14800 / 6600	20300 / 9000	0.73	-0.01 / -0,3	HH914449	HH914412	0.14 / 3,5	2.1250 / 53,975	4.17 / 106,0	3.36 / 85,3	0.13 / 3,3	1.4688 / 37,308	5.75 / 146,0	6.50 / 165,0
2.6875 / 68,262	4.3307 / 110,000	0.8661 / 22,000	4000 / 1790	2770 / 1235	1.45	-0.03 / -0,8	399A	394A	0.09 / 2,3	0.8660 / 21,996	3.07 / 78,0	2.91 / 74,0	0.05 / 1,3	0.7411 / 18,824	3.98 / 101,0	4.11 / 104,5
2.6875 / 68,262	4.3307 / 110,000	0.8661 / 22,000	4000 / 1790	2770 / 1235	1.45	-0.03 / -0,8	399AS	394A	0.20 / 5,0	0.8660 / 21,996	3.27 / 83,0	2.91 / 74,0	0.05 / 1,3	0.7411 / 18,824	3.98 / 101,0	4.11 / 104,5
2.6875 / 68,262	4.6250 / 117,475	1.1875 / 30,162	5950 / 2660	4450 / 1980	1.34	-0.11 / -2,8	33269	33462	0.14 / 3,5	1.1875 / 30,162	3.23 / 82,0	2.99 / 76,0	0.13 / 3,3	0.9375 / 23,812	4.09 / 104,0	4.41 / 112,0
2.6875 / 68,262	4.7244 / 120,000	1.1418 / 29,002	5900 / 2640	3900 / 1735	1.52	-0.16 / -4,1	480	472A	0.14 / 3,5	1.1420 / 29,007	3.23 / 82,0	2.95 / 75,0	0.13 / 3,3	0.9230 / 23,444	4.17 / 106,0	4.49 / 114,0
2.6875 / 68,262	4.8125 / 122,238	1.5000 / 38,100	7900 / 3520	4700 / 2080	1.69	-0.37 / -9,4	560S	553X	0.14 / 3,5	1.4440 / 36,678	3.27 / 83,0	2.99 / 76,0	0.13 / 3,3	1.1875 / 30,162	4.25 / 108,0	4.53 / 115,0
2.6875 / 68,262	5.1181 / 130,000	1.4542 / 36,937	8250 / 3660	5100 / 2280	1.61	-0.32 / -8,1	570	562X	0.14 / 3,5	1.4240 / 36,170	3.27 / 83,0	3.03 / 77,0	0.12 / 3,0	1.1417 / 29,000	4.49 / 114,0	4.76 / 121,0
2.6875 / 68,262	5.3750 / 136,525	1.6250 / 41,275	10900 / 4850	6750 / 3000	1.62	-0.43 / -10,9	H414245	H414210	0.14 / 3,5	1.6250 / 41,275	3.35 / 86,0	3.23 / 82,0	0.13 / 3,3	1.2500 / 31,750	4.76 / 121,0	5.08 / 129,0
2.6875 / 68,262	5.3750 / 136,525	1.6250 / 41,275	10900 / 4850	6750 / 3000	1.62	-0.43 / -10,9	H414245X	H414210	0.38 / 9,7	1.6250 / 41,275	3.86 / 98,0	3.23 / 82,0	0.13 / 3,3	1.2500 / 31,750	4.76 / 121,0	5.08 / 129,0
2.6875 / 68,262	5.3750 / 136,525	1.8125 / 46,038	11900 / 5300	9600 / 4280	1.24	-0.33 / -8,5	H715343	H715311	0.14 / 3,5	1.8125 / 46,038	3.54 / 90,0	3.31 / 84,0	0.13 / 3,3	1.4375 / 36,512	4.65 / 118,0	5.20 / 132,0
2.6875 / 68,262	6.0000 / 152,400	1.8750 / 47,625	10900 / 4850	12200 / 5450	0.89	-0.15 / -3,7	9185	9121	0.14 / 3,5	1.8125 / 46,038	3.70 / 94,0	3.20 / 81,3	0.13 / 3,3	1.2500 / 31,750	5.12 / 130,0	5.71 / 145,0
2.7500 / 69,850	3.8750 / 98,425	0.5313 / 13,495	1780 / 795	1340 / 595	1.33	0.17 / 4,4	LL713049	LL713010	0.06 / 1,5	0.5313 / 13,495	3.03 / 77,0	2.91 / 74,0	0.06 / 1,5	0.3750 / 9,525	3.62 / 92,0	3.70 / 94,0
2.7500 / 69,850	4.0000 / 101,600	0.7500 / 19,050	3110 / 1385	2450 / 1090	1.27	0.10 / 2,7	L713049	L713010	0.06 / 1,5	0.7500 / 19,050	3.07 / 78,0	2.95 / 75,0	0.06 / 1,5	0.5938 / 15,083	3.66 / 93,0	3.86 / 98,0
2.7500 / 69,850	4.0625 / 103,188	0.7500 / 19,050	3110 / 1385	2450 / 1090	1.27	0.10 / 2,7	L713049	L713012	0.06 / 1,5	0.7500 / 19,050	3.07 / 78,0	2.95 / 75,0	0.06 / 1,5	0.5938 / 15,083	3.70 / 94,0	3.90 / 99,0

① These maximum fillet radii will be cleared by the bearing corners.
② Minus value indicates center is inside cone backface.
†Dimension shown is maximum value—see note at bottom of fitting practice table page 4 in Reference Tables.
*For "J" part tolerances see metric tolerance, page 20 and fitting practice page 6 in Reference Tables.

SINGLE-ROW STRAIGHT BORE—TS

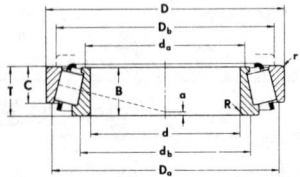

			cone		cup	

| bore | outside diameter | width | rating at 500 RPM for 3000 hours L10 one row radial | thrust | fac-tor | eff. load center | part numbers cone | cup | max. shaft fillet radius R[①] | width B | backing shoulder diameters d_b | d_a | max. hous-ing fillet radius r[①] | width C | backing shoulder D_b | D_a |
d	D	T	lb daN	lb daN	K	a[⊕]										
2.7500 69,850	4.4375 112,712	0.8750 22,225	4150 1840	2950 1315	1.40	0.0 0,0	LM613449	LM613410	0.06 1,5	0.8660 21,996	3.07 78,0	2.99 76,0	0.03 0,8	0.6250 15,875	4.09 104,0	4.21 107,0
2.7500 69,850	4.4375 112,712	1.0000 25,400	4900 2180	4100 1820	1.20	0.04 0,9	29675	29620	0.06 1,5	1.0000 25,400	3.15 80,0	3.03 77,0	0.13 3,3	0.7500 19,050	3.98 101,0	4.29 109,0
2.7500 69,850	4.6250 117,475	1.1875 30,162	5950 2660	4450 1980	1.34	-0.11 -2,8	33275	33462	0.14 3,5	1.1875 30,162	3.31 84,0	3.03 77,0	0.13 3,3	0.9375 23,812	4.09 104,0	4.41 112,0
2.7500 69,850	4.7244 120,000	1.1418 29,002	5900 2640	3900 1735	1.52	-0.16 -4,1	482	472A	0.14 3,5	1.1420 29,007	3.27 83,0	3.03 77,0	0.13 3,3	0.9230 23,444	4.17 106,0	4.49 114,0
2.7500 69,850	4.7244 120,000	1.2813 32,545	7600 3380	4700 2080	1.62	-0.25 -6,3	47487	47420	0.14 3,5	1.2813 32,545	3.31 84,0	3.07 78,0	0.13 3,3	1.0313 26,195	4.21 107,0	4.49 114,0
2.7500 69,850	5.0000 127,000	1.4375 36,512	8250 3660	5100 2280	1.61	-0.32 -8,1	566	563X	0.14 3,5	1.4240 36,170	3.35 85,0	3.07 78,0	0.03 0,8	1.1250 28,575	4.49 114,0	4.72 120,0
2.7500 69,850	5.0000 127,000	1.4375 36,512	8250 3660	5100 2280	1.61	-0.32 -8,1	566S	563X	0.03 0,8	1.4240 36,170	3.11 79,0	3.07 78,0	0.03 0,8	1.1250 28,575	4.49 114,0	4.72 120,0
2.7500 69,850	5.0000 127,000	1.4375 36,512	8050 3580	6950 3080	1.16	-0.15 -3,8	HM813846	HM813811	0.14 3,5	1.4375 36,512	3.46 88,0	3.19 81,0	0.06 1,5	1.0625 26,988	4.45 113,0	4.76 121,0
2.7500 69,850	5.1250 130,175	1.6250 41,275	9600 4260	5950 2640	1.61	-0.44 -11,2	643	633	0.14 3,5	1.6250 41,275	3.39 86,0	3.15 80,0	0.13 3,3	1.2500 31,750	4.57 116,0	4.88 124,0
2.7500 69,850	5.3750 136,525	1.8125 46,038	11900 5300	9600 4280	1.24	-0.33 -8,5	H715344	H715111	0.14 3,5	1.8125 46,038	3.62 92,0	3.35 85,0	0.13 3,3	1.4375 36,512	4.65 118,0	5.20 132,0
2.7500 69,850	5.7500 146,050	1.4375 36,512	6950 3100	11200 5000	0.62	0.50 12,7	HM914545	HM914510	0.16 4,0	1.3125 33,338	3.74 95,0	3.39 86,1	0.13 3,3	0.9375 23,812	4.80 122,0	5.47 139,0
2.7500 69,850	5.7500 146,050	1.6250 41,275	10300 4600	7150 3180	1.43	-0.31 -7,9	655	653	0.14 3,5	1.6250 41,275	3.46 88,0	3.23 82,0	0.13 3,3	1.2500 31,750	5.16 131,0	5.47 139,0
2.7500 69,850	5.7500 146,050	1.6250 41,275	8900 3960	11900 5300	0.75	0.17 4,3	H913849	H913810	0.14 3,5	1.5625 39,688	3.74 95,0	3.24 82,4	0.13 3,3	1.0000 25,400	4.88 124,0	5.43 138,0
2.7500 69,850	5.8750 149,225	2.1250 53,975	14700 6550	9100 4060	1.61	-0.59 -15,1	6454	6420	0.20 5,0	2.1350 54,229	3.70 94,0	3.35 85,0	0.13 3,3	1.7500 44,450	5.08 129,0	5.51 140,0
2.7500 69,850	5.9090 150,089	1.7500 44,450	13200 5850	7350 3260	1.80	-0.47 -11,9	745A	742	0.14 3,5	1.8375 46,672	3.46 88,0	3.23 82,0	0.13 3,3	1.4375 36,512	5.28 134,0	5.59 142,0
2.7500 69,850	6.6250 168,275	2.1250 53,975	16900 7550	8700 3860	1.95	-0.73 -18,4	835	832	0.14 3,5	2.2190 56,363	3.58 91,0	3.31 84,0	0.13 3,3	1.6250 41,275	5.87 149,0	6.10 155,0
2.7540 69,952	4.7812 121,442	0.9688 24,608	4250 1900	3270 1455	1.30	0.06 1,5	34274	34478	0.08 2,0	0.9060 23,012	3.19 81,0	3.07 78,0	0.08 2,0	0.6875 17,462	4.33 110,0	4.57 116,0
*2.7559 *70,000	*4.3307 *110,000	1.0236 26,000	4900 2200	4100 1820	1.20	0.01 0,4	JLM813049	JLM813010	0.04 1,0	0.9843 25,000	3.07 78,0	3.03 77,0	0.10 2,5	0.8071 20,500	3.86 98,0	4.13 105,0
*2.7559 *70,000	*4.5276 *115,000	1.1417 29,000	6150 2740	4500 2020	1.36	-0.10 -2,5	JM612949	JM612910	0.12 3,0	1.1417 29,000	3.27 83,0	3.03 77,0	0.10 2,5	0.9055 23,000	4.06 103,0	4.33 110,0
2.7559 70,000	4.7244 120,000	1.1418 29,002	5900 2640	3900 1735	1.52	-0.16 -4,1	484	472A	0.08 2,0	1.1420 29,007	3.15 80,0	3.03 77,0	0.13 3,3	0.9230 23,444	4.17 106,0	4.49 114,0
2.7559 70,000	4.9233 125,052	0.9343 23,731	4250 1900	3270 1455	1.30	0.06 1,5	34275	34492A	0.08 2,0	0.9060 23,012	3.23 82,0	3.07 78,0	0.08 2,0	0.6457 16,401	4.41 112,0	4.65 118,0

SINGLE-ROW STRAIGHT BORE **TS**

												cone				cup			
bore	outside diameter	width	rating at 500 RPM for 3000 hours L10		fac-tor	eff. load center	part numbers		max. shaft fillet radius	width	backing shoulder diameters		max. hous-ing fillet radius	width	backing shoulder	
			one row radial	thrust			cone	cup								
d	D	T	lb daN	lb daN	K	a③			R①	B	d_b	d_a	r①	C	D_b	D_a
2.7559 70,000	5.8750 149,225	2.1250 53,975	14700 6550	9100 4060	1.61	−0.59 −15,1	6459	6420	0.12 3,0	2.1350 54,229	3.54 90,0	3.35 85,0	0.13 3,3	1.7500 44,450	5.08 129,0	5.51 140,0
†2.7559 †70,000	6.9375 176,212	2.1563 54,770	14400 6450	17200 7650	0.84	−0.08 −2,0	H916642	H916610	0.13 3,3	2.0938 53,183	4.06 103,0	3.74 95,0	0.13 3,3	1.4375 36,512	5.79 147,0	6.46 164,0
2.7810 70,637	4.7500 120,650	1.0000 25,400	4900 2180	4100 1820	1.20	0.04 0,9	29680	29630	0.05 1,3	1.0000 25,400	3.15 80,0	3.07 78,0	0.13 3,3	0.7500 19,050	4.09 104,0	4.45 113,0
2.8125 71,438	4.6250 117,475	1.1875 30,162	5950 2660	4450 1980	1.34	−0.11 −2,8	33281	33462	0.14 3,5	1.1875 30,162	3.35 85,0	3.11 79,0	0.13 3,3	0.9375 23,812	4.09 104,0	4.41 112,0
2.8125 71,438	4.7244 120,000	1.2813 32,545	7600 3380	4700 2080	1.62	−0.25 −6,3	47490	47420	0.14 3,5	1.2813 32,545	3.39 86,0	3.11 79,0	0.13 3,3	1.0313 26,195	4.21 107,0	4.49 114,0
2.8125 71,438	5.0000 127,000	1.4375 36,512	8250 3660	5100 2280	1.61	−0.32 −8,1	567A	563X	0.14 3,5	1.4240 36,170	3.39 86,0	3.15 80,0	0.03 0,8	1.1250 28,575	4.49 114,0	4.72 120,0
2.8125 71,438	5.0000 127,000	1.4375 36,512	8250 3660	5100 2280	1.61	−0.32 −8,1	567S	563X	0.25 6,4	1.4240 36,170	3.62 92,0	3.15 80,0	0.03 0,8	1.1250 28,575	4.49 114,0	4.72 120,0
2.8125 71,438	5.0000 127,000	1.4375 36,512	8050 3580	6950 3080	1.16	−0.15 −3,8	HM813849	HM813811	0.14 3,5	1.4375 36,512	3.50 89,0	3.22 81,9	0.06 1,5	1.0625 26,988	4.45 113,0	4.76 121,0
2.8125 71,438	5.1250 130,175	1.6250 41,275	9600 4260	5950 2640	1.61	−0.44 −11,2	644	633	0.14 3,5	1.6250 41,275	3.43 87,0	3.19 81,0	0.13 3,3	1.2500 31,750	4.57 116,0	4.88 124,0
2.8125 71,438	5.1250 130,175	1.6250 41,275	9600 4260	5950 2640	1.61	−0.44 −11,2	645	633	0.25 6,4	1.6250 41,275	3.66 93,0	3.19 81,0	0.13 3,3	1.2500 31,750	4.57 116,0	4.88 124,0
2.8125 71,438	5.2500 133,350	1.1875 30,162	6550 2920	5000 2220	1.31	−0.03 −0,8	495S	492A	0.14 3,5	1.1720 29,769	3.46 88,0	3.23 82,0	0.13 3,3	0.8750 22,225	4.72 120,0	5.04 128,0
2.8125 71,438	5.2500 133,350	1.3125 33,338	7850 3500	5450 2420	1.44	−0.17 −4,3	47675	47620A	0.14 3,5	1.3125 33,338	3.46 88,0	3.23 82,0	0.03 0,8	1.0313 26,195	4.76 121,0	5.04 128,0
2.8125 71,438	5.3750 136,525	1.6250 41,275	10900 4850	6750 3000	1.62	−0.43 −10,9	H414249	H414210	0.14 3,5	1.6250 41,275	3.50 89,0	3.28 83,3	0.13 3,3	1.2500 31,750	4.76 121,0	5.08 129,0
2.8125 71,438	5.3750 136,525	1.8125 46,038	11900 5300	9600 4280	1.24	−0.33 −8,5	H715345	H715311	0.14 3,5	1.8125 46,038	3.66 93,0	3.43 87,0	0.13 3,3	1.4375 36,512	4.65 118,0	5.20 132,0
2.8125 71,438	5.7500 146,050	1.4375 36,512	6950 3100	11200 5000	0.62	0.50 12,7	HM914949	HM914910	0.16 4,0	1.3125 33,338	3.78 96,0	3.39 86,1	0.13 3,3	0.9375 23,812	4.80 122,0	5 47 139,0
2.8750 73,025	4.4375 112,712	1.0000 25,400	4900 2180	4100 1820	1.20	0.04 0,9	29685	29620	0.14 3,5	1.0000 25,400	3.39 86,0	3.15 80,0	0.13 3,3	0.7500 19,050	3.98 101,0	4.29 109,0
2.8750 73,025	4.6250 117,475	1.0000 25,400	5150 2280	4450 1980	1.15	0.09 2,2	LM814845	LM814810	0.14 3,5	1.0000 25,400	3.43 87,0	3.19 81,0	0.13 3,3	0.7500 19,050	4.13 105,0	4.35 113,0
2.8750 73,025	4.6250 117,475	1.1875 30,162	5950 2660	4450 1980	1.34	−0.11 −2,8	33287	33462	0.14 3,5	1.1875 30,162	3.43 87,0	3.15 80,0	0.13 3,3	0.9375 23,812	4.09 104,0	4.41 112,0
2.8750 73,025	4.9375 125,412	1.0000 25,400	5150 2300	3690 1640	1.40	0.02 0,5	27680	27620	0.14 3,5	1.0000 25,400	3.46 88,0	3.23 82,0	0.06 1,5	0.7813 19,845	4.53 115,0	4.72 120,0
2.8750 73,025	5.0000 127,000	1.1875 30,162	6750 3000	4850 2160	1.39	−0.11 −2,8	42683	42620	0.14 3,5	1.2205 31,000	3.46 88,0	3.19 81,0	0.13 3,3	0.8750 22,225	4.49 114,0	4.76 121,0
2.8750 73,025	5.0000 127,000	1.4375 36,512	8250 3660	5100 2280	1.61	−0.32 −8,1	567	563X	0.14 3,5	1.4240 36,170	3.46 88,0	3.19 81,0	0.03 0,8	1.1250 28,575	4.49 114,0	4.72 120,0
2.8750 73,025	5.0000 127,000	1.4375 36,512	8250 3660	5100 2280	1.61	−0.32 −8,1	567X	563X	0.19 4,8	1.4240 36,170	3.54 90,0	3.19 81,0	0.03 0,8	1.1250 28,575	4.49 114,0	4.72 120,0
2.8750 73,025	5.5000 139,700	1.4375 36,512	8800 3920	6100 2700	1.45	−0.21 −5,3	576	572X	0.14 3,5	1.4212 36,098	3.54 90,0	3.27 83,0	0.13 3,3	1.1250 28,575	4.92 125,0	5.24 133,0

① These maximum fillet radii will be cleared by the bearing corners.
③ Minus value indicates center is inside cone backface.
† Dimension shown is maximum value—see note at bottom of fitting practice table page 4 in Reference Tables.
* For "J" part tolerances see metric tolerance, page 20 and fitting practice page 6 in Reference Tables.

SINGLE-ROW STRAIGHT BORE—TS

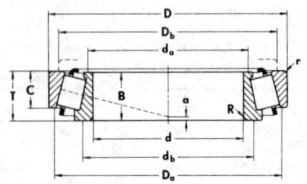

			cone							cone				cup		
bore	outside diameter	width	rating at 500 RPM for 3000 hours L10		fac-tor	eff. load center	part numbers		max. shaft fillet radius	width	backing shoulder diameters		max. hous-ing fillet radius	width	backing shoulder	
			one row radial	thrust												
d	D	T	lb daN	lb daN	K	a[①]	cone	cup	R[①]	B	d_b	d_a	r[①]	C	D_b	D_a
2.8750 73,025	5.8750 149,225	2.1250 53,975	14700 6550	9100 4060	1.61	−0.59 −15,1	6460	6420	0.14 3,5	2.1350 54,229	3.66 93,0	3.43 87,0	0.13 3,3	1.7500 44,450	5.08 129,0	5.51 140,0
2.8750 73,025	5.9055 150,000	1.7502 44,455	13200 5850	7350 3260	1.80	−0.47 −11,9	744	743	0.14 3,5	1.8375 46,672	3.58 91,0	3.35 85,0	0.13 3,3	1.3780 35,000	5.28 134,0	5.59 142,0
2.8750 73,025	6.3750 161,925	1.8750 47,625	13800 6100	8050 3580	1.71	−0.47 −11,9	762XA	752	0.14 3,5	1.9000 48,260	3.62 92,0	3.39 86,0	0.13 3,3	1.5000 38,100	5.67 144,0	5.91 150,0
2.9062 73,817	4.4375 112,712	1.0000 25,400	4900 2180	4100 1820	1.20	0.04 0,9	29688	29620	0.06 1,5	1.0000 25,400	3.27 83,0	3.19 81,0	0.13 3,3	0.7500 19,050	3.98 101,0	4.29 109,0
2.9062 73,817	5.0000 127,000	1.4375 36,512	8250 3660	5100 2280	1.61	−0.32 −8,1	568	563X	0.03 0,8	1.4240 36,170	3.27 83,0	3.23 82,0	0.03 0,8	1.1250 28,575	4.49 114,0	4.72 120,0
2.9375 74,612	5.5115 139,992	1.4375 36,512	8800 3920	6100 2700	1.45	−0.21 −5,3	577	572	0.14 3,5	1.4212 36,098	3.58 91,0	3.35 85,0	0.13 3,3	1.1250 28,575	4.92 125,0	5.24 133,0
2.9375 74,612	5.9055 150,000	1.6250 41,275	10300 4600	7150 3180	1.43	−0.31 −7,9	658	653X	0.14 3,5	1.6250 41,275	3.62 92,0	3.39 86,0	0.12 3,0	1.2500 31,750	5.24 133,0	5.55 141,0
*2.9528 *75,000	*4.5276 *115,000	0.9843 25,000	4950 2200	3900 1735	1.27	0.02 0,4	JLM714149	JLM714110	0.12 3,0	0.9843 25,000	3.43 87,0	3.19 81,0	0.10 2,5	0.7480 19,000	4.09 104,0	4.33 110,0
*2.9528 *75,000	*4.7244 *120,000	1.2205 31,000	6750 3020	5150 2300	1.31	−0.08 −2,0	JM714249	JM714210	0.12 3,0	1.1614 29,500	3.46 88,0	3.26 82,9	0.10 2,5	0.9843 25,000	4.25 108,0	4.53 115,0
*2.9528 *75,000	*5.7087 *145,000	2.0079 51,000	14700 6550	9100 4060	1.61	−0.56 −14,4	JH415647	JH415610	0.12 3,0	2.0079 51,000	3.70 94,0	3.50 89,0	0.10 2,5	1.6535 42,000	5.08 129,0	5.47 139,0
3.0000 76,200	4.1563 105,570	0.5313 13,495	1840 820	1480 660	1.24	0.26 6,5	LL714649	LL714610	0.06 1,5	0.5313 13,495	3.27 83,0	3.19 81,0	0.06 1,5	0.3750 9,525	3.90 99,0	4.02 102,0
3.0000 76,200	4.3125 109,538	0.7500 19,050	3270 1455	2820 1255	1.16	0.20 5,0	L814749	L814710	0.06 1,5	0.7500 19,050	3.31 84,0	3.23 82,0	0.06 1,5	0.5938 15,083	3.94 100,0	4.13 105,0
3.0000 76,200	4.7812 121,442	0.9688 24,608	4250 1900	3270 1455	1.30	0.06 1,5	34301	34478	0.14 3,5	0.9060 23,012	3.50 89,0	3.27 83,0	0.08 2,0	0.6875 17,462	4.33 110,0	4.57 116,0
3.0000 76,200	4.9375 125,412	1.0000 25,400	5150 2300	3690 1640	1.40	0.02 0,5	27684	27620	0.14 3,5	1.0000 25,400	3.58 91,0	3.31 84,0	0.06 1,5	0.7813 19,845	4.53 115,0	4.72 120,0
3.0000 76,200	5.0000 127,000	1.0625 26,988	4250 1900	3270 1455	1.30	0.06 1,5	34300	34500	0.08 2,0	0.9060 23,012	3.39 86,0	3.27 83,0	0.13 3,3	0.7812 19,842	4.41 112,0	4.65 118,0
3.0000 76,200	5.0000 127,000	1.1875 30,162	6750 3000	4850 2160	1.39	−0.11 −2,8	42687	42620	0.14 3,5	1.2205 31,000	3.54 90,0	3.31 84,0	0.13 3,3	0.8750 22,225	4.49 114,0	4.76 121,0
3.0000 76,200	5.0000 127,000	1.1875 30,162	6750 3000	4850 2160	1.39	−0.11 −2,8	42688	42620	0.25 6,4	1.2205 31,000	3.78 96,0	3.31 84,0	0.13 3,3	0.8750 22,225	4.49 114,0	4.76 121,0
3.0000 76,200	5.2500 133,350	1.1875 30,162	6550 2920	5000 2220	1.31	−0.03 −0,8	495AX	492A	0.25 6,4	1.1720 29,769	3.86 98,0	3.39 86,0	0.13 3,3	0.8750 22,225	4.72 120,0	5.04 128,0
3.0000 76,200	5.2500 133,350	1.3125 33,338	7850 3500	5450 2420	1.44	−0.17 −4,3	47678	47620A	0.25 6,4	1.3125 33,338	3.82 97,0	3.35 85,0	0.03 0,8	1.0313 26,195	4.76 121,0	5.04 128,0
3.0000 76,200	5.2500 133,350	1.3125 33,338	7850 3500	5450 2420	1.44	−0.17 −4,3	47679	47620A	0.14 3,5	1.3125 33,338	3.58 91,0	3.35 85,0	0.08 1,8	1.0313 26,195	4.76 121,0	5.04 128,0
3.0000 76,200	5.2500 133,350	1.3125 33,338	7850 3500	5450 2420	1.44	−0.17 −4,3	47680	47620	0.03 0,8	1.3125 33,338	3.39 86,0	3.35 85,0	0.13 3,3	1.0313 26,195	4.69 119,0	5.04 128,0

SINGLE-ROW STRAIGHT BORE **TS**

							cone		cone				cup			
			rating at 500 RPM for 3000 hours L10		fac-tor	eff. load center	part numbers		max. shaft fillet radius	width	backing shoulder diameters		max. hous-ing fillet radius	width	backing shoulder	
bore	outside diameter	width	one row radial	thrust			cone	cup								
d	D	T	lb daN	lb daN	K	a②	cone	cup	R①	B	d_b	d_a	r①	C	D_b	D_a
3.0000 76,200	5.2500 133,350	1.5625 39,688	10000 4440	6900 3060	1.45	−0.29 −7,4	HM516442	HM516410	0.14 3,5	1.5625 39,688	3.66 93,0	3.43 87,0	0.13 3,3	1.2813 32,545	4.65 118,0	5.04 128,0
3.0000 76,200	5.3438 135,733	1.7500 44,450	11200 5000	7800 3480	1.44	−0.46 −11,7	5760	5735	0.14 3,5	1.8150 46,101	3.70 94,0	3.46 88,0	0.13 3,3	1.3750 34,925	4.69 119,0	5.12 130,0
3.0000 76,200	5.3750 136,525	1.1875 30,162	6550 2920	5000 2220	1.31	−0.03 −0,8	495A	493	0.14 3,5	1.1720 29,769	3.62 92,0	3.39 86,0	0.13 3,3	0.8750 22,225	4.80 122,0	5.12 130,0
3.0000 76,200	5.5000 139,700	1.4375 36,512	8800 3920	6100 2700	1.45	−0.21 −5,3	575	572X	0.14 3,5	1.4212 36,098	3.62 92,0	3.39 86,0	0.13 3,3	1.1250 28,575	4.92 125,0	5.24 133,0
3.0000 76,200	5.5000 139,700	1.4375 36,512	8800 3920	6100 2700	1.45	−0.21 −5,3	575S	572X	0.27 6,8	1.4212 36,098	3.90 99,0	3.39 86,0	0.13 3,3	1.1250 28,575	4.92 125,0	5.24 133,0
3.0000 76,200	5.8125 147,638	1.4062 35,717	9350 4160	7100 3160	1.32	−0.10 −2,5	590A	592XE	0.14 3,5	1.4300 36,322	3.74 95,0	3.50 89,0	0.03 0,8	1.0312 26,192	5.31 135,0	5.59 142,0
3.0000 76,200	5.8750 149,225	2.1250 53,975	14700 6550	9100 4060	1.61	−0.59 −15,1	6461	6420	0.14 3,5	2.1350 54,229	3.78 96,0	3.52 89,5	0.13 3,3	1.7500 44,450	5.08 129,0	5.51 140,0
3.0000 76,200	5.8750 149,225	2.1250 53,975	14700 6550	9100 4060	1.61	−0.59 −15,1	6461A	6420	0.38 9,7	2.1350 54,229	4.25 108,0	3.52 89,5	0.13 3,3	1.7500 44,450	5.08 129,0	5.51 140,0
3.0000 76,200	5.9055 150,000	1.7502 44,455	13200 5850	7350 3260	1.80	−0.47 −11,9	748S	743	0.14 3,5	1.8375 46,672	3.66 93,0	3.43 87,0	0.13 3,3	1.3780 35,000	5.28 134,0	5.59 142,0
3.0000 76,200	6.0000 152,400	1.6250 41,275	10300 4600	7150 3180	1.43	−0.31 −7,9	659	652	0.14 3,5	1.6250 41,275	3.66 93,0	3.43 87,0	0.13 3,3	1.2500 31,750	5.28 134,0	5.55 141,0
3.0000 76,200	6.2992 160,000	2.1250 53,975	16000 7150	11000 4900	1.46	−0.52 −13,1	6576	6525X	0.14 3,5	2.1693 55,100	3.90 99,0	3.62 92,0	0.12 3,0	1.7500 44,450	5.55 141,0	6.04 153,4
3.0000 76,200	6.3750 161,925	1.9375 49,212	11500 5100	14000 6200	0.82	0.0 0,0	9285	9220	0.14 3,5	1.8125 46,038	4.06 103,0	3.56 90,4	0.13 3,3	1.2500 31,750	5.43 138,0	6.03 153,0
3.0000 76,200	6.3750 161,925	2.1250 53,975	16000 7150	11000 4900	1.46	−0.52 −13,1	6575	6536	0.25 6,4	2.1693 55,100	4.09 104,0	3.62 92,0	0.03 0,8	1.6875 42,862	5.67 144,0	6.06 154,0
3.0000 76,200	6.6250 168,275	1.8750 47,625	13800 6100	8050 3580	1.71	−0.47 −11,9	755	753	0.14 3,5	1.9000 48,260	3.74 95,0	3.46 88,0	0.13 3,3	1.5000 38,100	5.79 147,0	5.91 150,0
3.0000 76,200	6.6250 168,275	2.1250 53,975	16900 7550	8700 3860	1.95	−0.73 −18,4	837	832	0.03 0,8	2.2190 56,363	3.54 90,0	3.50 89,0	0.13 3,3	1.6250 41,275	5.87 149,0	6.10 155,0
3.0000 76,200	6.6250 168,275	2.1250 53,975	16900 7550	8700 3860	1.95	−0.73 −18,4	843	832	0.25 6,4	2.2190 56,363	3.98 101,0	3.50 89,0	0.13 3,3	1.6250 41,275	5.87 149,0	6.10 155,0
3.0000 76,200	6.7500 171,450	1.9375 49,212	12000 5350	15800 7000	0.76	0.17 4,4	9380	9321	0.14 3,5	1.8125 46,038	4.13 105,0	3.87 98,2	0.13 3,3	1.2500 31,750	5.79 147,0	6.46 164,0
3.0000 76,200	7.0000 177,800	2.1875 55,562	12000 5350	15800 7000	0.76	0.05 1,3	9378	9320	0.14 3,5	2.0000 50,800	4.13 105,0	3.87 98,2	0.13 3,3	1.3750 34,925	5.83 148,0	6.46 164,0
3.0000 76,200	7.1250 180,975	2.1250 53,975	15100 6700	18900 8400	0.80	0.02 0,5	H917840	H917810	0.14 3,5	2.0938 53,183	4.33 110,0	3.94 100,1	0.13 3,3	1.4063 35,720	5.98 152,0	6.69 170,0
3.0000 76,200	7.5000 190,500	2.2500 57,150	22000 9750	12600 5600	1.74	−0.59 −15,0	HH221430	HH221410	0.14 3,5	2.2650 57,531	3.98 101,0	3.74 95,0	0.13 3,3	1.8125 46,038	6.73 171,0	7.05 179,0
3.0625 77,788	5.1875 120,650	1.0938 27,783	5150 2280	4450 1980	1.15	0.09 2,2	LM814849	LM814814	0.14 3,5	1.0000 25,400	3.58 91,0	3.35 85,0	0.13 3,3	1.0313 26,195	4.21 107,0	4.56 115,8
3.0625 77,788	4.7812 121,442	0.9688 24,608	4250 1900	3270 1455	1.30	0.06 1,5	34306	34478	0.14 3,5	0.9060 23,012	3.54 90,0	3.31 84,0	0.08 2,0	0.6875 17,462	4.33 110,0	4.57 116,0
3.0625 77,788	4.7812 121,442	0.9688 24,608	4250 1900	3270 1455	1.30	0.06 1,5	34307	34478	0.25 6,4	0.9060 23,012	3.78 96,0	3.31 84,0	0.08 2,0	0.6875 17,462	4.33 110,0	4.57 116,0

① These maximum fillet radii will be cleared by the bearing corners.
② Minus value indicates center is inside cone backface.
*For "J" part tolerances see metric tolerance, page 20 and fitting practice page 6 in Reference Tables.

SINGLE-ROW STRAIGHT BORE—TS

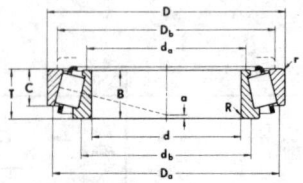

bore	outside diameter	width	rating at 500 RPM for 3000 hours L10		factor	eff. load center	part numbers		max. shaft fillet radius	width	backing shoulder diameters		max. housing fillet radius	width	backing shoulder	
			one row radial	thrust			cone	cup								
d	D	T	lb daN	lb daN	K	a[2]	cone	cup	R[1]	B	d_b	d_a	r[1]	C	D_b	D_a
3.0625 77,788	5.0000 127,000	1.1875 30,162	6750 3000	4850 2160	1.39	−0.11 −2,8	42690	42620	0.14 3,5	1.2205 31,000	3.58 91,0	3.35 85,0	0.13 3,3	0.8750 22,225	4.49 114,0	4.76 121,0
3.0625 77,788	5.2500 133,350	1.1875 30,162	6550 2920	5000 2220	1.31	−0.03 −0,8	495AS	492A	0.14 3,5	1.1720 29,769	3.66 93,0	3.43 87,0	0.13 3,3	0.8750 22,225	4.72 120,0	5.04 128,0
3.0625 77,788	5.3438 135,733	1.7500 44,450	11200 5000	7800 3480	1.44	−0.33 −11,7	5795	5735	0.14 3,5	1.8150 46,101	3.78 96,0	3.50 89,0	0.13 3,3	1.3750 34,925	4.69 119,0	5.12 130,0
3.0625 77,788	5.3750 136,525	1.8125 46,038	11900 5300	9600 4280	1.24	−0.33 −8,5	H715348	H715311	0.14 3,5	1.8125 46,038	3.86 98,0	3.48 88,5	0.13 3,3	1.4375 36,512	5.20 132,0	5.20 132,0
3.1250 79,375	5.7500 146,050	1.6250 41,275	10300 4600	7150 3180	1.43	−0.31 −7,9	661	653	0.14 3,5	1.6250 41,275	3.78 96,0	3.54 90,0	0.13 3,3	1.2500 31,750	5.16 131,0	5.47 139,0
3.1250 79,375	5.8125 147,638	1.4062 35,717	9350 4160	7100 3160	1.32	−0.10 −2,5	595A	592XS	0.14 3,5	1.4300 36,322	3.86 98,0	3.58 91,0	0.13 3,3	1.0312 26,192	5.24 133,0	5.59 142,0
3.1250 79,375	5.9055 150,000	1.7502 44,455	13200 5850	7350 3260	1.80	−0.47 −11,9	750	743	0.14 3,5	1.8375 46,672	3.78 96,0	3.54 90,0	0.13 3,3	1.3780 35,000	5.28 134,0	5.59 142,0
3.1250 79,375	6.3750 161,925	1.8750 47,625	13800 6100	8050 3580	1.71	−0.47 −11,9	756A	752	0.31 8,0	1.9000 48,260	4.17 106,0	3.58 91,0	0.13 3,3	1.5000 38,100	5.67 144,0	5.91 150,0
3.1250 79,375	7.5000 190,500	2.2500 57,150	22000 9750	12600 5600	1.74	−0.59 −15,0	HH221431	HH221410	0.14 3,5	2.2650 57,531	4.06 103,0	3.82 97,0	0.13 3,3	1.8125 46,038	6.73 171,0	7.05 179,0
*3.1496 *80,000	*5.1181 *130,000	1.3780 35,000	8550 3800	5700 2540	1.50	−0.20 −5,2	JM515649	JM515610	0.12 3,0	1.3386 34,000	3.70 94,0	3.46 88,0	0.10 2,5	1.1220 28,500	4.61 117,0	4.92 125,0
†3.1496 †80,000	*5.7874 †147,000	1.5748 40,000	11700 5200	6650 2960	1.76	−0.34 −8,6	HM218238	HM218210	0.28 7,0	1.5748 40,000	4.09 104,0	3.58 91,0	0.14 3,5	1.2795 32,500	5.24 133,0	5.55 141,0
3.1496 80,000	7.8740 200,000	2.0772 52,761	16500 7350	17900 8000	0.92	0.05 1,3	98316	98788	0.14 3,5	1.9375 49,212	4.37 111,0	4.13 105,0	0.13 3,3	1.3750 34,925	6.85 174,0	7.40 188,0
3.1875 80,962	5.2500 133,350	1.1875 30,162	6550 2920	5000 2220	1.31	−0.03 −0,8	496	492A	0.14 3,5	1.1720 29,769	3.74 95,0	3.50 89,0	0.13 3,3	0.8750 22,225	4.72 120,0	5.04 128,0
3.1875 80,962	5.2500 133,350	1.3125 33,338	7850 3500	5450 2420	1.44	−0.17 −4,3	47681	47620A	0.14 3,5	1.3125 33,338	3.74 95,0	3.50 89,0	0.03 0,8	1.0313 26,195	4.76 121,0	5.04 128,0
3.1875 80,962	5.2500 133,350	1.5625 39,688	10000 4440	6900 3060	1.45	−0.29 −7,4	HM516447	HM516410	0.14 3,5	1.5625 39,688	3.82 97,0	3.58 91,0	0.13 3,3	1.2813 32,545	4.65 118,0	5.04 128,0
3.1875 80,962	5.5000 139,700	1.4375 36,512	8800 3920	6100 2700	1.45	−0.21 −5,3	581	572X	0.14 3,5	1.4212 36,098	3.78 96,0	3.54 90,0	0.13 3,3	1.1250 28,575	4.92 125,0	5.24 133,0
3.1875 80,962	5.9055 150,000	1.7502 44,455	13200 5850	7350 3260	1.80	−0.47 −11,9	740	743	0.20 5,0	1.8375 46,672	3.98 101,0	3.58 91,0	0.13 3,3	1.3780 35,000	5.28 134,0	5.59 142,0
3.1875 80,962	6.6250 168,275	2.1250 53,975	16900 7550	8700 3860	1.95	−0.73 −18,4	838	832	0.03 0,8	2.2190 56,363	3.70 94,0	3.66 93,0	0.13 3,3	1.6250 41,275	5.87 149,0	6.10 155,0
3.2500 82,550	4.5625 115,888	0.8125 20,638	4150 1840	2170 965	1.90	−0.05 −1,3	L116149	L116110	0.06 1,5	0.8438 21,433	3.54 90,0	3.46 88,0	0.06 1,5	0.6563 16,670	4.25 108,0	4.37 111,0
3.2500 82,550	4.9375 125,412	1.0000 25,400	5150 2300	3690 1640	1.40	0.02 0,5	27687	27620	0.14 3,5	1.0000 25,400	3.78 96,0	3.50 89,0	0.06 1,5	0.7813 19,845	4.53 115,0	4.72 120,0
3.2500 82,550	5.2500 133,350	1.1875 30,162	6550 2920	5000 2220	1.31	−0.03 −0,8	495	492A	0.14 3,5	1.1720 29,769	3.82 97,0	3.54 90,0	0.13 3,3	0.8750 22,225	4.72 120,0	5.04 128,0

SINGLE-ROW STRAIGHT BORE

TS

			rating at 500 RPM for 3000 hours L10		fac-tor	eff. load center	part numbers		cone				cup			
			one row radial	thrust					max. shaft fillet radius	width	backing shoulder diameters		max. hous-ing fillet radius	width	backing shoulder	
bore	outside diameter	width					cone	cup								
d	D	T	lb daN	lb daN	K	a②			R①	B	d_b	d_a	r①	C	D_b	D_a
3.2500 82,550	5.2500 133,350	1.3125 33,338	7850 3500	5450 2420	1.44	−0.17 −4,3	47685	47620A	0.03 0,8	1.3125 33,338	3.58 91,0	3.54 90,0	0.03 0,8	1.0313 26,195	4.76 121,0	5.04 128,0
3.2500 82,550	5.2500 133,350	1.3125 33,338	7850 3500	5450 2420	1.44	−0.17 −4,3	47686	47620A	0.14 3,5	1.3125 33,338	3.82 97,0	3.54 90,0	0.03 0,8	1.0313 26,195	4.76 121,0	5.04 128,0
3.2500 82,550	5.2500 133,350	1.3125 33,338	7850 3500	5450 2420	1.44	−0.17 −4,3	47687	47620A	0.27 6,8	1.3125 33,338	4.06 103,0	3.54 90,0	0.03 0,8	1.0313 26,195	4.76 121,0	5.04 128,0
3.2500 82,550	5.2500 133,350	1.5625 39,688	10000 4440	6900 3060	1.45	−0.29 −7,4	HM516448	HM516410	0.27 6,8	1.5625 39,688	4.13 105,0	3.62 92,0	0.13 3,3	1.2813 32,545	4.65 118,0	5.04 128,0
3.2500 82,550	5.2500 133,350	1.5625 39,688	10000 4440	6900 3060	1.45	−0.29 −7,4	HM516449	HM516410	0.14 3,5	1.5625 39,688	3.90 99,0	3.62 92,0	0.13 3,3	1.2813 32,545	4.65 118,0	5.04 128,0
3.2500 82,550	5.5000 139,700	1.4375 36,512	8800 3920	6100 2700	1.45	−0.21 −5,3	580	572X	0.14 3,5	1.4212 36,098	3.86 98,0	3.58 91,0	0.13 3,3	1.1250 28,575	4.92 125,0	5.24 133,0
3.2500 82,550	5.5000 139,700	1.4375 36,512	8800 3920	6100 2700	1.45	−0.21 −5,3	582	572X	0.27 6,8	1.4212 36,098	4.09 104,0	3.58 91,0	0.13 3,3	1.1250 28,575	4.92 125,0	5.24 133,0
3.2500 82,550	5.7500 146,050	1.6250 41,275	10300 4600	7150 3180	1.43	−0.31 −7,9	663	653	0.14 3,5	1.6250 41,275	3.90 99,0	3.62 92,0	0.13 3,3	1.2500 31,750	5.16 131,0	5.47 139,0
3.2500 82,550	5.7500 146,050	1.6250 41,275	10300 4600	7150 3180	1.43	−0.31 −7,9	663A	653	0.27 6,8	1.6250 41,275	4.13 105,0	3.62 92,0	0.13 3,3	1.2500 31,750	5.16 131,0	5.47 139,0
3.2500 82,550	5.9055 150,000	1.4170 35,992	9350 4160	7100 3160	1.32	−0.10 −2,5	595	593X	0.14 3,5	1.4300 36,322	3.94 100,0	3.66 93,0	0.12 3,0	1.0630 27,000	5.28 134,0	5.59 142,0
3.2500 82,550	5.9055 150,000	1.7502 44,455	13200 5850	7350 3260	1.80	−0.47 −11,9	749A	743	0.14 3,5	1.8375 46,672	3.90 99,0	3.66 93,0	0.13 3,3	1.3780 35,000	5.28 134,0	5.59 142,0
3.2500 82,550	5.9055 150,000	1.7502 44,455	13200 5850	7350 3260	1.80	−0.47 −11,9	750A	743	0.27 6,8	1.8375 46,672	4.17 106,0	3.66 93,0	0.13 3,3	1.3780 35,000	5.28 134,0	5.59 142,0
3.2500 82,550	6.3750 161,925	1.8750 47,625	13800 6100	8050 3580	1.71	−0.47 −11,9	757	752	0.14 3,5	1.9000 48,260	3.94 100,0	3.70 94,0	0.13 3,3	1.5000 38,100	5.67 144,0	5.91 150,0
3.2500 82,550	6.3750 161,925	2.1250 53,975	16000 7150	11000 4900	1.46	−0.52 −13,1	6559	6535	0.14 3,5	2.1693 55,100	4.09 104,0	3.86 98,0	0.13 3,3	1.6875 42,862	5.55 141,0	6.06 154,0
3.2500 82,550	6.6250 168,275	2.1250 53,975	16900 7550	8700 3860	1.95	−0.73 −18,4	842	832	0.14 3,5	2.2190 56,363	3.98 101,0	3.70 94,0	0.13 3,3	1.6250 41,275	5.87 149,0	6.10 155,0
3.2500 82,550	7.1250 180,975	2.1250 53,975	15100 6700	18900 8400	0.80	0.02 0,5	H917849	H917810	0.13 3,3	2.0938 53,183	4.49 114,0	3.94 100,1	0.13 3,3	1.4063 35,720	5.98 152,0	6.69 170,0
3.2813 83,345	4.9375 125,412	1.0000 25,400	5150 2300	3690 1640	1.40	0.02 0,5	27689	27620	0.03 0,8	1.0000 25,400	3.54 90,0	3.54 90,0	0.06 1,5	0.7813 19,845	4.53 115,0	4.72 120,0
3.2813 83,345	4.9375 125,412	1.0000 25,400	5150 2300	3690 1640	1.40	0.02 0,5	27690	27620	0.14 3,5	1.0000 25,400	3.78 96,0	3.54 90,0	0.06 1,5	0.7813 19,845	4.53 115,0	4.72 120,0
3.2813 83,345	4.9375 125,412	1.0000 25,400	5150 2300	3690 1640	1.40	0.02 0,5	27691	27620	0.25 6,4	1.0000 25,400	4.02 102,0	3.54 90,0	0.06 1,5	0.7813 19,845	4.53 115,0	4.72 120,0
3.3125 84,138	5.2500 133,350	1.1875 30,162	6550 2920	5000 2220	1.31	−0.03 −0,8	498	492A	0.14 3,5	1.1720 29,769	3.86 98,0	3.58 91,0	0.13† 3,3	0.8750 22,225	4.72 120,0	5.04 128,0
3.3125 84,138	6.7500 171,450	1.9375 49,212	12000 5350	15800 7000	0.76	0.17 4,4	9385	9321	0.14 3,5	1.8125 46,038	4.37 111,0	3.87 98,2	0.13 3,3	1.2500 31,750	5.79 147,0	6.46 164,0
*3.3465 *85,000	*5.1181 *130,000	1.1811 30,000	7100 3160	5400 2400	1.31	−0.01 −0,2	JM716648	JM716610	0.24 6,0	1.1417 29,000	4.09 104,0	3.62 92,0	0.10 2,5	0.9449 24,000	4.61 117,0	4.92 125,0
*3.3465 *85,000	*5.1181 *130,000	1.1811 30,000	7100 3160	5400 2400	1.31	−0.01 −0,2	JM716649	JM716610	0.12 3,0	1.1417 29,000	3.86 98,0	3.62 92,0	0.10 2,5	0.9449 24,000	4.61 117,0	4.92 125,0

① These maximum fillet radii will be cleared by the bearing corners.
② Minus value indicates center is inside cone backface.
† Dimension shown is maximum value—see note at bottom of fitting practice table page 4 in Reference Tables.
*For "J" part tolerances see metric tolerance, page 20 and fitting practice page 6 in Reference Tables.

SINGLE-ROW STRAIGHT BORE—TS

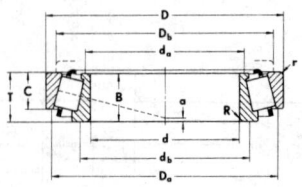

bore d	outside diameter D	width T	rating at 500 RPM for 3000 hours L10 — one row radial lb daN	thrust lb daN	fac-tor K	eff. load center a[2]	part numbers cone	part numbers cup	cone max. shaft fillet radius R[1]	cone width B	cone backing shoulder diameters d_b	cone backing shoulder diameters d_a	cup max. housing fillet radius r[1]	cup width C	cup backing shoulder D_b	cup backing shoulder D_a
*3.3465 *85,000	*5.5118 *140,000	1.5354 39,000	10300 4550	7150 3200	1.43	−0.23 −5,9	JHM516849	JHM516810	0.12 3,0	1.4961 38,000	3.94 100,0	3.70 93,9	0.10 2,5	1.2402 31,500	4.92 125,0	5.28 134,0
3.3465 85,000	5.7500 146,050	1.6250 41,275	10300 4600	7150 3180	1.43	−0.31 −7,9	665X	653	0.14 3,5	1.6250 41,275	3.98 101,0	3.74 95,0	0.13 3,3	1.2500 31,750	5.16 131,0	5.47 139,0
*3.3465 *85,000	*5.9055 *150,000	1.8110 46,000	13900 6200	7900 3520	1.76	−0.47 −11,9	JH217249	JH217210	0.12 3,0	1.8110 46,000	3.98 101,0	3.75 95,2	0.10 2,5	1.4961 38,000	5.28 134,0	5.59 142,0
3.3465 85,000	7.4375 188,912	2.0983 53,297	12900 5750	19200 8550	0.67	0.41 10,3	90334	90744	0.14 3,5	2.0772 52,761	4.57 116,0	4.41 112,0	0.13 3,3	1.2500 31,750	6.34 161,0	7.06 179,4
3.3465 85,000	7.8740 200,000	2.0772 52,761	16500 7350	17900 8000	0.92	0.05 1,3	98335	98788	0.14 3,5	1.9375 49,212	4.53 115,0	4.29 109,0	0.13 3,3	1.3750 34,925	6.85 174,0	7.40 188,0
3.3475 85,026	5.9055 150,000	1.7502 44,455	13200 5850	7350 3260	1.80	−0.47 −11,9	749	743	0.14 3,5	1.8375 46,672	3.98 101,0	3.74 95,0	0.13 3,3	1.3780 35,000	5.28 134,0	5.59 142,0
3.3475 85,026	5.9055 150,000	1.7502 44,455	13200 5850	7350 3260	1.80	−0.47 −11,9	749S	743	0.20 5,0	1.8375 46,672	4.09 104,0	3.74 95,0	0.13 3,3	1.3780 35,000	5.28 134,0	5.59 142,0
3.3750 85,725	5.2500 133,350	1.1875 30,162	6550 2920	5000 2220	1.31	−0.03 −0,8	497	492A	0.14 3,5	1.1720 29,769	3.90 99,0	3.66 93,0	0.13 3,3	0.8750 22,225	4.72 120,0	5.04 128,0
3.3750 85,725	5.5960 142,138	1.6875 42,862	11600 5150	8600 3820	1.35	−0.29 −7,4	HM617049	HM617010	0.19 4,8	1.6875 42,862	4.17 106,0	3.77 95,7	0.13 3,3	1.3438 34,133	4.92 125,0	5.39 137,0
3.3750 85,725	5.7500 146,050	1.6250 41,275	10300 4600	7150 3180	1.43	−0.31 −7,9	665	653	0.14 3,5	1.6250 41,275	4.02 102,0	3.74 95,0	0.13 3,3	1.2500 31,750	5.16 131,0	5.47 139,0
3.3750 85,725	5.7500 146,050	1.6250 41,275	10300 4600	7150 3180	1.43	−0.31 −7,9	665A	653	0.25 6,4	1.6250 41,275	4.21 107,0	3.74 95,0	0.13 3,3	1.2500 31,750	5.16 131,0	5.47 139,0
3.3750 85,725	6.0000 152,400	1.5625 39,688	9350 4160	7100 3160	1.32	−0.10 −2,5	596	592A	0.14 3,5	1.4300 36,322	4.02 102,0	3.78 96,0	0.13 3,3	1.1875 30,162	5.31 135,0	5.67 144,0
3.3750 85,725	6.3750 161,925	1.8750 47,625	13800 6100	8050 3580	1.71	−0.47 −11,9	758	752	0.14 3,5	1.9000 48,260	4.06 103,0	3.82 97,0	0.13 3,3	1.5000 38,100	5.67 144,0	5.91 150,0
3.3750 85,725	6.6250 168,275	1.6250 41,275	11500 5100	9250 4120	1.24	−0.11 −2,8	677	672	0.14 3,5	1.6250 41,275	4.13 105,0	3.90 99,0	0.13 3,3	1.1875 30,162	5.87 149,0	6.30 160,0
3.3750 85,725	6.6250 168,275	2.1250 53,975	16900 7550	8700 3860	1.95	−0.73 −18,4	841	832	0.14 3,5	2.2190 56,363	4.09 104,0	3.82 97,0	0.13 3,3	1.6250 41,275	5.87 149,0	6.10 155,0
3.4375 87,312	7.5000 190,500	2.2500 57,150	19300 8600	11100 4950	1.74	−0.60 −15,4	869	854	0.31 8,0	2.2650 57,531	4.61 117,0	4.02 102,0	0.13 3,3	1.7500 44,450	6.69 170,0	6.85 174,0
3.4375 87,312	7.5000 190,500	2.2500 57,150	22000 9750	12600 5600	1.74	−0.59 −15,0	HH221432	HH221410	0.31 8,0	2.2650 57,531	4.65 118,0	4.06 103,0	0.13 3,3	1.8125 46,038	6.73 171,0	7.05 179,0
3.4630 87,960	5.8437 148,430	1.1250 28,575	7100 3160	6000 2660	1.19	0.12 3,1	42346	42584	0.12 3,0	1.1406 28,971	4.06 103,0	3.86 98,0	0.12 3,0	0.8438 21,433	5.28 134,0	5.59 142,0
3.5000 88,900	4.7812 121,442	0.5938 15,083	2600 1160	1470 655	1.77	0.12 2,9	LL217849	LL217810	0.06 1,5	0.5938 15,083	3.82 97,0	3.70 94,0	0.06 1,5	0.4375 11,112	4.53 115,0	4.61 117,0
3.5000 88,900	4.8750 123,825	0.8125 20,638	4300 1920	2430 1080	1.77	0.0 0,0	L217849	L217810	0.06 1,5	0.8125 20,638	3.82 97,0	3.70 94,0	0.06 1,5	0.6563 16,670	4.57 116,0	4.69 119,0
3.5000 88,900	5.0000 127,000	0.8125 20,638	4300 1920	2430 1080	1.77	0.0 0,0	L217849	L217813	0.06 1,5	0.8125 20,638	3.82 97,0	3.70 94,0	0.06 1,5	0.7500 19,050	4.61 117,0	4.76 121,0

SINGLE-ROW STRAIGHT BORE

TS

bore	outside diameter	width	rating at 500 RPM for 3000 hours L10		factor	eff. load center	part numbers		cone				cup			
			one row radial	thrust			cone	cup	max. shaft fillet radius	width	backing shoulder diameters		max. housing fillet radius	width	backing shoulder	
d	D	T	lb daN	lb daN	K	a [2]			R [1]	B	d_b	d_a	r [1]	C	D_b	D_a
3.5000 88,900	5.8125 147,638	1.4062 35,717	9350 4160	7100 3160	1.32	-0.10 -2,5	593	592XE	0.14 3,5	1.4300 36,322	4.09 104,0	3.86 98,0	0.03 0,8	1.0312 26,192	5.31 135,0	5.59 142,0
3.5000 88,900	5.8125 147,638	1.4062 35,717	9350 4160	7100 3160	1.32	-0.10 -2,5	593A	592XE	0.25 6,4	1.4300 36,322	4.33 110,0	3.86 98,0	0.03 0,8	1.0312 26,192	5.31 135,0	5.59 142,0
3.5000 88,900	5.8750 149,225	1.2500 31,750	7100 3160	6000 2660	1.19	0.12 3,1	42350	42587	0.12 3,0	1.1406 28,971	4.09 104,0	3.86 98,0	0.13 3,3	0.9688 24,608	5.28 134,0	5.63 143,0
3.5000 88,900	6.2992 160,000	2.1250 53,975	16000 7150	11000 4900	1.46	-0.52 -13,1	6580	6525X	0.14 3,5	2.1693 55,100	4.29 109,0	4.01 101,9	0.12 3,0	1.7500 44,450	5.55 141,0	6.04 153,4
3.5000 88,900	6.3750 161,925	1.8750 47,625	13800 6100	8050 3580	1.71	-0.47 -11,9	759	752	0.14 3,5	1.9000 48,260	4.17 106,0	3.90 99,0	0.13 3,3	1.5000 38,100	5.67 144,0	5.91 150,0
3.5000 88,900	6.3750 161,925	1.8750 47,625	13800 6100	8050 3580	1.71	-0.47 -11,9	766	752	0.28 7,0	1.9000 48,260	4.45 113,0	3.90 99,0	0.13 3,3	1.5000 38,100	5.67 144,0	5.91 150,0
3.5000 88,900	6.6250 168,275	2.1250 53,975	16900 7550	8700 3860	1.95	-0.73 -18,4	850	832	0.14 3,5	2.2190 56,363	4.17 106,0	3.94 100,0	0.13 3,3	1.6250 41,275	5.87 149,0	6.10 155,0
3.5000 88,900	6.6929 170,000	1.6250 41,275	11500 5100	9250 4120	1.24	-0.11 -2,8	679	673X	0.14 3,5	1.6250 41,275	4.21 107,0	3.98 101,0	0.12 3,0	1.1875 30,162	5.91 150,0	6.30 160,0
3.5000 88,900	6.7500 171,450	1.8750 47,625	14300 6400	9000 4000	1.59	-0.38 -9,7	77350	77675	0.20 5,0	1.9000 48,260	4.33 110,0	3.98 101,0	0.13 3,3	1.5000 38,100	6.02 153,0	6.34 161,0
3.5000 88,900	7.5000 190,500	2.2500 57,150	19300 8600	11100 4950	1.74	-0.60 -15,4	855	854	0.31 8,0	2.2650 57,531	4.65 118,0	4.06 103,0	0.13 3,3	1.7500 44,450	6.69 170,0	6.85 174,0
3.5000 88,900	7.5000 190,500	2.2500 57,150	22000 9750	12600 5600	1.74	-0.59 -15,0	HH221434	HH221410	0.31 8,0	2.2650 57,531	4.72 120,0	4.13 105,0	0.13 3,3	1.8125 46,038	6.73 171,0	7.05 179,0
3.5000 88,900	7.8740 200,000	2.0772 52,761	16500 7350	17900 8000	0.92	0.05 1,3	98350	98788	0.14 3,5	1.9375 49,212	4.65 118,0	4.41 112,0	0.13 3,3	1.3750 34,925	6.85 174,0	7.40 188,0
*3.5433 *90,000	*5.7087 *145,000	1.3780 35,000	9450 4200	7200 3200	1.31	-0.08 -2,0	JM718149	JM718110	0.12 3,0	1.3386 34,000	4.13 105,0	3.90 99,0	0.10 2,5	1.0630 27,000	5.16 131,0	5.46 138,8
3.5433 90,000	5.8125 147,638	1.4062 35,717	9350 4160	7100 3160	1.32	-0.10 -2,5	597X	592XE	0.12 3,0	1.4300 36,322	4.09 104,0	3.90 99,0	0.03 0,8	1.0312 26,192	5.31 135,0	5.59 142,0
†3.5433 †90,000	6.0000 152,400	1.5748 40,000	11700 5200	6650 2960	1.76	-0.34 -8,6	HM218248	HM218215	0.28 7,0	1.5748 40,000	4.41 112,0	3.90 99,0	0.13 3,3	1.2795 32,500	5.31 135,0	5.63 143,0
*3.5433 *90,000	*6.1024 *155,000	1.7323 44,000	13800 6100	8050 3580	1.71	-0.39 -10,0	JHM318448	JHM318410	0.12 3,0	1.7323 44,000	4.17 106,0	3.94 100,0	0.10 2,5	1.3976 35,500	5.51 140,0	5.83 148,0
3.5433 90,000	6.2992 160,000	2.1250 53,975	16000 7150	11000 4900	1.46	-0.52 -13,1	6581X	6525X	0.12 3,0	2.1693 55,100	4.29 109,0	4.01 101,9	0.12 3,0	1.7500 44,450	5.55 141,0	6.04 153,4
3.5433 90,000	6.3750 161,925	1.8750 47,625	13800 6100	8050 3580	1.71	-0.47 -11,9	767X	752	0.12 3,0	1.9000 48,260	4.17 106,0	3.94 100,0	0.13 3,3	1.5000 38,100	5.67 144,0	5.91 150,0
3.5625 90,488	6.3750 161,925	1.8750 47,625	13800 6100	8050 3580	1.71	-0.47 -11,9	760	752	0.14 3,5	1.9000 48,260	4.21 107,0	3.98 101,0	0.13 3,3	1.5000 38,100	5.67 144,0	5.91 150,0
†3.6220 †92,000	5.6250 142,875	1.1811 30,000	6950 3080	5700 2520	1.22	0.07 1,8	LM718947	LM718910	0.14 3,5	1.1811 30,000	4.17 106,0	3.94 100,0	0.13 3,3	0.8661 22,000	5.08 129,0	5.43 138,0
3.6250 92,075	5.7500 146,050	1.3125 33,338	8750 3900	6750 3000	1.30	-0.04 -1,0	47890	47820	0.14 3,5	1.3750 34,925	4.21 107,0	3.98 101,0	0.13 3,3	1.0313 26,195	5.16 131,0	5.51 140,0
3.6250 92,075	5.8125 147,638	1.4062 35,717	9350 4160	7100 3160	1.32	-0.10 -2,5	598	592XE	0.14 3,5	1.4300 36,322	4.21 107,0	3.98 101,0	0.03 0,8	1.0312 26,192	5.31 135,0	5.59 142,0
3.6250 92,075	5.8125 147,638	1.4062 35,717	9350 4160	7100 3160	1.32	-0.10 -2,5	598A	592XE	0.25 6,4	1.4300 36,322	4.45 113,0	3.98 101,0	0.03 0,8	1.0312 26,192	5.31 135,0	5.59 142,0

① These maximum fillet radii will be cleared by the bearing corners.
② Minus value indicates center is inside cone backface.
†Dimension shown is maximum value—see note at bottom of fitting practice table page 4 in Reference Tables.
*For "J" part tolerances see metric tolerance, page 20 and fitting practice page 6 in Reference Tables.

SINGLE-ROW STRAIGHT BORE—TS

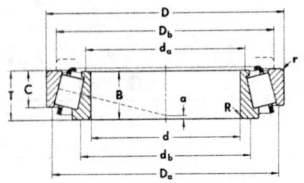

| bore | outside diameter | width | rating at 500 RPM for 3000 hours L10 | | fac-tor | eff. load center | part numbers | | cone max. shaft fillet radius | width | backing shoulder diameters | | cup max. hous-ing fillet radius | width | backing shoulder | |
| | | | one row radial | thrust | | | cone | cup | | | | | | | | |
d	D	T	lb daN	lb daN	K	a			R	B	d_b	d_a	r	C	D_b	D_a
3.6250 92,075	5.8125 147,638	1.4062 35,717	9350 4160	7100 3160	1.32	-0.10 -2,5	598X	592XE	0.14 3,5	1.4300 36,322	4.21 107,0	4.09 104,0	0.03 0,8	1.0312 26,192	5.31 135,0	5.59 142,0
3.5250 92,075	5.8437 148,430	1.1250 28,575	7100 3160	6000 2660	1.19	0.12 3,1	42362	42584	0.14 3,5	1.1406 28,971	4.21 107,0	3.98 101,0	0.12 3,0	0.8438 21,433	5.28 134,0	5.59 142,0
3.6250 92,075	6.6250 168,275	1.6250 41,275	11500 5100	9250 4120	1.24	-0.11 -2,8	681	672	0.14 3,5	1.6250 41,275	4.33 110,0	4.09 104,0	0.13 3,3	1.1875 30,162	5.87 149,0	6.30 160,0
3.6250 92,075	6.6250 168,275	1.6250 41,275	11500 5100	9250 4120	1.24	-0.11 -2,8	681A	672	0.25 6,4	1.6250 41,275	4.57 116,0	4.09 104,0	0.13 3,3	1.1875 30,162	5.87 149,0	6.30 160,0
3.6250 92,075	7.1250 180,975	1.8750 47,625	14900 6600	9850 4380	1.51	-0.32 -8,1	778	772	0.14 3,5	1.8900 48,006	4.37 111,0	4.13 105,0	0.13 3,3	1.5000 38,100	6.34 161,0	6.61 168,0
3.6250 92,075	7.5000 190,500	2.2500 57,150	19300 8600	11100 4950	1.74	-0.60 -15,4	857	854	0.31 8,0	2.2650 57,531	4.76 121,0	4.17 106,0	0.13 3,3	1.7500 44,450	6.69 170,0	6.85 174,0
3.6875 93,662	5.8125 147,638	1.4062 35,717	9350 4160	7100 3160	1.32	-0.10 -2,5	597	592XE	0.14 3,5	1.4300 36,322	4.21 109,0	4.02 102,0	0.03 0,8	1.0312 26,192	5.31 135,0	5.59 142,0
3.5875 93,662	5.8437 148,430	1.1250 28,575	7100 3160	6000 2660	1.19	0.12 3,1	42368	42584	0.12 3,0	1.1406 28,971	4.21 107,0	4.02 102,0	0.12 3,0	0.8438 21,433	5.28 134,0	5.59 142,0
*3.7402 *95,000	*5.9055 *150,000	1.3780 35,000	9350 4160	7100 3160	1.32	-0.06 -1,6	JM719149	JM719113	0.12 3,0	1.3386 34,000	4.29 109,0	4.09 104,0	0.10 2,5	1.0630 27,000	5.31 135,0	5.63 143,0
3.7500 95,250	5.0625 128,588	0.6250 15,875	2760 1225	1660 740	1.66	0.17 4,3	LL319349	LL319310	0.06 1,5	0.5938 15,083	4.06 103,0	3.94 100,0	0.06 1,5	0.4688 11,908	4.80 122,0	4.88 124,0
3.7500 95,250	5.1250 130,175	0.8125 20,638	4450 1980	2670 1190	1.67	0.05 1,3	L319249	L319210	0.06 1,5	0.8438 21,433	4.06 103,0	3.98 101,0	0.06 1,5	0.6563 16,670	4.80 122,0	4.92 125,0
3.7500 95,250	5.7500 146,050	1.3125 33,338	8750 3900	6750 3000	1.30	-0.04 -1,0	47896	47820	0.14 3,5	1.3750 34,925	4.33 110,0	4.06 103,0	0.13 3,3	1.0313 26,195	5.16 131,0	5.51 140,0
3.7500 95,250	5.8125 147,638	1.4062 35,717	9350 4160	7100 3160	1.32	-0.10 -2,5	594	592XE	0.14 3,5	1.4300 36,322	4.33 110,0	4.09 104,0	0.03 0,8	1.0312 26,192	5.31 135,0	5.59 142,0
3.7500 95,250	5.8125 147,638	1.4062 35,717	9350 4160	7100 3160	1.32	-0.10 -2,5	594A	592XE	0.20 5,0	1.4300 36,322	4.45 113,0	4.09 104,0	0.03 0,8	1.0312 26,192	5.31 135,0	5.59 142,0
3.7500 95,250	5.8437 148,430	1.1250 28,575	7100 3160	6000 2660	1.19	0.12 3,1	42375	42584	0.12 3,0	1.1406 28,971	4.25 108,0	4.06 103,0	0.12 3,0	0.8438 21,433	5.28 134,0	5.59 142,0
3.7500 95,250	5.8437 148,430	1.1250 28,575	7100 3160	6000 2660	1.19	0.12 3,1	42376	42584	0.14 3,5	1.1406 28,971	4.29 109,0	4.06 103,0	0.12 3,0	0.8438 21,433	5.28 134,0	5.59 142,0
3.7500 95,250	6.1875 157,162	1.4375 36,512	9900 4400	8050 3580	1.23	-0.01 -0,4	52375	52618	0.14 3,5	1.4219 36,116	4.41 112,0	4.13 105,0	0.13 3,3	1.0313 26,195	5.59 142,0	5.98 152,0
3.7500 95,250	6.6250 168,275	1.6250 41,275	11500 5100	9250 4120	1.24	-0.11 -2,8	683	672	0.14 3,5	1.6250 41,275	4.45 113,0	4.17 106,0	0.13 3,3	1.1875 30,162	5.87 149,0	6.30 160,0
3.7500 95,250	6.7500 171,450	2.0000 50,800	14300 6400	9000 4000	1.59	-0.38 -9,7	77375	77676X	0.14 3,5	1.9000 48,260	4.45 113,0	4.17 106,0	0.13 3,3	1.6250 41,275	5.98 152,0	6.34 161,0
3.7500 95,250	7.1250 180,975	1.8750 47,625	14900 6600	9850 4380	1.51	-0.32 -8,1	776	772	0.14 3,5	1.8900 48,006	4.49 114,0	4.21 107,0	0.13 3,3	1.5000 38,100	6.34 161,0	6.61 168,0
3.7500 95,250	7.5000 190,500	2.2500 57,150	19300 8600	11100 4950	1.74	-0.60 -15,4	864	854	0.31 8,0	2.2650 57,531	4.84 123,0	4.25 108,0	0.13 3,3	1.7500 44,450	6.69 170,0	6.85 174,0

bore	outside diameter	width	rating at 500 RPM for 3000 hours L10		factor	eff. load center	part numbers		cone				cup			
			one row radial	thrust					max. shaft fillet radius	width	backing shoulder diameters		max. housing fillet radius	width	backing shoulder	
d	D	T	lb daN	lb daN	K	a[1]	cone	cup	R[1]	B	d_b	d_a	r[1]	C	D_b	D_a
3.7500 95,250	7.5000 190,500	2.2500 57,150	22000 9750	12600 5600	1.74	-0.59 -15,0	HH221440	HH221410	0.31 8,0	2.2650 57,531	4.92 125,0	4.33 110,0	0.13 3,3	1.8125 46,038	6.73 171,0	7.05 179,0
3.8125 96,838	5.8437 148,430	1.1250 28,575	7100 3160	6000 2660	1.19	0.12 3,1	42381	42584	0.14 3,5	1.1406 28,971	4.33 110,0	4.09 104,0	0.12 3,0	0.8438 21,433	5.28 134,0	5.59 142,0
3.8125 96,838	7.4375 188,912	2.0000 50,800	12900 5750	19200 8550	0.67	0.51 12,8	90381	90744	0.14 3,5	1.8125 46,038	4.92 125,0	4.44 112,8	0.13 3,3	1.2500 31,750	6.34 161,0	7.06 179,4
3.8750 98,425	6.3750 161,925	1.4375 36,512	9900 4400	8050 3580	1.23	-0.01 -0,4	52387	52637	0.14 3,5	1.4219 36,116	4.49 114,0	4.25 108,0	0.13 3,3	1.0313 26,195	5.67 144,0	6.06 154,0
3.8750 98,425	6.6250 168,275	1.6250 41,275	11500 5100	9250 4120	1.24	-0.11 -2,8	685	672	0.14 3,5	1.6250 41,275	4.57 116,0	4.29 109,0	0.13 3,3	1.1875 30,162	5.87 149,0	6.30 160,0
3.8750 98,425	7.1250 180,975	1.8750 47,625	14900 6600	9850 4380	1.51	-0.32 -8,1	779	772	0.14 3,5	1.8900 48,006	4.57 116,0	4.33 110,0	0.13 3,3	1.5000 38,100	6.34 161,0	6.61 168,0
3.8750 98,425	7.2500 184,150	2.5000 63,500	23200 10350	14900 6600	1.56	-0.66 -16,8	HH421246	HH421210	0.25 6,4	2.5000 63,500	5.00 127,0	4.53 115,1	0.13 3,3	2.0625 52,388	6.42 163,0	6.93 176,0
3.8750 98,425	7.5000 190,500	2.2500 57,150	19300 8600	11100 4950	1.74	-0.60 -15,4	866	854	0.14 3,5	2.2650 57,531	4.65 118,0	4.37 111,0	0.13 3,3	1.7500 44,450	6.69 170,0	6.85 174,0
3.8750 98,425	7.5000 190,500	2.2500 57,150	22000 9750	12600 5600	1.74	-0.59 -15,0	HH221442	HH221410	0.14 3,5	2.2650 57,531	4.69 119,0	4.45 113,0	0.13 3,3	1.8125 46,038	6.73 171,0	7.05 179,0
3.9060 99,212	6.7500 171,450	1.9375 49,212	14800 6600	8750 3880	1.70	-0.44 -11,3	HM321245	HM321210	0.14 3,5	1.9375 49,212	4.57 116,0	4.29 109,0	0.13 3,3	1.5000 38,100	6.10 155,0	6.46 164,0
3.9362 99,979	5.9048 149,982	1.2598 32,000	7100 3160	6100 2720	1.16	0.18 4,6	LM820048	LM820012	0.09 2,3	1.1811 30,000	4.37 111,0	4.25 108,0	0.09 2,3	1.0236 26,000	5.31 135,0	5.67 144,0
3.9363 99,982	7.5000 190,500	2.2500 57,150	22000 9750	12600 5600	1.74	-0.59 -15,0	HH221447	HH221410	0.25 6,4	2.2650 57,531	4.96 126,0	4.49 114,0	0.13 3,3	1.8125 46,038	6.73 171,0	7.05 179,0
*3.9370 *100,000	*6.1024 *155,000	1.4173 36,000	10100 4480	8100 3620	1.24	0.01 0,3	JM720249	JM720210	0.12 3,0	1.3780 35,000	4.53 115,0	4.29 109,0	0.10 2,5	1.1024 28,000	5.51 140,0	5.87 149,0
*3.9370 *100,000	*6.2992 *160,000	1.6142 41,000	12200 5450	9850 4380	1.24	-0.10 -2,5	JHM720249	JHM720210	0.12 3,0	1.5748 40,000	4.61 117,0	4.31 109,4	0.10 2,5	1.2598 32,000	5.63 143,0	6.06 153,9
3.9370 100,000	7.1250 180,975	1.8750 47,625	14900 6600	9850 4380	1.51	-0.32 -8,1	783	772	0.14 3,5	1.8900 48,006	4.65 118,0	4.37 111,0	0.13 3,3	1.5000 38,100	6.34 161,0	6.61 168,0
3.9370 100,000	7.8740 200,000	2.0772 52,761	16500 7350	17900 8000	0.92	0.05 1,3	98394X	98788	0.14 3,5	1.9375 49,212	4.96 126,0	4.76 120,8	0.13 3,3	1.3750 34,925	6.85 174,0	7.40 188,0
3.9375 100,012	6.1875 157,162	1.4375 36,512	9900 4400	8050 3580	1.23	-0.01 -0,4	52393	52618	0.14 3,5	1.4219 36,116	4.57 116,0	4.29 109,0	0.13 3,3	1.0313 26,195	5.59 142,0	5.98 152,0
4.0000 101,600	5.3125 134,938	0.6250 15,875	2800 1245	1770 790	1.58	0.22 5,6	LL420549	LL420510	0.06 1,5	0.5938 15,083	4.29 109,0	4.21 107,0	0.06 1,5	0.4688 11,908	5.04 128,0	5.12 130,0
4.0000 101,600	5.3750 136,525	0.8438 21,433	4600 2060	2900 1290	1.59	0.11 2,8	L420449	L420410	0.06 1,5	0.8438 21,433	4.29 109,0	4.21 107,0	0.06 1,5	0.6563 16,670	5.04 128,0	5.20 132,0
4.0000 101,600	5.7500 146,050	0.8438 21,433	4700 2080	3140 1400	1.49	0.19 4,8	L521945	L521910	0.06 1,5	0.8438 21,433	4.41 112,0	4.29 109,0	0.06 1,5	0.6563 16,670	5.35 136,0	5.55 141,0
4.0000 101,600	6.1875 157,162	1.4375 36,512	9900 4400	8050 3580	1.23	-0.01 -0,4	52400	52618	0.14 3,5	1.4219 36,116	4.61 117,0	4.37 111,0	0.13 3,3	1.0313 26,195	5.59 142,0	5.98 152,0
4.0000 101,600	6.1875 157,162	1.4375 36,512	9900 4400	8050 3580	1.23	-0.01 -0,4	52401	52618	0.31 8,0	1.4219 36,116	4.96 126,0	4.37 111,0	0.13 3,3	1.0313 26,195	5.59 142,0	5.98 152,0
4.0000 101,600	6.6250 168,275	1.6250 41,275	11500 5100	9250 4120	1.24	-0.11 -2,8	687	672	0.14 3,5	1.6250 41,275	4.96 118,0	4.41 112,0	0.13 3,3	1.1875 30,162	5.87 149,0	6.30 160,0

[1] These maximum fillet radii will be cleared by the bearing corners.
[2] Minus value indicates center is inside cone backface.
*For "J" part tolerances see metric tolerance, page 20 and fitting practice page 6 in Reference Tables.

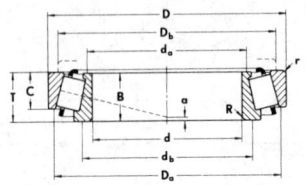

			rating at 500 RPM for 3000 hours L10		factor	eff. load center	part numbers		cone				cup			
bore	outside diameter	width	one row radial	thrust					max. shaft fillet radius	width	backing shoulder diameters		max. housing fillet radius	width	backing shoulder	
d	D	T	lb daN	lb daN	K	a [2]	cone	cup	R [1]	B	d_b	d_a	r [1]	C	D_b	D_a
4.0000 / 101,600	7.0000 / 177,800	1.3750 / 34,925	6950 / 3100	13900 / 6200	0.50	1.36 / 34.5	LM921845	LM921810	0.13 / 3,3	1.2500 / 31,750	4.84 / 123,0	4.69 / 119,0	0.13 / 3,3	0.7500 / 19,050	6.06 / 154,0	6.77 / 172,0
4.0000 / 101,600	7.1250 / 180,975	1.8750 / 47,625	14900 / 6600	9850 / 4380	1.51	-0.32 / -8,1	780	772	0.14 / 3,5	1.8900 / 48,006	4.69 / 119,0	4.45 / 113,0	0.13 / 3,3	1.5000 / 38,100	6.34 / 161,0	6.61 / 168,0
4.0000 / 101,600	7.5000 / 190,500	2.2500 / 57,150	19300 / 8600	11100 / 4950	1.74	-0.60 / -15,4	861	854	0.31 / 8,0	2.2650 / 57,531	5.08 / 129,0	4.49 / 114,0	0.13 / 3,3	1.7500 / 44,450	6.69 / 170,0	6.85 / 174,0
4.0000 / 101,600	7.5000 / 190,500	2.2500 / 57,150	22000 / 9750	12600 / 5600	1.74	-0.59 / -15,0	HH221449	HH221410	0.31 / 8,0	2.2650 / 57,531	5.16 / 131,0	4.56 / 115,9	0.13 / 3,3	1.8125 / 46,038	6.73 / 171,0	7.05 / 179,0
4.0000 / 101,600	7.8740 / 200,000	2.0772 / 52,761	16500 / 7350	17900 / 8000	0.92	0.05 / 1,3	98400	98788	0.14 / 3,5	1.9375 / 49,212	5.04 / 128,0	4.76 / 120,8	0.13 / 3,3	1.3750 / 34,925	6.85 / 174,0	7.40 / 188,0
4.0000 / 101,600	8.3750 / 212,725	2.6250 / 66,675	24300 / 10800	13600 / 6050	1.79	-0.78 / -19,7	941	932	0.28 / 7,0	2.6250 / 66,675	5.12 / 130,0	4.61 / 117,0	0.13 / 3,3	2.1250 / 53,975	7.36 / 187,0	7.60 / 193,1
4.0000 / 101,600	8.3750 / 212,725	2.6250 / 66,675	28300 / 12600	15800 / 7050	1.79	-0.74 / -18,9	HH224335	HH224310	0.28 / 7,0	2.6250 / 66,675	5.20 / 132,0	4.76 / 121,0	0.13 / 3,3	2.1250 / 53,975	7.56 / 192,0	7.94 / 201,7
4.0000 / 101,600	8.4375 / 214,312	2.1875 / 55,562	19200 / 8550	22100 / 9800	0.87	0.27 / 6,8	H924033	H924010	0.14 / 3,5	2.0625 / 52,388	5.20 / 132,0	5.04 / 128,0	0.13 / 3,3	1.5625 / 39,688	7.32 / 186,0	8.07 / 205,0
4.0000 / 101,600	9.8750 / 250,825	3.0000 / 76,200	27900 / 12400	33200 / 14750	0.84	-0.13 / -3,4	HH923649	HH923610	0.25 / 6,4	2.8750 / 73,025	5.87 / 149,0	5.15 / 130,8	0.25 / 6,4	2.0000 / 50,800	8.15 / 207,0	9.01 / 228,8
4.0000 / 101,600	9.8750 / 250,825	3.0000 / 76,200	27900 / 12400	33200 / 14750	0.84	-0.13 / -3,4	HH923649	HH923611	0.25 / 6,4	2.8750 / 73,025	5.87 / 149,0	5.15 / 130,8	0.13 / 3,3	2.0000 / 50,800	8.27 / 210,0	9.01 / 228,8
4.1250 / 104,775	7.1250 / 180,975	1.8750 / 47,625	14900 / 6600	9850 / 4380	1.51	-0.32 / -8,1	782	772	0.14 / 3,5	1.8900 / 48,006	4.80 / 122,0	4.57 / 116,0	0.13 / 3,3	1.5000 / 38,100	6.34 / 161,0	6.61 / 168,0
4.1250 / 104,775	7.1250 / 180,975	1.8750 / 47,625	14900 / 6600	9850 / 4380	1.51	-0.32 / -8,1	786	772	0.25 / 6,4	1.8900 / 48,006	5.04 / 128,0	4.57 / 116,0	0.13 / 3,3	1.5000 / 38,100	6.34 / 161,0	6.61 / 168,0
4.1250 / 104,775	7.1250 / 180,975	1.8750 / 47,625	14900 / 6600	9850 / 4380	1.51	-0.32 / -8,1	787	772	0.28 / 7,0	1.8900 / 48,006	5.08 / 129,0	4.57 / 116,0	0.13 / 3,3	1.5000 / 38,100	6.34 / 161,0	6.61 / 168,0
4.1250 / 104,775	7.5000 / 190,500	1.8750 / 47,625	15900 / 7050	11300 / 5050	1.40	-0.26 / -6,5	71412	71750	0.14 / 3,5	1.9375 / 49,212	4.88 / 124,0	4.65 / 118,0	0.13 / 3,3	1.3750 / 34,925	6.73 / 171,0	7.13 / 181,0
4.1875 / 106,362	6.5000 / 165,100	1.4375 / 36,512	10100 / 4500	8600 / 3820	1.18	0.08 / 2,0	56418	56650	0.14 / 3,5	1.4375 / 36,512	4.80 / 122,0	4.57 / 116,0	0.13 / 3,3	1.0625 / 26,988	5.87 / 149,0	6.26 / 159,0
4.2500 / 107,950	5.7500 / 146,050	0.8438 / 21,433	4700 / 2080	3140 / 1400	1.49	0.19 / 4,8	L521949	L521910	0.06 / 1,5	0.8438 / 21,433	4.57 / 116,0	4.49 / 114,0	0.06 / 1,5	0.6563 / 16,670	5.35 / 136,0	5.55 / 141,0
4.2500 / 107,950	6.2500 / 158,750	0.9063 / 23,020	5050 / 2240	5250 / 2340	0.96	0.54 / 13,7	37425	37625	0.14 / 3,5	0.8440 / 21,438	4.80 / 122,0	4.53 / 115,0	0.13 / 3,3	0.6250 / 15,875	5.63 / 143,0	5.98 / 152,0
4.2500 / 107,950	6.2987 / 159,987	1.3750 / 34,925	9350 / 4160	6450 / 2860	1.45	-0.06 / -1,4	LM522546	LM522510	0.14 / 3,5	1.3750 / 34,925	4.80 / 122,0	4.57 / 116,0	0.13 / 3,3	1.0625 / 26,988	5.75 / 146,0	6.06 / 154,0
4.2500 / 107,950	6.3750 / 161,925	1.3750 / 34,925	8700 / 3860	7500 / 3340	1.16	0.15 / 3,9	48190	48120	0.14 / 3,5	1.3750 / 34,925	4.80 / 122,0	4.57 / 116,0	0.13 / 3,3	1.0625 / 26,988	5.75 / 146,0	6.14 / 156,0
4.2500 / 107,950	6.5000 / 165,100	1.4375 / 36,512	10100 / 4500	8600 / 3820	1.18	0.08 / 2,0	56425	56650	0.14 / 3,5	1.4375 / 36,512	4.84 / 123,0	4.61 / 117,0	0.13 / 3,3	1.0625 / 26,988	5.87 / 149,0	6.26 / 159,0
4.2500 / 107,950	6.7500 / 171,450	1.3386 / 34,000	7950 / 3540	6450 / 2860	1.24	0.18 / 4,6	67425	67675	0.14 / 3,5	1.1875 / 30,162	4.84 / 123,0	4.57 / 116,0	0.13 / 3,3	0.9948 / 25,268	6.14 / 156,0	6.46 / 164,0

SINGLE-ROW STRAIGHT BORE

TS

bore	outside diameter	width	rating at 500 RPM for 3000 hours L10		factor	eff. load center	part numbers		cone				cup			
			one row radial	thrust			cone	cup	max shaft fillet radius	width	backing shoulder diameters		max housing fillet radius	width	backing shoulder	
d	D	T	lb daN	lb daN	K	a			R	B	d_b	d_a	r	C	D_b	D_a
4.2500	7.5000	1.8750	15900	11300	1.40	−0.26	71425	71750	0.14	1.9375	4.96	4.72	0.13	1.3750	6.73	7.13
107,950	190,500	47,625	7050	5050		−6,5			3,5	49,212	126,0	120,0	3,3	34,925	171,0	181,0
4.2500	8.3750	2.6250	24300	13600	1.79	−0.78	936	932	0.31	2.6250	5.39	4.80	0.13	2.1250	7.36	7.60
107,950	212,725	66,675	10800	6050		−19,7			8,0	66,675	137,0	122,0	3,3	53,975	187,0	193,1
4.2500	8.3750	2.6250	28300	15800	1.79	−0.74	HH224340	HH224310	0.31	2.6250	5.47	4.96	0.13	2.1250	7.56	7.94
107,950	212,725	66,675	12600	7050		−18,9			8,0	66,675	139,0	126,0	3,3	53,975	192,0	201,7
4.3125	6.2500	0.9063	5050	5250	0.96	0.54	37431	37625	0.14	0.8440	4.84	4.57	0.13	0.6250	5.63	5.98
109,538	158,750	23,020	2240	2340		13,7			3,5	21,438	123,0	116,0	3,3	15,875	143,0	152,0
4.3302	6.2987	1.3750	9350	6450	1.45	−0.06	LM522548	LM522510	0.31	1.3750	5.24	4.65	0.13	1.0625	5.75	6.06
109,987	159,987	34,925	4160	2860		−1,4			8,0	34,925	133,0	118,0	3,3	26,988	146,0	154,0
4.3302	6.2987	1.3750	9350	6450	1.45	−0.06	LM522549	LM522510	0.14	1.3750	4.88	4.65	0.13	1.0625	5.75	6.06
109,987	159,987	34,925	4160	2860		−1,4			3,5	34,925	124,0	118,0	3,3	26,988	146,0	154,0
4.3304	7.0000	1.6250	12100	10700	1.13	0.05	64433	64700	0.14	1.6250	5.04	4.76	0.13	1.1875	6.30	6.77
109,992	177,800	41,275	5400	4750		1,2			3,5	41,275	128,0	121,0	3,3	30,162	160,0	172,0
4.3307	*6.4961	1.3780	10100	8600	1.18	0.12	JM822049	JM822010	0.12	1.3780	4.88	4.69	0.10	1.0433	5.87	6.26
110,000	*165,000	35,000	4500	3820		3,0			3,0	35,000	124,0	119,0	2,5	26,500	149,0	159,0
4.3307	*7.0866	1.8504	16200	11200	1.44	−0.23	JHM522649	JHM522610	0.12	1.8110	5.00	4.79	0.10	1.4961	6.38	6.77
110,000	*180,000	47,000	7200	5000		−6,0			3,0	46,000	127,0	121,8	2,5	38,000	162,0	172,0
4.3307	8.3750	2.6250	24300	13600	1.79	−0.78	942	932	0.25	2.6250	5.35	4.88	0.13	2.1250	7.36	7.60
110,000	212,725	66,675	10800	6050		−19,7			6,4	66,675	136,0	124,0	3,3	53,975	187,0	193,1
4.3750	7.5000	1.8750	15900	11300	1.40	−0.26	71437	71750	0.14	1.9375	5.08	4.84	0.13	1.3750	6.73	7.13
111,125	190,500	47,625	7050	5050		−6,5			3,5	49,212	129,0	123,0	3,3	34,925	171,0	181,0
4.3750	8.4375	2.1875	19200	22100	0.87	0.27	H924045	H924010	0.14	2.0625	5.47	5.16	0.13	1.5625	7.32	8.07
111,125	214,312	55,562	8550	9800		6,8			3,5	52,388	139,0	131,2	3,3	39,688	186,0	205,0
4.5000	6.0000	0.8438	4900	3480	1.41	0.25	L623149	L623110	0.06	0.8438	4.84	4.72	0.06	0.6563	5.63	5.79
114,300	152,400	21,433	2180	1550		6,4			1,5	21,433	123,0	120,0	1,5	16,670	143,0	147,0
4.5000	7.0079	1.6250	12100	10700	1.13	0.05	64450	64701X	0.14	1.6250	5.16	4.92	0.12	1.1875	6.30	6.77
114,300	178,000	41,275	5400	4750		1,2			3,5	41,275	131,0	125,0	3,0	30,162	160,0	172,0
4.5000	†7.0866	1.3750	8200	6950	1.18	0.21	68450	68709	0.14	1.2500	5.12	4.84	0.03	1.0000	6.50	6.77
114,300	†180,000	34,925	3640	3080		5,3			3,5	31,750	130,0	123,0	0,8	25,400	165,0	172,0
4.5000	7.5000	1.8750	15900	11300	1.40	−0.26	71450	71750	0.14	1.9375	5.20	4.92	0.13	1.3750	6.73	7.13
114,300	190,500	47,625	7050	5050		−6,5			3,5	49,212	132,0	125,0	3,3	34,925	171,0	181,0
4.5000	8.3750	2.6250	24300	13600	1.79	−0.78	938	932	0.28	2.6250	5.55	5.04	0.13	2.1250	7.36	7.60
114,300	212,725	66,675	10800	6050		−19,7			7,0	66,675	141,0	128,0	3,3	53,975	187,0	193,1
4.5000	8.3750	2.6250	28300	15800	1.79	−0.74	HH224346	HH224310	0.28	2.6250	5.63	5.16	0.13	2.1250	7.56	7.94
114,300	212,725	66,675	12600	7050		−18,9			7,0	66,675	143,0	131,0	3,3	53,975	192,0	201,7
4.5000	9.0000	2.1250	20500	25900	0.79	0.53	HM926740	HM926710	0.14	1.9460	5.75	5.59	0.13	1.5000	7.87	8.63
114,300	228,600	53,975	9100	11550		13,4			3,5	49,428	146,0	142,0	3,3	38,100	200,0	219,3
4.5000	10.7500	3.2500	35900	39100	0.92	−0.26	HH926744	HH926710	0.25	3.2500	6.46	5.80	0.25	2.1250	9.06	9.97
114,300	273,050	82,550	16000	17350		−6,6			6,4	82,550	164,0	147,2	6,4	53,975	230,0	253,3
*4.5276	7.0000	1.6250	12100	10700	1.13	0.05	64452	64700	0.14	1.6250	5.20	4.96	0.13	1.1875	6.30	6.77
115,000	177,800	41,275	5400	4750		1,2			3,5	41,275	132,0	125,9	3,3	30,162	160,0	172,0
4.5310	7.5000	1.8750	15900	11300	1.40	−0.26	71453	71750	0.14	1.9375	5.24	4.96	0.13	1.3750	6.73	7.13
115,087	190,500	47,625	7050	5050		−6,5			3,5	49,212	133,0	126,0	3,3	34,925	171,0	181,0
4.5310	7.5000	1.8750	15900	11300	1.40	−0.26	71455	71750	0.31	1.9375	5.55	4.96	0.13	1.3750	6.73	7.13
115,087	190,500	47,625	7050	5050		−6,5			8,0	49,212	141,0	126,0	3,3	34,925	171,0	181,0

▪These maximum fillet radii will be cleared by the bearing corners.
▪Minus value indicates center is inside cone backface.
①Dimension shown is maximum value—see note at bottom of fitting practice table page 4 in Reference Tables.
For "J" part tolerances see metric tolerance, page 20 and fitting practice page 6 in Reference Tables.

SINGLE-ROW STRAIGHT BORE—TS

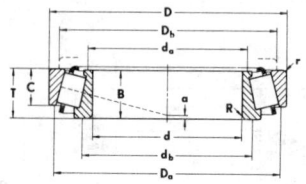

bore	outside diameter	width	rating at 500 RPM for 3000 hours L10 one row radial	thrust	factor K	eff. load center a①	cone	cup	cone max shaft fillet radius R①	width B	db	da	cup max housing fillet radius r①	width C	Db	Da
d (lb daN)	D	T	lb daN	lb daN												
4.6250 / 117,475	7.1250 / 180,975	1.3750 / 34,925	8200 / 3640	6950 / 3080	1.18	0.21 / 5,3	68462	68712	0.14 / 3,5	1.2500 / 31,750	5.20 / 132,0	4.92 / 125,0	0.13 / 3,3	1.0000 / 25,400	6.42 / 163,0	6. / 172
4.7230 / 119,964	8.4646 / 215,000	1.8750 / 47,625	17200 / 7650	14300 / 6400	1.20	0.09 / 2,2	74472	74846X	0.14 / 3,5	1.8750 / 47,625	5.59 / 142,0	5.35 / 136,0	0.13 / 3,3	1.3750 / 34,925	7.72 / 196,0	8. / 208
†4.7244 / †120,000	6.5625 / 166,688	1.0000 / 25,400	6500 / 2880	5100 / 2260	1.27	0.31 / 7,9	L724348	L724310	0.13 / 3,3	1.0000 / 25,400	5.20 / 132,0	5.00 / 127,0	0.13 / 3,3	0.7500 / 19,050	6.06 / 154,0	6. / 16?
†4.7244 / †120,000	†7.0866 / †180,000	1.4173 / 36,000	10800 / 4800	7650 / 3420	1.41	0.0 / 0,0	M624649	M624610	0.14 / 3,5	1.4173 / 36,000	5.31 / 135,0	5.04 / 128,0	0.06 / 1,5	1.0236 / 26,000	6.54 / 173	6.
4.7500 / 120,650	6.3125 / 160,338	0.8438 / 21,433	5150 / 2280	3830 / 1700	1.34	0.33 / 8,4	L624549	L624510	0.06 / 1,5	0.8438 / 21,433	5.08 / 129,0	5.00 / 127,0	0.06 / 1,5	0.6563 / 16,670	5.91 / 150,0	6. / 155
4.7500 / 120,650	6.6875 / 169,862	1.0000 / 25,400	7000 / 3120	3990 / 1775	1.76	0.10 / 2,4	L225842	L225810	0.06 / 1,5	1.0313 / 26,195	5.16 / 131,0	5.08 / 129,0	0.06 / 1,5	0.8125 / 20,638	6.30 / 160,0	6. / 164
4.7500 / 120,650	†6.6929 / †170,000	1.0000 / 25,400	6500 / 2880	5100 / 2260	1.27	0.31 / 7,9	L724349	L724314	0.13 / 3,3	1.0000 / 25,400	5.24 / 133,0	5.04 / 128,0	0.13 / 3,3	0.7500 / 19,050	6.14 / 156,0	6. / 163
4.7500 / 120,650	6.8750 / 174,625	1.4063 / 35,720	11300 / 5000	6400 / 2840	1.76	-0.14 / -3,6	M224749	M224710	0.14 / 3,5	1.4375 / 36,512	5.31 / 135,0	5.08 / 129,0	0.06 / 1,5	1.0938 / 27,783	6.42 / 163,0	6. / 168
4.7500 / 120,650	7.1875 / 182,562	1.5625 / 39,688	12900 / 5750	6750 / 3000	1.91	-0.22 / -5,6	48282	48220	0.14 / 3,5	1.5000 / 38,100	5.39 / 137,0	5.16 / 131,0	0.13 / 3,3	1.3125 / 33,338	6.61 / 168,0	6. / 176
4.7500 / 120,650	7.5000 / 190,500	1.8125 / 46,038	15900 / 7050	11600 / 5150	1.37	-0.15 / -3,8	HM624749	HM624710	0.14 / 3,5	1.8125 / 46,038	5.43 / 138,0	5.20 / 132,0	0.06 / 1,5	1.3750 / 34,925	6.85 / 174,0	7. / 184
4.7500 / 120,650	8.1250 / 206,375	1.8750 / 47,625	16800 / 7450	13200 / 5900	1.27	-0.07 / -1,9	795	792	0.13 / 3,3	1.8750 / 47,625	5.47 / 139,0	5.28 / 134,0	0.13 / 3,3	1.3750 / 34,925	7.32 / 198	7. / 198
4.7500 / 120,650	9.2500 / 234,950	2.5000 / 63,500	27300 / 12150	17300 / 7700	1.58	-0.55 / -13,9	95475	95925	0.25 / 6,4	2.5000 / 63,500	5.87 / 149,0	5.39 / 137,0	0.13 / 3,3	1.9375 / 49,212	8.23 / 209,0	8. / 217
4.7500 / 120,650	10.0000 / 254,000	3.0625 / 77,788	38200 / 17000	21000 / 9350	1.82	-0.92 / -23,3	HH228340	HH228310	0.38 / 9,7	3.2500 / 82,550	6.22 / 158,0	5.59 / 142,0	0.25 / 6,4	2.4375 / 61,912	8.78 / 223,0	9. / 233
4.7500 / 120,650	11.0000 / 279,400	3.2500 / 82,550	35900 / 16000	39100 / 17350	0.92	-0.26 / -6,6	HH926749	HH926716	0.25 / 6,4	3.2500 / 82,550	6.61 / 168,0	5.80 / 147,2	0.25 / 6,4	2.1250 / 53,975	9.17 / 233,0	9. / 253
4.8750 / 123,825	7.1875 / 182,562	1.5625 / 39,688	12900 / 5750	6750 / 3000	1.91	-0.22 / -5,6	48286	48220	0.14 / 3,5	1.5000 / 38,100	5.47 / 139,0	5.24 / 133,0	0.13 / 3,3	1.3125 / 33,338	6.61 / 168,0	6. / 176
4.9190 / 124,943	9.2500 / 234,950	2.5000 / 63,500	27300 / 12150	17300 / 7700	1.58	-0.55 / -13,9	95491	95925	0.25 / 6,4	2.5000 / 63,500	5.98 / 152,0	5.51 / 140,0	0.13 / 3,3	1.9375 / 49,212	8.23 / 209,0	8. / 217
4.9330 / 125,298	9.0000 / 228,600	2.1250 / 53,975	20500 / 9100	25900 / 11550	0.79	0.53 / 13,4	HM926745	HM926710	0.14 / 3,5	1.9460 / 49,428	6.06 / 154,0	5.63 / 143,0	0.13 / 3,3	1.5000 / 38,100	7.87 / 200,0	8. / 219
5.0000 / 127,000	6.5313 / 165,895	0.7188 / 18,258	4150 / 1840	2350 / 1045	0.24	0.24 / 6,1	LL225749	LL225710	0.06 / 1,5	0.6875 / 17,462	5.31 / 135,0	5.24 / 133,0	0.06 / 1,5	0.5313 / 13,495	6.22 / 158,0	6. / 160
5.0000 / 127,000	6.7500 / 171,450	1.0000 / 25,400	6750 / 3000	5450 / 2440	1.23	0.36 / 9,2	L725349	L725311	0.13 / 3,3	1.0000 / 25,400	5.47 / 139,0	5.28 / 134,0	0.13 / 3,3	0.7200 / 18,288	6.30 / 160,0	6. / 167
5.0000 / 127,000	7.1250 / 180,975	1.0000 / 25,400	7000 / 3120	3990 / 1775	1.76	0.10 / 2,4	L225849	L225818	0.06 / 1,5	1.0313 / 26,195	5.35 / 136,0	5.28 / 134,0	0.06 / 1,5	0.8125 / 20,638	6.46 / 164,0	6. / 166
5.0000 / 127,000	7.1875 / 182,562	1.5625 / 39,688	12900 / 5750	6750 / 3000	1.91	-0.22 / -5,6	48290	48220	0.14 / 3,5	1.5000 / 38,100	5.55 / 141,0	5.31 / 135,0	0.13 / 3,3	1.3125 / 33,338	6.61 / 168,0	6. / 176

SINGLE-ROW STRAIGHT BORE **TS**

bore	outside diameter	width	rating at 500 RPM for 3000 hours L10 one row radial	thrust	factor	eff. load center	part numbers cone	cup	cone max shaft fillet radius	width	backing shoulder diameters		cup max housing fillet radius	width	backing shoulder	
d	D	T	lb daN	lb daN	K	a	cone	cup	R	B	d_b	d_a	r	C	D_b	D_a
5.0000 127,000	7.7500 196,850	1.8125 46,038	16900 7500	9950 4420	1.70	−0.25 −6,3	67388	67322	0.14 3,5	1.8125 46,038	5.67 144,0	5.43 138,0	0.13 3,3	1.5000 38,100	7.09 180,0	7.44 189,0
5.0000 127,000	8.5000 215,900	1.8750 47,625	17200 7650	14300 6400	1.20	0.09 2,2	74500	74850	0.14 3,5	1.8750 47,625	5.83 148,0	5.55 141,0	0.13 3,3	1.3750 34,925	7.72 196,0	8.19 208,0
5.0000 127,000	9.0000 228,600	2.1250 53,975	20500 9100	25900 11550	0.79	0.53 13,4	HM926747	HM926710	0.14 3,5	1.9460 49,428	6.14 156,0	5.63 143,0	0.13 3,3	1.5000 38,100	7.87 200,0	8.63 219,3
5.0000 127,000	9.2500 234,950	2.5000 63,500	27300 12150	17300 7700	1.58	−0.55 −13,9	95500	95925	0.25 6,4	2.5000 63,500	6.06 154,0	5.59 142,0	0.13 3,3	1.9375 49,212	8.23 209,0	8.54 217,0
5.0000 127,000	10.0000 254,000	3.0625 77,788	38200 17000	21000 9350	1.82	−0.92 −23,3	HH228349	HH228310	0.38 9,7	3.2500 82,550	6.46 164,0	5.83 148,0	0.25 6,4	2.4375 61,912	8.78 223,0	9.20 233,6
5.0000 127,000	11.3750 288,925	3.2500 82,550	43000 19000	23400 10400	1.83	−1.05 −26,6	HH231637	HH231610	0.53 13,5	3.4375 87,312	6.85 174,0	5.91 150,0	0.25 6,4	2.2500 57,150	10.04 255,0	10.38 263,7
5.0000 127,000	12.0000 304,800	3.5000 88,900	34500 15350	43000 19200	0.80	0.07 1,7	EE516050	516120	0.25 6,4	3.2500 82,550	6.93 176,0	6.46 164,0	0.25 6,4	2.2500 57,150	10.08 256,0	10.98 278,9
5.0000 127,000	12.0000 304,800	3.5000 88,900	39400 17550	49500 22000	0.80	0.07 1,8	HH932132	HH932110	0.25 6,4	3.2500 82,550	7.17 182,0	6.77 172,0	0.25 6,4	2.2500 57,150	10.24 260,0	11.34 288,1
5.0312 127,792	9.0000 228,600	2.1250 53,975	20500 9100	25900 11550	0.79	0.53 13,4	HM926749	HM926710	0.14 3,5	1.9460 49,428	6.14 156,0	5.63 143,0	0.13 3,3	1.5000 38,100	7.87 200,0	8.63 219,3
5.0625 128,588	7.5000 190,500	1.3750 34,925	8150 3620	9150 4060	0.89	0.65 16,5	48506	48750	0.14 3,5	1.2500 31,750	5.67 144,0	5.43 138,0	0.13 3,3	1.0000 25,400	6.69 170,0	7.20 183,0
5.0625 128,588	8.1250 206,375	1.8750 47,625	16800 7450	13200 5900	1.27	−0.07 −1,9	799	792	0.13 3,3	1.8750 47,625	5.75 146,0	5.51 140,0	0.13 3,3	1.3750 34,925	7.32 186,0	7.80 198,0
5.1181 130,000	8.1250 206,375	1.8750 47,625	16800 7450	13200 5900	1.27	−0.07 −1,9	797	792	0.14 3,5	1.8750 47,625	5.83 148,0	5.55 141,0	0.13 3,3	1.3750 34,925	7.32 186,0	7.80 198,0
5.1250 130,175	8.0000 203,200	1.8125 46,038	16900 7500	9950 4420	1.70	−0.25 −6,3	67389	67320	0.14 3,5	1.8125 46,038	5.75 146,0	5.55 141,0	0.13 3,3	1.5000 38,100	7.20 183,0	7.52 191,0
5.1250 130,175	8.1250 206,375	1.8750 47,625	16800 7450	13200 5900	1.27	−0.07 −1,9	799A	792	0.14 3,5	1.8750 47,625	5.83 148,0	5.59 142,0	0.13 3,3	1.3750 34,925	7.32 186,0	7.80 198,0
5.2500 133,350	6.8125 173,038	0.7500 19,050	4300 1920	2570 1145	1.68	0.30 7,6	LL327049	LL327010	0.06 1,5	0.6875 17,462	5.55 141,0	5.47 139,0	0.06 1,5	0.5625 14,288	6.46 164,0	6.57 167,0
5.2500 133,350	6.9688 177,008	1.0000 25,400	7250 3220	4300 1920	1.68	0.16 3,9	L327249	L327210	0.06 1,5	1.0313 26,195	5.59 142,0	5.51 140,0	0.06 1,5	0.8125 20,638	6.57 167,0	6.73 171,0
5.2500 133,350	7.5000 190,500	1.5625 39,688	13700 6100	7500 3340	1.82	−0.16 −4,0	48385	48320	0.14 3,5	1.5625 39,688	5.83 148,0	5.59 142,0	0.13 3,3	1.3125 33,338	6.97 177,0	7.24 184,0
5.2500 133,350	7.7500 196,850	1.8125 46,038	16900 7500	9950 4420	1.70	−0.25 −6,3	67391	67322	0.31 8,0	1.8125 46,038	6.18 157,0	5.63 143,0	0.13 3,3	1.5000 38,100	7.09 180,0	7.44 189,0
5.2500 133,350	8.0000 203,200	1.8125 46,038	16900 7500	9950 4420	1.70	−0.25 −6,3	67390	67324	0.14 3,5	1.8125 46,038	5.87 149,0	5.63 143,0	0.13 3,3	1.8125 46,038	7.20 183,0	7.59 192,8
5.2500 133,350	8.4646 215,000	1.8750 47,625	17200 7650	14300 6400	1.20	0.09 2,2	74525	74846X	0.14 3,5	1.8750 47,625	5.98 152,0	5.75 146,0	0.13 3,3	1.3750 34,925	7.72 196,0	8.19 208,0
5.2500 133,350	9.2500 234,950	2.5000 63,500	27300 12150	17300 7700	1.58	−0.55 −13,9	95525	95925	0.38 9,7	2.5000 63,500	6.54 166,0	5.83 148,0	0.13 3,3	1.9375 49,212	8.23 209,0	8.54 217,0
5.2500 133,350	9.2500 234,950	2.5000 63,500	27300 12150	17300 7700	1.58	−0.55 −13,9	95528	95925	0.19 4,8	2.5000 63,500	6.18 157,0	5.83 148,0	0.13 3,3	1.9375 49,212	8.23 209,0	8.54 217,0
5.3750 136,525	7.3750 187,325	1.1250 28,575	9400 4180	5700 2540	1.65	0.14 3,6	LM328344	LM328410	0.06 1,5	1.1563 29,370	5.79 147,0	5.71 145,0	0.06 1,5	0.9063 23,020	6.93 176,0	7.17 182,0

① These maximum fillet radii will be cleared by the bearing corners.
② Minus value indicates center is inside backface.
† Dimension shown is maximum value—see note at bottom of fitting practice table page 4 in Reference Tables.

SINGLE-ROW STRAIGHT BORE—TS

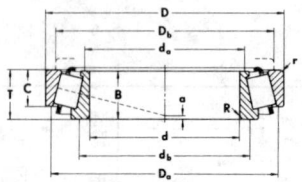

| | | | rating at 500 RPM for 3000 hours L10 | | fac-tor | eff. load center | part numbers | | cone max shaft fillet radius | cone width | cone backing shoulder diameters | | cup max hous-ing fillet radius | cup width | cup backing shoulder | |
| bore | outside diameter | width | one row radial | thrust | | | cone | cup | | | | | | | | |
d	D	T	lb daN	lb daN	K	a[①]			R[①]	B	d_b	d_a	r[①]	C	D_b	D_a
5.3750 136,525	7.5000 190,500	1.5625 39,688	13700 6100	7500 3340	1.82	−0.16 −4,0	48393	48320	0.14 3,5	1.5625 39,688	5.94 151,0	5.67 144,0	0.13 3,3	1.3125 33,338	6.97 177,0	7.24 184,0
5.3750 136,525	†6.6772 †195,000	1.2992 33,000	12000 5350	6800 3040	1.76	0.04 0,9	LM229139	LM229110	0.14 3,5	1.2992 33,000	5.98 152,0	5.75 146,0	0.14 3,5	1.0827 27,500	7.17 182,0	7.48 190,0
5.3750 136,525	8.4646 215,000	1.8750 47,625	17200 7650	14300 6400	1.20	0.09 2,2	74537	74846X	0.14 3,5	1.8750 47,625	6.10 155,0	5.83 148,0	0.13 3,3	1.3750 34,925	7.72 196,0	8.19 208,0
5.3750 136,525	9.0000 228,600	2.2500 57,150	23000 10250	16500 7350	1.39	−0.23 −6,0	896	892	0.14 3,5	2.2500 57,150	6.14 156,0	5.91 150,0	0.13 3,3	1.7500 44,450	8.07 205,0	8.50 216,0
5.5000 139,700	7.1250 180,975	0.8438 21,433	5250 2340	3290 1465	1.60	0.31 7,9	LL428349	LL428310	0.06 1,5	0.8125 20,638	5.83 148,0	5.75 146,0	0.06 1,5	0.6563 16,670	6.77 172,0	6.89 175,0
5.5000 139,700	7.3750 187,325	1.1250 28,575	9400 4180	5700 2540	1.65	0.14 3,6	LM328448	LM328410	0.06 1,5	1.1563 29,370	5.87 149,0	5.79 147,0	0.06 1,5	0.9063 23,020	6.93 176,0	7.17 182,0
5.5000 139,700	8.4646 215,000	1.8750 47,625	17200 7650	14300 6400	1.20	0.09 2,2	74550	74846X	0.14 3,5	1.8750 47,625	6.22 158,0	5.94 151,0	0.13 3,3	1.3750 34,925	7.72 196,0	8.19 208,0
5.5000 139,700	8.4646 215,000	1.8750 47,625	17200 7650	14300 6400	1.20	0.09 2,2	74550A	74846X	0.25 6,4	1.8750 47,625	6.42 163,0	5.94 151,0	0.13 3,3	1.3750 34,925	7.72 196,0	8.19 208,0
5.5000 139,700	9.0000 228,600	2.2500 57,150	23000 10250	16500 7350	1.39	−0.23 −6,0	898	892	0.14 3,5	2.2500 57,150	6.30 160,0	6.02 153,0	0.13 3,3	1.7500 44,450	8.07 205,0	8.50 216,0
5.5000 139,700	9.0000 228,600	2.2500 57,150	23000 10250	16500 7350	1.39	−0.23 −6,0	898A	892	0.25 6,4	2.2500 57,150	6.50 165,0	6.02 153,0	0.13 3,3	1.7500 44,450	8.07 205,0	8.50 216,0
5.5000 139,700	9.3125 236,538	2.2500 57,150	23000 10200	17400 7750	1.32	−0.14 −3,4	82550	82931	0.14 3,5	2.2300 56,642	6.34 161,0	6.06 154,0	0.13 3,3	1.7500 44,450	8.39 213,0	8.90 226,0
5.5000 139,700	9.8425 250,000	2.6250 66,675	29200 12950	20400 9050	1.43	−0.48 −12,2	99550	99098X	0.28 7,0	2.6250 66,675	6.69 170,0	6.14 156,0	0.13 3,3	1.8750 47,625	8.90 226,0	9.37 238,0
5.5000 139,700	11.6250 295,275	3.2500 82,550	43000 19000	23400 10400	1.83	−1.05 −26,6	HH231649	HH231615	0.38 9,7	3.4375 87,312	6.97 177,0	6.34 161,0	0.25 6,4	2.2500 57,150	10.16 258,0	10.38 263,7
5.5000 139,700	12.1250 307,975	3.5000 88,900	49500 22200	27800 12350	1.79	−1.04 −26,4	HH234031	HH234010	0.38 9,7	3.6875 93,662	7.09 180,0	6.61 168,0	0.27 6,8	2.6250 66,675	10.87 276,0	11.24 285,4
5.5000 139,700	12.2500 311,150	3.5000 88,900	34500 15350	43000 19200	0.80	0.07 1,7	EE516055	516122	0.25 6,4	3.2500 82,550	7.28 185,0	6.81 173,0	0.25 6,4	2.2500 57,150	10.20 259,0	10.98 278,9
5.5118 140,000	8.4646 215,000	1.8750 47,625	17200 7650	14300 6400	1.20	0.09 2,2	74551X	74846X	0.14 3,5	1.8750 47,625	6.22 158,0	6.02 153,0	0.13 3,3	1.3750 34,925	7.72 196,0	8.19 208,0
5.6250 142,875	7.6250 193,675	1.1250 28,575	9700 4320	6100 2720	1.59	0.19 4,8	36686	36620	0.06 1,5	1.1250 28,575	6.02 153,0	5.94 151,0	0.06 1,5	0.9063 23,020	7.17 182,0	7.40 188,0
5.6250 142,875	†6.6772 †195,000	1.2992 33,000	12000 5350	6800 3040	1.76	0.04 0,9	LM229146	LM229110	0.14 3,5	1.2992 33,000	6.18 157,0	5.91 150,0	0.14 3,5	1.0827 27,500	7.17 182,0	7.48 190,0
5.6250 142,875	7.8750 200,025	1.6250 41,275	13900 6200	8000 3560	1.74	−0.12 −3,0	48684	48620	0.31 8,0	1.5625 39,688	6.54 166,0	5.94 151,0	0.13 3,3	1.3437 34,130	7.28 185,0	7.60 193,0
5.6250 142,875	7.8750 200,025	1.6250 41,275	13900 6200	8000 3560	1.74	−0.12 −3,0	48685	48620	0.14 3,5	1.5625 39,688	6.22 158,0	5.94 151,0	0.13 3,3	1.3437 34,130	7.28 185,0	7.60 193,0
5.7500 146,050	7.4063 188,120	0.8750 22,225	5400 2400	3540 1575	1.53	0.37 9,4	LL529749	LL529710	0.06 1,5	0.8125 20,638	6.10 155,0	5.98 152,0	0.06 1,5	0.6563 16,670	7.05 179,0	7.17 182,0

| bore | outside diameter | width | rating at 500 RPM for 3000 hours L10 | | fac-tor | eff. load center | part numbers | | cone | | | | cup | | | |
| | | | one row radial | thrust | | | cone | cup | max. shaft fillet radius | width | backing shoulder diameters | | max. hous-ing fillet radius | width | backing shoulder | |
d	D	T	lb daN	lb daN	K	a②			R①	B	d_b	d_a	r①	C	D_b	D_a
5.7500 146,050	7.6250 193,675	1.1250 28,575	9700 4320	6100 2720	1.59	0.19 4,8	36691	36620	0.19 4,8	1.1250 28,575	6.38 162,0	6.02 153,0	0.06 1,5	0.9063 23,020	7.17 182,0	7.40 188,0
5.7500 146,050	8.0000 203,200	1.1250 28,575	9700 4320	6100 2720	1.59	0.19 4,8	36690	36626	0.06 1,5	1.1250 28,575	6.10 155,0	6.02 153,0	0.06 1,5	0.9063 23,020	7.32 186,0	7.48 190,0
5.7500 146,050	9.3125 236,538	2.2500 57,150	26300 11700	14400 6400	1.83	-0.45 -11,4	HM231140	HM231110	0.14 3,5	2.2300 56,642	6.46 164,0	6.30 160,0	0.13 3,3	1.7500 44,450	8.54 217,0	8.82 224,0
5.7500 146,050	9.5000 241,300	2.2500 57,150	23000 10200	17400 7750	1.32	-0.14 -3,4	82576	82950	0.14 3,5	2.2300 56,642	6.54 166,0	6.30 160,0	0.13 3,3	1.7500 44,450	8.46 215,0	8.90 226,0
5.7500 146,050	10.0000 254,000	2.6250 66,675	29200 12950	20400 9050	1.43	-0.48 -12,2	99575	99100	0.28 7,0	2.6250 66,675	6.89 175,0	6.38 162,0	0.13 3,3	1.8750 47,625	8.94 227,0	9.37 238,0
5.7500 146,050	10.5625 268,288	2.9375 74,612	34400 15300	22800 10150	1.51	-0.59 -15,0	EE107057	107105	0.25 6,4	2.9375 74,612	6.93 176,0	6.54 166,0	0.25 6,4	2.2500 57,150	9.33 237,0	9.82 249,4
5.7500 146,050	12.0000 304,800	3.5000 88,900	34500 15350	43000 19200	0.80	0.07 1,7	EE516057	516120	0.25 6,4	3.2500 82,550	7.48 190,0	6.90 175,2	0.25 6,4	2.2500 57,150	10.08 256,0	10.98 278,9
5.7500 146,050	12.0000 304,800	3.5000 88,900	39400 17550	49500 22000	0.80	0.07 1,8	HH932145	HH932110	0.25 6,4	3.2500 82,550	7.68 195,0	6.87 174,4	0.25 6,4	2.2500 57,150	10.24 260,0	11.34 288,1
5.8750 149,225	9.3125 236,538	2.2500 57,150	26300 11700	14400 6400	1.83	-0.45 -11,4	HM231148	HM231110	0.25 6,4	2.2300 56,642	6.77 172,0	6.42 163,0	0.13 3,3	1.7500 44,450	8.54 217,0	8.82 224,0
5.8750 149,225	9.5000 241,300	2.2500 57,150	26300 11700	14400 6400	1.83	-0.45 -11,4	HM231149	HM231115	0.14 3,5	2.2300 56,642	6.57 167,0	6.42 163,0	0.13 3,3	1.7500 44,450	8.62 219,0	8.82 224,0
5.8750 149,225	9.8425 250,000	2.6250 66,675	29200 12950	20400 9050	1.43	-0.48 -12,2	99587	99098X	0.28 7,0	2.6250 66,675	7.01 178,0	6.50 165,0	0.13 3,3	1.8750 47,625	8.90 226,0	9.37 238,0
6.0000 152,400	7.5625 192,088	0.9843 25,000	6950 3080	4950 2200	1.40	0.40 10,0	L630349	L630310	0.08 2,0	0.9449 24,000	6.38 162,0	6.22 158,0	0.08 2,0	0.7480 19,000	7.20 183,0	7.36 187,0
6.0000 152,400	8.0000 203,200	1.1250 28,575	8850 3940	6950 3100	1.27	0.45 11,4	L730649	L730610	0.13 3,3	1.1250 28,575	6.50 165,0	6.30 160,0	0.13 3,3	0.8440 21,438	7.48 190,0	7.80 198,0
6.0000 152,400	8.7500 222,250	1.8437 46,830	17400 7750	9900 4400	1.76	-0.23 -6,0	M231649	M231610	0.14 3,5	1.8437 46,830	6.65 169,0	6.42 163,0	0.06 1,5	1.3750 34,925	8.15 207,0	8.39 213,0
6.0000 152,400	9.8425 250,000	2.6250 66,675	29200 12950	20400 9050	1.43	-0.48 -12,2	99600	99098X	0.28 7,0	2.6250 66,675	7.13 181,0	6.57 167,0	0.13 3,3	1.8750 47,625	8.90 226,0	9.37 238,0
6.0000 152,400	10.5625 268,288	2.9375 74,612	34400 15300	22800 10150	1.51	-0.59 -15,0	EE107060	107105	0.25 6,4	2.9375 74,612	7.13 181,0	6.73 171,0	0.25 6,4	2.2500 57,150	9.33 237,0	9.82 249,4
6.0000 152,400	12.1250 307,975	3.5000 88,900	49500 22200	27800 12350	1.79	-1.04 -26,4	HH234048	HH234010	0.38 9,7	3.6875 93,662	7.52 191,0	7.05 179,0	0.27 6,8	2.6250 66,675	10.87 276,0	11.24 285,4
6.0000 152,400	12.1250 307,975	3.5000 88,900	44000 19600	24600 10950	1.79	-1.11 -28,3	EE450601	451212	0.38 9,7	3.6875 93,662	7.44 189,0	6.97 177,0	0.27 6,8	2.4375 61,912	10.59 269,0	10.82 274,8
6.1250 155,575	13.0000 330,200	3.3750 85,725	42500 18800	59000 26200	0.72	0.67 16,9	H936340	H936310	0.25 6,4	3.1250 79,375	8.23 209,0	7.58 192,4	0.25 6,4	2.1250 53,975	11.10 282,0	12.26 311,4
6.2500 158,750	8.0938 205,583	0.9375 23,812	7000 3120	4450 1980	1.57	0.37 9,4	L432348	L432310	0.19 4,8	0.9375 23,812	6.85 174,0	6.54 166,0	0.06 1,5	0.7188 18,258	7.68 195,0	7.83 199,0
6.2500 158,750	8.0938 205,583	0.9375 23,812	7000 3120	4450 1980	1.57	0.37 9,4	L432349	L432310	0.06 1,5	0.9375 23,812	6.61 168,0	6.54 166,0	0.06 1,5	0.7188 18,258	7.68 195,0	7.83 199,0
6.2500 158,750	8.8750 225,425	1.6250 41,275	15100 6750	9950 4420	1.52	0.10 2,5	46780	46720	0.14 3,5	1.5625 39,688	6.93 176,0	6.65 169,0	0.13 3,3	1.3125 33,338	8.23 209,0	8.58 218,0
6.3120 160,325	11.3750 288,925	2.5000 63,500	35500 15800	19400 8600	1.83	-0.46 -11,6	HM237532	HM237510	0.28 7,0	2.5000 63,500	7.56 192,0	7.13 181,0	0.13 3,3	1.8750 47,625	10.47 266,0	10.68 271,3

① These maximum fillet radii will be cleared by the bearing corners.
② Minus value indicates center is inside cone backface.
† Dimension shown is maximum value—see note at bottom of fitting practice table page 4 in Reference Tables.

SINGLE-ROW STRAIGHT BORE—TS

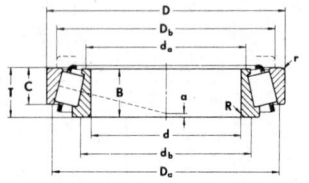

bore	outside diameter	width	rating at 500 RPM for 3000 hours L10		fac-tor	eff. load center	part numbers		cone				cup			
---	---	---	one row radial	thrust			cone	cup	max. shaft fillet radius	width	backing shoulder diameters		max. housing fillet radius	width	backing shoulder	
d	D	T	lb daN	lb daN	K	a②			R①	B	d_b	d_a	r①	C	D_b	D_a
6.5000 165,100	8.5000 215,900	1.0313 26,195	8400 3740	5250 2340	1.60	0.34 8,6	L433749	L433710	0.06 1,5	1.0313 26,195	6.85 174,0	6.77 172,0	0.06 1,5	0.8125 20,638	8.07 205,0	8.23 209,0
6.5000 165,100	8.8750 225,425	1.6250 41,275	15100 6750	9950 4420	1.52	0.10 2,5	46790	46720	0.14 3,5	1.5625 39,688	7.13 181,0	6.85 174,0	0.13 3,3	1.3125 33,338	8.23 209,0	8.58 218,0
6.5000 165,100	9.7500 247,650	1.8750 47,625	19500 8650	14700 6500	1.33	0.19 4,8	67780	67720	0.14 3,5	1.8750 47,625	7.28 185,0	7.05 179,0	0.13 3,3	1.5000 38,100	9.02 229,0	9.45 240,0
6.5000 165,100	10.0000 254,000	1.8125 46,038	18100 8050	11500 5100	1.58	-0.06 -1,5	86650	86100	0.19 4,8	1.8125 46,038	7.28 185,0	6.93 176,0	0.13 3,3	1.3125 33,338	9.21 234,0	9.41 239,0
6.5000 165,100	11.3750 288,925	2.5000 63,500	30000 13350	24000 10650	1.25	-0.03 -0,8	94649	94113	0.28 7,0	2.5000 63,500	7.76 197,0	7.32 186,0	0.13 3,3	1.8750 47,625	10.20 259,0	10.71 272,0
6.5000 165,100	11.3750 288,925	2.5000 63,500	35500 15800	19400 8600	1.83	-0.46 -11,6	HM237535	HM237510	0.28 7,0	2.5000 63,500	7.68 195,0	7.24 184,0	0.13 3,3	1.8750 47,625	10.47 266,0	10.68 271,3
6.5000 165,100	12.2500 311,150	3.2500 82,550	46000 20400	25900 11550	1.77	-0.73 -18,5	H238140	H238110	0.25 6,4	3.2500 82,550	7.80 198,0	7.40 188,0	0.25 6,4	2.5625 65,088	11.02 280,0	11.36 288,5
6.5000 165,100	13.2500 336,550	3.6250 92,075	58000 25800	37100 16500	1.57	-0.84 -21,5	HH437549	HH437510	0.13 3,3	3.7500 95,250	7.72 196,0	7.72 196,0	0.25 6,4	2.7500 69,850	11.69 297,0	12.12 307,7
6.5000 165,100	14.1732 560,000	3.6250 92,075	48500 21600	33500 14900	1.45	-0.61 -15,6	EE420651	421417	0.38 9,7	3.4999 88,897	8.46 215,0	7.83 199,0	0.13 3,3	2.5000 63,500	12.87 327,0	13.16 334,4
6.6250 168,275	9.7500 247,650	1.8750 47,625	19500 8650	14700 6500	1.33	0.19 4,8	67782	67720	0.14 3,5	1.8750 47,625	7.36 187,0	7.13 181,0	0.13 3,3	1.5000 38,100	9.02 229,0	9.45 240,0
6.6250 168,275	13.5000 342,900	3.3750 85,725	42500 18800	59000 26200	0.72	0.67 16,9	H936349	H936316	0.25 6,4	3.1250 79,375	8.58 218,0	7.58 192,4	0.25 6,4	2.1250 53,975	11.30 287,0	12.26 311,4
*6.6929 *170,000	*9.0551 *230,000	1.5354 39,000	15500 6900	10200 4550	1.52	0.18 4,6	JHM534149	JHM534110	0.12 3,0	1.4961 38,000	7.24 184,0	7.01 178,0	0.10 2,5	1.2205 31,000	8.54 217,0	8.82 224,0
*6.6929 *170,000	*9.4488 *240,000	1.8110 46,000	19900 8850	14900 6600	1.34	0.20 5,0	JM734449	JM734410	0.12 3,0	1.7520 44,500	7.28 185,0	7.09 180,0	0.10 2,5	1.4567 37,000	8.74 222,0	9.12 231,7
6.6929 170,000	10.0000 254,000	1.8125 46,038	18100 8050	11500 5100	1.58	-0.06 -1,5	86669	86100	0.19 4,8	1.8125 46,038	7.44 189,0	7.09 180,0	0.13 3,3	1.3125 33,338	9.21 234,0	9.41 239,0
6.7500 171,450	8.7500 222,250	1.0000 25,400	7850 3480	5050 2240	1.55	0.42 10,7	L435049	L435010	0.06 1,5	0.9688 24,608	7.13 181,0	7.05 179,0	0.06 1,5	0.7500 19,050	8.31 211,0	8.46 215,0
6.7500 171,450	10.2500 260,350	2.6250 66,675	31000 13800	21400 9500	1.45	-0.34 -8,5	HM535349	HM535310	0.14 3,5	2.6250 66,675	7.56 192,0	7.40 186,1	0.13 3,3	2.0625 52,388	9.29 236,0	9.84 250,0
6.7500 171,450	11.7500 298,450	2.5000 63,500	30000 13350	24000 10650	1.25	-0.03 -0,8	94675	94118	0.28 7,0	2.5000 63,500	7.95 202,0	7.52 191,0	0.13 3,3	1.8750 47,625	10.35 263,0	10.71 272,0
6.7500 171,450	13.5000 342,900	3.1250 79,375	34500 15350	29200 13000	1.18	-0.18 -4,5	EE590675	591350	0.25 6,4	3.1875 80,962	8.07 205,0	7.72 196,0	0.25 6,4	2.1250 53,975	11.73 298,0	12.08 306,8
6.8750 174,625	9.7500 247,650	1.8750 47,625	19500 8650	14700 6500	1.33	0.19 4,8	67786	67720	0.31 8,0	1.8750 47,625	7.87 200,0	7.28 185,0	0.13 3,3	1.5000 38,100	9.02 229,0	9.45 240,0
6.8750 174,625	9.7500 247,650	1.8750 47,625	19500 8650	14700 6500	1.33	0.19 4,8	67787	67720	0.14 3,5	1.8750 47,625	7.56 192,0	7.28 185,0	0.13 3,3	1.5000 38,100	9.02 229,0	9.45 240,0
6.8750 174,625	10.2500 260,350	2.1250 53,975	24800 11050	14100 6300	1.76	-0.25 -6,5	M236845	M236810	0.14 3,5	2.1250 53,975	7.60 193,0	7.44 189,0	0.13 3,3	1.6250 41,275	9.49 241,0	9.80 249,0

			rating at 500 RPM for 3000 hours L10		fac-tor	eff. load center	part numbers		cone				cup			
			one row radial	thrust					max. shaft fillet radius	width	backing shoulder diameters		max. hous-ing fillet radius	width	backing shoulder	
bore	outside diameter	width	lb daN	lb daN			cone	cup								
d	D	T	lb daN	lb daN	K	a②	cone	cup	R①	B	d_b	d_a	r①	C	D_b	D_a
6.8750	11.3750	2.5000	30000	24000	1.25	−0.03	94687	94113	0.28	2.5000	8.03	7.60	0.13	1.8750	10.20	10.71
174,625	288,925	63,500	13350	10650		−0,8			7,0	63,500	204,0	193,0	3,3	47,625	259,0	272,0
6.8750	11.3750	2.5000	35500	19400	1.83	−0.46	HM237542	HM237510	0.28	2.5000	7.95	7.52	0.13	1.8750	10.47	10.68
174,625	288,925	63,500	15800	8600		−11,6			7,0	63,500	202,0	191,0	3,3	47,625	266,0	271,3
6.8750	11.7500	3.2500	43500	28000	1.55	−0.60	EE219068	219117	0.25	3.2500	8.03	7.60	0.25	2.5000	10.59	11.10
174,625	298,450	82,550	19400	12450		−15,3			6,4	82,550	204,0	193,0	6,4	63,500	269,0	282,0
6.8750	12.2500	3.2500	43500	28000	1.55	−0.60	EE219068	219122	0.25	3.2500	8.03	7.60	0.25	2.5000	10.83	11.10
174,625	311,150	82,550	19400	12450		−15,3			6,4	82,550	204,0	193,0	6,4	63,500	275,0	282,0
6.8750	12.2500	3.2500	46000	25900	1.77	−0.73	H238148	H238110	0.25	3.2500	8.07	7.68	0.25	2.5625	11.02	11.36
174,625	311,150	82,550	20400	11550		−18,5			6,4	82,550	205,0	195,0	6,4	65,088	280,0	288,5
7.0000	8.9375	1.1875	10600	8000	1.33	0.50	36990	36920	0.06	1.1875	7.40	7.32	0.06	0.9063	8.43	8.70
177,800	227,012	30,162	4700	3540		12,7			1,5	30,162	188,0	186,0	1,5	23,020	214,0	221,0
7.0000	9.7500	1.8750	19500	14700	1.33	0.19	67790	67720	0.14	1.8750	7.64	7.40	0.13	1.5000	9.02	9.45
177,800	247,650	47,625	8650	6500		4,8			3,5	47,625	194,0	188,0	3,3	38,100	229,0	240,0
7.0000	9.7500	1.8750	19500	14700	1.33	0.19	67791	67720	0.41	1.8750	8.19	7.40	0.13	1.5000	9.02	9.45
177,800	247,650	47,625	8650	6500		4,8			10,4	47,625	208,0	188,0	3,3	38,100	229,0	240,0
7.0000	10.2500	2.1250	24800	14100	1.76	−0.25	M236848	M236810	0.31	2.1250	8.03	7.52	0.13	1.6250	9.49	9.80
177,800	260,350	53,975	11050	6300		−6,5			8,0	53,975	204,0	191,0	3,3	41,275	241,0	249,0
7.0000	10.2500	2.1250	24800	14100	1.76	−0.25	M236849	M236810	0.14	2.1250	7.68	7.52	0.13	1.6250	9.49	9.80
177,800	260,350	53,975	11050	6300		−6,5			3,5	53,975	195,0	191,0	3,3	41,275	241,0	249,0
7.0000	10.6250	2.1875	24200	13700	1.76	−0.24	M238840	M238810	0.14	2.1875	7.80	7.64	0.13	1.6875	9.84	10.08
177,800	269,875	55,562	10750	6100		−6,0			3,5	55,562	198,0	194,0	3,3	42,862	250,0	256,0
7.0000	11.3750	2.5000	30000	24000	1.25	−0.03	94700	94113	0.28	2.5000	8.15	7.68	0.13	1.8750	10.20	10.71
177,800	288,925	63,500	13350	10650		−0,8			7,0	63,500	207,0	195,0	3,3	47,625	259,0	272,0
7.0000	11.3750	2.5000	35500	19400	1.83	−0.46	HM237545	HM237510	0.28	2.5000	8.07	7.64	0.13	1.8750	10.47	10.68
177,800	288,925	63,500	15800	8600		−11,6			7,0	63,500	205,0	194,0	3,3	47,625	266,0	271,3
7.0000	12.5970	3.5000	44500	24300	1.83	−0.88	H239640	H239610	0.14	3.3750	7.95	7.80	0.19	2.5625	11.54	11.84
177,800	319,964	88,900	19800	10800		−22,3			3,5	85,725	202,0	198,0	4,8	65,088	293,0	300,8
7.0000	12.8750	3.5625	43500	27200	1.60	−0.86	EE470078X	470128	0.38	3.6250	8.54	7.91	0.25	2.5000	11.57	12.07
177,800	327,025	90,488	19400	12100		−22,0			9,7	92,075	217,0	201,0	6,4	63,500	294,0	306,5
7.0000	14.0000	3.1250	41000	38400	1.07	0.14	EE607070	607140	0.25	3.0625	8.43	8.03	0.25	2.1250	12.28	12.84
177,800	355,600	79,375	18200	17100		3,4			6,4	77,788	214,0	204,0	6,4	53,975	312,0	326,1
7.0000	14.3720	3.6250	48500	33500	1.45	−0.61	EE420701	421437	0.50	3.4999	9.09	8.19	0.13	2.5000	12.95	13.16
177,800	365,049	92,075	21600	14900		−15,6			12,7	88,897	231,0	208,0	3,3	63,500	329,0	334,4
7.0000	16.8750	4.1875	51000	66000	0.77	0.51	EE350701	351687	0.25	3.7500	9.06	8.70	0.25	2.4375	14.37	15.08
177,800	428,625	106,362	22600	29400		13,0			6,4	95,250	230,0	221,0	6,4	61,912	365,0	383,0
*7.0866	*9.8425	1.8504	20600	16900	1.22	0.35	JM736149	JM736110	0.12	1.7717	7.72	7.50	0.10	1.4567	9.13	9.55
*180,000	*250,000	47,000	9150	7500		9,0			3,0	45,000	196,0	190,5	2,5	37,000	232,0	242,6
7.0866	10.5000	1.8543	19200	15800	1.22	0.42	67875	67820	0.25	1.8110	8.15	7.87	0.13	1.5000	9.69	10.20
180,000	266,700	47,099	8550	7000		10,6			6,4	46,000	207,0	200,0	3,3	38,100	246,0	259,0
†7.0866	12.5000	2.5000	32900	29400	1.12	0.31	93708	93125	0.14	2.5000	8.23	8.03	0.13	1.8125	11.26	11.81
†180,000	317,500	63,500	14650	13050		7,9			3,5	63,500	209,0	204,0	3,3	46,038	286,0	300,0
7.2500	9.2610	1.3386	13700	7900	1.74	0.20	LM236749	LM236710A	0.08	1.2992	7.68	7.52	0.08	1.1024	8.82	9.02
184,150	235,229	34,000	6100	3540		5,1			2,0	33,000	195,0	191,0	2,0	28,000	224,0	229,0
7.2500	11.0236	1.8317	19200	15800	1.22	0.40	67883	67830	0.13	1.8438	8.03	7.80	0.13	1.4173	9.92	10.20
184,150	280,000	46,526	8550	7000		10,1			3,5	46,833	204,0	198,0	3,3	36,000	252,0	259,0

① These maximum fillet radii will be cleared by the bearing corners.
② Minus value indicates center is inside cone backface.
† Dimension shown is maximum value—see note at bottom of fitting practice table page 4 in Reference Tables.
* For "J" part tolerances see metric tolerance, page 20 and fitting practice page 6 in Reference Tables.

SINGLE-ROW STRAIGHT BORE—TS

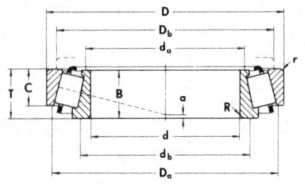

						cone	cup							

bore	outside diameter	width	rating at 500 RPM for 3000 hours L10 — one row radial	rating at 500 RPM for 3000 hours L10 — thrust	fac-tor	eff. load center	part numbers — cone	part numbers — cup	cone — max shaft fillet radius	cone — width	cone — db	cone — da	cup — max housing fillet radius	cup — width	cup — Db	cup — Da
d	D	T	lb daN	lb daN	K	a②	cone	cup	R①	B	db	da	r①	C	Db	Da
7.3750 / 187,325	10.6250 / 269,875	2.1875 / 55,562	24200 / 10750	13700 / 6100	1.76	−0.24 / −6,0	M238849	M238810	0.14 / 3,5	2.1875 / 55,562	8.07 / 205,0	7.91 / 201,0	0.13 / 3,3	1.6875 / 42,862	9.84 / 250,0	10.08 / 256,0
7.3750 / 187,325	11.1250 / 282,575	2.0000 / 50,800	17200 / 7650	12200 / 5400	1.41	0.15 / 3,8	87737	87111	0.14 / 3,5	1.8750 / 47,625	8.15 / 207,0	7.91 / 201,0	0.13 / 3,3	1.4375 / 36,512	10.28 / 261,0	10.50 / 266,6
7.3750 / 187,325	11.4170 / 289,992	1.8317 / 46,526	19200 / 8550	15800 / 7000	1.22	0.40 / 10,1	67884	67835	0.14 / 3,5	1.8438 / 46,833	8.11 / 206,0	7.91 / 201,0	0.13 / 3,3	1.4173 / 36,000	10.08 / 256,0	10.20 / 259,0
7.3750 / 187,325	12.6250 / 320,675	3.5000 / 88,900	44500 / 19800	24300 / 10800	1.83	−0.88 / −22,3	H239649	H239612	0.22 / 5,5	3.3750 / 85,725	8.43 / 214,0	8.07 / 205,0	0.19 / 4,8	2.5625 / 65,088	11.54 / 293,0	11.84 / 300,8
*7.4803 / *190,000	*10.2362 / *260,000	1.8110 / 46,000	19200 / 8550	15700 / 7000	1.22	0.43 / 10,8	JM738249	JM738210	0.12 / 3,0	1.7323 / 44,000	8.11 / 206,0	7.87 / 200,0	0.10 / 2,5	1.4370 / 36,500	9.53 / 242,0	9.92 / 252,0
7.4834 / 190,078	10.5000 / 266,700	1.8543 / 47,099	19200 / 8550	15800 / 7000	1.22	0.42 / 10,6	67886	67820	0.25 / 6,4	1.8110 / 46,000	8.43 / 214,0	7.99 / 203,0	0.13 / 3,3	1.5000 / 38,100	9.69 / 246,0	10.20 / 259,0
7.5000 / 190,500	10.5000 / 266,700	1.8750 / 47,625	19200 / 8550	15800 / 7000	1.22	0.40 / 10,1	67885	67820	0.14 / 3,5	1.8438 / 46,833	8.23 / 209,0	7.99 / 203,0	0.13 / 3,3	1.5000 / 38,100	9.69 / 246,0	10.20 / 259,0
7.5000 / 190,500	11.1250 / 282,575	2.0000 / 50,800	17200 / 7650	12200 / 5400	1.41	0.15 / 3,8	87750	87111	0.14 / 3,5	1.8750 / 47,625	8.23 / 209,0	7.99 / 203,0	0.13 / 3,3	1.4375 / 36,512	10.28 / 261,0	10.50 / 266,6
7.5000 / 190,500	12.5000 / 317,500	2.6875 / 68,262	32900 / 14650	29400 / 13050	1.12	0.31 / 7,9	93750	93126	0.17 / 4,3	2.5000 / 63,500	8.58 / 218,0	8.35 / 212,0	0.13 / 3,3	2.0000 / 50,800	11.22 / 285,0	11.81 / 300,0
7.5000 / 190,500	12.8750 / 327,025	3.5625 / 90,488	43500 / 19400	27200 / 12100	1.60	−0.88 / −22,0	EE470075	470128	0.25 / 6,4	3.6250 / 92,075	8.66 / 220,0	8.27 / 210,0	0.25 / 6,4	2.5000 / 63,500	11.57 / 294,0	12.07 / 306,5
7.5000 / 190,500	13.2500 / 336,550	3.8750 / 98,425	55000 / 24600	54500 / 24200	1.01	−0.21 / −5,5	HH840249	HH840210	0.25 / 6,4	3.7500 / 95,250	9.21 / 234,0	8.49 / 215,7	0.25 / 6,4	2.8750 / 73,025	11.42 / 290,0	12.52 / 318,0
7.5000 / 190,500	14.5000 / 368,300	3.6250 / 92,075	48500 / 21600	33500 / 14900	1.45	−0.61 / −15,6	EE420751	421450	0.25 / 6,4	3.4999 / 88,897	8.94 / 227,0	8.58 / 218,0	0.13 / 3,3	2.5000 / 63,500	13.03 / 331,0	13.16 / 334,4
7.5000 / 190,500	16.8750 / 428,625	4.1875 / 106,362	51000 / 22600	66000 / 29400	0.77	0.51 / 13,0	EE350750	351687	0.25 / 6,4	3.7500 / 95,250	9.45 / 240,0	9.33 / 236,9	0.25 / 6,4	2.4375 / 61,912	14.37 / 365,0	15.08 / 383,0
7.5625 / 192,088	10.5000 / 266,700	1.8750 / 47,625	19200 / 8550	15800 / 7000	1.22	0.40 / 10,1	67887	67820	0.41 / 10,4	1.8438 / 46,833	8.78 / 223,0	8.03 / 204,0	0.13 / 3,3	1.5000 / 38,100	9.69 / 246,0	10.20 / 259,0
7.6250 / 193,675	11.1250 / 282,575	2.0000 / 50,800	17200 / 7650	12200 / 5400	1.41	0.15 / 3,8	87762	87111	0.14 / 3,5	1.8750 / 47,625	8.31 / 211,0	8.11 / 206,0	0.13 / 3,3	1.4375 / 36,512	10.28 / 261,0	10.50 / 266,6
7.7500 / 196,850	9.5000 / 241,300	0.9375 / 23,812	7550 / 3360	5400 / 2400	1.40	0.69 / 17,4	LL639249	LL639210	0.06 / 1,5	0.9062 / 23,017	8.07 / 205,0	7.99 / 203,0	0.06 / 1,5	0.6875 / 17,462	9.13 / 232,0	9.29 / 236,0
7.7500 / 196,850	10.0000 / 254,000	1.1250 / 28,575	8900 / 3960	6050 / 2700	1.47	0.56 / 14,2	L540049	L540010	0.06 / 1,5	1.0938 / 27,783	8.15 / 207,0	8.07 / 205,0	0.06 / 1,5	0.8438 / 21,433	9.57 / 243,0	9.72 / 247,0
7.7500 / 196,850	10.1250 / 257,175	1.5625 / 39,688	15600 / 6950	11900 / 5300	1.31	0.45 / 11,4	LM739749	LM739710	0.14 / 3,5	1.5625 / 39,688	8.39 / 213,0	8.11 / 206,0	0.13 / 3,3	1.1875 / 30,162	9.47 / 239,0	9.88 / 251,0
7.7500 / 196,850	12.5000 / 317,500	2.5000 / 63,500	32900 / 14650	29400 / 13050	1.12	0.31 / 7,9	93775	93125	0.17 / 4,3	2.5000 / 63,500	8.78 / 223,0	8.50 / 216,0	0.13 / 3,3	1.8125 / 46,038	11.26 / 286,0	11.81 / 300,0
*7.8740 / *200,000	*11.8110 / *300,000	2.5591 / 65,000	33200 / 14750	29700 / 13200	1.12	0.32 / 8,1	JHM840449	JHM840410	0.14 / 3,5	2.4409 / 62,000	8.78 / 223,0	8.46 / 214,8	0.10 / 2,5	2.0079 / 51,000	10.75 / 273,0	11.37 / 288,9
7.8750 / 200,025	12.5000 / 317,500	2.5000 / 63,500	32900 / 14650	29400 / 13050	1.12	0.31 / 7,9	93787	93125	0.17 / 4,3	2.5000 / 63,500	8.86 / 225,0	8.62 / 219,0	0.13 / 3,3	1.8125 / 46,038	11.26 / 286,0	11.81 / 300,0

| bore | outside diameter | width | rating at 500 RPM for 3000 hours L10 | | fac-tor | eff. load center | part numbers | | cone | | | | cup | | | |
| | | | one row radial | thrust | | | cone | cup | max. shaft fillet radius | width | backing shoulder diameters | | max. hous-ing fillet radius | width | backing shoulder | |
d	D	T	lb daN	lb daN	K	a[2]			R[1]	B	d_b	d_a	r[1]	C	D_b	D_a
7.8750 200,025	13.1250 333,375	2.7500 69,850	41000 18200	30700 13650	1.33	0.03 0,8	HM743337	HM743310	0.25 6,4	2.7500 69,850	9.09 231,0	8.70 221,0	0.25 6,4	2.0625 52,388	11.93 303,0	12.48 317,1
7.8750 200,025	15.1250 384,175	4.4375 112,712	81500 36200	46500 20600	1.76	-1.10 -28,1	H247535	H247510	0.25 6,4	4.4375 112,712	9.49 241,0	9.09 231,0	0.25 6,4	3.5625 90,488	13.62 346,0	14.26 362,1
7.8750 200,025	15.5000 393,700	4.3750 111,125	72500 32200	37000 16450	1.96	-1.33 -33,9	HH144642	HH144614	0.25 6,4	4.3750 111,125	9.25 235,0	8.90 226,0	0.25 6,4	3.3125 84,138	13.86 352,0	14.04 356,6
8.0000 203,200	10.2812 261,142	1.1250 28,575	9000 4020	6300 2800	1.43	0.62 15,7	LL641149	LL641110	0.06 1,5	1.0938 27,783	8.43 214,0	8.35 212,0	0.06 1,5	0.8438 21,433	9.80 249,0	10.00 254,0
8.0000 203,200	10.8750 276,225	1.6875 42,862	19100 8450	10400 4650	1.83	0.07 1,7	LM241149	LM241110	0.14 3,5	1.6875 42,862	8.62 219,0	8.43 214,0	0.13 3,3	1.3438 34,133	10.24 260,0	10.51 267,0
8.0000 203,200	11.1250 282,575	1.8125 46,038	19900 8850	17300 7700	1.15	0.63 16,0	67983	67920	0.14 3,5	1.8125 46,038	8.74 222,0	8.50 216,0	0.13 3,3	1.4375 36,512	10.24 260,0	10.83 275,0
8.0000 203,200	11.5000 292,100	2.2813 57,945	28500 12700	16200 7200	1.76	-0.18 -4,7	M241547	M241510	0.14 3,5	2.2813 57,945	8.70 221,0	8.54 217,0	0.13 3,3	1.8125 46,038	10.71 272,0	10.98 279,0
8.0000 203,200	12.5000 317,500	2.5000 63,500	32900 14650	29400 13050	1.12	0.31 7,9	93800	93125	0.17 4,3	2.5000 63,500	8.94 227,0	8.74 222,0	0.13 3,3	1.8125 46,038	11.26 286,0	11.81 300,0
8.0000 203,200	12.5000 317,500	2.5000 63,500	32900 14650	29400 13050	1.12	0.31 7,9	93800A	93125	0.31 8,0	2.5000 63,500	9.21 234,0	8.74 222,0	0.13 3,3	1.8125 46,038	11.26 286,0	11.81 300,0
8.0000 203,200	14.1732 360,000	3.6250 92,075	48500 21600	33500 14900	1.45	-0.61 -15,6	EE420801	421417	0.13 3,3	3.4999 88,897	9.06 230,0	8.94 227,0	0.13 3,3	2.5000 63,500	12.87 327,0	13.16 334,4
8.0000 203,200	19.0000 482,600	4.6250 117,475	58000 25800	86500 38600	0.67	1.35 34,3	EE380080	380190	0.25 6,4	3.7500 95,250	10.31 262,0	10.08 256,0	0.25 6,4	2.8750 73,025	15.83 402,0	16.85 428,1
8.0625 204,788	11.5000 292,100	2.2813 57,945	28500 12700	16200 7200	1.76	-0.18 -4,7	M241549	M241510	0.14 3,5	2.2813 57,945	8.78 223,0	8.62 219,0	0.13 3,3	1.8125 46,038	10.71 272,0	10.98 279,0
8.0625 204,788	12.5000 317,500	2.5000 63,500	32900 14650	29400 13050	1.12	0.31 7,9	93806A	93125	0.17 4,3	2.5000 63,500	9.02 229,0	8.78 223,0	0.13 3,3	1.8125 46,038	11.26 286,0	11.81 300,0
8.1250 206,375	11.1250 282,575	1.8125 46,038	19900 8850	17300 7700	1.15	0.63 16,0	67985	67920	0.14 3,5	1.8125 46,038	8.82 224,0	8.62 219,0	0.13 3,3	1.4375 36,512	10.24 260,0	10.83 275,0
8.1250 206,375	12.5000 317,500	2.1250 53,975	23000 10250	12400 5500	1.86	-0.24 -6,2	EE132084	132125	0.16 4,0	2.1250 53,975	8.94 227,0	8.66 220,0	0.13 3,3	1.3750 34,925	11.57 294,0	11.54 293,0
8.1250 206,375	12.5000 317,500	2.5000 63,500	32900 14650	29400 13050	1.12	0.31 7,9	93812	93125	0.17 4,3	2.5000 63,500	9.06 230,0	8.82 224,0	0.13 3,3	1.8125 46,038	11.26 286,0	11.81 300,0
8.1250 206,375	13.2500 336,550	3.8750 98,425	61000 27200	34800 15500	1.76	-1.00 -25,5	H242649	H242610	0.13 3,3	3.9375 100,012	9.09 231,0	8.94 227,0	0.13 3,3	3.0625 77,788	12.05 306,0	12.51 317,7
8.1250 206,375	14.1732 360,000	3.6250 92,075	48500 21600	33500 14900	1.45	-0.61 -15,6	EE420812X	421417	0.25 6,4	3.4999 88,897	9.41 239,0	9.02 229,0	0.13 3,3	2.5000 63,500	12.87 327,0	13.16 334,4
8.1250 206,375	19.0000 482,600	4.6250 117,475	58000 25800	86500 38600	0.67	1.35 34,3	EE380081	380190	0.25 6,4	3.7500 95,250	10.39 264,0	10.16 258,0	0.25 6,4	2.8750 73,025	15.83 402,0	16.85 428,1
8.2500 209,550	12.5000 317,500	2.5000 63,500	32900 14650	29400 13050	1.12	0.31 7,9	93825	93125	0.17 4,3	2.5000 63,500	9.17 233,0	8.93 226,9	0.13 3,3	1.8125 46,038	11.26 286,0	11.81 300,0
8.2500 209,550	12.5000 317,500	2.5000 63,500	32900 14650	29400 13050	1.12	0.31 7,9	93825A	93125	0.50 12,7	2.5000 63,500	9.84 250,0	8.93 226,9	0.13 3,3	1.8125 46,038	11.26 286,0	11.81 300,0
8.2500 209,550	13.1250 333,375	2.7500 69,850	41000 18200	30700 13650	1.33	0.03 0,8	HM743345	HM743310	0.25 6,4	2.7500 69,850	9.37 238,0	8.98 228,0	0.25 6,4	2.0625 52,388	11.93 303,0	12.48 317,1
8.2500 209,550	14.0000 355,600	2.6875 68,262	35300 15700	35600 15850	0.99	0.67 17,0	96825	96140	0.28 7,0	2.6250 66,675	9.69 246,0	9.25 235,0	0.13 3,3	1.8750 47,625	12.52 318,0	13.15 334,0

① These maximum fillet radii will be cleared by the bearing corners.
② Minus value indicates center is inside cone backface.
*For "J" part tolerances see metric tolerance, page 20 and fitting practice page 6 in Reference Tables.

SINGLE-ROW STRAIGHT BORE—TS

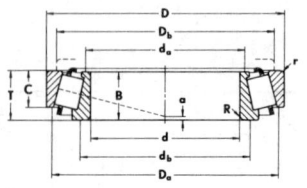

| bore | outside diameter | width | rating at 500 RPM for 3000 hours L10 | | factor | eff. load center | part numbers | | cone max shaft fillet radius | width | backing shoulder diameters | | cup max housing fillet radius | width | backing shoulder | |
| | | | one row radial | thrust | | | cone | cup | | | | | | | | |
d	D	T	lb daN	lb daN	K	a②	cone	cup	R①	B	d_b	d_a	r①	C	D_b	D_a
8.3750 212,725	11.2500 285,750	1.8125 46,038	20100 8950	16600 7400	1.21	0.56 14,2	LM742745	LM742710	0.14 3,5	1.8125 46,038	9.06 230,0	8.86 225,0	0.13 3,3	1.3750 34,925	10.47 266,0	10.98 279,0
8.5000 215,900	11.3750 288,925	1.8125 46,038	20100 8950	16600 7400	1.21	0.56 14,2	LM742749	LM742714	0.14 3,5	1.8125 46,038	9.17 233,0	8.94 227,0	0.13 3,3	1.3750 34,925	10.51 267,0	11.02 280,0
8.5000 215,900	11.4177 290,009	1.2500 31,750	10300 4550	6750 3000	1.52	0.51 12,9	543085	543114	0.14 3,5	1.2500 31,750	9.13 232,0	8.90 226,0	0.13 3,3	0.8750 22,225	10.71 272,0	10.87 276,0
8.5000 215,900	14.0000 355,600	2.7500 69,850	36100 16050	20400 9050	1.77	-0.39 -9,8	EE130851	131400	0.27 6,8	2.7500 69,850	9.76 248,0	9.33 237,0	0.06 1,5	1.9375 49,212	12.95 329,0	13.01 330,4
8.5000 215,900	14.1732 360,000	3.2500 82,550	48500 21600	33500 14900	1.45	-0.24 -6,1	EE420850	421417	0.06 1,5	3.1249 79,372	9.29 236,0	9.29 236,0	0.13 3,3	2.5000 63,500	12.87 327,0	13.16 334,4
8.6602 219,969	11.4177 290,009	1.2500 31,750	10300 4550	6750 3000	1.52	0.51 12,9	543086	543114	0.14 3,5	1.2500 31,750	9.25 235,0	9.02 229,0	0.13 3,3	0.8750 22,225	10.71 272,0	10.87 276,0
8.6875 220,662	12.3750 314,325	2.4375 61,912	33700 15000	19100 8500	1.76	-0.17 -4,4	M244249	M244210	0.25 6,4	2.4375 61,912	9.65 245,0	9.25 235,0	0.13 3,3	1.9375 49,212	11.54 293,0	11.81 300,0
8.7500 222,250	19.0000 482,600	4.6250 117,475	58000 25800	86500 38600	0.67	1.35 34,3	EE380875	380190	0.25 6,4	3.7500 95,250	10.91 277,0	10.51 267,0	0.25 6,4	2.8750 73,025	15.83 402,0	16.85 428,1
8.8750 225,425	14.0000 355,600	2.7500 69,850	36100 16050	20400 9050	1.77	-0.39 -9,8	EE130889	131400	0.27 6,8	2.7500 69,850	10.04 255,0	9.61 244,0	0.06 1,5	1.9375 49,212	12.95 329,0	13.01 330,4
8.8750 225,425	15.7500 400,050	3.5000 88,900	50500 22400	38000 16900	1.33	-0.19 -4,8	EE430888	431575	0.06 1,5	3.4375 87,312	9.88 251,0	9.88 251,0	0.13 3,3	2.5000 63,500	14.17 360,0	14.34 364,2
8.9920 228,397	17.0000 431,800	3.6250 92,075	45500 20200	69000 30800	0.66	1.63 41,5	EE113089	113170	0.25 6,4	3.3750 85,725	10.79 274,0	10.51 267,0	0.25 6,4	1.9375 49,212	14.76 375,0	15.64 397,2
8.9945 228,460	17.0000 431,800	3.6250 92,075	45500 20200	69000 30800	0.66	1.63 41,5	EE113091	113170	0.25 6,4	3.3750 85,725	10.79 274,0	10.51 267,0	0.25 6,4	1.9375 49,212	14.76 375,0	15.64 397,2
9.0000 228,600	11.6250 295,275	1.3125 33,338	10600 4700	7300 3240	1.45	0.62 15,7	544090	544116	0.14 3,5	1.2500 31,750	9.61 244,0	9.45 240,0	0.13 3,3	0.9375 23,812	11.02 280,0	11.30 287,0
9.0000 228,600	12.6250 320,675	2.0000 50,800	19500 8650	16200 7200	1.20	0.56 14,2	88900	88126	0.25 6,4	1.9375 49,212	9.96 253,0	9.53 242,0	0.13 3,3	1.3125 33,338	11.77 299,0	12.17 309,0
9.0000 228,600	12.8750 327,025	2.0625 52,388	24900 11100	17300 7700	1.44	0.30 7,7	8573	8520	0.25 6,4	2.0625 52,388	10.04 255,0	9.61 244,0	0.13 3,3	1.4375 36,512	12.01 305,0	12.32 313,0
9.0000 228,600	14.0000 355,600	2.6875 68,262	35300 15700	35600 15850	0.99	0.67 17,0	96900	96140	0.28 7,0	2.6250 66,675	10.24 260,0	9.80 249,0	0.13 3,3	1.8750 47,625	12.52 318,0	13.15 334,0
9.0000 228,600	14.0000 355,600	2.7500 69,850	36100 16050	20400 9050	1.77	-0.39 -9,8	EE130902	131400	0.27 6,8	2.7500 69,850	10.12 257,0	9.72 247,0	0.06 1,5	1.9375 49,212	12.95 329,0	13.01 330,4
9.0000 228,600	14.1250 358,775	2.8125 71,438	45000 20200	25700 11450	1.76	-0.27 -6,9	M249732	M249710	0.14 3,5	2.8125 71,438	10.08 256,0	9.88 251,0	0.13 3,3	2.1250 53,975	13.19 335,0	13.50 343,0
9.0000 228,600	15.7500 400,050	3.5000 88,900	50500 22400	38000 16900	1.33	-0.19 -4,8	EE430900	431575	0.41 10,4	3.4375 87,312	10.67 271,0	9.96 253,0	0.13 3,3	2.5000 63,500	14.17 360,0	14.34 364,2
9.0000 228,600	19.2500 488,950	4.8750 123,825	74000 33000	119000 53000	0.62	1.57 39,9	HH949549	HH949510	0.25 6,4	4.3750 111,125	11.69 297,0	11.02 279,9	0.25 6,4	2.8750 73,025	16.38 416,0	17.94 455,7
9.0000 228,600	20.0000 508,000	4.6250 117,475	60000 26800	97000 43200	0.62	1.95 49,5	EE390090	390200	0.25 6,4	3.7500 95,250	11.30 287,0	10.91 277,0	0.25 6,4	2.8750 73,025	16.65 423,0	17.96 456,2

bore d	outside diameter D	width T	rating 500 RPM 3000 hrs L10 — one row radial (lb / daN)	thrust (lb / daN)	factor K	eff. load center a②	cone	cup	cone max shaft fillet radius R①	cone width B	cone db	cone da	cup max hous. fillet radius r①	cup width C	cup Db	cup Da
9.1250 / 231,775	10.5625 / 268,288	0.8858 / 22,500	7150 / 3180	4050 / 1800	1.76	0.62 / 15,7	LL244549	LL244510	0.08 / 2,0	0.8465 / 21,500	9.49 / 241,0	9.33 / 237,0	0.08 / 2,0	0.7283 / 18,500	10.28 / 261,0	10.35 / 263,0
9.1250 / 231,775	11.8125 / 300,038	1.3125 / 33,338	10600 / 4700	7300 / 3240	1.45	0.62 / 15,7	544091	544118	0.14 / 3,5	1.2500 / 31,750	9.72 / 247,0	9.57 / 243,0	0.13 / 3,3	0.9375 / 23,812	11.10 / 282,0	11.30 / 287,0
9.1250 / 231,775	13.2500 / 336,550	2.5625 / 65,088	38700 / 17200	22000 / 9750	1.76	-0.19 / -4,8	M246942	M246910	0.25 / 6,4	2.5625 / 65,088	10.16 / 258,0	9.80 / 249,0	0.13 / 3,3	2.0000 / 50,800	12.32 / 313,0	12.68 / 322,0
9.1250 / 231,775	14.1250 / 358,775	2.8125 / 71,438	45000 / 20200	25700 / 11450	1.76	-0.27 / -6,9	M249734	M249710	0.25 / 6,4	2.8125 / 71,438	10.35 / 263,0	10.00 / 254,0	0.13 / 3,3	2.1250 / 53,975	13.19 / 335,0	13.50 / 343,0
9.2500 / 234,950	12.3750 / 314,325	1.9375 / 49,212	25200 / 11200	17100 / 7600	1.47	0.33 / 8,4	LM545849	LM545810	0.14 / 3,5	1.9375 / 49,212	9.92 / 252,0	9.69 / 246,0	0.13 / 3,3	1.4375 / 36,512	11.65 / 296,0	12.05 / 306,0
9.2500 / 234,950	12.5000 / 317,500	1.9375 / 49,212	25200 / 11200	17100 / 7600	1.47	0.33 / 8,4	LM545849	LM545812	0.14 / 3,5	1.9375 / 49,212	9.92 / 252,0	9.69 / 246,0	0.13 / 3,3	1.4375 / 36,512	11.69 / 297,0	12.05 / 306,0
9.2500 / 234,950	12.8750 / 327,025	2.0625 / 52,388	24900 / 11100	17300 / 7700	1.44	0.30 / 7,7	8575	8520	0.25 / 6,4	2.0625 / 52,388	10.20 / 259,0	9.76 / 248,0	0.13 / 3,3	1.4375 / 36,512	12.01 / 305,0	12.32 / 313,0
9.2500 / 234,950	12.8750 / 327,025	2.0625 / 52,388	19500 / 8650	16200 / 7200	1.20	0.56 / 14,2	88925	88128	0.25 / 6,4	1.9375 / 49,212	10.16 / 258,0	9.69 / 246,0	0.13 / 3,3	1.3750 / 34,925	11.89 / 302,0	12.17 / 309,0
9.2500 / 234,950	14.0000 / 355,600	2.6875 / 68,262	35300 / 15700	35600 / 15850	0.99	0.67 / 17,0	96925	96140	0.28 / 7,0	2.6250 / 66,675	10.43 / 265,0	10.00 / 254,0	0.13 / 3,3	1.8750 / 47,625	12.52 / 318,0	13.15 / 334,0
9.2500 / 234,950	15.1250 / 384,175	4.4375 / 112,712	81500 / 36200	46500 / 20600	1.76	-1.10 / -28,1	H247549	H247510	0.25 / 6,4	4.4375 / 112,712	10.59 / 269,0	10.20 / 259,0	0.25 / 6,4	3.5625 / 90,488	13.62 / 346,0	14.26 / 362,1
9.3437 / 237,330	13.2500 / 336,550	2.5625 / 65,088	38700 / 17200	22000 / 9750	1.76	-0.19 / -4,8	M246949	M246910	0.25 / 6,4	2.5625 / 65,088	10.31 / 262,0	9.96 / 253,0	0.13 / 3,3	2.0000 / 50,800	12.32 / 313,0	12.68 / 322,0
9.3437 / 237,330	14.1250 / 358,775	2.8125 / 71,438	45000 / 20200	25700 / 11450	1.76	-0.27 / -6,9	M249736	M249710	0.25 / 6,4	2.8125 / 71,438	10.51 / 267,0	10.16 / 258,0	0.13 / 3,3	2.1250 / 53,975	13.19 / 335,0	13.50 / 343,0
9.5000 / 241,300	12.8750 / 327,025	2.0625 / 52,388	24900 / 11100	17300 / 7700	1.44	0.30 / 7,7	8578	8520	0.25 / 6,4	2.0625 / 52,388	10.39 / 264,0	9.96 / 253,0	0.13 / 3,3	1.4375 / 36,512	12.01 / 305,0	12.32 / 313,0
9.5000 / 241,300	14.3720 / 365,049	2.0000 / 50,800	25500 / 11350	15800 / 7050	1.61	0.23 / 5,8	EE170950	171436	0.25 / 6,4	2.0000 / 50,800	10.59 / 269,0	10.24 / 260,0	0.13 / 3,3	1.3125 / 33,338	13.31 / 338,0	13.27 / 337,0
9.5000 / 241,300	15.5000 / 393,700	2.9062 / 73,817	40000 / 17800	27600 / 12300	1.45	0.10 / 2,6	EE275095	275155	0.25 / 6,4	2.7500 / 69,850	10.94 / 278,0	10.55 / 268,0	0.25 / 6,4	1.9687 / 50,005	14.41 / 366,0	14.89 / 378,1
9.5000 / 241,300	17.5000 / 444,500	4.0000 / 101,600	66500 / 29600	38500 / 17100	1.73	-0.76 / -19,2	EE923095	923175	0.25 / 6,4	3.9375 / 100,112	10.91 / 277,0	10.55 / 268,0	0.19 / 4,8	3.0000 / 76,200	15.87 / 403,0	16.02 / 407,0
9.5000 / 241,300	19.2500 / 488,950	4.7500 / 120,650	90500 / 40200	48500 / 21400	1.87	-1.22 / -31,1	EE295950	295193	0.25 / 6,4	4.7500 / 120,650	11.22 / 285,0	10.87 / 276,0	0.25 / 6,4	3.6250 / 92,075	17.48 / 444,0	17.74 / 450,5
9.5000 / 241,300	20.0000 / 508,000	4.6250 / 117,475	97000 / 43200	60250 / 26800	0.62	1.95 / 49,5	EE390095	390200	0.25 / 6,4	3.7500 / 95,250	11.69 / 297,0	11.34 / 288,0	0.25 / 6,4	2.8750 / 73,025	16.65 / 423,0	17.96 / 456,2
9.6250 / 244,475	15.0000 / 381,000	3.1250 / 79,375	43000 / 19200	38200 / 17000	1.13	0.38 / 9,5	EE126097	126150	0.25 / 6,4	3.0000 / 76,200	10.83 / 275,0	10.47 / 266,0	0.19 / 4,8	2.2500 / 57,150	13.50 / 343,0	14.09 / 358,0
9.7500 / 247,650	12.0000 / 304,800	0.8750 / 22,225	7600 / 3380	4250 / 1880	1.80	0.68 / 17,3	28880	28820	0.06 / 1,5	0.8750 / 22,225	10.16 / 258,0	10.08 / 256,0	0.06 / 1,5	0.6250 / 15,875	11.46 / 291,0	11.57 / 294,0
9.7500 / 247,650	13.6250 / 346,075	2.5000 / 63,500	39600 / 17600	23300 / 10350	1.70	-0.05 / -1,3	M348449	M348410	0.25 / 6,4	2.5000 / 63,500	10.75 / 273,0	10.35 / 263,0	0.25 / 6,4	2.0000 / 50,800	12.64 / 321,0	13.07 / 332,0
9.7500 / 247,650	14.5000 / 368,300	2.0000 / 50,800	25500 / 11350	15800 / 7050	1.61	0.23 / 5,8	EE170975	171450	0.25 / 6,4	2.0000 / 50,800	10.79 / 274,0	10.39 / 264,0	0.13 / 3,3	1.3125 / 33,338	13.39 / 340,0	13.27 / 337,0
9.7500 / 247,650	16.0000 / 406,400	4.5625 / 115,888	96500 / 43000	55000 / 24400	1.76	-1.13 / -28,8	HH249949	HH249910	0.25 / 6,4	4.6250 / 117,475	11.18 / 284,0	10.83 / 275,0	0.25 / 6,4	3.6875 / 93,662	14.41 / 366,0	15.08 / 382,9

① These maximum fillet radii will be cleared by the bearing corners.
② Minus value indicates center is inside cone backface.

SINGLE-ROW STRAIGHT BORE—TS

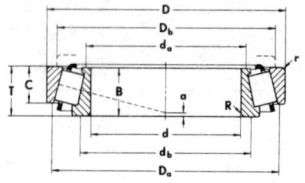

bore	outside diameter	width	rating at 500 RPM for 3000 hours L10 one row radial	rating at 500 RPM for 3000 hours L10 thrust	factor	eff. load center	part numbers cone	part numbers cup	cone max. shaft fillet radius	cone width	cone backing shoulder diameters		cup max. housing fillet radius	cup width	cup backing shoulder	
d	D	T	lb daN	lb daN	K	a [?]	cone	cup	R [1]	B	d_b	d_a	r [1]	C	D_b	D_a
9.8130 249,250	15.0000 381,000	3.1250 79,375	43000 19200	38200 17000	1.13	0.38 9,5	EE126098	126150	0.25 6,4	3.0000 76,200	10.98 279,0	10.59 269,0	0.19 4,8	2.2500 57,150	13.50 343,0	14.09 358,0
10.0000 254,000	12.7500 323,850	0.8750 22,225	7900 3500	4650 2080	1.69	0.83 21,1	29875	29820	0.06 1,5	0.8750 22,225	10.51 267,0	10.47 266,0	0.06 1,5	0.6250 15,875	12.20 310,0	12.28 312,0
10.0000 254,000	14.1250 358,775	2.8125 71,438	45000 20200	25700 11450	1.76	-0.27 -6,9	M249749	M249710	0.14 3,5	2.8125 71,438	10.79 274,0	10.63 270,0	0.13 3,3	2.1250 53,975	13.19 335,0	13.50 343,0
10.0000 254,000	14.3750 365,125	2.3125 58,738	32200 14350	20700 9200	1.56	0.20 5,1	EE134100	134143	0.25 6,4	2.3125 58,738	11.06 281,0	10.71 272,0	0.25 6,4	1.6875 42,862	13.35 339,0	13.66 347,0
10.0000 254,000	15.5000 393,700	2.9062 73,817	40000 17800	27600 12300	1.45	0.10 2,6	EE275100	275155	0.25 6,4	2.7500 69,850	11.30 287,0	10.91 277,0	0.25 6,4	1.9687 50,005	14.41 366,0	14.89 378,1
10.0000 254,000	16.6250 422,275	3.3906 86,121	54000 24000	30700 13650	1.76	-0.37 -9,3	HM252343	HM252310	0.27 6,8	3.1406 79,771	11.30 287,0	11.06 281,0	0.13 3,3	2.6250 66,675	15.43 392,0	15.73 399,5
10.0000 254,000	17.5000 444,500	3.0000 76,200	46500 20600	27300 12150	1.71	-0.21 -5,3	EE822100X	822175	0.25 6,4	3.0000 76,200	11.34 288,0	11.10 282,0	0.25 6,4	2.0000 50,800	15.94 405,0	16.06 408,0
10.0000 254,000	21.0000 533,400	5.2500 133,350	90000 40000	145000 64500	0.62	1.79 45,5	HH953749	HH953710	0.25 6,4	4.7500 120,650	12.91 328,0	12.06 306,3	0.25 6,4	3.0625 77,788	17.91 455,0	19.51 495,6
10.1250 257,175	13.5000 342,900	2.2500 57,150	33400 14850	19900 8850	1.68	0.10 2,5	M349549	M349510	0.25 6,4	2.2500 57,150	11.06 281,0	10.59 269,0	0.13 3,3	1.7500 44,450	12.68 322,0	13.11 333,0
10.2500 260,350	14.3750 365,125	2.3125 58,738	32200 14350	20700 9200	1.56	0.20 5,1	EE134102	134143	0.25 6,4	2.3125 58,738	11.26 286,0	10.87 276,0	0.25 6,4	1.6875 42,862	13.35 339,0	13.66 347,0
10.2500 260,350	15.7500 400,050	2.7500 69,850	37100 16500	25100 11150	1.48	0.03 0,8	EE221026	221575	0.38 9,7	2.6563 67,470	11.65 296,0	11.02 280,0	0.25 6,4	1.8125 46,038	14.41 366,0	14.63 371,5
10.2500 260,350	16.6250 422,275	3.3906 86,121	54000 24000	30700 13650	1.76	-0.37 -9,3	HM252348	HM252310	0.27 6,8	3.1406 79,771	11.50 292,0	11.22 285,0	0.13 3,3	2.6250 66,675	15.43 392,0	15.73 399,5
10.2500 260,350	16.6250 422,275	3.3906 86,121	56000 24800	31700 14100	1.76	-0.37 -9,3	HM252349	HM252310	0.27 6,8	3.1406 79,771	11.50 292,0	11.22 285,0	0.13 3,3	2.6250 66,675	15.43 392,0	15.73 399,5
10.2500 260,350	16.6250 422,275	3.3907 86,124	51000 22600	29000 12900	1.76	-0.39 -9,8	EE551026	551662	0.27 6,8	3.1406 79,771	11.54 293,0	11.30 287,0	0.13 3,3	2.6250 66,675	15.31 389,0	15.44 392,1
10.2500 260,350	19.2500 488,950	4.7500 120,650	90500 40200	48500 21400	1.87	-1.22 -31,1	EE295102	295193	0.25 6,4	4.7500 120,650	11.77 299,0	11.42 290,0	0.25 6,4	3.6250 92,075	17.48 444,0	17.74 450,5
10.3750 263,525	12.8125 325,438	1.1250 28,575	11500 5100	7150 3180	1.60	0.80 20,4	38880	38820	0.06 1,5	1.1250 28,575	10.83 275,0	10.83 275,0	0.06 1,5	1.0000 25,400	12.28 312,0	12.40 315,0
10.3750 263,525	14.0000 355,600	2.2500 57,150	34700 15450	21400 9500	1.62	0.20 5,0	LM451345	LM451310	0.14 3,5	2.2500 57,150	11.14 283,0	10.98 279,0	0.13 3,3	1.7500 44,450	13.19 335,0	13.50 343,0
10.5000 266,700	12.7500 323,850	0.8750 22,225	7900 3500	4650 2080	1.69	0.83 21,1	29880	29820	0.06 1,5	0.8750 22,225	10.91 277,0	10.83 275,0	0.06 1,5	0.6250 15,875	12.20 310,0	12.28 312,0
10.5000 266,700	12.8125 325,438	1.1250 28,575	11500 5100	7150 3180	1.60	0.80 20,4	38885	38820	0.06 1,5	1.1250 28,575	10.91 277,0	10.91 277,0	0.06 1,5	1.0000 25,400	12.28 312,0	12.40 315,0
10.5000 266,700	14.0000 355,600	2.2500 57,150	34700 15450	21400 9500	1.62	0.20 5,0	LM451349	LM451310	0.14 3,5	2.2500 57,150	11.22 285,0	11.06 281,0	0.13 3,3	1.7500 44,450	13.19 335,0	13.50 343,0
10.5000 266,700	14.0000 355,600	2.2500 57,150	34700 15450	21400 9500	1.62	0.20 5,0	LM451349A	LM451310	0.41 10,4	2.2500 57,150	11.77 299,0	11.06 281,0	0.13 3,3	1.7500 44,450	13.19 335,0	13.50 343,0

bore d	outside diameter D	width T	rating at 500 RPM for 3000 hours L10 one row radial (lb daN)	thrust (lb daN)	fac-tor K	eff. load center a[②]	cone part number	cup part number	cone max shaft fillet radius R[①]	cone width B	d_b	d_a	cup max housing fillet radius r[①]	cup width C	D_b	D_a
10.5000 / 266.700	15.5000 / 393,700	2.9062 / 73,817	40000 / 17800	27600 / 12300	1.45	0.10 / 2,6	EE275105	275155	0.25 / 6,4	2.7500 / 69,850	11.65 / 296,0	11.30 / 287,0	0.25 / 6,4	1.9687 / 50,005	14.41 / 366,0	14.89 / 378,1
10.5000 / 266.700	16.9970 / 431,723	3.2500 / 82,550	51000 / 22600	29000 / 12900	1.76	-0.39 / -9,8	EE551050	551700	0.27 / 6,8	3.1406 / 79,771	11.73 / 298,0	11.46 / 291,0	0.14 / 3,5	2.3750 / 60,325	15.51 / 394,0	15.51 / 394,0
10.5000 / 266.700	17.5000 / 444,500	4.7500 / 120,650	91000 / 40400	90000 / 40000	1.01	-0.02 / -0,5	H852849	H852810	0.25 / 6,4	4.6250 / 117,475	12.40 / 315,0	11.69 / 296,9	0.25 / 6,4	3.5000 / 88,900	15.35 / 390,0	16.63 / 422,3
10.6250 / 269.875	15.0000 / 381,000	2.9375 / 74,612	50000 / 22200	28300 / 12600	1.76	-0.26 / -6,6	M252349	M252310	0.25 / 6,4	2.9375 / 74,612	11.65 / 296,0	11.30 / 287,0	0.13 / 3,3	2.2500 / 57,150	14.02 / 356,0	14.32 / 363,8
10.7500 / 273.050	15.5000 / 393,700	2.9062 / 73,817	40000 / 17800	27600 / 12300	1.45	0.10 / 2,6	EE275108	275155	0.25 / 6,4	2.7500 / 69,850	11.85 / 301,0	11.46 / 291,0	0.25 / 6,4	1.9687 / 50,005	14.41 / 366,0	14.89 / 378,1
10.8750 / 276.225	13.8750 / 352,425	1.4375 / 36,512	15700 / 7000	14600 / 6500	1.08	1.37 / 34,9	L853049	L853010	0.14 / 3,5	1.3750 / 34,925	11.54 / 293,0	11.34 / 288,0	0.13 / 3,3	0.9375 / 23,812	13.07 / 332,0	13.46 / 342,0
11.0000 / 279.400	12.5000 / 317,500	0.9600 / 24,384	8800 / 3920	5200 / 2320	1.69	0.80 / 20,3	LL352149	LL352110	0.06 / 1,5	0.9600 / 24,384	11.34 / 288,0	11.26 / 286,0	0.06 / 1,5	0.7200 / 18,288	12.17 / 309,0	12.28 / 312,0
11.0000 / 279.400	18.5000 / 469,900	3.7500 / 95,250	62500 / 27800	40000 / 17800	1.55	-0.29 / -7,5	EE722110	722185	0.38 / 9,7	3.6875 / 93,662	12.64 / 321,0	12.36 / 314,0	0.13 / 3,3	2.7500 / 69,850	16.93 / 430,0	17.04 / 432,9
11.0000 / 279.400	19.2500 / 488,950	4.7500 / 120,650	90500 / 40200	48500 / 21400	1.87	-1.22 / -31,1	EE295110	295193	0.05 / 1,3	4.7500 / 120,650	11.93 / 303,0	11.97 / 304,0	0.25 / 6,4	3.6250 / 92,075	17.48 / 444,0	17.74 / 450,5
11.0229 / 279.981	14.9610 / 380,009	2.5625 / 65,088	38800 / 17300	28800 / 12800	1.35	0.45 / 11,5	LM654642	LM654611	0.14 / 3,5	2.5625 / 65,088	11.89 / 302,0	11.73 / 298,0	0.13 / 3,3	1.9375 / 49,212	14.02 / 356,0	14.49 / 368,0
11.0312 / 280.192	15.7500 / 400,050	2.0625 / 52,388	28300 / 12600	19800 / 8800	1.43	0.62 / 15,8	EE101103	101575	0.27 / 6,8	1.9768 / 50,211	12.17 / 309,0	12.09 / 307,0	0.13 / 3,3	1.3750 / 34,925	14.72 / 374,0	14.80 / 376,0
11.0312 / 280.192	16.0000 / 406,400	2.7500 / 69,850	41000 / 18200	27200 / 12100	1.51	0.26 / 6,6	EE128111	128160	0.27 / 6,8	2.6643 / 67,673	12.17 / 309,0	12.09 / 307,0	0.13 / 3,3	2.1250 / 53,975	14.88 / 378,0	15.12 / 384,0
11.2500 / 285.750	13.9375 / 354,012	1.3125 / 33,338	12500 / 5550	10500 / 4650	1.19	1.29 / 32,7	545112	545139	0.14 / 3,5	1.2500 / 31,750	11.89 / 302,0	11.73 / 298,0	0.13 / 3,3	0.8750 / 22,225	13.31 / 338,0	13.58 / 345,0
11.2500 / 285.750	14.1250 / 358,775	1.3125 / 33,338	12500 / 5550	10500 / 4650	1.19	1.29 / 32,7	545112	545141	0.14 / 3,5	1.2500 / 31,750	11.89 / 302,0	11.73 / 298,0	0.13 / 3,3	0.8750 / 22,225	13.39 / 340,0	13.58 / 345,0
11.2500 / 285.750	14.9960 / 380,898	2.5625 / 65,088	38800 / 17300	28800 / 12800	1.35	0.45 / 11,5	LM654649	LM654610	0.14 / 3,5	2.5625 / 65,088	12.05 / 306,0	11.89 / 302,0	0.13 / 3,3	1.9375 / 49,212	14.02 / 356,0	14.49 / 368,0
11.3750 / 288.925	16.0000 / 406,400	3.0625 / 77,788	59500 / 26600	34500 / 15350	1.73	-0.16 / -4,0	M255449	M255410	0.25 / 6,4	3.0625 / 77,788	12.44 / 316,0	12.20 / 310,0	0.13 / 3,3	2.3750 / 60,325	14.92 / 379,0	15.27 / 387,9
11.5000 / 292.100	14.7500 / 374,650	1.8750 / 47,625	25500 / 11350	17600 / 7800	1.45	0.69 / 17,5	L555249	L555210	0.14 / 3,5	1.8750 / 47,625	12.17 / 309,0	12.01 / 305,0	0.13 / 3,3	1.3750 / 34,925	13.98 / 355,0	14.25 / 362,0
11.5000 / 292.100	15.5000 / 393,700	2.5000 / 63,500	21900 / 9750	22800 / 10150	0.96	1.44 / 36,7	84115	84155	0.14 / 3,5	2.0000 / 50,800	12.32 / 313,0	12.17 / 309,0	0.25 / 6,4	1.7500 / 44,450	14.29 / 363,0	14.88 / 378,0
11.5000 / 292.100	18.5000 / 469,900	3.7500 / 95,250	62500 / 27800	40000 / 17800	1.55	-0.29 / -7,5	EE722115	722185	0.38 / 9,7	3.6875 / 93,662	12.99 / 330,0	12.76 / 324,0	0.13 / 3,3	2.7500 / 69,850	16.93 / 430,0	17.04 / 432,9
11.5000 / 292.100	22.0000 / 558,800	5.3750 / 136,525	115000 / 51000	78000 / 34600	1.48	-0.96 / -24,3	EE790114	790221	0.25 / 6,4	5.3750 / 136,525	13.19 / 335,0	12.95 / 329,0	0.25 / 6,4	3.8750 / 98,425	19.72 / 501,0	20.24 / 514,2
11.7500 / 298.450	17.5000 / 444,500	2.5000 / 63,500	35200 / 15650	22700 / 10100	1.55	0.30 / 7,7	EE291175	291750	0.31 / 8,0	2.4375 / 61,912	13.07 / 332,0	12.60 / 320,0	0.06 / 1,5	1.5625 / 39,688	16.38 / 416,0	16.34 / 415,0
11.8125 / 300.038	16.6250 / 422,275	3.2500 / 82,550	65000 / 29000	37600 / 16750	1.73	-0.22 / -5,6	HM256849	HM256810	0.25 / 6,4	3.2500 / 82,550	12.91 / 328,0	12.56 / 319,0	0.13 / 3,3	2.5000 / 63,500	15.51 / 394,0	15.88 / 403,3
12.0000 / 304.800	15.5000 / 393,700	2.0000 / 50,800	29200 / 13000	17900 / 7950	1.63	0.50 / 12,7	L357049	L357010	0.25 / 6,4	2.0000 / 50,800	12.95 / 329,0	12.56 / 319,0	0.13 / 3,3	1.5000 / 38,100	14.72 / 374,0	14.96 / 380,0

① These maximum fillet radii will be cleared by the bearing corners.
② Minus value indicates center is inside cone backface.

SINGLE-ROW STRAIGHT BORE—TS

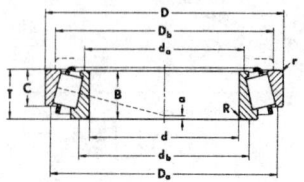

bore	outside diameter	width	rating at 500 RPM for 3000 hours L10 one row radial	rating at 500 RPM for 3000 hours L10 thrust	fac-tor	eff. load center	part numbers cone	part numbers cup	cone max. shaft fillet radius	cone width	cone backing shoulder diameters	cone backing shoulder diameters	cup max. hous-ing fillet radius	cup width	cup backing shoulder	cup backing shoulder
d	D	T	lb daN	lb daN	K	a②	cone	cup	R①	B	d_b	d_a	r①	C	D_b	D_a
12.0000 304,800	16.0000 406,400	2.5000 63,500	40500 18000	30700 13650	1.32	0.64 16,3	LM757049	LM757010	0.25 6,4	2.5000 63,500	13.03 331,0	12.68 322,0	0.13 3,3	1.8750 47,625	14.96 380,0	15.47 393,0
12.0000 304,800	17.5000 444,500	2.5000 63,500	35200 15650	22700 10100	1.55	0.30 7,7	EE291201	291749	0.31 8,0	2.4375 61,912	13.27 337,0	12.76 324,0	0.13 3,3	1.5625 39,688	16.34 415,0	16.34 415,0
12.0000 304,800	19.5000 495,300	3.0000 76,200	54000 24200	37400 16650	1.45	0.36 9,2	EE941205X	941950	0.25 6,4	3.0656 77,866	13.35 339,0	13.07 332,0	0.13 3,3	2.1250 53,975	18.07 459,0	18.22 462,7
12.0000 304,800	19.5000 495,300	3.7500 95,250	68000 30200	47000 21000	1.45	-0.06 -1,4	EE724119	724195	0.63 16,0	3.6250 92,075	14.13 359,0	12.99 330,0	0.25 6,4	2.7500 69,850	17.72 450,0	18.07 458,9
12.0000 304,800	19.5000 495,300	3.7500 95,250	66500 29600	46000 20400	1.45	-0.06 -1,4	EE724120	724195	0.63 16,0	3.6250 92,075	14.13 359,0	12.99 330,0	0.25 6,4	2.7500 69,850	17.72 450,0	18.07 458,9
12.0000 304,800	†19.6850 †500,000	4.0000 101,600	51000 22800	102000 45500	0.50	4.15 105,3	M959442	M959410	0.25 6,4	3.1250 79,375	13.90 353,0	13.54 344,0	0.25 6,4	2.1250 53,975	17.24 438,0	18.94 481,1
12.0000 304,800	22.0000 558,800	5.3750 136,525	115000 51000	78000 34600	1.48	-0.96 -24,3	EE790120	790221	0.05 1,3	5.3750 136,525	13.19 335,0	13.19 335,0	0.25 6,4	3.8750 98,425	19.72 501,0	20.24 514,2
12.3125 312,738	14.1250 358,775	0.8750 22,225	6450 2860	9100 4040	0.71	3.13 79,6	LL957049	LL957010	0.09 2,3	0.8125 20,638	12.80 325,0	12.68 322,0	0.06 1,5	0.5625 14,288	13.62 346,0	13.94 354,0
12.5000 317,500	17.5000 444,500	2.5000 63,500	35200 15650	22700 10100	1.55	0.30 7,7	EE291250	291750	0.31 8,0	2.4375 61,912	13.62 346,0	13.15 334,0	0.06 1,5	1.5625 39,688	16.38 416,0	16.34 415,0
12.5000 317,500	17.6250 447,675	3.3750 85,725	73500 32800	42500 18800	1.74	-0.19 -4,8	HM259049	HM259010	0.14 3,5	3.3750 85,725	13.43 341,0	13.27 337,0	0.13 3,3	2.6875 68,262	16.46 418,0	16.84 427,7
12.5000 317,500	23.5000 596,900	5.3750 136,525	126000 56000	91000 40400	1.38	-0.66 -16,7	EE720125	720236	0.78 19,8	5.3750 136,525	15.35 390,0	13.90 353,0	0.25 6,4	3.8750 98,425	21.02 534,0	21.55 547,4
12.5000 317,500	24.5000 622,300	5.8125 147,638	118000 52500	190000 84500	0.62	2.38 60,6	H961649	H961610	0.56 14,3	5.1875 131,762	16.14 410,0	14.69 373,0	0.50 12,7	3.2500 82,550	20.91 531,0	22.90 581,6
12.7500 323,850	15.0000 381,000	1.1250 28,575	12800 5650	9600 4260	1.33	1.37 34,9	LL758744	LL758715	0.14 3,5	1.1250 28,575	13.35 339,0	13.11 333,0	0.13 3,3	0.8125 20,638	14.37 365,0	14.69 373,0
12.8125 325,438	23.5000 596,900	5.3750 136,525	126000 56000	91000 40400	1.38	-0.66 -16,7	EE720128	720236	0.25 6,4	5.3750 136,525	14.53 369,0	14.13 359,0	0.25 6,4	3.8750 98,425	21.02 534,0	21.55 547,4
13.0000 330,200	16.3750 415,925	1.8750 47,625	24900 11100	21300 9500	1.17	1.39 35,4	L860048	L860010	0.50 12,7	1.8750 47,625	14.45 367,0	13.58 345,0	0.13 3,3	1.3750 34,925	15.51 394,0	15.83 402,0
13.0000 330,200	16.3750 415,925	1.8750 47,625	24900 11100	21300 9500	1.17	1.39 35,4	L860049	L860010	0.14 3,5	1.8750 47,625	13.74 349,0	13.58 345,0	0.13 3,3	1.3750 34,925	15.51 394,0	15.83 402,0
13.0000 330,200	18.5000 469,900	2.3750 60,325	27300 12150	23300 10350	1.33	1.33 33,8	EE161300	161850	0.28 7,0	1.2578 31,948	14.45 367,0	14.02 356,0	0.25 6,4	1.5000 38,100	17.52 445,0	17.91 455,0
13.0000 330,200	19.0000 482,600	3.3750 85,725	57000 25400	38400 17100	1.49	0.19 4,8	EE526130	526190	0.25 6,4	3.1562 80,167	14.17 360,0	13.82 351,0	0.13 3,3	2.3750 60,325	17.68 449,0	17.87 454,0
13.0000 330,200	19.0000 482,600	3.3750 85,725	57000 25400	38400 17100	1.49	0.19 4,8	EE526132	526190	0.13 3,3	3.1562 80,167	13.94 354,0	13.82 351,0	0.13 3,3	2.3750 60,325	17.68 449,0	17.87 454,0
13.1250 333,375	18.5000 469,900	3.5625 90,488	81000 36000	46500 20600	1.74	-0.24 -6,2	HM261049	HM261010	0.25 6,4	3.5625 90,488	14.29 363,0	14.06 357,0	0.13 3,3	2.8125 71,438	17.28 439,0	17.69 449,2
13.5000 342,900	17.7500 450,850	2.6250 66,675	51000 22600	30700 13650	1.66	0.35 8,9	LM361649	LM361610	0.33 8,5	2.6250 66,675	14.69 373,0	14.17 360,0	0.14 3,5	2.0625 52,388	16.73 425,0	17.13 435,0

outside diameter D	width T	one row radial (lb daN)	thrust (lb daN)	factor K	eff. load center a	cone	cup	max. shaft fillet radius R	width B	d_b	d_a	max. housing fillet radius r	width C	D_b	D_a
17.9960 / 457,098	2.6250 / 66,675	43500 / 19400	53500 / 23800	0.82	2.22 / 56,4	LM961548	LM961510	0.13 / 3,3	2.5000 / 63,500	14.45 / 376,0	14.29 / 363,0	0.13 / 3,3	1.8125 / 46,038	16.65 / 423,0	17.44 / 443,1
21.0000 / 533,400	3.0000 / 76,200	62500 / 27800	35400 / 15750	1.76	0.15 / 3,8	EE971354	972100	0.19 / 4,8	3.0000 / 76,200	14.69 / 373,0	14.45 / 367,0	0.13 / 3,3	2.0000 / 50,800	19.72 / 501,0	19.72 / 501,0
19.0000 / 482,600	2.3750 / 60,325	27300 / 12150	23300 / 10350	1.17	1.33 / 33,8	EE161363	161900	0.28 / 7,0	2.1875 / 55,562	14.92 / 379,0	14.49 / 368,0	0.25 / 6,4	1.5000 / 38,100	17.76 / 451,0	17.91 / 455,0
19.0000 / 482,600	2.6250 / 66,675	42000 / 18600	29900 / 13300	1.40	0.64 / 16,3	EE203136	203190	0.27 / 6,8	2.5000 / 63,500	14.80 / 376,0	14.41 / 366,0	0.27 / 6,8	1.7500 / 44,450	17.68 / 449,0	17.96 / 456,1
19.0000 / 482,600	2.6250 / 66,675	42000 / 18600	29900 / 13300	1.40	0.64 / 16,3	EE203137	203190	0.50 / 12,7	2.5000 / 63,500	15.28 / 388,0	14.41 / 366,0	0.27 / 6,8	1.7500 / 44,450	17.68 / 449,0	17.96 / 456,1
19.2500 / 488,950	3.7500 / 95,250	88000 / 39200	50500 / 22600	1.74	-0.25 / -6,4	HM262749	HM262710	0.25 / 6,4	3.7500 / 95,250	14.84 / 377,0	14.45 / 367,0	0.13 / 3,3	2.9375 / 74,612	17.95 / 456,0	18.39 / 467,0
19.7500 / 501,650	3.5625 / 90,488	66500 / 29600	42000 / 18600	1.59	0.14 / 3,6	EE333137	333197	0.25 / 6,4	3.3125 / 84,138	15.04 / 382,0	14.65 / 372,0	0.13 / 3,3	2.7500 / 69,850	18.50 / 470,0	18.83 / 478,2
17.5000 / 444,500	2.3750 / 60,325	42000 / 18600	22000 / 9800	1.90	0.28 / 7,2	L163149	L163110	0.14 / 3,5	2.3750 / 60,325	14.72 / 374,0	14.57 / 370,0	0.13 / 3,3	1.8750 / 47,625	16.61 / 422,0	16.93 / 430,0
18.5000 / 469,900	2.3750 / 60,325	27300 / 12150	23300 / 10350	1.17	1.33 / 33,8	EE161400	161850	0.28 / 7,0	2.1875 / 55,562	15.20 / 386,0	14.76 / 375,0	0.25 / 6,4	1.5000 / 38,100	17.52 / 445,0	17.91 / 455,0
19.7500 / 501,650	2.9375 / 74,612	43500 / 19400	32700 / 14550	1.33	0.77 / 19,7	EE231400	231975	0.25 / 6,4	2.6250 / 66,675	15.28 / 388,0	14.92 / 379,0	0.13 / 3,3	2.0000 / 50,800	18.58 / 472,0	18.94 / 481,1
19.7500 / 501,650	3.5625 / 90,488	66500 / 29600	42000 / 18600	1.59	0.14 / 3,6	EE333140	333197	0.25 / 6,4	3.3125 / 84,138	15.24 / 387,0	14.84 / 377,0	0.13 / 3,3	2.7500 / 69,850	18.50 / 470,0	18.83 / 478,2
15.8125 / 401,638	0.8437 / 21,430	8900 / 3960	6750 / 3000	1.32	1.73 / 43,9	LL762648	LL762610	0.08 / 2,0	0.8437 / 21,430	14.61 / 371,0	14.53 / 369,0	0.08 / 2,0	0.6250 / 15,875	15.43 / 392,0	15.63 / 397,0
16.0000 / 406,400	0.9375 / 23,812	10600 / 4700	7350 / 3260	1.45	1.49 / 37,8	LL562749	LL562710	0.09 / 2,3	0.9375 / 23,812	14.65 / 372,0	14.61 / 371,0	0.06 / 1,5	0.6875 / 17,462	15.59 / 396,0	15.79 / 401,0
20.6250 / 523,875	4.0000 / 101,600	102000 / 45000	57500 / 25600	1.76	-0.33 / -8,3	HM265049	HM265010	0.25 / 6,4	4.0000 / 101,600	15.75 / 400,0	15.51 / 394,0	0.25 / 6,4	3.1250 / 79,375	19.17 / 487,0	19.63 / 498,7
20.2500 / 514,350	2.9375 / 74,612	43500 / 19400	32700 / 14550	1.33	0.77 / 19,7	EE231462	232025	0.25 / 6,4	2.6250 / 66,675	15.75 / 400,0	15.35 / 390,0	0.13 / 3,3	2.0000 / 50,800	18.82 / 478,0	18.94 / 481,1
17.0000 / 431,800	1.1250 / 28,575	13800 / 6100	7850 / 3500	1.76	1.10 / 27,9	LL264648	LL264610	0.14 / 3,5	1.1250 / 28,575	15.31 / 389,0	15.12 / 384,0	0.13 / 3,3	0.8125 / 20,638	16.42 / 417,0	16.69 / 424,0
18.8750 / 479,425	1.9375 / 49,212	29000 / 12900	24600 / 10950	1.18	1.69 / 43,0	L865547	L865512	0.25 / 6,4	1.8750 / 47,625	16.02 / 407,0	15.55 / 395,0	0.13 / 3,3	1.3750 / 34,925	17.95 / 456,0	18.31 / 465,0
18.8750 / 479,425	1.9375 / 49,212	29000 / 12900	24600 / 10950	1.18	1.69 / 43,0	L865548	L865512	0.50 / 12,7	1.8750 / 47,625	16.50 / 419,0	15.55 / 395,0	0.13 / 3,3	1.3750 / 34,925	17.95 / 456,0	18.31 / 465,0
20.5625 / 522,288	3.3750 / 85,725	69500 / 31000	46000 / 20400	1.51	0.35 / 9,0	LM565949	LM565910	0.25 / 6,4	3.3125 / 84,138	16.18 / 411,0	15.83 / 402,0	0.13 / 3,3	2.4375 / 61,912	19.41 / 493,0	19.67 / 499,5
20.6250 / 523,875	3.3750 / 85,725	69500 / 31000	46000 / 20400	1.51	0.35 / 9,0	LM565949	LM565912	0.25 / 6,4	3.3125 / 84,138	16.18 / 411,0	15.83 / 402,0	0.13 / 3,3	2.4375 / 61,912	19.41 / 493,0	19.67 / 499,5
21.5000 / 546,100	4.1250 / 104,775	110000 / 49000	63000 / 28000	1.76	-0.27 / -7,0	HM266447	HM266410	0.25 / 6,4	4.1250 / 104,775	16.34 / 415,0	15.94 / 405,0	0.25 / 6,4	3.2500 / 82,550	19.94 / 507,0	20.47 / 520,0
23.2500 / 590,550	4.5000 / 114,300	130000 / 58000	73500 / 32600	1.76	-0.37 / -9,4	M268730	M268710	0.25 / 6,4	4.5000 / 114,300	16.73 / 425,0	16.34 / 415,0	0.25 / 6,4	3.5000 / 88,900	21.61 / 549,0	22.14 / 562,4
17.3750 / 441,325	1.1250 / 28,575	13300 / 5900	7700 / 3440	1.72	1.18 / 30,0	LL365348	LL365310	0.14 / 3,5	1.1250 / 28,575	15.71 / 399,0	15.47 / 393,0	0.13 / 3,3	0.8125 / 20,638	16.81 / 427,0	17.05 / 433,0

maximum fillet radii will be cleared by the bearing corners.

value indicates center is inside cone backface.

nsion shown is maximum value—see note at bottom of fitting practice table page 4 in Reference Tables.

SINGLE-ROW STRAIGHT BORE—TS

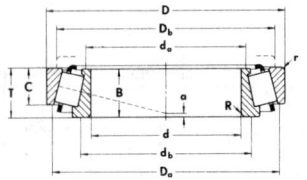

			cone		cup	

bore d	outside diameter D	width T	rating at 500 RPM for 3000 hours L10 — one row radial (lb/daN)	thrust (lb/daN)	fac-tor K	eff. load center a	part numbers cone	cup	max. shaft fillet radius R	width B	backing shoulder diameters d_b	d_a	max. hous-ing fillet radius r	width C	backing shoulder D_b	D_a
15.1250 / 384,175	21.5000 / 546,100	4.1250 / 104,775	110000 / 49000	63000 / 28000	1.76	-0.27 / -7,0	HM266449	HM266410	0.25 / 6,4	4.1250 / 104,775	16.42 / 417,0	16.02 / 407,0	0.25 / 6,4	3.2500 / 82,550	19.96 / 507,0	20.47 / 520,0
15.1875 / 385,762	20.2500 / 514,350	3.2500 / 82,550	72000 / 32000	51500 / 22800	1.40	0.64 / 16,3	LM665949	LM665910	0.25 / 6,4	3.2500 / 82,550	16.34 / 415,0	15.98 / 406,0	0.13 / 3,3	2.5000 / 63,500	18.98 / 482,0	19.49 / 495,0
15.6250 / 396,875	21.5000 / 546,100	3.0000 / 76,200	46000 / 20400	37300 / 16600	1.23	1.40 / 35,7	EE234156	234215	0.25 / 6,4	2.4063 / 61,120	16.85 / 428,0	16.46 / 418,0	0.25 / 6,4	2.1875 / 55,562	19.84 / 504,0	20.30 / 515,6
15.8750 / 403,225	18.1250 / 460,375	1.1250 / 28,575	13100 / 5800	9050 / 4020	1.45	1.63 / 41,4	LL566848	LL566810	0.14 / 3,5	1.1250 / 28,575	16.46 / 418,0	16.30 / 414,0	0.13 / 3,3	0.8125 / 20,638	17.52 / 445,0	17.80 / 452,0
16.0000 / 406,400	20.0000 / 508,000	2.4375 / 61,912	48000 / 21200	29900 / 13300	1.60	0.80 / 20,4	L467549	L467510	0.13 / 3,3	2.4375 / 61,912	16.77 / 426,0	16.65 / 423,0	0.13 / 3,3	1.8750 / 47,625	19.02 / 483,0	19.37 / 492,0
16.0000 / 406,400	21.6250 / 549,275	3.3750 / 85,725	72500 / 32200	50500 / 22600	1.43	0.61 / 15,6	LM567949	LM567910	0.25 / 6,4	3.3125 / 84,138	17.20 / 437,0	16.81 / 427,0	0.13 / 3,3	2.4375 / 61,912	20.43 / 519,0	20.72 / 526,3
16.0000 / 406,400	22.0000 / 558,800	2.5625 / 65,088	46000 / 20400	37300 / 16600	1.23	1.40 / 35,7	EE234160	234220	0.25 / 6,4	2.4063 / 61,120	17.13 / 435,0	16.73 / 425,0	0.25 / 6,4	1.7500 / 44,450	20.31 / 516,0	20.31 / 516,0
16.0000 / 406,400	23.2500 / 590,550	4.2500 / 107,950	114000 / 50500	63500 / 28200	1.80	-0.31 / -7,9	EE833160X	833232	0.38 / 9,7	4.2500 / 107,950	17.64 / 448,0	17.13 / 435,0	0.25 / 6,4	3.1875 / 80,962	21.61 / 549,0	22.07 / 560,5
16.0000 / 406,400	24.0000 / 609,600	3.6250 / 92,075	69500 / 31000	46000 / 20400	1.52	0.47 / 12,0	EE911600	912400	0.27 / 6,8	3.3125 / 84,138	17.44 / 443,0	17.28 / 439,0	0.25 / 6,4	2.3750 / 60,325	22.32 / 567,0	22.44 / 570,0
16.3750 / 415,925	23.2500 / 590,550	4.5000 / 114,300	130000 / 58000	73500 / 32600	1.76	-0.37 / -9,4	M268749	M268710	0.25 / 6,4	4.5000 / 114,300	17.76 / 451,0	17.36 / 441,0	0.25 / 6,4	3.5000 / 88,900	21.61 / 549,0	22.14 / 562,4
16.7500 / 425,450	26.9960 / 685,698	5.6250 / 142,875	151000 / 67000	104000 / 46000	1.45	-0.32 / -8,1	EE328167	328269	0.50 / 12,7	5.6220 / 142,799	18.98 / 482,0	18.23 / 463,0	0.25 / 6,4	4.1250 / 104,775	24.57 / 624,0	25.04 / 636,1
17.0000 / 431,800	21.0000 / 533,400	1.8125 / 46,038	32000 / 14250	16800 / 7450	1.91	0.92 / 23,5	80385	80325	0.13 / 3,3	1.8125 / 46,038	17.72 / 450,0	17.56 / 446,0	0.13 / 3,3	1.3750 / 34,925	20.08 / 510,0	20.08 / 510,0
17.0000 / 431,800	21.7500 / 552,450	1.7500 / 44,450	32400 / 14400	17700 / 7900	1.83	1.03 / 26,2	80170	80217	0.13 / 3,3	1.7500 / 44,450	17.95 / 456,0	17.80 / 452,0	0.13 / 3,3	1.2500 / 31,750	20.91 / 531,0	20.91 / 531,0
17.0000 / 431,800	22.5000 / 571,500	2.9375 / 74,612	63000 / 28000	59000 / 26200	1.07	1.97 / 50,0	LM869448	LM869410	0.13 / 3,3	2.9375 / 74,612	17.99 / 457,0	17.83 / 453,0	0.13 / 3,3	2.0625 / 52,388	21.14 / 537,0	21.61 / 549,0
17.0000 / 431,800	23.7500 / 603,250	3.0000 / 76,200	49000 / 21800	44000 / 19600	1.11	1.85 / 47,0	EE241701	242375	0.25 / 6,4	2.8750 / 73,025	18.35 / 446,0	17.99 / 457,0	0.25 / 6,4	2.0000 / 50,800	21.97 / 558,0	22.16 / 562,8
17.6250 / 447,675	21.7500 / 552,450	1.7500 / 44,450	32400 / 14400	17700 / 7900	1.83	1.03 / 26,2	80176	80217	0.13 / 3,3	1.7500 / 44,450	18.39 / 467,0	18.27 / 464,0	0.13 / 3,3	1.2500 / 31,750	20.91 / 531,0	20.91 / 531,0
17.6250 / 447,675	25.0000 / 635,000	4.7500 / 120,650	150000 / 66500	85000 / 37800	1.76	-0.32 / -8,1	M270749	M270710	0.25 / 6,4	4.7500 / 120,650	19.06 / 484,0	18.66 / 474,0	0.25 / 6,4	3.7500 / 95,250	23.27 / 591,0	23.82 / 605,1
18.0000 / 457,200	22.5625 / 573,088	2.9375 / 74,612	69000 / 30600	47500 / 21200	1.45	1.07 / 27,2	L570649	L570610	0.25 / 6,4	2.9375 / 74,612	19.09 / 485,0	18.70 / 475,0	0.25 / 6,4	2.2500 / 57,150	21.38 / 543,0	21.97 / 558,0
18.0000 / 457,200	23.5000 / 596,900	3.0000 / 76,200	63500 / 28200	44000 / 19600	1.44	1.05 / 26,7	EE244180	244235	0.38 / 9,7	2.8750 / 73,025	19.45 / 494,0	18.82 / 478,0	0.13 / 3,3	2.1250 / 53,975	22.32 / 567,0	22.47 / 570,7
18.0000 / 457,200	23.7500 / 603,250	3.3750 / 85,725	77500 / 34600	60500 / 26800	1.29	1.20 / 30,5	LM770949	LM770910	0.25 / 6,4	3.3125 / 84,138	19.25 / 489,0	18.86 / 479,0	0.13 / 3,3	2.3750 / 60,325	22.44 / 570,0	22.82 / 579,7
18.7500 / 476,250	22.2500 / 565,150	1.6250 / 41,275	26000 / 11550	21000 / 9350	1.24	2.30 / 58,4	LL771948	LL771911	0.13 / 3,3	1.6250 / 41,275	19.49 / 495,0	19.33 / 491,0	0.13 / 3,3	1.2500 / 31,750	21.38 / 543,0	21.61 / 549,0

| bore | outside diameter | width | rating at 500 RPM for 3000 hours L10 | | factor | eff. load center | part numbers | | cone max. shaft fillet radius | width | backing shoulder diameters | | cup max. housing fillet radius | width | backing shoulder | |
| | | | one row radial | thrust | | | cone | cup | | | | | | | | |
d	D	T	lb daN	lb daN	K	a②	cone	cup	R①	B	d_b	d_a	r①	C	D_b	D_a
18.8750 479.425	26.7500 679.450	5.0625 128,588	172000 76500	98000 43600	1.76	−0.35 −8,9	M272749	M272710	0.25 6,4	5.0625 128,588	20.31 516,0	19.96 507,0	0.25 6,4	4.0000 101,600	24.92 633,0	25.52 648,2
19.0000 482,600	24.2500 615,950	3.3750 85,725	91000 40400	51500 23000	1.76	0.49 12,4	LM272249	LM272210	0.25 6,4	3.3750 85,725	20.20 513,0	19.72 501,0	0.25 6,4	2.6250 66,675	23.03 585,0	23.48 596,4
19.0000 482,600	24.9950 634,873	3.1875 80,962	79500 35400	47000 21000	1.70	0.75 19,0	EE243190	243250	0.25 6,4	3.1875 80,962	20.08 516,0	20.08 510,0	0.13 3,3	2.5000 63,500	24.00 603,0	24.00 609,6
19.2500 488,950	24.9950 634,873	3.3125 84,138	86500 38400	69500 31000	1.24	1.61 41,0	LM772748	LM772710	0.25 6,4	3.3125 84,138	20.55 522,0	20.08 510,0	0.13 3,3	2.4375 61,912	23.62 600,0	24.15 613,3
19.2500 488,950	26.0000 660,400	3.6875 93,662	104000 46000	55000 24400	1.90	0.19 4,8	EE640192	640260	0.25 6,4	3.7188 94,458	20.55 522,0	20.20 513,0	0.25 6,4	2.7500 69,850	24.57 624,0	24.82 630,5
19.2530 489,026	24.9950 634,873	3.1875 80,962	79500 35400	47000 21000	1.70	0.75 19,0	EE243192	243250	0.25 6,4	3.1875 80,962	20.55 522,0	20.31 516,0	0.13 3,3	2.5000 63,500	24.00 603,0	24.00 609,6
19.6250 498,475	24.9950 634,873	3.1875 80,962	79500 35400	47000 21000	1.70	0.75 19,0	EE243196	243250	0.25 6,4	3.1875 80,962	20.79 528,0	20.55 522,0	0.13 3,3	2.5000 63,500	24.00 603,0	24.00 609,6
20.5000 520,700	29.0000 736,600	3.5000 88,900	79500 35400	64500 28800	1.23	1.79 45,5	EE982051	982900	0.25 6,4	3.2188 81,758	21.97 558,0	21.73 552,0	0.13 3,3	2.1250 53,975	27.28 693,0	27.28 693,0
21.0000 533,400	25.0000 635,000	2.0000 50,800	40500 18000	28200 12550	1.44	2.00 50,8	LL575343	LL575310	0.25 6,4	2.0000 50,800	21.97 558,0	21.61 549,0	0.25 6,4	1.5000 38,100	24.09 612,0	24.45 621,0
21.1250 536,575	29.9950 761,873	5.7500 146,050	216000 96000	122000 54500	1.76	−0.38 −9,8	M276449	M276410	0.25 6,4	5.7500 146,050	22.68 576,0	22.44 570,0	0.25 6,4	4.5000 114,300	27.99 711,0	28.57 725,6
21.2500 539,750	25.0000 635,000	2.0000 50,800	40500 18000	28200 12550	1.44	2.00 50,8	LL575349	LL575310	0.25 6,4	2.0000 50,800	22.20 564,0	21.85 555,0	0.25 6,4	1.5000 38,100	24.09 612,0	24.45 621,0
21.6250 549,275	27.2500 692,150	3.1875 80,962	84500 37600	54500 24200	1.55	1.27 32,2	L476549	L476510	0.25 6,4	3.1875 80,962	22.80 579,0	22.44 570,0	0.25 6,4	2.4375 61,912	25.87 657,0	26.22 666,0
22.0000 558,800	28.5000 723,900	2.8750 73,025	75000 33400	63500 28400	1.18	2.54 64,5	EE647220	647285	0.19 4,8	2.8750 73,025	23.15 588,0	22.91 582,0	0.19 4,8	2.2500 57,150	27.05 687,0	27.60 701,1
22.0000 558,800	29.0000 736,600	3.4688 88,108	103000 45500	60500 26800	1.70	0.89 22,6	EE843220	843290	0.25 6,4	3.4688 88,108	23.27 591,0	23.03 585,0	0.25 6,4	2.5000 63,500	27.52 699,0	27.84 707,1
22.0000 558,800	29.0000 736,600	4.1250 104,775	140000 62500	82500 36600	1.69	0.62 15,8	LM377449	LM377410	0.25 6,4	4.1250 104,775	23.39 594,0	23.03 585,0	0.25 6,4	3.1875 80,962	27.40 696,0	27.84 707,1
23.0000 584,200	27.0000 685,800	1.9375 49,212	43500 19400	32500 14450	1.34	2.54 64,5	LL778149	LL778110	0.14 3,5	1.9375 49,212	23.74 603,0	23.62 600,0	0.13 3,3	1.3750 34,925	26.10 663,0	26.34 669,0
23.5000 596,900	27.0000 685,800	1.2500 31,750	18400 8200	16600 7400	1.11	3.78 96,1	680235	680270	0.14 3,5	1.2500 31,750	24.21 615,0	24.21 615,0	0.13 3,3	1.0000 25,400	26.10 663,0	26.34 669,0
24.0000 609,600	30.0000 762,000	3.7500 95,250	115000 51000	96000 42600	1.20	2.28 57,9	L879947	L879910	0.25 6,4	3.6250 92,075	25.28 642,0	24.92 633,0	0.25 6,4	2.8125 71,438	28.35 720,0	29.17 741,0
24.0000 609,600	30.5000 774,700	3.3750 85,725	101000 45000	69500 31000	1.45	1.79 45,3	L580049	L580010	0.25 6,4	3.1250 79,375	25.28 642,0	24.92 633,0	0.25 6,4	2.3750 60,325	29.17 741,0	29.51 749,3
24.0000 609,600	31.0000 787,400	3.6875 93,662	121000 54000	76500 34000	1.58	1.24 31,5	EE649240	649310	0.25 6,4	3.6875 93,662	25.28 642,0	24.92 633,0	0.25 6,4	2.7500 69,850	29.41 747,0	29.74 755,3
26.7500 679,450	35.5000 901,700	5.6250 142,875	245000 109000	139000 62000	1.76	0.27 7,0	LM281849	LM281810	0.38 9,7	5.6250 142,875	28.58 726,0	28.11 714,0	0.25 6,4	4.3750 111,125	33.54 852,0	34.12 866,6
27.0000 685,800	34.5000 876,300	3.6875 93,662	131000 58000	94000 41800	1.40	2.13 54,1	EE655270	655345	0.25 6,4	3.6250 92,075	28.46 723,0	28.11 714,0	0.25 6,4	2.7500 69,850	32.72 831,0	33.13 841,4
28.0000 711,200	36.0000 914,400	3.3750 85,725	108000 48000	70500 31400	1.54	2.11 53,5	EE755280	755360	0.25 6,4	3.2500 82,550	29.53 750,0	29.17 741,0	0.25 6,4	2.3750 60,325	34.37 873,0	34.53 877,0

①These maximum fillet radii will be cleared by the bearing corners.
②Minus value indicates center is inside cone backface.

SINGLE-ROW STRAIGHT BORE—TS

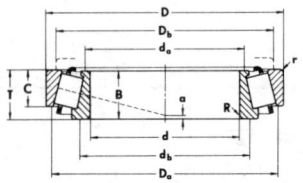

			cone						cup			

bore	outside diameter	width	rating at 500 RPM for 3000 hours L10 one row radial	thrust	factor K	eff. load center a[2]	part numbers cone	cup	max. shaft fillet radius R[1]	width B	d_b	d_a	max. housing fillet radius r[1]	width C	D_b	D_a
d	D	T	lb daN	lb daN	K	a[2]	cone	cup	R[1]	B	d_b	d_a	r[1]	C	D_b	D_a
28.5000 723,900	36.0000 914,400	3.3125 84,138	108000 48000	70500 31400	1.54	2.17 55,1	EE755285	755360	0.13 3,3	3.1875 80,962	29.65 753,0	29.53 750,0	0.25 6,4	2.3750 60,325	34.37 873,0	34.53 877,0
29.5000 749,300	39.0000 990,600	6.2795 159,500	299000 133000	170000 75500	1.76	0.24 6,1	LM283649	LM283610	0.25 6,4	6.3125 160,338	31.18 792,0	30.94 786,0	0.25 6,4	4.8425 123,000	36.85 936,0	37.50 952,4
†29.9213 †760,000	35.0000 889,000	2.7500 69,850	83500 37200	54500 24200	1.54	2.45 62,3	LL483448	LL483418	0.13 3,3	2.7500 69,850	30.83 783,0	30.59 777,0	0.13 3,3	2.0000 50,800	33.66 855,0	33.78 858,0
30.0000 762,000	35.0000 889,000	2.7500 69,850	83500 37200	54500 24200	1.54	2.45 62,3	LL483449	LL483418	0.13 3,3	2.7500 69,850	30.83 783,0	30.71 780,0	0.13 3,3	2.0000 50,800	33.66 855,0	33.78 858,0
30.0000 762,000	38.0000 965,200	3.6875 93,662	101000 45000	70000 31200	1.45	2.50 63,6	EE752300	752380	0.25 6,4	3.1875 80,962	31.42 798,0	31.06 789,0	0.13 3,3	2.6250 66,675	36.26 921,0	36.36 923,5
31.5625 801,688	36.0000 914,400	2.3125 58,738	65500 29200	44500 19800	1.47	3.11 79,0	LL584449	LL584410	0.14 3,5	2.3125 58,738	32.36 822,0	32.24 819,0	0.13 3,3	1.6250 41,275	34.96 888,0	35.20 894,0
33.0000 838,200	41.0000 1041,400	3.6875 93,662	119000 53000	89500 39800	1.33	3.27 83,1	EE763330	763410	0.25 6,4	3.5000 88,900	34.49 876,0	34.25 870,0	0.25 6,4	2.6250 66,675	39.21 996,0	39.41 1000,9
33.7500 857,250	43.0000 1092,200	4.7500 120,650	158000 70500	150000 66500	1.05	4.43 112,6	EE157337	157430	0.75 19,0	4.3750 111,125	36.50 927,0	35.20 894,0	0.25 6,4	3.0000 76,200	40.75 1035,0	41.23 1047,4
38.5000 977,900	44.5000 1130,300	2.6250 66,675	96500 43000	72000 32000	1.34	4.52 114,7	LL687949	LL687910	0.25 6,4	2.5000 63,500	39.76 1010,0	39.57 1005,0	0.25 6,4	1.8750 47,625	43.11 1095,0	43.32 1100,4
40.0000 1016,000	50.0000 1270,000	4.0000 101,600	159000 71000	134000 59500	1.19	5.03 127,8	EE168400	168500	0.38 9,7	4.0000 101,600	42.13 1070,0	41.54 1055,0	0.38 9,7	2.6250 66,675	47.64 1210,0	47.80 1214,1
41.8750 1063,625	48.0000 1219,200	2.5625 65,088	101000 45000	82500 36600	1.23	5.61 142,4	LL788345	LL788310	0.13 3,3	2.5625 65,088	42.91 1090,0	42.72 1085,0	0.13 3,3	1.6875 42,862	46.65 1185,0	46.80 1188,8
42.0000 1066,800	48.0000 1219,200	2.5625 65,088	101000 45000	82500 36600	1.23	5.61 142,4	LL788349	LL788310	0.13 3,3	2.5625 65,088	42.91 1090,0	42.91 1090,0	0.13 3,3	1.6875 42,862	46.65 1185,0	46.80 1188,8
42.0000 1066,800	52.0000 1320,800	3.7500 95,250	134000 59500	132000 58500	1.02	6.93 175,9	EE776420	776520	0.25 6,4	3.5000 88,900	43.90 1115,0	43.90 1115,0	0.25 6,4	2.7500 69,850	49.61 1260,0	50.14 1273,5
45.5000 1155,700	56.5000 1435,100	4.7500 120,650	244000 108500	151000 67000	1.62	3.46 87,9	EE277455	277565	0.25 6,4	4.7500 120,650	47.44 1205,0	47.05 1195,0	0.25 6,4	3.7500 95,250	53.94 1370,0	53.94 1370,0
50.0000 1270,000	56.5000 1435,100	2.7500 69,850	113000 50500	111000 49500	1.02	8.54 216,8	LL889049	LL889010	0.25 6,4	2.5625 65,088	51.38 1305,0	51.18 1300,0	0.25 6,4	1.8750 47,625	54.92 1395,0	55.24 1403,2
67.0000 1701,800	81.5000 2070,099	5.5000 139,700	331000 147000	218000 97000	1.52	6.24 158,5	EE289670	289815	0.50 12,7	5.5000 139,700	69.69 1770,0	69.29 1760,0	0.50 12,7	4.5000 114,300	77.76 1975,0	77.56 1970,0

①These maximum fillet radii will be cleared by the bearing corners.
②Specific cone part number indicated in ( ) when dimension "T" varies from others in series.
†Dimension shown is maximum value—See note at bottom of fitting practice table page 4 in Reference Tables.

SINGLE-ROW STRAIGHT BORE
ISO METRIC SERIES

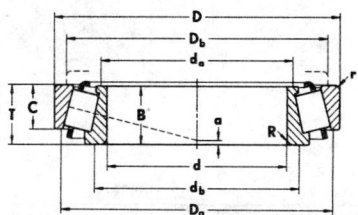

STANDARD TOLERANCES (in μm)

CONE BORE			
over	inclusive	high	low
10	18	0	− 8
18	30	0	−10
30	50	0	−12
50	80	0	−15
80	120	0	−20

CUP O.D.			
over	inclusive	high	low
30	50	0	−11
50	80	0	−13
80	120	0	−15
120	150	0	−18
150	180	0	−25
180	250	0	−30

OVERALL BEARING WIDTH			
over	inclusive	high	low
10	18	+200	− 0
18	30	+200	− 0
30	50	+200	− 0
50	80	+200	− 0
80	120	+200	−200

bore	outside diameter	width	rating at 500 RPM for 3000 hours L10		fac-tor	eff. load center	bearing number	cone				cup			
			one row radial	thrust				max. shaft fillet radius	width	backing shoulder diameters		max. housing fillet radius	width	backing shoulder	
d	D	T	daN	daN	K	a[2]		R[1]	B	d_b	d_a	r[1]	C	D_b	D_a
15,000	42,000	14,250	418	204	2,05	−4,5	30302	1,5	13,000	22	20	1,5	11,000	35,5	39
17,000	40,000	13,250	362	214	1,69	−3,5	30203	1,5	12,000	23,5	20,5	1,5	11,000	34	37
17,000	47,000	15,250	520	254	2,05	−4,8	30303	1,5	14,000	24	21,5	1,5	12,000	39,5	43
20,000	47,000	15,250	510	302	1,69	−4,0	30204	1,5	14,000	27	24,5	1,5	12,000	39,5	44
20,000	52,000	16,250	605	312	1,95	−4,8	30304	2,0	15,000	28,5	25,5	2,0	13,000	44	48
20,000	52,000	22,250	840	430	1,95	−8,3	32304	2,0	21,000	28,5	26	2,0	18,000	42	48
25,000	52,000	16,250	580	372	1,56	−3,5	30205	1,5	15,000	32	30	1,5	13,000	44	49
25,000	52,000	22,000	1000	600	1,66	−7,6	33205	1,5	22,000	34	30,5	1,5	18,000	45	49,5
25,000	62,000	18,250	850	434	1,95	−5,0	30305	2,0	17,000	33,5	31	2,0	15,000	53	57
30,000	62,000	17,250	740	475	1,56	−3,3	30206	1,5	16,000	36,5	35	1,5	14,000	53	58
30,000	62,000	21,250	940	605	1,56	−5,8	32206	1,5	20,000	38	35,5	1,5	17,000	52	59
30,000	72,000	20,750	1035	560	1,85	−5,8	30306	2,0	19,000	39,5	36,5	2,0	16,000	61	67
35,000	72,000	18,250	965	615	1,56	−2,8	30207	2,0	17,000	43	41,5	2,0	15,000	62	67
35,000	72,000	24,250	1290	825	1,56	−6,3	32207	2,0	23,000	44,5	42	2,0	19,000	60	67
35,000	80,000	32,750	1960	1055	1,85	−12,1	32307	2,5	31,000	47,5	43	2,5	25,000	67	75

The dimensions for **d** and **D** are maximum metric values.
[1] These maximum fillet radii will be cleared by the bearing corners.
[2] Minus value indicates center is inside cone backface.

SINGLE-ROW STRAIGHT BORE
ISO METRIC SERIES

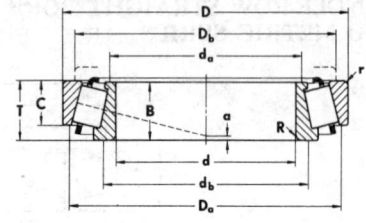

bore	outside diameter	width	rating at 500 RPM for 3000 hours L10		fac-tor	eff. load center	bearing number	cone				cup			
			one-row radial	thrust				max. shaft fillet radius	width	backing shoulder diameters		max. hous-ing fillet radius	width	backing shoulder	
d	D	T	daN	daN	K	a[2]		R[1]	B	d_b	d_a	r[1]	C	D_b	D_a
40,000	80,000	19,750	1070	685	1,56	−3,0	30208	2,0	18,000	47	46	2,0	16,000	69	75
40,000	80,000	24,750	1380	885	1,56	−5,5	32208	2,0	23,000	49	47	2,0	19,000	68	75
40,000	90,000	35,250	2320	1370	1,69	−11,8	32308	2,5	33,000	54	49	2,5	27,000	75	83
45,000	80,000	26,000	1735	1140	1,52	−6,5	33109	2,0	26,000	55	51,5	2,0	20,500	72	76,5
45,000	85,000	20,750	1175	815	1,44	−2,2	30209	2,0	19,000	54	51,5	2,0	16,000	74	80
45,000	85,000	24,750	1515	1050	1,44	−4,3	32209	2,0	23,000	54	51,5	2,0	19,000	73	81
50,000	90,000	21,750	1360	975	1,39	−2,0	30210	2,0	20,000	59	56	2,0	17,000	79	85
50,000	90,000	24,750	1540	1110	1,39	−3,5	32210	2,0	23,000	59	56	2,0	19,000	78	86
50,000	110,000	42,250	3300	1960	1,69	−14,1	32310	3,0	40,000	65	62	3,0	33,000	92	103
55,000	100,000	22,750	1735	1205	1,44	−2,0	30211	2,5	21,000	65	62	2,5	18,000	87	94
55,000	100,000	26,750	2100	1455	1,44	−4,0	32211	2,5	25,000	67	63	2,5	21,000	86	94
55,000	120,000	45,500	4020	2380	1,69	−15,4	32311	3,0	43,000	71	67	3,0	35,000	100	113
60,000	110,000	23,750	1800	1250	1,44	−1,7	30212	2,5	22,000	70	67	2,5	19,000	95	103
60,000	110,000	29,750	2400	1665	1,44	−5,0	32212	2,5	28,000	71	68	2,5	24,000	95	104
60,000	130,000	48,500	4650	2760	1,69	−16,6	32312	3,5	46,000	78	73	3,5	37,000	108	121
65,000	110,000	34,000	3120	2080	1,51	−7,8	33113	2,0	34,000	77	72,5	2,0	26,500	99	106
65,000	120,000	32,750	3060	2120	1,44	−5,5	32213	2,5	31,000	78	74	2,5	27,000	105	114
65,000	140,000	36,000	3220	4550	0,71	8,0	31313	3,5	33,000	87	79	3,5	23,000	116	133
70,000	125,000	26,250	2360	1705	1,39	−0,5	30214	2,5	24,000	81	78	2,5	21,000	111	118
70,000	125,000	33,250	3240	2320	1,39	−4,5	32214	2,5	31,000	83	79	2,5	27,000	110	119
75,000	125,000	37,000	3900	2640	1,47	−7,5	33115	2,5	37,000	88	83,5	2,5	29,000	112	120
75,000	130,000	33,250	3280	2440	1,34	−3,5	32215	2,5	31,000	87	84	2,5	27,000	114	125
80,000	140,000	35,250	3640	2620	1,39	−4,5	32216	3,0	33,000	94	90	3,0	28,000	124	133
85,000	150,000	38,500	4360	3140	1,39	−4,5	32217	3,0	36,000	100	95	3,0	30,000	130	143
90,000	160,000	32,500	3700	2660	1,39	−0,7	30218	3,0	30,000	103	100	3,0	26,000	141	151
90,000	160,000	42,500	5000	3600	1,39	−6,2	32218	3,0	40,000	106	102	3,0	34,000	141	152
95,000	145,000	39,000	4900	2320	2,10	−10,1	33019	2,5	39,000	106	102	2,5	32,500	133	139
95,000	170,000	45,500	5650	4080	1,39	−6,2	32219	3,5	43,000	113	108	3,5	37,000	148	162
100,000	180,000	49,000	6650	4750	1,39	−7,2	32220	3,5	46,000	119	114	3,5	39,000	159	171
105,000	160,000	35,000	4380	3340	1,31	−0,3	32021X	3,0	35,000	119	114,5	3,0	26,000	146	153,5
105,000	160,000	43,000	5800	2780	2,07	−12,1	33021	3,0	43,000	118	114	3,0	34,000	147	153
105,000	190,000	53,000	7300	5250	1,39	−7,8	32221	3,5	50,000	124	119	3,5	43,000	167	179

The dimensions for d and D are maximum metric values.
[1]These maximum fillet radii will be cleared by the bearing corners.
[2]Minus value indicates center is inside cone backface.

SINGLE-ROW FLANGED CUP

TSF

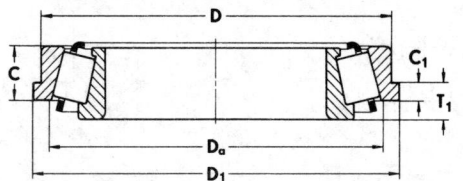

for available cones refer to bearing selection index under series indicated

cup								cone					
		flange		backing shoulder diameter	part number						rating at 500 RPM for 3000 hours L10		
outside diameter	width	diameter	width			cup	series	bore range			one row radial lb daN	thrust lb daN	factor
D	C	D₁	C₁	Dₐ				d	T₁				K
1.3775 34,988	0.3437 8,730	1.4985 38,062	0.0930 2,362	1.32 33,5	A4138B		A4000	0.4992 — †0.5906 12,680 — †15,000	0.1823 4,630		500 222	387 172	1.29
1.5745 39,992	0.3750 9,525	1.6955 43,066	0.0930 2,362	1.50 38,0	A6157B		A6000	0.6250 — 0.7500 15,875 — 19,050	0.1910 4,851		530 236	480 212	1.11
1.6875 42,862	0.5313 13,495	1.8085 45,936	0.1250 3,175	1.59 40,5	17520B		17500	0.6250 15,875	0.2500 6,350		1150 515	655 292	1.76
1.8504 47,000	0.4375 11,112	2.0024 50,861	0.1090 2,769	1.75 44,5	05185B		05000	0.6250 — †0.7874 15,875 — †20,000	0.2377 6,038		1020 450	620 276	1.64
1.9380 49,225	0.5625 14,288	2.0898 53,081	0.1280 3,251	1.83 46,5	09195AB		09000 (09067)①	0.7500 19,050	①0.2755 6,998		1600 715	730 324	2.20
1.9380 49,225	0.5625 14,288	2.0898 53,081	0.1280 3,251	1.83 46,5	09195AB		09000	0.6250 — 0.8115 15,875 — 20,612	0.3468 8,809		1600 715	730 324	2.20
1.9687 50,005	0.3750 9,525	2.1209 53,871	0.1094 2,779	1.93 49,0	07196B		07000	0.7874 — 1.0000 20,000 — 25,400	0.2657 6,749		1130 500	780 346	1.45
2.0470 51,994	0.5000 12,700	2.1990 55,855	0.1090 2,769	1.97 50,0	07204B		07000	0.7874 — 1.0000 20,000 — 25,400	0.2000 5,080		1130 500	780 346	1.45
2.0472 52,000	0.5000 12,700	2.2030 55,956	0.1090 2,769	1.97 50,0	07205B		07000	0.7874 — 1.0000 20,000 — 25,400	0.2000 5,080		1130 500	780 346	1.45
2.0625 52,388	0.5625 14,288	2.2147 56,253	0.1560 3,962	1.97 50,0	1328B		1300	0.8750 22,225	0.3560 9,042		1820 810	910 404	2.00
2.2400 56,896	0.6250 15,875	2.3920 60,757	0.1560 3,962	2.09 53,0	1729B		1700	0.7500 — 1.0000 19,050 — 25,400	0.2935 7,455		1740 775	915 408	1.90
2.2500 57,150	0.5313 13,495	2.4022 61,016	0.1563 3,970	2.17 55,0	15520B		15500	1.0000 — 1.1250 25,400 — 28,575	0.3125 7,938		1800 800	1070 475	1.69
2.3125 58,738	0.4219 10,716	2.4645 62,598	0.1090 2,769	2.24 57,0	08231B		08000	1.1875 — 1.2500 30,162 — 31,750	0.2652 6,736		1280 570	1040 465	1.23
2.3125 58,738	0.5937 15,080	2.4645 62,598	0.1562 3,967	2.20 56,0	1932B		1900	0.8750 — 1.1250 22,225 — 28,575	0.3125 7,938		1850 825	1050 465	1.77
2.3750 60,325	0.6250 15,875	2.5270 64,186	0.1562 3,967	2.24 57,0	1931B		1900	0.8750 — 1.1250 22,225 — 28,575	0.3125 7,938		1850 825	1050 465	1.77
2.4375 61,912	0.9375 23,812	2.6209 66,571	0.1875 4,762	2.32 59,0	3620B		3600	0.9375 23,812	0.3750 9,525		3360 1495	1630 725	2.07
2.4409 62,000	0.5625 14,288	2.5930 65,862	0.1400 3,556	2.32 59,0	17244B		17000	0.9835 — 1.1875 24,981 — 30,162	0.2075 5,270		1620 720	1060 470	1.53
2.5000 63,500	0.6250 15,875	2.6522 67,366	0.1562 3,967	2.36 60,0	15250B		15000 (15100SR)①	1.0000 25,400	①0.3087 7,841		1990 885	1190 530	1.67
2.5000 63,500	0.6250 15,875	2.6522 67,366	0.1562 3,967	2.36 60,0	15250B		15000 (15123)①	1.2500 31,750	①0.3087 7,841		1990 885	1190 530	1.67

①Specific cone part number indicated in ( ) when dimension "T₁" varies from others in series.

†Dimension shown is maximum value—see note at bottom of fitting practice table page 4 in Reference Tables.

Single-Row Flanged Cup — TSF

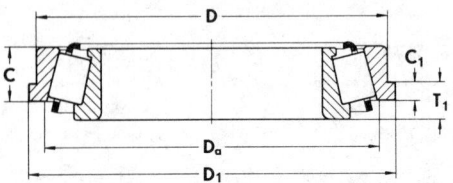

for available cones refer to bearing selection index under series indicated

cup							cone				
		flange		backing shoulder diameter	part number				rating at 500 RPM for 3000 hours L10		
outside diameter	width	diameter	width				bore range		one row radial	thrust	factor
D	C	D_1	C_1	D_a	cup	series	d	T_1	lb daN	lb daN	K
2.5000 63,500	0.6250 15,875	2.6522 67,366	0.1562 3,967	2.36 60,0	15250B	15000	1.0000 — 1.2500 25,400 — 31,750	0.3437 8,730	1990 885	1190 530	1.67
2.5312 64,292	0.6563 16,670	2.7180 69,037	0.1563 3,970	2.48 63,0	M86610B	M86600	1.0000 — 1.2187 25,400 — 30,955	0.3438 8,733	2450 1090	2290 1020	1.07
2.5625 65,088	0.3750 9,525	2.6835 68,161	0.1090 2,769	2.48 63,0	13836B	13800	1.5000 38,100	0.2340 5,944	1140 510	675 300	1.69
2.5625 65,088	0.6250 15,875	2.7147 68,953	0.1563 3,970	2.48 63,0	23256B	23000	0.9375 — 1.0000 23,812 — 25,400	0.4063 10,320	2050 910	2560 1140	0.80
2.6150 66,421	0.7500 19,050	2.7670 70,282	0.1560 3,962	2.44 62,0	2631B	2600	0.8750 — 1.1562 22,225 — 29,367	0.3435 8,725	2970 1320	1290 575	2.30
2.6875 68,262	0.4688 11,908	2.8397 72,128	0.1406 3,571	2.64 67,0	19268B	19000	1.3770 — 1.5000 34,976 — 38,100	0.2968 7,539	2000 890	1530 680	1.31
2.6875 68,262	0.6875 17,462	2.8397 72,128	0.1562 3,967	2.56 65,0	02420B	02400	1.0000 — †1.2598 25,400 — †32,000	0.3437 8,730	2490 1110	1780 790	1.40
2.7170 69,012	0.6250 15,875	2.8690 72,873	0.1560 3,962	2.56 65,0	14276B	14000	1.1811 — 1.3770 30,000 — 34,976	0.3123 7,932	2180 970	1420 635	1.53
2.7500 69,850	0.7500 19,050	2.9020 73,711	0.1560 3,962	2.60 66,0	2523B	2500	1.1250 — 1.3125 28,575 — 33,338	0.3435 8,725	3280 1460	1530 685	2.14
2.8125 71,438	0.3750 9,525	2.9225 74,231	0.1100 2,794	2.72 69,0	LL103010B	LL103000	1.7500 44,450	0.2350 5,969	1420 630	740 330	1.91
2.8346 72,000	0.5625 14,288	2.9865 75,857	0.1400 3,556	2.68 68,0	19283B	19000	1.3770 — 1.5000 34,976 — 38,100	0.2475 6,286	2000 890	1530 680	1.31
2.8440 72,238	0.6250 15,875	2.9960 76,098	0.1563 3,970	2.72 69,0	16284B	16000	1.5000 38,100	0.3438 8,733	2280 1015	1570 700	1.45
2.8593 72,626	0.9375 23,812	3.0433 77,300	0.1875 4,762	2.72 69,0	3120B	3100	1.0000 — 1.3125 25,400 — 33,338	0.4375 11,112	3700 1645	2100 935	1.76
3.0000 76,200	0.5625 14,288	3.1836 80,863	0.1406 3,571	2.87 73,0	11300B	11000	1.6250 41,275	0.2871 7,292	1930 860	1610 715	1.20
3.0000 76,200	0.7500 19,050	3.2500 82,550	0.2500 6,350	2.87 73,0	2720B	2700	1.3125 — 1.5625 33,338 — 39,688	0.4375 11,112	3460 1540	1790 800	1.93
3.0000 76,200	0.9375 23,812	3.1836 80,863	0.1875 4,762	2.91 74,0	31520B	31500	1.3125 — 1.4375 33,338 — 36,512	0.4063 10,320	3770 1680	2600 1155	1.45
3.1250 79,375	0.5313 13,495	3.3086 84,038	0.1406 3,571	3.03 77,0	18620B	18600	1.7500 — 1.8125 44,450 — 46,038	0.2968 7,539	2090 930	1340 595	1.56
3.1250 79,375	0.6875 17,462	3.3390 84,811	0.2188 5,558	3.03 77,0	43312B	43000	0.9600 — 1.3125 24,384 — 33,338	0.5313 13,495	2880 1285	3320 1475	0.87
3.1250 79,375	0.7500 19,050	3.2772 83,241	0.1563 3,970	2.99 76,0	26822B	26800	1.3780 — 1.6880 35,000 — 42,875	0.3438 8,733	3660 1630	2000 890	1.83

†Dimension shown is maximum value—see note at bottom of fitting practice table page 4 in Reference Tables.

SINGLE-ROW FLANGED CUP

for available cones refer to bearing selection index under series **indicated**

cup							cone			rating at 500 RPM for 3000 hours L10		factor
		flange		backing shoulder diameter	part number					one row radial lb daN	thrust lb daN	
outside diameter D	width C	diameter D_1	width C_1	D_a	cup	series	bore range d	T_1				K
3.1250 79,375	0.9375 23,812	3.3090 84,049	0.1875 4,762	2.99 76,0	3420B	3400	1.1875 — 1.5000 30,162 — 38,100	0.4063 10,320		4150 1840	2590 1155	1.60
3.1496 80,000	0.6250 15,875	3.3015 83,858	0.1560 3,962	2.87 73,0	28315B	28000	1.1875 — 1.5748 30,162 — 40,000	0.3580 9,093		2440 1085	1680 750	1.45
3.1496 80,000	0.7018 17,826	3.3330 84,658	0.1875 4,762	3.03 77,0	332B	335	1.2500 — 1.6880 31,750 — 42,875	0.3125 7,938		3000 1335	1400 625	2.14
3.1562 80,167	0.9375 23,812	3.3396 84,826	0.1875 4,762	3.03 77,0	3320B	3300	1.3750 — 1.5625 34,925 — 39,688	0.4063 10,320		4300 1900	2000 890	2.14
3.1875 80,962	0.5625 14,288	3.3085 84,036	0.1250 3,175	3.07 78,0	L305610B	L305600	2.0000 50,800	0.2813 7,145		2680 1190	1630 725	1.64
3.2187 81,755	0.9375 23,812	3.4021 86,413	0.1875 4,762	3.03 77,0	3329B	3300	1.3750 — 1.5625 34,925 — 39,688	0.4063 10,320		4300 1900	2000 890	2.14
3.2700 83,058	0.7500 19,050	3.4220 86,919	0.1563 3,970	3.15 80,0	25521B	25500	1.4375 — 1.7960 36,512 — 45,618	0.3438 8,733		3680 1635	2110 940	1.74
3.3465 85,000	0.5313 13,495	3.4870 88,570	0.1406 3,571	3.23 82,0	18720B	18700	1.8125 — 2.0000 46,038 — 50,800	0.2968 7,539		2240 995	1550 690	1.44
3.3465 85,000	0.6875 17,462	3.5299 89,659	0.1875 4,762	3.23 82,0	354B	355	1.5748 — 1.8125 40,000 — 46,038	0.3125 7,938		3140 1395	1640 730	1.91
3.3465 85,000	0.8125 20,638	3.5340 89,764	0.1875 4,762	3.23 82,0	2924B	2900	1.8125 46,038	0.3750 9,525		3830 1705	2270 1010	1.69
3.3750 85,725	0.9375 23,812	3.5270 89,586	0.1875 4,762	3.27 83,0	3820B	3800	1.3750 — 1.6250 34,925 — 41,275	0.4375 11,112		5000 2220	3450 1535	1.45
3.4375 87,312	0.5625 14,288	3.5625 90,488	0.1250 3,175	3.35 85,0	L507910B	L507900	2.2500 57,150	0.2813 7,145		2810 1250	1870 835	1.50
3.4375 87,312	0.9375 23,812	3.6215 91,986	0.1870 4,750	3.23 82,0	3525B	3500	1.5000 — 1.7810 38,100 — 45,237	0.4370 11,100		4550 2020	2380 1060	1.91
3.4843 88,501	0.6875 17,462	3.6983 93,937	0.2187 5,555	3.39 86,0	44348B	44000 (44157X)①	1.5748 40,000	①0.5062 12,857		3180 1410	4250 1880	0.75
3.4843 88,501	0.6875 17,462	3.6983 93,937	0.2187 5,555	3.39 86,0	44348B	44000	1.3125 — 1.6250 33,338 — 41,275	0.5312 13,492		3180 1410	4250 1880	0.75
3.5433 90,000	0.6250 15,875	3.7268 94,661	0.1875 4,762	3.39 86,0	362B	365	1.6250 — 2.0312 41,275 — 51,592	0.3499 8,887		3310 1475	1810 805	1.83
3.6250 92,075	0.7813 19,845	3.7772 95,941	0.1562 3,967	3.50 89,0	28521B	28500	1.7665 — 2.0625 44,869 — 52,388	0.3437 8,730		4100 1840	2660 1185	1.55
3.6718 93,264	0.8750 22,225	3.8558 97,937	0.1875 4,762	3.58 91,0	33820B	33800	1.5000 — 2.1250 38,100 — 53,975	0.4063 10,320		5250 2320	2960 1315	1.77
3.6718 93,264	0.9375 23,812	3.8558 97,937	0.1875 4,762	3.54 90,0	3720B	3700	1.7500 — 2.0625 44,450 — 52,388	0.4375 11,112		5000 2220	2890 1285	1.73
3.7500 95,250	0.8750 22,225	3.9640 100,686	0.2188 5,558	3.43 87,0	432B	435	1.2500 — 1.8125 31,750 — 46,038	0.4376 11,115		4950 2200	2410 1070	2.05
3.8125 96,838	0.7018 17,826	3.9960 101,498	0.1875 4,762	3.70 94,0	382B	385	1.8750 — 2.2650 47,625 — 57,531	0.3125 7,938		3590 1595	2180 970	1.65
3.8437 97,630	0.7656 19,446	3.9960 101,498	0.1560 3,962	3.70 94,0	28622B	28600	2.0000 — 2.2500 50,800 — 57,150	0.3592 9,124		4400 1960	3040 1350	1.45
3.9370 100,000	0.7813 19,845	4.0930 103,962	0.1563 3,970	3.86 98,0	28921B	28900 (28990)①	2.4400 61,976	①0.3438 8,733		4550 2020	3310 1470	1.37
3.9370 100,000	0.7813 19,845	4.0930 103,962	0.1563 3,970	3.86 98,0	28921B	28900	2.3750 — 2.4700 60,325 — 62,738	0.3750 9,525		4550 2020	3310 1470	1.37

①Specific cone part number indicated in ( ) when dimension "T_1" varies from others in series.

Single-Row Flanged Cup — TSF

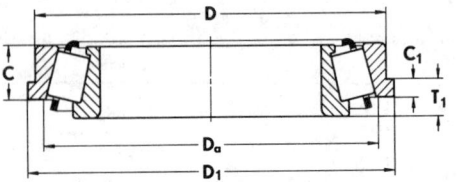

for available cones refer to bearing selection index under series indicated

cup								cone				
		flange		backing shoulder diameter	part number						rating at 500 RPM for 3000 hours L10	
outside diameter	width	diameter	width					bore range			one row radial	thrust
D	C	D₁	C₁	Dₐ	cup	series		d	T₁	lb daN	lb daN	factor K
4.0000 101,600	1.0625 26,988	4.2460 107,848	0.2500 6,350	3.82 97,0	522B	525		1.5000 — 2.0000 38,100 — 50,800	0.5625 14,288	6550 2920	3200 1425	2.05
4.1250 104,775	0.6250 15,875	4.3084 109,433	0.1875 4,762	4.02 102,0	39412B	39000		†2.3622 — 2.5000 †60,000 — 63,500	0.4063 10,320	3880 1725	2570 1145	1.51
4.2500 107,950	0.7500 19,050	4.4022 111,816	0.1563 3,970	4.13 105,0	29520B	29500		2.3622 — 2.6250 60,000 — 66,675	0.4063 10,320	4650 2080	3670 1630	1.27
4.2500 107,950	0.8750 22,225	4.4640 113,386	0.2188 5,558	3.94 100,0	453B	455		1.6250 — 2.2500 41,275 — 57,150	0.4376 11,115	5400 2400	3090 1375	1.74
4.3307 110,000	0.7411 18,824	4.5147 114,673	0.1870 4,750	4.17 106,0	394AB	395		1.9685 — 2.6875 50,000 — 68,262	0.3120 7,925	4000 1790	2770 1235	1.45
4.3307 110,000	0.7500 19,050	4.4803 113,800	0.1563 3,970	4.13 105,0	29521B	29500		2.3622 — 2.6250 60,000 — 66,675	0.4063 10,320	4650 2080	3670 1630	1.27
4.3750 111,125	0.8125 20,638	4.5938 116,683	0.2188 5,558	4.21 107,0	55437B	55000		1.7500 — 2.0625 44,450 — 52,388	0.5938 15,083	4150 1840	6300 2800	0.66
4.3750 111,125	1.1875 30,162	4.6210 117,373	0.2500 6,350	3.94 100,0	532B	535		1.5748 — 2.1250 40,000 — 53,975	0.5625 14,288	6900 3060	3500 1560	1.97
4.4375 112,712	0.7500 19,050	4.5900 116,586	0.1563 3,970	4.33 110,0	29620B	29600		2.7500 — 2.9062 69,850 — 73,817	0.4063 10,320	4900 2180	4100 1820	1.20
4.4375 112,712	0.9375 23,812	4.6210 117,373	0.1875 4,762	4.25 108,0	3920B	3900		2.0000 — 2.6250 50,800 — 66,675	0.4375 11,112	5900 2620	4050 1800	1.45
4.4375 112,712	0.9375 23,812	4.6523 118,168	0.2188 5,558	4.33 110,0	39520B	39500		2.0000 — 2.6250 50,800 — 66,675	0.4688 11,908	7000 3100	4050 1800¢	1.72
4.5000 114,300	1.3750 34,925	4.7772 121,341	0.2813 7,145	4.21 107,0	65320B	65300		1.9375 49,212	0.6563 16,670	8850 3940	6500 2900	1.36
4.5625 115,888	0.6563 16,670	4.7187 119,855	0.1563 3,970	4.45 113,0	L116110B	L116100		3.2500 82,550	0.3125 7,938	4150 1840	2170 965	1.90
4.6250 117,475	0.9375 23,812	4.8084 122,133	0.1875 4,762	4.49 114,0	33462B	33000		2.2500 — 2.8750 57,150 — 73,025	0.4375 11,112	5950 2660	4450 1980	1.34
4.6250 117,475	0.9375 23,812	4.8750 123,825	0.2500 6,350	4.45 113,0	66462B	66000		2.0000 — 2.2500 50,800 — 57,150	0.6250 15,875	5750 2560	6200 2760	0.93
4.7244 120,000	0.9542 24,237	4.9384 125,435	0.2180 5,537	4.53 115,0	472B	475		2.1654 — 2.7559 55,000 — 70,000	0.4368 11,095	5900 2640	3900 1735	1.52
4.7500 120,650	1.2500 31,750	5.0275 127,691	0.2812 7,142	4.33 110,0	612B	615		1.7500 — 2.2500 44,450 — 57,150	0.6562 16,667	8300 3700	4450 1980	1.86
4.8125 122,238	0.8437 21,430	4.9961 126,901	0.1875 4,762	4.65 118,0	34481B	34000		2.7540 — 3.0625 69,952 — 77,788	0.3126 7,940	4250 1900	3270 1455	1.30
4.8750 123,825	1.1875 30,162	5.1210 130,073	0.2500 6,350	4.57 116,0	552B	555		2.0000 — 2.6875 50,800 — 68,262	0.5625 14,288	7900 3520	4700 2080	1.69

†Dimension shown is maximum value—see note at bottom of fitting practice table 4 in Reference Tables.

SINGLE-ROW FLANGED CUP

for available cones refer to bearing selection index under series indicated

cup							cone				
		flange		backing shoulder diameter	part number				rating at 500 RPM for 3000 hours L10		factor
outside diameter	width	diameter	width		cup	series	bore range		one row radial	thrust	
D	C	D_1	C_1	D_a			d	T_1	lb daN	lb daN	K
4.9375 125,412	0.7813 19,845	5.1211 130,076	0.1875 4,762	4.84 123,0	27620B	27600	2.8750 — 3.2813 73,025 — 83,345	0.4062 10,317	5150 2300	3690 1640	1.40
5.0000 127,000	0.8750 22,225	5.2460 133,248	0.2188 5,558	4.88 124,0	42620B	42600	2.8750 — 3.0625 73,025 — 77,788	0.5313 13,495	6750 3000	4850 2160	1.39
5.0000 127,000	1.1250 28,575	5.2460 133,248	0.2500 6,350	4.76 121,0	563B	565	2.5000 — 2.9062 63,500 — 73,817	0.5625 14,288	8250 3660	5100 2280	1.61
5.0000 127,000	1.3750 34,925	5.2772 134,041	0.2813 7,145	4.72 120,0	65500B	65000	2.0000 — 2.3750 50,800 — 60,325	0.6563 16,670	9850 4380	8200 3660	1.20
5.2500 133,350	1.0313 26,195	5.4650 138,811	0.2188 5,558	5.12 130,0	47620B	47600	2.8125 — 3.2500 71,438 — 82,550	0.5000 12,700	7850 3500	5450 2420	1.44
5.3750 136,525	0.8750 22,225	5.5890 141,961	0.2180 5,537	5.16 131,0	493B	495	2.8125 — 3.3750 71,438 — 85,725	0.5305 13,475	6550 2920	5000 2220	1.31
5.3750 136,525	1.2500 31,750	5.6520 143,561	0.2810 7,137	4.92 125,0	632B	635	2.1250 — 2.8125 53,975 — 71,438	0.6560 16,662	9600 4260	5950 2640	1.61
5.3750 136,525	1.2813 32,545	5.6875 144,462	0.2038 5,177	5.16 131,0	HM516414B	HM516400	3.0000 — 3.2500 76,200 — 82,550	0.4850 12,319	10000 4440	6900 3060	1.45
5.5000 139,700	1.4375 36,512	6.0000 152,400	0.3125 7,938	5.31 135,0	H715310B	H715300	2.3750 — 3.0625 60,325 — 77,788	0.6875 17,462	11900 5300	9600 4280	1.24
5.5115 139,992	1.1250 28,575	5.7575 146,240	0.2500 6,350	5.28 134,0	572B	575	2.8750 — 3.2500 73,025 — 82,550	0.5625 14,288	8800 3920	6100 2700	1.45
5.6250 142,875	1.0313 26,195	5.8710 149,123	0.3125 7,938	5.59 142,0	47825B	47800	3.6250 — 3.7500 92,075 — 95,250	0.5937 15,080	8750 3900	6750 3000	1.30
5.8750 149,225	0.9688 24,608	6.0898 154,681	0.2188 5,558	5.67 144,0	42587B	42000	3.4630 — 3.8125 87,960 — 96,838	0.5000 12,700	7100 3160	6000 2660	1.19
5.8750 149,225	1.7500 44,450	6.1835 157,061	0.3125 7,938	5.51 140,0	6420B	6400	2.2500 — 3.0000 57,150 — 76,200	0.6875 17,462	14700 6550	9100 4060	1.61
5.9090 150,089	1.4375 36,512	6.2170 157,912	0.3125 7,938	5.63 143,0	742B	745	2.5000 — 3.3475 63,500 — 85,026	0.6250 15,875	13200 5850	7350 3260	1.80
6.0000 152,400	1.1875 30,162	6.2460 158,648	0.2500 6,350	5.67 144,0	592B	595	3.0000 — 3.7500 76,200 — 95,250	0.6250 15,875	9350 4160	7100 3160	1.32
6.0000 152,400	1.2500 31,750	6.2772 159,441	0.2812 7,142	5.55 141,0	652B	655	2.7500 — 3.3750 69,850 — 85,725	0.6562 16,667	10300 4600	7150 3180	1.43
6.2500 158,750	0.6250 15,875	6.4336 163,413	0.1875 4,762	6.02 153,0	37625B	37000	4.2500 — 4.3125 107,950 — 109,538	0.4688 11,908	5050 2240	5250 2340	0.96
6.2992 160,000	1.0313 26,195	6.5490 166,345	0.2500 6,350	6.10 155,0	52630XB	52000	3.7500 — 4.0000 95,250 — 101,600	0.6562 16,667	9900 4400	8050 3580	1.23
6.3125 160,338	0.6563 16,670	6.4647 164,203	0.1563 3,970	6.18 157,0	L624510B	L624500	4.7500 120,650	0.3438 8,733	5150 2280	3830 1700	1.34
6.3750 161,925	1.0313 26,195	6.6210 168,173	0.2500 6,350	6.10 155,0	52637B	52000	3.7500 — 4.0000 95,250 — 101,600	0.6562 16,667	9900 4400	8050 3580	1.23
6.3750 161,925	1.1875 30,162	6.7500 171,450	0.2810 7,137	6.03 153,0	9221B	9200 (9275)①	2.3750 76,200	①0.9060 23,012	11500 5100	14000 6200	0.82
6.3750 161,925	1.1875 30,162	6.7500 171,450	0.2810 7,137	6.03 153,0	9221B	9200	3.0000 76,200	0.9685 24,600	11500 5100	14000 6200	0.82
6.3750 161,925	1.5000 38,100	6.6830 169,748	0.3120 7,925	5.91 150,0	752B	755	2.8750 — 3.5625 73,025 — 90,488	0.6870 17,450	13800 6100	8050 3580	1.71
6.3750 161,925	1.6875 42,862	6.7500 171,450	0.3125 7,938	6.10 155,0	6535B	6500	3.0000 — 3.5433 76,200 — 90,000	0.7500 19,050	16000 7150	11000 4900	1.46

①Specific cone part number indicated in ( ) when dimension "T_1" varies from others in series.

Single-Row Flanged Cup — TSF

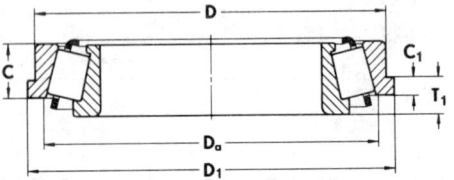

for available cones refer to bearing selection index under series indicated

cup							cone					
		flange		backing shoulder diameter	part number				rating at 500 RPM for 3000 hours L10			
outside diameter D	width C	diameter D_1	width C_1	D_a	cup	series	bore range d	T_1	one row radial lb daN	thrust lb daN	factor K
6.5000 165,100	1.0625 26,988	6.7460 171,348	0.2500 6,350	6.38 162,0	56650B	56000	4.1875 — 4.2500 106,362 — 107,950	0.6250 15,875	10100 4500	8600 3820	1.18
6.6250 168,275	1.1875 30,162	6.9030 175,336	0.2812 7,142	6.30 160,0	672B	675	3.3750 — 4.0000 85,725 — 101,600	0.7187 18,255	11500 5100	9250 4120	1.24
6.6250 168,275	1.6250 41,275	6.9960 177,698	0.3750 9,525	6.10 155,0	832B	835	2.7500 — 3.5000 69,850 — 88,900	0.8750 22,225	16900 7550	8700 3860	1.95
6.7500 171,450	0.9948 25,268	7.0272 178,491	0.2812 7,142	6.50 165,0	67675B	67000	4.2500 107,950	0.6250 15,875	7950 3540	6450 2860	1.24
7.0000 177,800	1.1875 30,162	7.2772 184,841	0.2813 7,145	6.85 174,0	64700B	64000	4.3304 — †4.5276 109,992 — †115,000	0.7188 18,258	12100 5400	10700 4750	1.13
†7.0866 †180,000	1.0236 26,000	7.3996 187,950	0.2500 6,350	6.89 175,0	M624610B	M624600	†4.7244 †120,000	0.6437 16,350	10800 4800	7650 3420	1.41
†7.0866 †180,000	1.1875 30,162	7.3602 186,949	0.2813 7,145	6.85 174,0	64708B	64000	4.3304 — †4.5276 109,992 — †115,000	0.7188 18,258	12100 5400	10700 4750	1.13
7.1250 180,975	1.5000 38,100	7.4330 188,798	0.3125 7,938	6.61 168,0	772B	775	3.6250 — 4.1250 92,075 — 104,775	0.6875 17,462	14900 6600	9850 4380	1.51
7.1875 182,562	1.3125 33,338	7.4435 188,811	0.2500 6,350	6.97 177,0	48220B	48200	4.7500 — 5.0000 120,650 — 127,000	0.5000 12,700	12900 5750	6750 3000	1.91
7.5000 190,500	1.3125 33,338	7.7148 195,956	0.2188 5,558	7.32 186,0	48320B	48300	5.2500 — 5.3750 133,350 — 136,525	0.4688 11,908	13700 6100	7500 3340	1.82
7.5000 190,500	1.3750 34,925	7.8080 198,323	0.3125 7,938	7.13 181,0	71750B	71000	4.1250 — 4.5310 104,775 — 115,087	0.8125 20,638	15900 7050	11300 5050	1.40
7.5000 190,500	1.7500 44,450	7.8710 199,923	0.3750 9,525	6.85 174,0	854B	855	3.4375 — 4.0000 87,312 — 101,600	0.8750 22,225	19300 8600	11100 4950	1.74
7.6250 193,675	0.9063 23,020	7.7772 197,541	0.1563 3,970	7.48 190,0	36620B	36600	5.6250 — 5.7500 142,875 — 146,050	0.3750 9,525	9700 4320	6100 2720	1.59
7.7500 196,850	1.5000 38,100	8.0272 203,891	0.2813 7,145	7.52 191,0	67322B	67300	5.0000 — 5.2500 127,000 — 133,350	0.5938 15,083	16900 7500	9950 4420	1.70
7.8740 200,000	1.3750 34,925	8.2500 209,550	0.3750 9,525	7.40 188,0	98788B	98000	3.1496 — 4.0000 80,000 — 101,600	1.0772 27,361	16500 7350	17900 8000	0.92
7.8750 200,025	1.3437 34,130	8.0898 205,481	0.2187 5,555	7.64 194,0	48620B	48600	5.6250 142,875	0.5000 12,700	13900 6200	8000 3560	1.74
8.0000 203,200	1.5000 38,100	8.2772 210,241	0.2813 7,145	7.52 191,0	67320B	67300	5.0000 — 5.2500 127,000 — 133,350	0.5938 15,083	16900 7500	9950 4420	1.70
8.1250 206,375	1.3750 34,925	8.4336 214,213	0.3125 7,938	7.80 198,0	792B	795	4.7500 — 5.1250 120,650 — 130,175	0.8125 20,638	16800 7450	13200 5900	1.27
8.3750 212,725	2.1250 53,975	8.8085 223,736	0.4375 11,112	7.83 199,0	932B	935	4.0000 — 4.5000 101,600 — 114,300	0.9375 23,812	24300 10800	13600 6050	1.79

†Dimension shown is maximum value—see note at bottom of fitting practice table page 4 in Reference Tables.

for available cones refer to bearing selection index under series indicated

| | | flange | | backing shoulder diameter | part number | | bore range | | rating at 500 RPM for 3000 hours L10 | | factor |
| | | | | | | | | | one row radial lb | thrust lb | |
outside diameter D	width C	diameter D_1	width C_1	D_a	cup	series	d	T_1			K
8.5000 215,900	0.8125 20,688	8.7500 222,250	0.1875 4,762	8.31 211,0	L433710B	L433700	6.5000 165,100	0.4063 10,320	8400 3740	5250 2340	1.60
8.5000 215,900	1.3750 34,925	8.8084 223,733	0.3125 7,938	8.23 209,0	74850B	74000	4.7230 — 5.5118 119,964 — 140,000	0.8125 20,638	17200 7650	14300 6400	1.20
8.8750 225,425	1.3125 33,338	9.0898 230,881	0.2188 5,558	8.62 219,0	46720B	46700	6.2500 — 6.5000 158,750 — 165,100	0.5313 13,495	15100 6750	9950 4420	1.52
9.0000 228,600	1.7500 44,450	9.3710 238,023	0.3750 9,525	8.50 216,0	892B	895	5.3750 — 5.5000 136,525 — 139,700	0.8750 22,225	23000 10250	16500 7350	1.39
9.5000 241,300	1.7500 44,450	9.8710 250,723	0.3750 9,525	8.90 226,0	82950B	82000	5.5000 — 5.7500 139,700 — 146,050	0.8750 22,225	23000 10200	17400 7750	1.32
9.7500 247,650	1.5000 38,100	10.0272 254,691	0.2813 7,145	9.49 241,0	67720B	67700	6.5000 — 7.0000 165,100 — 177,800	0.6563 16,670	19500 8650	14700 6500	1.33
10.0000 254,000	1.8750 47,625	10.4320 264,973	0.4375 11,112	9.37 238,0	99100B	99000	5.5000 — 6.0000 139,700 — 152,400	1.1875 30,162	29200 12950	20400 9050	1.43
10.5000 266,700	1.5000 38,100	10.7772 273,741	0.2813 7,145	10.20 259,0	67820B	67800 (67875)①	7.0866 180,000	①0.6356 16,144	19200 8550	15800 7000	1.22
10.5000 266,700	1.5000 38,100	10.7772 273,741	0.2813 7,145	10.20 259,0	67820B	67800 (67886)①	7.4830 190,068	①0.6356 16,144	19200 8550	15800 7000	1.22
10.5000 266,700	1.5000 38,100	10.7772 273,741	0.2813 7,145	10.20 259,0	67820B	67800	7.2500 — 7.5625 184,150 — 192,088	0.6563 16,670	19200 8550	15800 7000	1.22
11.1250 282,575	1.4375 36,512	11.4022 289,616	0.2813 7,145	10.83 275,0	67920B	67900	8.0000 — 8.1250 203,200 — 206,375	0.6563 16,670	19900 8850	17300 7700	1.15
11.2500 285,750	1.3750 34,925	11.5624 293,685	0.3125 7,938	11.02 280,0	LM742710B	LM742700	8.3750 — 8.5000 212,725 — 215,900	0.7500 19,050	20100 8950	16600 7400	1.21
11.3750 288,925	1.8750 47,625	11.8084 299,933	0.4375 11,112	10.71 272,0	94113B	94000	6.5000 — 7.0000 165,100 — 177,800	1.0625 26,988	30000 13350	24000 10650	1.25
11.3750 288,925	1.8750 47,625	11.8084 299,933	0.4375 11,112	10.98 279,0	HM237510B	HM237500	6.3120 — 7.0000 160,325 — 177,800	1.0625 26,988	35500 15800	19400 8600	1.83
12.5000 317,500	1.8125 46,038	12.9340 328,523	0.4375 11,112	11.81 300,0	93125B	93000	†7.0866 — 8.2500 †180,000 — 209,550	1.1250 28,575	32900 14650	29400 13050	1.12
12.8750 327,025	1.4375 36,512	13.2460 336,448	0.3750 9,525	12.32 313,0	8520B	8500	9.0000 — 9.5000 228,600 — 241,300	1.0000 25,400	24900 11100	17300 7700	1.44
13.5000 342,900	1.7500 44,450	13.8750 352,425	0.3750 9,525	13.11 333,0	M349510B	M349500	10.1250 257,175	0.8750 22,225	33400 14850	19900 8850	1.68
*13.7795 *350,000	0.9375 23,812	14.0925 357,950	0.2362 6,000	13.46 342,0	L853011B	L853000	10.8750 276,225	0.7362 18,700	15700 7000	14600 6500	1.08
14.0000 355,600	1.7500 44,450	14.3750 365,125	0.3750 9,525	13.54 344,0	LM451310B	LM451300	10.3750 — 10.5000 263,525 — 266,700	0.8750 22,225	34700 15450	21400 9500	1.62
14.9960 380,898	1.9375 49,212	15.3710 390,423	0.3750 9,525	14.49 368,0	LM654610B	LM654600	11.0229 — 11.2500 279,981 — 285,750	1.0000 25,400	38800 17300	28800 12800	1.35
*15.9449 *405,000	1.5000 38,100	16.5324 419,923	0.3750 9,525	14.96 380,0	L357019B	L357000	12.0000 304,800	0.8750 22,225	29200 13000	17900 7950	1.63
17.5000 444,500	1.5625 39,688	17.9960 457,098	0.5000 12,700	16.85 428,0	291750B	290000	11.7500 — 12.5000 298,450 — 317,500	1.4375 36,512	35200 15650	22700 10100	1.55
18.8125 477,838	1.8125 46,038	19.3125 490,538	0.3750 9,525	18.27 464,0	LM763811B	LM763800	14.2500 361,950	1.0625 26,988	50000 22200	40500 17950	1.24

①Specific cone part number indicated in ( ) when dimension "T_1" varies from others in series.
*Dimension shown is maximum value—see note at bottom of fitting practice table page 4 in Reference Tables.

Single-Row Flanged Cup — TSF

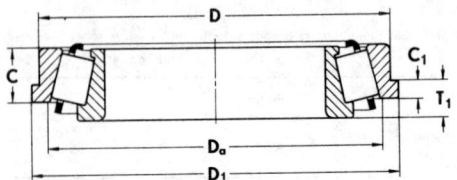

for available cones refer to bearing selection index under series indicated

cup								cone				
		flange		backing shoulder diameter	part number						rating at 500 RPM for 3000 hours L10	
outside diameter D	width C	diameter D₁	width C₁	Dₐ	cup	series		bore range d	T₁	one row radial lb daN	thrust lb daN	factor K
19.0000 482,600	2.3750 60,325	19.6210 498,373	0.6250 15,875	18.27 464,0	526190B	526000		13.0000 330,200	1.6250 41,275	57000 25400	38400 17100	1.49
20.0000 508,000	1.8750 47,625	20.4336 519,013	0.4375 11,112	19.37 492,0	L467510B	L467500		16.0000 406,400	1.0000 25,400	48000 21200	29900 13300	1.60
20.5625 522,288	2.4375 61,912	21.1211 536,476	0.5625 14,288	19.96 507,0	LM565910B	LM565900		15.0000 381,000	1.5000 38,100	69500 31000	46000 20400	1.51
21.6250 549,275	2.4375 61,912	22.1836 563,463	0.5625 14,288	20.91 531,0	LM567910B	LM567900		16.0000 406,400	1.5000 38,100	72500 32200	50500 22600	1.43
23.7500 603,250	2.3750 60,325	24.3086 617,438	0.5625 14,288	22.82 579,7	LM770910B	LM770900		18.0000 457,200	1.5625 39,688	77500 34600	60500 26800	1.29
27.0000 685,800	1.2500 31,750	27.2772 692,840	0.2812 7,142	26.34 669,0	LL379010B	LL379000		23.5000 596,900	0.5312 13,492	31700 14100	18500 8250	1.71
28.5625 725,488	1.3125 33,338	28.8711 733,325	0.3125 7,938	27.87 708,0	LL780210B	LL780200		24.5000 622,300	0.8125 20,638	43500 19400	34700 15450	1.25
29.0000 736,600	1.2500 31,750	29.3120 744,524	0.2812 7,142	28.35 720,0	LL480710B	LL480700		25.5000 647,700	0.5312 13,492	33400 14850	21100 9400	1.58
32.5000 825,500	1.0000 25,400	32.8124 833,435	0.2500 6,350	31.77 807,0	LL582910B	LL582900		29.0000 736,600	0.5000 12,700	25000 11100	17000 7550	1.47
38.5000 977,900	1.3125 33,338	38.8750 987,425	0.3125 7,938	37.20 945,0	LL586018B	LL586000		34.0000 863,600	0.7500 19,050	46000 20400	31600 14050	1.45
48.0000 1219,200	1.6875 42,862	48.5000 1231,900	0.5000 12,700	47.24 1200,0	LL788310B	LL788300		41.8750 — 42.0000 1063,625 — 1066,800	1.3750 34,925	101000 45000	82500 36600	1.23
56.5000 1435,100	1.8750 47,625	57.2500 1454,149	0.5625 14,288	55.71 1415,0	LL889010B	LL889000		50.0000 1270,000	1.4375 36,512	113000 50500	111000 49500	1.02

SINGLE-ROW — "DUO-FACE" SEAL

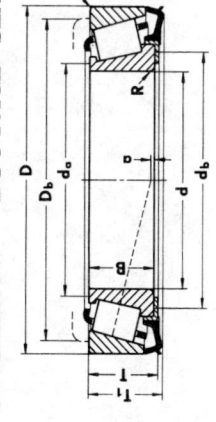

bore d	outside diameter D	width over stamp'g T	width over seal T₁	rating at 500 RPM 3000 hours L10 one row radial daN	rating thrust daN	factor K	eff. load center a	part numbers cone	cup	seal	cone max short fillet radius R	width B	backing shoulder diameters d_b	d_a	cup D_b	max housing fillet radius r
0.7500 19.050	1.7810 45.237	0.641 16.28	0.67 17.0	1230 545	635 282	1.94	-0.22 -5.6	*LM11949L	LM11910	LM11900L	0.05 1.3	0.6550 16.637	1.11—1.19 28.2—30.2	0.93 23.6	1.56 39.5	0.05 1.3
0.7500 19.050	1.7810 45.237	0.641 16.28	0.67 17.0	1230 545	635 282	1.94	-0.22 -5.6	*LM11949L	LM11910	LM11900E	0.05 1.3	0.6550 16.637	0.97 24.6	0.93 23.6	1.56 39.5	0.05 1.3
0.8437 21.438	1.9687 50.005	0.721 18.31	0.75 19.0	1660 740	790 352	2.10	-0.25 -6.4	*M12649L	M12610	M12600L	0.05 1.3	0.7200 18.288	1.14—1.30 29.0—33.0	1.00 25.4	1.73 44.0	0.05 1.3
1.0000 25.400	1.9687 50.005	0.562 14.28	0.59 15.0	1130 500	780 346	1.45	-0.11 -2.9	07100L	07196	07000L	0.04 1.0	0.5614 14.260	1.31—1.44 33.3—36.6	1.16 29.5	1.75 44.5	0.04 1.0
1.0000 25.400	1.9800 50.292	0.591 15.01	0.63 16.0	1200 535	770 342	1.56	-0.13 -3.3	*L44643L	L44610	L44600L	0.05 1.3	0.5800 14.732	1.25 31.8	1.16 29.5	1.75 44.5	0.05 1.3
1.0000 25.400	1.9800 50.292	0.591 15.01	0.63 16.0	1200 535	770 342	1.56	-0.13 -3.3	*L44643LA O-Ring in bore	L44610	L44600L	0.05 1.3	0.5800 14.732	1.25 31.8	1.16 29.5	1.75 44.5	0.05 1.3
1.2500 31.750	2.3280 59.131	0.656 16.66	0.70 17.8	1580 700	1110 495	1.42	-0.12 -2.9	*LM67048L	LM67010	LM67000L	Spec	0.6600 16.764	1.75 44.5	1.42 36.1	2.05 52.0	0.05 1.3
1.3750 34.925	2.5625 65.088	0.741 18.82	0.78 19.8	2140 950	1380 615	1.55	-0.15 -3.7	*LM48548L	LM48510	LM48500L	Spec	0.7200 18.288	1.89 48.0	1.57 39.9	2.28 58.0	0.05 1.3
1.5000 38.100	2.5625 65.088	0.741 18.82	0.78 19.8	2020 900	1150 510	1.76	-0.16 -4.2	LM29748L	LM29710	LM29700L	Spec	0.7200 18.288	1.98 50.3	1.67 42.4	2.32 59.0	0.05 1.3
1.5000 38.100	2.7170 69.012	0.781 19.84	0.83 21.1	2230 990	1540 685	1.45	-0.12 -3.0	13685L	13621	13600L	0.14 3.5	0.7500 19.050	2.05 52.1	1.69 42.9	2.40 61.0	0.09 2.3
2.6875 68.262	4.3307 110.000	0.916 23.27	0.97 24.6	4000 1790	2770 1235	1.45	-0.03 -0.8	399AL	394A	395LL	0.09 2.3	0.8660 21.996	3.19—3.34 81.0—84.8	2.91 73.9	3.98 101.0	0.05 1.3

Ⓡ These maximum fillet radii will be cleared by the bearing corners.
Ⓐ Minus value indicates center is inside cone backface.
*Non-standard tolerances, see Inch System bearing tolerance page 18, in Reference Tables.

THRUST BEARINGS · STEERING PIVOT
WITH RETAINERS

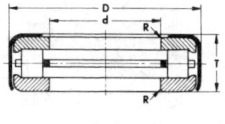

fig. 1

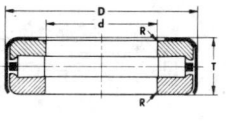

fig. 2

STANDARD TOLERANCES

inch tolerances in .0001" metric tolerances in micrometers
1 micrometer = 0,001 mm

bore d		High	Low	outside diameter D		High	Low	width T bearing bore size		High	Low
up to	1.0000" incl. 25,400 mm	30 76	30 76	up to	5.0000" incl. 127,000 mm	100 254	0 0	up to	3.0000" incl. 76,200 mm	100 254	100 254
1.0000" 25,400 mm	3.0000" incl. 76,200 mm	40 102	40 102	5.0000" 127,000 mm	8.0000" incl. 203,200 mm	150 381	0 0	3.0000" 76,200 mm	5.0000" incl. 127,000 mm	150 381	150 381
3.0000" 76,200 mm	and over	50 127	50 127	8.0000" 203,200 mm	and over	200 508	0 0	5.0000" 127,000 mm	and over	200 508	200 508

bore d	outside diameter D	width T	max. shaft fillet radius R①	steering pivot rating lb daN	bearing number no oil holes in retainer	oil holes in retainer	figure no.
0.6350 16,129	1.6250 41,275	0.5000 12,700	0.03 0,8	2400 1070	T63	T63W	1
0.7600 19,304	1.6250 41,275	0.5000 12,700	0.03 0,8	2400 1070	T77	T77W	1
0.7600 19,304	1.6250 41,275	0.5310 13,487	0.03 0,8	2400 1070	T76	T76W	1
.07975 20,256	1.5625 39,688	0.5625 14,288	0.05 1,3	2400 1070	T86		1
0.8220 20,879	1.6250 41,275	0.5310 13,487	0.03 0,8	2400 1070	T82	T82W	1
0.8220 20,879	1.6600 42,164	0.5310 13,487	0.03 0,8	2960 1320	T83	T83W	2
0.8850 22,279	1.8906 48,021	0.5940 15,088	0.03 0,8	3890 1730	T88	T88W	1
0.9470 24,054	1.8906 48,021	0.5940 15,088	0.03 0,8	3890 1730	T94	T94W	1
0.9500 24,130	2.0000 50,800	0.6250 15,875	0.03 0,8	4200 1860	T95	T95W	1
1.0100 25,654	2.0000 50,800	0.6250 15,875	0.03 0,8	4200 1860	T101	T101W	1
1.0350 26,289	2.0000 50,800	0.6250 15,875	0.03 0,8	4200 1860	T104	T104W	1
1.0720 27,229	2.0000 50,800	0.6250 15,875	0.03 0,8	4200 1860	T107	T107W	1
1.1350 28,829	2.0940 53,188	0.6250 15,875	0.03 0,8	4500 2000	T110	T110W	1

①These maximum fillet radii will be cleared by the bearing corners.

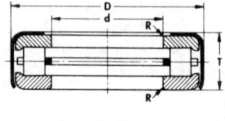

fig. 1

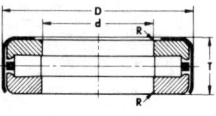

fig. 2

inch tolerances in .0001"				**STANDARD TOLERANCES**				metric tolerances in micrometers 1 micrometer = 0,001 mm			
bore				**outside diameter**				**width**			
d		**High**	**Low**	**D**		**High**	**Low**	bearing bore size		**High**	**Low**
up to	1.0000" incl. 25,400 mm	30 76	30 76	up to	5.0000" incl. 127,000 mm	100 254	0 0	up to	3.0000" incl. 76,200 mm	100 254	100 254
1.0000" 25,400 mm	3.0000" incl. 76,200 mm	40 102	40 102	5.0000" 127,000 mm	8.0000" incl. 203,200 mm	150 381	0 0	3.0000" 76,200 mm	5.0000" incl. 127,000 mm	150 381	150 381
3.0000" 76,200 mm	and over	50 127	50 127	8.0000" 203,200 mm	and over	200 508	0 0	5.0000" 127,000 mm	and over	200 508	200 508

bore	outside diameter	width	max. shaft fillet radius	steering pivot rating	bearing number		figure
d	D	T	R①	lb daN	no oil holes in retainer	oil holes in retainer	no.
1.1350 28,829	2.1875 55,562	0.6250 15,875	0.03 0,8	4500 2000	T113	T113W	1
1.1975 30,416	2.1553 54,745	0.4500 11,430	0.03 0,8	3690 1640	T120		2
1.1975 30,416	2.1875 55,562	0.6250 15,875	0.03 0,8	4500 2000	T119	T119W	1
1.2600 32,004	2.1875 55,562	0.6250 15,875	0.03 0,8	4500 2000	T126	T126W	1
1.3850 35,179	2.3125 58,738	0.6250 15,875	0.03 0,8	4750 2120	T139	T139W	1
1.3850 35,179	2.4688 62,708	0.7650 19,431	0.03 0,8	5050 2240	T142	T142W	1
1.5080 38,303	2.5938 65,883	0.7650 19,431	0.03 0,8	5300 2360	T149	T149W	1
1.5840 40,234	2.5938 65,883	0.7650 19,431	0.03 0,8	5300 2360	T158		1
2.0100 51,054	2.9375 74,612	0.6250 15,875	0.03 0,8	5850 2600	T199	T199W	1
3.0938 78,583	4.0313 102,395	0.6250 15,875	0.03 0,8	8000 3540	T309	T309W	1
3.8750 98,425	5.0000 127,000	0.6875 17,462	0.03 0,8	9700 4300	T387	T387W	1
4.8430 123,012	6.0000 152,400	0.6875 17,462	0.03 0,8	10600 4750	T484		1
5.8125 147,638	7.0000 177,800	0.6875 17,462	0.03 0,8	11600 5150	T581		1

①These maximum fillet radii will be cleared by the bearing corners.

THRUST BEARINGS · CAGELESS · WITH RETAINERS

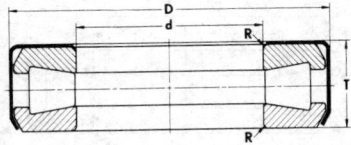

type TTC
fig. 1

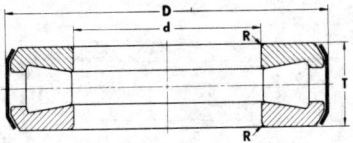

type TTCS
fig. 2

STANDARD TOLERANCES

inch tolerances in .0001"   metric tolerances in micrometers
1 micrometer = 0,001 mm

bore d		High	Low	outside diameter D		High	Low	width T bearing bore size		High	Low
ɔ to	1.0000" incl. 25,400 mm	30 76	30 76	up to	5.0000" incl. 127,000 mm	100 254	0 0	up to	3.0000" incl. 76,200 mm	100 254	100 254
0000" 5,400 mm	3.0000" incl. 76,200 mm	40 102	40 102	5.0000" 127,000 mm	8.0000" incl. 203,200 mm	150 381	0	3.0000" 76,200 mm	5.0000" incl. 127,000 mm	150 381	150 381
0000" 5,200 mm	and over	50 127	50 127	8.0000" 203,200 mm	and over	200 508	0	5.0000" 127,000 mm	and over	200 508	200 508

bore d	outside diameter D	width T	max. shaft fillet radius R①	steering pivot rating lb daN	bearing number no holes in retainer	oil holes in retainer	figure no.
1.2600 32,004	2.1875 55,562	0.6250 15,875	0.03 0,8	6200 2760	T1260		1
1.2600 32,004	2.6250 66,675	0.7656 14,446	0.03 0,8	9450 4220	T127	T127W	1
1.3850 35,179	2.6250 66,675	0.7656 19,446	0.03 0,8	9450 4220	T138	T138W	1
1.4470 36,754	2.6250 66,675	0.7656 19,446	0.06 1,5	9450 4220	T144	T144W	1
1.5100 38,354	2.8590 72,619	0.8125 20,638	0.03 0,8	10600 4700	T152		2
1.5100 38,354	2.8590 72,619	0.8438 21,433	0.03 0,8	10600 4700	T151	T151W	1
1.5730 39,954	2.8590 72,619	0.8438 21,433	0.03 0,8	10600 4700	T157	T157W	1
1.6350 41,529	2.8590 72,619	0.8438 21,433	0.03 0,8	10600 4700	T163	T163W	1
1.6970 43,104	3.2660 82,956	0.9375 23,812	0.03 0,8	14300 6400	T169	T169W	1
1.7600 44,704	3.2660 82,956	0.9375 23,812	0.03 0,8	14300 6400	T176	T176W	1
1.7717 45,000	2.8740 73,000	0.7874 20,000	0.03 0,8	10700 4750	T177		1
1.8220 46,279	3.2660 82,956	0.9375 23,812	0.03 0,8	14300 6400	T182	T182W	1
1.8850 - 47,879	3.2660 82,956	0.9063 23,020	0.03 0,8	14300 6400	T189	T189W	2

①These maximum fillet radii will be cleared by the bearing corners.

THRUST BEARINGS - CAGELESS - WITH RETAINERS — TTC-TTCS

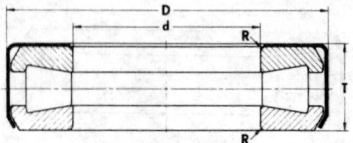

type TTC
fig. 1

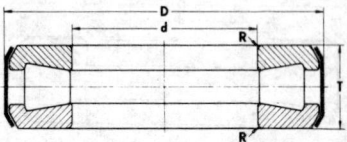

type TTCS
fig. 2

STANDARD TOLERANCES

inch tolerances in .0001"

metric tolerances in micrometers
1 micrometer = 0,001 mm

bore				outside diameter				width T			
d		High	Low	**D**		High	Low	bearing bore size		High	Low
up to	1.0000" incl. 25,400 mm	30 76	30 76	up to	5.0000" incl. 127,000 mm	100 254	0 0	up to	3.0000" incl. 76,200 mm	100 254	100 254
1.0000" 25,400 mm	3.0000" incl. 76,200 mm	40 102	40 102	5.0000" 127,000 mm	8.0000" incl. 203,200 mm	150 381	0 0	3.0000" 76,200 mm	5.0000" incl. 127,000 mm	150 381	150 381
3.0000" 76,200 mm	and over	50 127	50 127	8.0000" 203,200 mm	and over	200 508	0 0	5.0000" 127,000 mm	and over	200 508	200 508

bore d	outside diameter D	width T	max. shaft fillet radius R[①]	steering pivot rating lb daN	bearing number		figure no.
					no holes in retainer	oil holes in retainer	
1.8850 47,879	3.2660 82,956	0.9375 23,812	0.03 0,8	14300 6400	T188	T188W	1
1.9470 49,454	3.6720 93,269	1.0310 26,187	0.03 0,8	19400 8600	T193	T193W	2
1.9470 49,454	3.6720 93,269	1.0620 26,975	0.03 0,8	19400 8600	T194	T194W	1
2.0100 51,054	3.6720 93,269	1.0310 26,187	0.13 3,3	19400 8600	T201	T201W	2
2.0100 51,054	3.6720 93,269	1.0620 26,975	0.13 3,3	19400 8600	T202	T202W	1
2.0720 52,629	3.6720 93,269	1.0310 26,187	0.03 0,8	19400 8600	T209	T209W	2
2.0720 52,629	3.6720 93,269	1.0620 26,975	0.03 0,8	19400 8600	T208	T208W	1
2.5100 63,754	4.3750 111,125	1.0156 25,796	0.03 0,8	27900 12400	T252	T252W	2
2.5100 63,754	4.3750 111,125	1.0625 26,988	0.03 0,8	27900 12400	T251	T251W	1
3.0100 76,454	5.2500 133,350	1.3125 33,338	0.09 2,3	40000 17850	T301	T301W	2
3.0100 76,454	5.2500 133,350	1.3750 34,925	0.09 2,3	40000 17850	T302	T302W	1
3.5000 88,900	5.2500 133,350	1.3124 33,335	0.11 2,8	26000 11550	T350		2
4.0200 102,108	7.0716 179,619	1.7500 44,450	0.06 1,5	77500 34400	T402		2

①These maximum fillet radii will be cleared by the bearing corners.

THRUST BEARING · HEAVY DUTY

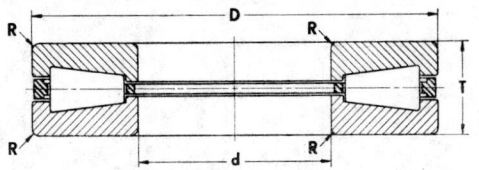

STANDARD TOLERANCES

inch tolerances in .0001" metric tolerances in micrometers
1 micrometer = 0,001 mm

bore				outside diameter				width		
d		High	Low	D		High	Low	T	High	Low
up to	12.0000" incl.
304,800 mm	10
25	0
0	up to	12.0000" incl.
304,800 mm	10
25	0
0			
12.0000"
304,800 mm	24.0000" incl.
609,600 mm	20
51	0
0	12.0000"
304,800 mm	24.0000" incl.
609,600 mm	20
51	0
0			
24.0000"
609,600 mm	36.0000" incl.
914,400 mm	30
76	0
0	24.0000"
609,600 mm	36.0000" incl.
914,400 mm	30
76	0
0	all sizes =	150
381	150
381
36.0000"
914,400 mm	48.0000" incl.
1219,200 mm	40
102	0
0	36.0000"
914,400 mm	48.0000" incl.
1219,200 mm	40
102	0
0			
				48.0000"
1219,200 mm	and over	50
127	0
0			

bore	outside diameter	width	max. shaft and housing fillet radii	rating at 500 RPM for 3000 hours L10	bearing number
d	D	T	R[①]	lb daN	
1.3750
34,925	3.0000
76,200	0.6250
15,875	0.06
1,5	5400
2400	T135
1.7500
44,450	3.3360
84,734	0.7188
18,258	0.09
2,3	7250
3220	T1750
2.0000
50,800	4.3125
109,538	0.8750
22,225	0.09
2,3	13400
5950	T200A
2.5000
63,500	4.6250
117,475	1.0000
25,400	0.09
2,3	13300
5950	T2520
3.0000
76,200	6.3750
161,925	1.3125
33,338	0.13
3,3	29300
13050	T311
4.0000
101,600	8.5000
215,900	1.8125
46,038	0.13
3,3	50500
22600	T411
4.4000
111,760	8.8000
223,520	2.2000
55,880	0.13
3,3	54000
24000	T441
4.5000
114,300	9.8750
250,825	2.1250
53,975	0.16
4,0	73000
32600	T451
5.0000
127,000	9.8750
250,825	2.1875
55,562	0.19
4,8	61500
27400	T520
5.0000
127,000	10.5000
266,700	2.3125
58,738	0.19
4,8	76500
34000	T511
5.0625
128,588	10.5000
266,700	2.3125
58,738	0.19
4,8	76500
34000	T511A
6.0000
152,400	12.5000
317,500	2.7500
69,850	0.25
6,4	111000
49500	T611
6.5000
165,100	12.2500
311,150	3.5000
88,900	0.25
6,4	95500
42600	T651
6.6250
168,275	12.0000
304,800	2.7500
69,850	0.25
6,4	89000
39600	T661
6.8750
174,625	14.1250
358,775	3.2500
82,550	0.25
6,4	131000
58500	T691

①These maximum fillet radii will be cleared by the bearing corners.

THRUST BEARING - HEAVY DUTY — TTHD

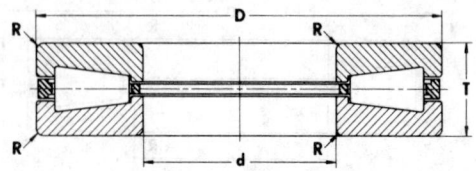

STANDARD TOLERANCES

inch tolerances in .0001" | metric tolerances in micrometers 1 micrometer = 0,001 mm

bore				outside diameter				width		
d		High	Low	D		High	Low	T	High	Low
up to	12.0000" incl. 304,800 mm	10 25	0 0	up to	12.0000" incl. 304,800 mm	10 25	0 0			
12.0000" 304,800 mm	24.0000" incl. 609,600 mm	20 51	0 0	12.0000" 304,800 mm	24.0000" incl. 609,600 mm	20 51	0 0			
24.0000" 609,600 mm	36.0000" incl. 914,400 mm	30 76	0 0	24.0000" 609,600 mm	36.0000" incl. 914,400 mm	30 76	0 0	all sizes =	150 381	150 381
36.0000" 914,400 mm	48.0000" incl. 1219,200 mm	40 102	0 0	36.0000" 914,400 mm	48.0000" incl. 1219,200 mm	40 102	0 0			
				48.0000" 1219,200 mm	and over	50 127	0 0			

bore	outside diameter	width	max. shaft and housing fillet radii	rating at 500 RPM for 3000 hours L10	bearing number
d	D	T	R[1]	lb daN	
7.0000 177,800	14.5000 368,300	3.2500 82,550	0.31 8,0	149000 66500	T711
7.4803 190,000	14.0000 355,600	2.9220 74,219	0.25 6,4	116000 51500	T7519
8.0000 203,200	16.5000 419,100	3.6250 92,075	0.38 9,7	190000 84500	T811
8.0000 203,200	16.5000 419,100	4.7500 120,650	0.38 9,7	190000 84500	T811X
9.0000 228,600	17.0000 431,800	3.4950 88,773	0.38 9,7	184000 81500	T9020
9.0000 228,600	19.0000 482,600	4.1250 104,775	0.44 11,2	255000 113500	T911
9.2500 234,950	19.0000 482,600	4.1250 104,775	0.44 11,2	255000 113500	T911A
9.2500 234,950	21.5000 546,100	5.0000 127,000	0.63 16,0	362000 161000	T921
10.0000 254,000	21.2500 539,750	4.6250 117,475	0.44 11,2	323000 144000	T1011
11.0000 279,400	23.7500 603,250	5.3750 136,525	0.44 11,2	420000 188000	T1120
14.5000 368,300	23.7500 603,250	4.7500 120,650	0.38 9,7	301000 134000	T14520
16.0000 406,400	28.0000 711,200	5.7500 146,050	0.38 9,7	475000 212000	T16021
16.0000 406,400	33.0000 838,200	7.0000 177,800	0.50 12,7	800000 356000	T16050
20.0000 508,000	39.0000 990,600	7.7500 196,850	0.50 12,7	1100000 495000	T20020
48.0000 1219,200	60.0000 1524,000	5.3750 136,525	0.38 9,7	945000 420000	T48000

[1] These maximum fillet radii will be cleared by the bearing corners.

BEARING TABLES

Two-row Assemblies

PAGE

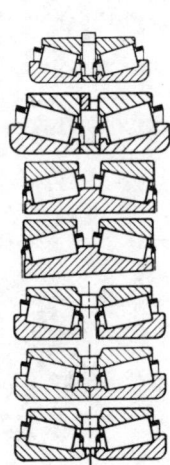

Tolerances .... I-III

"SS" Assemblies 1

"SR" Assemblies 2-7

TDI Type 9-15

TDIT Type 17-19

TDO — TDODC Types 21-35

TNA — TNADC Types 37-41

TNASW — TNASWE Types 43-45

Note: The ratings shown in these tables are in pounds and decanewtons. The unit for force —newton—within the International System of Units (SI) was adopted in March, 1968 by the International Organization for Standardization (ISO) as the official unit for bearing rating in the metric system. Specifically, the newton is the **force** required to give a mass of 1 kilogram an acceleration of 1 meter per second per second. Comparing a decanewton unit with a kilogram or pound technically requires a comparison of a unit of force (newton) with a unit of mass (kilogram or pound). The **newton** was introduced as a unit of **force** to avoid the confusion of using the same name for units of both force and mass.

Despite this difference, the user of this journal will want to know the conversion factors that apply. They are as follows:

1 decanewton = 10 newtons = 1.02 kilograms = 2.25 pounds

1 kilogram = 9.81 newtons = .98 decanewtons = 2.20 pounds

TWO-ROW
BEARINGS

SEE REFERENCE TABLES FOR ADDITIONAL BEARING TOLERANCES.

					CLASS									
					4 All Sizes		**2** 24.0000 609,600 Max. Cone Bore		**3** All Sizes		**0** 12.0000 304,800 Max. Cup O.D.		**00** 10.5000 266,700 Max. Cup O.D.	

CONE BORE TOLERANCE †

DEVIATION IN .0001 INCH AND MICROMETERS

BEARING TYPES	CONE BORE OVER	CONE BORE INCL.	CUP O.D. OVER	CUP O.D. INCL.	HIGH	LOW	HIGH	LOW	HIGH	LOW	HIGH	LOW	HIGH	LOW
SS ASSEM. TDI TDIT TDO TDODC TNA TNADC TNASW TNASWE		3.0000 76,200			+ 5 ▲ +13	0 0	+ 5 +13	0 0	+ 5 +13	0 0	+ 5 +13	0 0	+3 +8	0 0
	3.0000 76,200	12.0000 304,800			+ 10 + 25	0 0	+10 +25	0 0	+ 5 +13	0 0	+ 5 +13	0 0	+3 +8	0 0
	12.0000 304,800	24.0000 609,600			+ 20 + 51	0 0	+20 +51	0 0	+ 10 + 25	0 0	—	—	—	—
	24.0000 609,600	36.0000 914,400			+ 30 + 76	0 0	—	—	+ 15 + 38	0 0	—	—	—	—
	36.0000 914,400	48.0000 1219,200			+ 40 +102	0 0	—	—	+ 20 + 51	0 0	—	—	—	—
	48.0000 1219,200				+ 50 +127	0 0	—	—	+ 30 + 76	0 0	—	—	—	—

▲Cone bore deviation = 8 High, 0 Low (20 High, 0 Low) for cones in series LM11700, LM11900, M12600, LM12700, L44600, L45400, LM48500, LM67000 and L68100.

†Inch system bearings in the dimension tables with this sign (†) are shown with maximum cone bore; the tolerance is minus by the same magnitude as shown.

CUP O.D. TOLERANCE †

BEARING TYPES	CONE BORE OVER	CONE BORE INCL.	CUP O.D. OVER	CUP O.D. INCL.	HIGH	LOW	HIGH	LOW	HIGH	LOW	HIGH	LOW	HIGH	LOW
SS ASSEM. TDI TDIT TDO TDODC TNA TNADC TNASW TNASWE				12.0000 304,800	+ 10 + 25	0 0	+10 +25	0 0	+ 5 +13	0 0	+ 5 +13	0 0	+3 +8	0 0
			12.0000 304,800	24.0000 609,600	+ 20 + 51	0 0	+20 +51	0 0	+ 10 + 25	0 0	—	—	—	—
			24.0000 609,600	36.0000 914,400	+ 30 + 76	0 0	+30 +76	0 0	+ 15 + 38	0 0	—	—	—	—
			36.0000 914,400	48.0000 1219,200	+ 40 +102	0 0	—	—	+ 20 + 51	0 0	—	—	—	—
			48.0000 1219,200		+ 50 +127	0 0	—	—	+ 30 + 76	0 0	—	—	—	—

†Inch system bearings in the dimension tables with this sign (†) are shown with maximum cup O.D.; the tolerance is minus by the same magnitude as shown.

OVERALL BEARING WIDTH TOLERANCE

BEARING TYPES	CONE BORE OVER	CONE BORE INCL.	CUP O.D. OVER	CUP O.D. INCL.	HIGH	LOW	HIGH	LOW	HIGH	LOW	HIGH	LOW	HIGH	LOW
TNA TNADC TNASW TNASWE		5.0000 127,000			+100 +254	0 0	+100 +254	0 0	+100 +254	0 0	—	—	—	—
	5.0000 127,000				+300 +762	0 0	+300 +762	0 0	+300 +762	0 0	—	—	—	—
TDI TDIT TDO TDODC		4.0000 101,600			+160 +406	0 0	+160 +406	0 0	+160 +406	−160 −406	+160 +406	−160 −406	+160 +406	−160 −406
	4.0000 101,600	12.0000 304,800			+280 +711	−200 −508	+160 +406	− 80 −203	+160 +406	−160 −406	+160 +406	−160 −406	+160 +406	−160 −406
	12.0000 304,800	24.0000 609,600		20.0000 508,000	+300 +762	−300 −762	+300 +762	−300 −762	+160 +406	−160 −406	—	—	—	—
	12.0000 304,800	24.0000 609,600	20.0000 508,000		+300 +762	−300 −762	+300 +762	−300 −762	+300 +762	−300 −762	—	—	—	—
	24.0000 609,600				+300 +762	−300 −762	—	—	+300 +762	−300 −762	—	—	—	—
SS ASSEM.		4.0000 101,600			+180 ◆ +459	− 20 − 51	+180 +459	− 20 − 51	—	—	—	—	—	—

▲Overall bearing width deviation = 140 High, 0 Low (356 High, 0 Low) for series LM11700, LM11900, M12600, LM12700, L44600, L45400, LM48500, LM67000 and L68100.

◆Overall bearing width deviation = 300 High, 20 Low (762 High, 51 Low) for SS assemblies in series LM11700, LM11900, M12600, LM12700, L44600, L45400, LM48500, LM67000 and L68100.

ASSEMBLED BEARING MAXIMUM RADIAL RUNOUT

BEARING TYPES	CONE BORE OVER	CONE BORE INCL.	CUP O.D. OVER	CUP O.D. INCL.					
SS ASSEM. TDI TDIT TDO TDODC TNA TNADC TNASW TNASWE				12.0000 304,800	20 51	15 38	3 8	1.5 4	0.75 2
			12.0000 304,800	24.0000 609,600	20 51	15 38	7 18	—	—
			24.0000 609,600	36.0000 914,400	30 76	20 51	20 51	—	—
			36.0000 914,400		30 76		30 76	—	—

1

METRIC SYSTEM BEARING TOLERANCES (FOR "J" PREFIX PARTS)

SEE REFERENCE TABLES FOR ADDITIONAL BEARING TOLERANCES.

Values shown as .0001 Inch (top) / Micrometers (bottom).

CONE BORE TOLERANCE

BEARING TYPES	CONE BORE OVER	CONE BORE INCL.	K ALL SIZES HIGH	K LOW	N 19.6850/500 Max. Cone Bore & Max. Cup O.D. HIGH	N LOW	C 62.9921/1600 Max. Cone Bore & Max. Cup O.D. HIGH	C LOW	B 12.4016/315 Max. Cone Bore & Max. Cup O.D. HIGH	B LOW
SR ASSEM. TDO	0.3937 / 10	0.7087 / 18	0 / 0	−5 / −13	0 / 0	−5 / −13	0 / 0	−4 / −10	0 / 0	−3 / −8
	0.7087 / 18	1.1811 / 30	0 / 0	−5 / −13	0 / 0	−5 / −13	0 / 0	−4 / −10	0 / 0	−3 / −8
	1.1811 / 30	1.9685 / 50	0 / 0	−5 / −13	0 / 0	−5 / −13	0 / 0	−4 / −10	0 / 0	−4 / −10
	1.9685 / 50	3.1496 / 80	0 / 0	−6 / −15	0 / 0	−6 / −15	0 / 0	−5 / −13	0 / 0	−4 / −10
	3.1496 / 80	4.7244 / 120	0 / 0	−8 / −20	0 / 0	−8 / −20	0 / 0	−5 / −13	0 / 0	−4 / −10
	4.7244 / 120	7.0866 / 180	0 / 0	−10 / −25	0 / 0	−10 / −25	0 / 0	−5 / −13	0 / 0	−4 / −10
	7.0866 / 180	9.8425 / 250	0 / 0	−12 / −30	0 / 0	−12 / −30	0 / 0	−6 / −15	0 / 0	−5 / −13
	9.8425 / 250	12.4016 / 315	0 / 0	−14 / −35	0 / 0	−14 / −35	0 / 0	−7 / −18	0 / 0	−5 / −13
	12.4016 / 315	15.7480 / 400	0 / 0	−16 / −40	0 / 0	−16 / −40	0 / 0	−8 / −20	−	−
	15.7480 / 400	19.6850 / 500	0 / 0	−18 / −45	0 / 0	−18 / −45	0 / 0	−10 / −25	−	−
	19.6850 / 500	24.8031 / 630	0 / 0	−20 / −50	−	−	0 / 0	−12 / −30	−	−
	24.8031 / 630	31.4961 / 800	0 / 0	−31 / −80	−	−	0 / 0	−16 / −40	−	−
	31.4961 / 800	39.3700 / 1000	0 / 0	−39 / −100	−	−	0 / 0	−20 / −50	−	−
	39.3700 / 1000	47.2441 / 1200	0 / 0	−51 / −130	−	−	0 / 0	−24 / −60	−	−
	47.2441 / 1200	62.9921 / 1600	0 / 0	−59 / −150	−	−	0 / 0	−31 / −80	−	−
	62.9921 / 1600	78.7402 / 2000	0 / 0	−79 / −200	−	−	−	−	−	−
	78.7402 / 2000	———	0 / 0	−98 / −250	−	−	−	−	−	−

CUP O.D. TOLERANCE

BEARING TYPES	CUP O.D. OVER	CUP O.D. INCL.	K HIGH	K LOW	N HIGH	N LOW	C HIGH	C LOW	B HIGH	B LOW
SR ASSEM. TDO	0.7087 / 18	1.1811 / 30	0 / 0	−8 / −20	0 / 0	−8 / −20	0 / 0	−3 / −8	0 / 0	−3 / −8
	1.1811 / 30	1.9685 / 50	0 / 0	−8 / −20	0 / 0	−8 / −20	0 / 0	−4 / −10	0 / 0	−3 / −8
	1.9685 / 50	3.1496 / 80	0 / 0	−8 / −20	0 / 0	−8 / −20	0 / 0	−4 / −10	0 / 0	−3.5 / −9
	3.1496 / 80	4.7244 / 120	0 / 0	−8 / −20	0 / 0	−8 / −20	0 / 0	−5 / −13	0 / 0	−4 / −10
	4.7244 / 120	5.9055 / 150	0 / 0	−10 / −25	0 / 0	−10 / −25	0 / 0	−5 / −13	0 / 0	−4 / −10
	5.9055 / 150	7.0866 / 180	0 / 0	−10 / −25	0 / 0	−10 / −25	0 / 0	−5 / −13	0 / 0	−4 / −10
	7.0866 / 180	9.8425 / 250	0 / 0	−12 / −30	0 / 0	−12 / −30	0 / 0	−6 / −15	0 / 0	−5 / −13
	9.8425 / 250	12.4016 / 315	0 / 0	−16 / −40	0 / 0	−16 / −40	0 / 0	−8 / −20	0 / 0	−6 / −15
	12.4016 / 315	15.7480 / 400	0 / 0	−16 / −40	0 / 0	−16 / −40	0 / 0	−8 / −20	−	−
	15.7480 / 400	19.6850 / 500	0 / 0	−20 / −50	0 / 0	−20 / −50	0 / 0	−10 / −25	−	−
	19.6850 / 500	24.8031 / 630	0 / 0	−20 / −50	−	−	0 / 0	−10 / −25	−	−
	24.8031 / 630	31.4961 / 800	0 / 0	−31 / −80	−	−	0 / 0	−16 / −40	−	−
	31.4961 / 800	39.3700 / 1000	0 / 0	−39 / −100	−	−	0 / 0	−20 / −50	−	−
	39.3700 / 1000	47.2441 / 1200	0 / 0	−51 / −130	−	−	0 / 0	−24 / −60	−	−
	47.2441 / 1200	62.9921 / 1600	0 / 0	−65 / −165	−	−	0 / 0	−31 / −80	−	−
	62.9921 / 1600	78.7402 / 2000	0 / 0	−79 / −200	−	−	−	−	−	−
	78.7402 / 2000	———	0 / 0	−98 / −250	−	−	−	−	−	−

METRIC SYSTEM
BEARING TOLERANCES
(FOR "J" PREFIX PARTS)

SEE REFERENCE TABLES FOR
ADDITIONAL BEARING TOLERANCES.

OVERALL BEARING WIDTH TOLERANCE

BEARING TYPES	CONE BORE		K ALL SIZES		N 19.6850 500 Max. Cone Bore & Max. Cup O.D.		C 62.9921 1600 Max. Cone Bore & Max. Cup O.D.		B 12.4016 315 Max. Cone Bore & Max. Cup O.D.	
	OVER	INCL.	HIGH	LOW	HIGH	LOW	HIGH	LOW	HIGH	LOW
			DEVIATION—In .0001 Inch and Micrometers							
SR ASSEM.	0.3937 10	4.7244 120	– –	– –	0 0	– 59 –150	– –	– –	– –	– –
	4.7244 120	9.8425 250	– –	– –	0 0	– 59 –150	– –	– –	– –	– –
	9.8425 250	19.6850 500	– –	– –	0 0	– 59 –150	– –	– –	– –	– –

ASSEMBLED BEARING MAXIMUM RADIAL RUNOUT

BEARING TYPES	CUP O.D.					
	OVER	INCL.				
	0.7087 18	1.1811 30	12 30	12 30	2 5	1 2.5
	1.1811 30	1.9685 50	12 30	12 30	2.4 6	1 2.5
	1.9685 50	3.1496 80	12 30	12 30	2.4 6	1.4 3.5
	3.1496 80	4.7244 120	16 40	16 40	2.4 6	1.4 3.5
	4.7244 120	5.9055 150	16 40	16 40	2.8 7	1.4 3.5
	5.9055 150	7.0866 180	16 40	16 40	3 8	1.5 4
	7.0866 180	9.8425 250	20 50	20 50	4 10	2 5
	9.8425 250	12.4016 315	20 50	20 50	4.3 11	2 5
SR ASSEM. TDO	12.4016 315	15.7480 400	20 50	20 50	5 13	–
	15.7480 400	19.6850 500	25 65	25 65	7 18	–
	19.6850 500	24.8031 630	25 65	–	10 25	–
	24.8031 630	31.4961 800	25 65	–	14 35	–
	31.4961 800	39.3700 1000	35 90	–	20 50	–
	39.3700 1000	47.2441 1200	35 90	–	24 60	–
	47.2441 1200	62.9921 1600	35 90	–	31 80	–
	62.9921 1600	78.7402 2000	35 90	–	–	–
	78.7402 2000		35 90	–	–	–

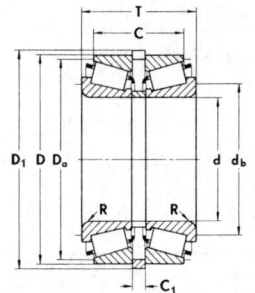

bore	outside diameter	width		rating at 500 RPM for 3000 hours L10			fac-tor	bearing assembly part numbers		cone	cup	snap ring spacer	
		through cones	over cups	one row radial	thrust	two row radial				max. shaft fillet radius	backing shoulder diameters	assembled outside diameter	nom. width
		T	C	lb daN	lb daN	lb daN	K	cone	cup	R[1]	d_b D_a	D_1	C_1
d	D												
0.6875 17,462	1.5700 39,878	1.1880 30,175	0.9380 23,825	935 416	460 204	1790 795	2.04	▲LM11749 Spcr. K106398R	LM11710 Spcr. K106397R	0.05 1,3	0.91 1.46 23,0 37,0	1.6500 41,910	0.100 2,54
0.7500 19,050	1.7810 45,237	1.4990 38,075	1.2290 31,217	1230 545	635 282	2340 1040	1.94	▲LM11949 Spcr. K107061R	LM11910 Spcr. K107087R	0.05 1,3	0.98 1.63 25,0 41,5	1.8430 46,812	0.280 7,11
1.0000 25,400	1.9800 50,292	1.2430 31,572	0.9630 24,460	1200 535	770 342	2280 1015	1.56	▲L44643 Spcr. K106790R	L44610 Spcr. K106789R	0.05 1,3	1.24 1.85 31,5 47,0	2.0780 52,781	0.125 3,18
1.0625 26,988	1.9800 50,292	1.2430 31,572	0.9630 24,460	1200 535	770 342	2280 1015	1.56	▲L44649 Spcr. K302683R	L44610 Spcr. K106789R	0.14 3,5	1.48 1.85 37,5 47,0	2.0780 52,781	0.125 3,18
1.2500 31,750	2.3280 59,131	1.4040 35,662	1.0840 27,534	1580 700	1110 495	3000 1335	1.42	▲LM67048 Spcr. K106817R	LM67010 Spcr. K106610R	Spec	1.67 2.20 42,5 56,0	2.4060 61,112	0.156 3,96
1.3750 34,925	2.5625 65.088	1.5580 39,573	1.2380 31,445	2140 950	1380 615	4100 1820	1.55	▲LM48548 Spcr. K106389R	LM48510 Spcr. K106390R	Spec	1.81 2.40 46,0 61,0	2.6560 67,462	0.140 3,56
1.3750 34,925	2.7170 69,012	1.6536 42,000	1.3410 34,061	2180 970	1420 635	4150 1840	1.53	14137A Spcr. K106389R	14276 Spcr. K109540R	0.06 1,5	1.65 2.48 42,0 63,0	2.8420 72,187	0,093 2.36
1.5000 38,100	2.5625 65,088	1.5580 39,573	1.2380 31,445	2020 900	1150 510	3850 1710	1.76	LM29749 Spcr. K106393R	LM29710 Spcr. K106390R	0.09 2,3	1.81 2.44 46,0 62,0	2.6560 67,462	0.140 3,56
1.7812 45,242	3.0625 77,788	1.7410 44,221	1.3660 34,696	2610 1160	1910 850	5000 2220	1.37	LM603049 Spcr. K109152R	LM603011 Spcr. K109151R	0.14 3,5	2.24 2.91 57,0 74,0	3.2020 81,331	0.1796 4,562
2.0625 52,388	3.6250 92,075	2.1516 54,651	1.7766 45,126	4100 1840	2660 1185	7850 3500	1.55	28584 Spcr. K107577R	28521 (Spcr. K107578R two required)	0.14 3,5	2.56 3.43 65,0 87,0	3.7730 95,834	0.218 5,54
2.1250 53,975	3.5000 88.900	1.7140 43,536	1.2764 32,421	2690 1200	2520 1120	5150 2280	1.07	LM806649 Spcr. K114294R	LM806610 (Spcr. K114295R two required)	0.09 2,3	2.48 3.35 63,0 85,0	3.6460 92,608	0.218 5,54
2.4375 61,912	4.3307 110,000	1.9462 49,433	1.6962 43,083	4000 1790	2770 1235	7650 3400	1.45	392 Spcr. K444667R	394A (Spcr. K444668R two required)	0.03 0,8	2.76 4.11 70,0 104,5	4.5710 116,103	0.218 5,54
2.6250 66.675	4.4375 112,712	2.6230 66,624	2.1230 53,924	7000 3100	4050 1800	13300 5900	1.72	39590 Spcr. K326056R	39521 (Spcr. K326057R two required)	0.14 3,5	3.15 4.21 80,0 107,0	4.5960 116,738	0.250 6,35
3.2813 83,345	4.9375 125,412	2.1540 54,712	1.7166 43,602	5150 2300	3690 1640	9850 4380	1.40	27690 Spcr. K107581R	27620 Spcr. K107582R	0.14 3,5	3.78 4.72 96,0 120,0	5.1210 130,073	0.156 3,96

①These maximum fillet radii will be cleared by the bearing corners.
▲Non-standard tolerances, see Inch System bearing tolerance page 18, in Reference Tables.

TWO-ROW "SET RIGHT" SPACER ASSEMBLIES

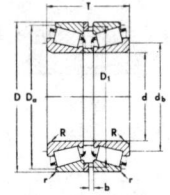

bore	outside diameter	width	rating at 500 RPM for 3000 hours L10			factor	bearing assembly	cone		cup		spacer	
			one row radial lb daN	thrust lb daN	two row radial lb daN			max. shaft fillet rad.	backing shoulder diameter	max. housing fillet rad.	backing shoulder diameter	max. groove O.D.	min. groove width
d	D	T				K		R①	d_b	r①	D_a	D_1	b
1.9685 50	3.2283 82	1.9291 49	3370 1500	1760 785	6400 2860	1.91	JLM104948 - JLM104910 Cone Spcr - LM104948XS Cup Spcr - LM104910ES	0.12 3	2.36 60	0.015 0,4	3.07 78	2.995 76,07	0.117 2,97
1.9685 50	3.5433 90	2.4409 62	5000 2220	2800 1245	9500 4220	1.78	JM205149 - JM205110 Cone Spcr - M205149XS Cup Spcr - M205110ES	0.12 3	2.44 62	0.02 0,5	3.35 85	3.185 80,90	0.133 3,38
1.9685 50	4.1339 105	3.1496 80	7150 3180	5950 2660	13600 6050	1.20	JHM807045 - JHM807012 Cone Spcr - HM807045XS Cup Spcr - HM807012ES	0.12 3	2.72 69	0.03 0,8	3.94 100	3.755 95,33	0.117 2,97
2.1654 55	3.5433 90	2.0472 52	3790 1685	2610 1165	7200 3220	1.45	JLM506849 - JLM506810 Cone Spcr - LM506849XS Cup Spcr - LM506810ES	0.06 1,5	2.48 63	0.02 0,5	3.39 86	3.185 80,90	0.133 3,38
2.1654 55	3.7402 95	2.5197 64	5400 2400	3110 1380	10300 4600	1.74	JM207049 - JM207010 Cone Spcr - M207049XS Cup Spcr - M207010ES	0.06 1,5	2.52 64	0.02 0,5	3.58 91	3.380 85,85	0.117 2,97
2.1654 55	4.3307 110	3.3858 86	8500 3780	5050 2240	16200 7200	1.69	JH307749 - JH307710 Cone Spcr - H307749XS Cup Spcr - H307710ES	0.12 3	2.80 71	0.03 0,8	4.09 104	3.965 100,71	0.133 3,38
2.3622 60	3.7402 95	2.1260 54	4100 1820	2830 1260	7800 3480	1.45	JLM508748 - JLM508710 Cone Spcr - LM508748XS Cup Spcr - LM508710ES	0.20 5	2.95 75	0.02 0,5	3.58 91	3.380 85,85	0.117 2,97
2.5591 65	4.1339 105	2.1260 54	4450 1980	3450 1535	8500 3780	1.29	JLM710949 - JLM710910 Cone Spcr - LM710949XS Cup Spcr - LM710910ES	0.12 3	3.03 77	0.015 0,4	3.96 100	3.755 95,38	0.117 2,97
2.5591 65	4.3307 110	2.4409 62	5900 2620	4050 1800	11200 5000	1.45	JM511946 - JM511910 Cone Spcr - M511946XS Cup Spcr - M511910ES	0.12 3	3.07 78	0.03 0,8	4.13 105	3.970 100,84	0.133 3,38
2.5591 65	4.7244 120	3.3858 86	9200 4100	5300 2360	17500 7800	1.73	JH211749 - JH211710 Cone Spcr - H211749XS Cup Spcr - H211710ES	0.12 3	3.15 80	0.04 1,0	4.49 114	4.360 110,74	0.133 3,38
2.7559 70	4.3307 110	2.2835 58	4900 2200	4100 1820	9400 4180	1.20	JLM813049 - JLM813010 Cone Spcr - LM813049XS Cup Spcr - LM813010ES	0.04 1	3.07 78	0.02 0,5	4.13 105	3.970 100,84	0.133 3,38

①These maximum fillet radii will be cleared by the bearing corners.

This bearing is not a matched assembly. Fixed length cup and cone spacers permit shipping of these bearing parts as individual components or as complete assemblies.

Cup spacer is designed so that a commercial snap ring can be used to locate the bearing assembly. It is also provided with oil slots and groove for lubrication purposes.

Floating bearing application requires certain design criteria which should be reviewed by Timken Company engineers before adopting the design.

IMPORTANT - Fitting practice shown must be used with these assemblies.

fits

cone bore d		rotating cone cone seat	fit	cup seat	fit	rotating cup cone seat	fit	cup seat	fit	mounted setting possible	probable
1.9685 50	r6	1.9705 1.9699 50,050 50,034	0.0025T 0.0014T 63T 34T	G7 3.2288 3.2302 82,012 82,047	0.0005L 0.0027L 12L 67L	f6 1.9675 1.9669 49,975 49,959	0.0005L 0.0016L 12L 41L	R6 3.2257 3.2266 81,934 81,956	0.0026T 0.0009T 66T 24T	0.004PL 0.019EP 0.11PL 0.49EP	0.003EP 0.012EP 0.07EP 0.30EP
1.9685 50	r6	1.9705 1.9699 50,050 50,034	0.0025T 0.0014T 63T 34T	G7 3.5438 3.5452 90,012 90,047	0.0005L 0.0027L 12L 67L	f6 1.9675 1.9669 49,975 49,959	0.0005L 0.0016L 12L 41L	R6 3.5407 3.5416 89,934 89,956	0.0026T 0.0009T 66T 24T	0.004PL 0.019EP 0.10PL 0.48EP	0.003EP 0.012EP 0.08EP 0.30EP
1.9685 50	r6	1.9705 1.9699 50,050 50,034	0.0025T 0.0014T 63T 34T	G7 4.1344 4.1358 105,012 105,047	0.0005L 0.0027L 12L 67L	f6 1.9675 1.9669 49,975 49,959	0.0005L 0.0016L 12L 41L	R6 4.1313 4.1322 104,931 104,953	0.0026T 0.0009T 69T 27T	0.004PL 0.016EP 0.12PL 0.41EP	0.002EP 0.010EP 0.04EP 0.26EP
2.1654 55	p6	2.1675 2.1668 55,051 55,032	0.0027T 0.0014T 66T 32T	G7 3.5438 3.5452 90,012 90,047	0.0005L 0.0027L 12L 67L	f6 2.1642 2.1635 54,970 54,951	0.0006L 0.0019L 15L 49L	R6 3.5407 3.5416 89,934 89,956	0.0026T 0.0009T 66T 24T	0.005PL 0.016EP 0.12PL 0.44EP	0.001EP 0.010EP 0.05EP 0.27EP
2.1654 55	p6	2.1675 2.1668 55,051 55,032	0.0027T 0.0014T 66T 32T	G7 3.7407 3.7422 95,012 95,047	0.0005L 0.0027L 12L 67L	f6 2.1642 2.1635 54,970 54,951	0.0006L 0.0019L 15L 49L	R6 3.7376 3.7385 94,934 94,956	0.0026T 0.0009T 66T 24T	0.004PL 0.019EP 0.07PL 0.51EP	0.003EP 0.012EP 0.10EP 0.33EP
2.1654 55	p6	2.1675 2.1668 55,051 55,032	0.0027T 0.0014T 66T 32T	G7 4.3312 4.3326 110,012 110,047	0.0005L 0.0027L 12L 67L	f6 2.1642 2.1635 54,970 54,951	0.0006L 0.0019L 15L 49L	R6 4.3281 4.3290 109,931 109,953	0.0026T 0.0009T 69T 27T	0.003PL 0.020EP 0.08PL 0.50EP	0.004EP 0.013EP 0.10EP 0.33EP
2.3622 60	p6	2.3643 2.3636 60,051 60,032	0.0027T 0.0014T 66T 32T	G7 3.7407 3.7421 95,012 95,047	0.0005L 0.0027L 12L 67L	f6 2.3610 2.3603 59,970 59,951	0.0006L 0.0019L 15L 49L	R6 3.7376 3.7385 94,934 94,956	0.0026T 0.0009T 66T 24T	0.004PL 0.017EP 0.10PL 0.45EP	0.002EP 0.011EP 0.06EP 0.28EP
2.5591 65	p6	2.5612 2.5605 65,051 65,032	0.0027T 0.0014T 66T 32T	G7 4.1344 4.1358 105,012 105,047	0.0005L 0.0027L 12L 67L	f6 2.5579 2.5572 64,970 64,951	0.0006L 0.0019L 15L 49L	R6 4.1313 4.1322 104,931 104,953	0.0026T 0.0009T 69T 27T	0.004PL 0.016EP 0.11PL 0.42EP	0.002EP 0.010EP 0.05EP 0.26EP
2.5591 65	p6	2.5612 2.5605 65,051 65,032	0.0027T 0.0014T 66T 32T	G7 4.3312 4.3326 110,012 110,047	0.0005L 0.0027L 12L 67L	f6 2.5579 2.5572 64,970 64,951	0.0006L 0.0019L 15L 49L	R6 4.3281 4.3290 109,931 109,953	0.0026T 0.0009T 69T 27T	0.004PL 0.017EP 0.11PL 0.44EP	0.002EP 0.011EP 0.06EP 0.28EP
2.5591 65	p6	2.5612 2.5605 65,051 65,032	0.0027T 0.0014T 66T 32T	G7 4.7249 4.7263 120,012 120,047	0.0005L 0.0027L 12L 67L	f6 2.5579 2.5572 64,970 64,951	0.0006L 0.0019L 15L 49L	R6 4.7218 4.7227 119,931 119,953	0.0026T 0.0009T 69T 27T	0.003PL 0.020EP 0.07PL 0.51EP	0.004EP 0.013EP 0.11EP 0.33EP
2.7559 70	p6	2.7580 2.7573 70,051 70,032	0.0027T 0.0014T 66T 32T	G7 4.3312 4.3326 110,012 110,047	0.0005L 0.0027L 12L 67L	f6 2.7547 2.7540 69,970 69,951	0.0006L 0.0019L 15L 49L	R6 4.3281 4.3290 109,931 109,953	0.0026T 0.0009T 69T 27T	0.004PL 0.017EP 0.10PL 0.43EP	0.002EP 0.011EP 0.06EP 0.27EP

① These spacer assemblies employ the "Set-Right" automated bearing setting technique. The resulting probable mounted setting range listed in these tables can be expected for 99.73% of the assemblies.

L = Loose   T = Tight   PL = Preload   EP = End Play

TWO-ROW "SET RIGHT" SPACER ASSEMBLIES

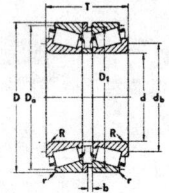

| | | | rating at 500 RPM for 3000 hours L10 | | | | | cone | | cup | | spacer | |
| bore | outside diameter | width | one row radial lb daN | thrust lb daN | two row radial lb daN | factor | bearing assembly | max. shaft fillet rad. | backing shoulder diameter | max. housing fillet rad. | backing shoulder diameter | max. groove O.D. | min. groove width |
d	D	T				K		R[①]	d_b	r[①]	D_a	D_1	b
2.7559 70	4.5276 115	2.5197 64	6150 2740	4500 2020	11700 5200	1.36	JM612949 - JM612910 Cone Spcr - M612949XS Cup Spcr - M612910ES	0.12 3	3.27 83	0.03 0,8	4.33 110	4.135 105,03	0.117 2,97
2.9528 75	4.5276 115	2.2047 56	4950 2200	3900 1735	9450 4200	1.27	JLM714149 - JLM714110 Cone Spcr - LM714149XS Cup Spcr - LM714110ES	0.12 3	3.43 87	0.02 0,5	4.33 110	4.135 105,03	0.117 2,97
2.9528 75	4.7244 120	2.7165 69	6750 3020	5150 2300	12900 5750	1.31	JM714249 - JM714210 Cone Srcr - M714249XS Cup Spcr - M714210ES	0.12 3	3.46 88	0.025 0,6	4.53 115	4.365 110,87	0.133 3,38
2.9528 75	5.7087 145	4.4094 112	14700 6550	9100 4060	28000 12450	1.61	JH415647 - JH415610 Cone Spcr - H415647XS Cup Spcr - H415610ES	0.12 3	3.70 94	0.03 0,8	5.47 139	5.255 133,48	0.133 3,38
3.1496 80	5.1181 130	3.0709 78	8550 3800	5700 2540	16300 7250	1.50	JM515649 - JM515610 Cone Spcr - M515649XS Cup Spcr - M515610ES	0.12 3	3.70 94	0.03 0,8	4.92 125	4.660 118,36	0.164 4,17
3.3465 85	5.1181 130	2.5984 66	7100 3160	5400 2400	13500 6000	1.31	JM716649 - JM716610 Cone Spcr - M716649XS Cup Spcr - M716610ES	0.12 3	3.86 98	0.03 0,8	4.92 125	4.710 119,63	0.117 2,97
3.3465 85	5.5118 140	3.3858 86	10300 4550	7150 3200	19500 8700	1.43	JHM516849 - JHM516810 Cone Spcr - HM516849XS Cup Spcr - HM516810ES	0.12 3	3.94 100	0.04 1,0	5.28 134	5.050 128,27	0.164 4,17
3.3465 85	5.9055 150	4.0157 102	13900 6200	7900 3520	26500 11800	1.76	JH217249 - JH217210 Cone Spcr - H217249XS Cup Spcr - H217210ES	0.12 3 .	3.98 101	0.05 1,3	5.59 142	5.445 138,30	0.164 4,17
3.5433 90	5.7087 145	3.1102 79	9450 4200	7200 3200	18000 8000	1.31	JM718149 - JM718110 Cone Spcr - M718149XS Cup Spcr - M718110ES	0.12 3	4.13 105	0.04 1,0	5.46 139	5.255 133,48	0.133 3,38
3.5433 90	6.1024 155	3.8583 98	13800 6100	8050 3580	26200 11650	1.71	JHM318448 - JHM318410 Cone Spcr - HM318448XS Cup Spcr - HM318841ES	0.12 3	4.17 106	0.03 0,8	5.83 148	5.625 142,88	0.164 4,17
3.7402 95	5.9055 150	3.0709 78	9350 4160	7100 3160	17900 7950	1.32	JM719149 - JM719113 Cone Spcr - M719149XS Cup Spcr - M719113ES	0.12 3	4.29 109	0.03 0,8	5.63 143	5.445 138,30	0.164 4,17

①These maximum fillet radii will be cleared by the bearing corners.

This bearing is not a matched assembly. Fixed length cup and cone spacers permit shipping of these bearing parts as individual components or as complete assemblies.

Cup spacer is designed so that a commercial snap ring can be used to locate the bearing assembly. It is also provided with oil slots and groove for lubrication purposes.

Floating bearing application requires certain design criteria which should be reviewed by Timken Company engineers before adopting the design.

IMPORTANT - Fitting practice shown must be used with these assemblies.

fits

cone bore d		rotating cone cone seat	cone fit		rotating cone cup seat	cup fit		rotating cup cone seat	cone fit		rotating cup cup seat	cup fit	mounted setting possible	probable
2.7559 70	p6	2.7580 2.7573 70,051 70,032	0.0027T 0.0014T 66T 32T	G7	4.5281 4.5295 115,012 115,047	0.0005L 0.0027L 12L 67L	f6	2.7547 2.7540 69,970 69,951	0.0006L 0.0019L 15L 49L	R6	4.5250 4.5259 114,931 114,953	0.0026T 0.0009T 69T 27T	0.004PL 0.017EP 0.11PL 0.43EP	0.002EP 0.011EP 0.05EP 0.27EP
2.9528 75	p6	2.9549 2.9542 75,051 75,032	0.0027T 0.0014T 66T 32T	G7	4.5281 4.5295 115,012 115,047	0.0005L 0.0027L 12L 67L	f6	2.9516 2.9509 74,970 74,951	0.0006L 0.0019L 15L 49L	R6	4.5250 4.5259 114,931 114,953	0.0026T 0.0009T 69T 27T	0.004PL 0.017EP 0.10PL 0.44EP	0.002EP 0.011EP 0.06EP 0.28EP
2.9528 75	p6	2.9549 2.9542 75,051 75,032	0.0027T 0.0014T 66T 32T	G7	4.7249 4.7263 120,012 120,047	0.0005L 0.0027L 12L 67L	f6	2.9516 2.9509 74,970 74,951	0.0006L 0.0019L 15L 49L	R6	4.7218 4.7227 119,931 119,953	0.0026T 0.0009T 69T 27T	0.004PL 0.017EP 0.09PL 0.45EP	0.002EP 0.011EP 0.07EP 0.28EP
2.9528 75	p6	2.9549 2.9542 75,051 75,032	0.0027T 0.0014T 66T 32T	G7	5.7093 5.7109 145,014 145,054	0.0006L 0.0032L 14L 79L	f6	2.9516 2.9509 74,970 74,951	0.0006L 0.0019L 15L 49L	P6	5.7062 5.7072 144,939 144,964	0.0025T 0.0005T 61T 11T	0.002PL 0.021EP 0.02PL 0.58EP	0.005EP 0.014EP 0.14EP 0.39EP
3.1496 80	p6	3.1517 3.1510 80,051 80,032	0.0027T 0.0014T 66T 32T	G7	5.1187 5.1203 130,014 130,054	0.0006L 0.0032L 14L 79L	f6	3.1484 3.1477 79,970 79,951	0.0006L 0.0019L 15L 49L	P6	5.1156 5.1166 129,939 129,964	0.0025T 0.0005T 61T 11T	0.003PL 0.020EP 0.07PL 0.53EP	0.004EP 0.013EP 0.09EP 0.35EP
3.3465 85	n6	3.3484 3.3475 85,045 85,023	0.0027T 0.0010T 65T 23T	G7	5.1187 5.1203 130,014 130,054	0.0006L 0.0032L 14L 79L	f6	3.3451 3.3442 84,964 84,942	0.0006L 0.0023L 16L 58L	P6	5.1156 5.1166 129,939 129,964	0.0025T 0.0005T 61T 11T	0.004PL 0.019EP 0.07PL 0.50EP	0.003EP 0.012EP 0.09EP 0.32EP
3.3465 85	n6	3.3484 3.3475 85,045 85,023	0.0027T 0.0010T 65T 23T	G7	5.5124 5.5140 140,014 140,054	0.0006L 0.0032L 14L 79L	f6	3.3451 3.3442 84,964 84,942	0.0006L 0.0023L 16L 58L	P6	5.5093 5.5103 139,939 139,964	0.0025T 0.0005T 61T 11T	0.003PL 0.020EP 0.07PL 0.52EP	0.004EP 0.013EP 0.10EP 0.34EP
3.3465 85	n6	3.3484 3.3475 85,045 85,023	0.0027T 0.0010T 65T 23T	G7	5.9061 5.9077 150,014 150,054	0.0006L 0.0032L 14L 79L	f6	3.3451 3.3442 84,964 84,942	0.0006L 0.0023L 16L 58L	P6	5.9030 5.9040 149,939 149,964	0.0025T 0.0005T 61T 11T	0.002PL 0.021EP 0.04PL 0.59EP	0.005EP 0.014EP 0.14EP 0.39EP
3.5433 90	n6	3.5452 3.5443 90,045 90,023	0.0027T 0.0010T 65T 23T	G7	5.7093 5.7109 145,014 145,054	0.0006L 0.0032L 14L 79L	f6	3.5419 3.5410 89,964 89,942	0.0006L 0.0023L 16L 58L	P6	5.7062 5.7072 144,939 144,964	0.0025T 0.0005T 61T 11T	0.004PL 0.019EP 0.07PL 0.50EP	0.003EP 0.012EP 0.09EP 0.33EP
3.5433 90	p6	3.5458 3.5449 90,059 90,037	0.0033T 0.0016T 79T 37T	G7	6.1030 6.1046 155,014 155,054	0.0006L 0.0032L 14L 79L	f6	3.5419 3.5410 89,964 89,942	0.0006L 0.0023L 16L 58L	R6	6.0992 6.1002 154,917 154,942	0.0032T 0.0012T 83T 33T	0.002PL 0.024EP 0.04PL 0.57EP	0.006EP 0.016EP 0.15EP 0.39EP
3.7402 95	n6	3.7421 3.7412 95,045 95,023	0.0027T 0.0010T 65T 23T	G7	5.9061 5.9077 150,014 150,054	0.0006L 0.0032L 14L 79L	f6	3.7388 3.7379 94,964 94,942	0.0006L 0.0023L 16L 58L	P6	5.9030 5.9040 149,939 149,964	0.0025T 0.0005T 61T 11T	0.003PL 0.020EP 0.05PL 0.52EP	0.004EP 0.013EP 0.11EP 0.35EP

① These spacer assemblies employ the "Set-Right" automated bearing setting technique. The resulting probable mounted setting range listed in these tables can be expected for 99.73% of the assemblies.

L = Loose   T = Tight   PL = Preload   EP = End Play

TWO-ROW "SET RIGHT" SPACER ASSEMBLIES

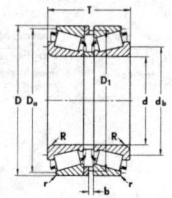

bore	outside diameter	width	rating at 500 RPM for 3000 hours L10			factor	bearing assembly	cone		cup		spacer	
			one row radial lb daN	thrust lb daN	two row radial lb daN			max. shaft fillet rad.	backing shoulder diameter	max. housing fillet rad.	backing shoulder diameter	max. groove O.D.	min. groove width
d	D	T				K		R[1]	d_b	r[1]	D_a	D_1	b
3.9370 100	6.1024 155	3.1496 80	10100 4480	8100 3620	19200 8550	1.24	JM720249 - JM720210 Cone Spcr - M720249XS Cup Spcr - M720210ES	0.12 3	4.53 115	0.03 0,8	5.87 149	5.625 142,88	0.164 4,17
3.9370 100	6.2992 160	3.5433 90	12200 5450	9850 4380	23300 10350	1.24	JHM720249 - JHM720210 Cone Spcr - HM720249XS Cup Spcr - HM720210ES	0.12 3	4.61 117	0.03 0,8	6.06 154	5.820 147,83	0.164 4,17
4.3307 110	6.4961 165	3.1496 80	10100 4500	8600 3820	19300 8600	1.18	JM822049 - JM822010 Cone Spcr - M822049XS Cup Spcr - M822010ES	0.12 3	4.88 124	0.03 0,8	6.26 159	5.975 151,77	0.164 4,17
4.3307 110	7.0866 180	4.0551 103	16200 7200	11200 5000	30800 13700	1.44	JHM522649 - JHM522610 Cone Spcr - HM522649XS Cup Spcr - HM522610ES	0.12 3	5.00 127	0.03 0,8	6.77 172	6.530 165,86	0.200 5,08
6.6929 170	9.0551 230	3.4646 88	15500 6900	10200 4550	29600 13150	1.52	JHM534149 - JHM534110 Cone Spcr - HM534149XS Cup Spcr - HM534110ES	0.12 3	7.24 184	0.015 0,4	8.82 224	8.585 218,06	0.200 5,08
6.6929 170	9.4488 240	3.9764 101	19900 8850	14900 6600	38000 16900	1.34	JM734449 - JM734410 Cone Spcr - M734449XS Cup Spcr - M734410ES	0.12 3	7.28 185	0.06 1,5	9.12 232	8.815 223,90	0.200 5,08
7.0866 180	9.8425 250	4.0551 103	20600 9150	16900 7500	39200 17450	1.22	JM736149 - JM736110 Cone Spcr - M736149XS Cup Spcr - M736110ES	0.12 3	7.72 196	0.04 1,0	9.55 243	9.120 231,65	0.200 5,08
7.4803 190	10.2362 260	4.0157 102	19200 8550	15700 7000	38400 17100	1.22	JM738249 - JM738210 Cone Spcr - M738249XS Cup Spcr - M738210ES	0.12 3	8.11 206	0.04 1,0	9.92 252	9.765 248,03	0.200 5,08
7.8740 200	11.8110 300	5.5512 141	33200 14750	29700 13200	66400 29500	1.12	JHM840449 - JHM840410 Cone Spcr - HM840449XS Cup Spcr - HM840410ES	0.14 3,5	8.78 223	0.06 1,5	11.37 289	11.215 284,86	0.200 5,08

[1]These maximum fillet radii will be cleared by the bearing corners.

This bearing is not a matched assembly. Fixed length cup and cone spacers permit shipping of these bearing parts as individual components or as complete assemblies.

Cup spacer is designed so that a commercial snap ring can be used to locate the bearing assembly. It is also provided with oil slots and groove for lubrication purposes.

Floating bearing application requires certain design criteria which should be reviewed by Timken Company engineers before adopting the design.

IMPORTANT - Fitting practice shown must be used with these assemblies.

fits

cone bore d	rotating cone cone seat	fit	cup seat	fit	rotating cup cone seat	fit	cup seat	fit	mounted setting possible	probable
3.9370 100	3.9395 3.9386 100,059 100,037	p6 0.0033T 0.0016T 79T 37T	6.1030 6.1046 155,014 155,054	G7 0.0006L 0.0032L 14L 79L	3.9356 3.9347 99,964 99,942	f6 0.0006L 0.0023L 16L 58L	6.0992 6.1002 154,917 154,942	R6 0.0032T 0.0012T 83T 33T	0.002PL 0.020EP 0.12EP 0.51EP	0.005EP 0.014EP 0.12EP 0.34EP
3.9370 100	3.9395 3.9386 100,059 100,037	p6 0.0033T 0.0016T 79T 37T	6.2998 6.3014 160,014 160,054	G7 0.0006L 0.0032L 14L 79L	3.9356 3.9347 99,964 99,942	f6 0.0006L 0.0023L 16L 58L	6.2960 6.2970 159,917 159,942	R6 0.0032T 0.0012T 83T 33T	0.002PL 0.020EP 0.04PL 0.51EP	0.005EP 0.014EP 0.12EP 0.35EP
4.3307 110	4.3332 4.3323 110,059 110,037	p6 0.0033T 0.0016T 79T 37T	6.4967 6.4983 165,014 165,054	G7 0.0006L 0.0032L 14L 79L	4.3293 4.3284 109,964 109,942	f6 0.0006L 0.0023L 16L 58L	6.4929 6.4939 164,917 164,939	R6 0.0032T 0.0012T 86T 36T	0.002PL 0.020EP 0.04PL 0.51EP	0.005EP 0.014EP 0.12EP 0.35EP
4.3307 110	4.3332 4.3323 110,059 110,037	p6 0.0033T 0.0016T 79T 37T	7.0872 7.0888 180,014 180,054	G7 0.0006L 0.0032L 14L 79L	4.3293 4.3284 109,964 109,942	f6 0.0006L 0.0023L 16L 58L	7.0834 7.0844 179,914 179,939	R6 0.0032T 0.0012T 86T 36T	0.002PL 0.022EP 0.05PL 0.54EP	0.005EP 0.015EP 0.13EP 0.37EP
6.6929 170	6.6957 6.6947 170,068 170,043	p6 0.0038T 0.0018T 93T 43T	9.0557 9.0575 230,015 230,061	G7 0.0006L 0.0036L 15L 91L	6.6913 6.6903 169,957 169,932	f6 0.0006L 0.0026L 18L 68L	9.0513 9.0525 229,896 229,925	R6 0.0038T 0.0014T 104T 45T	0.004PL 0.025EP 0.11PL 0.63EP	0.005EP 0.016EP 0.10EP 0.42EP
6.6929 170	6.6957 6.6947 170,068 170,043	p6 0.0038T 0.0018T 93T 43T	9.4494 9.4512 240,015 240,061	G7 0.0006L 0.0036L 15L 91L	6.6913 6.6903 169,957 169,932	f6 0.0006L 0.0026L 18L 68L	9.4450 9.4462 239,896 239,925	R6 0.0038T 0.0014T 104T 45T	0.004PL 0.025EP 0.10PL 0.61EP	0.005EP 0.016EP 0.10EP 0.42EP
7.0866 180	7.0894 7.0884 180,068 180,043	p6 0.0038T 0.0018T 93T 43T	9.8431 9.8449 250,015 250,061	G7 0.0006L 0.0036L 15L 91L	7.0850 7.0840 179,957 179,932	f6 0.0006L 0.0026L 18L 68L	9.8387 9.8399 249,896 249,925	R6 0.0038T 0.0014T 104T 45T	0.004PL 0.025EP 0.09PL 0.61EP	0.005EP 0.016EP 0.11EP 0.42EP
7.4803 190	7.4835 7.4823 190,079 190,050	p6 0.0044T 0.0020T 109T 50T	10.2369 10.2389 260,017 260,069	G7 0.0007L 0.0043L 17L 109L	7.4783 7.4771 189,950 189,921	f6 0.0008L 0.0032L 20L 79L	10.2318 10.2330 259,883 259,915	R6 0.0044T 0.0016T 117T 45T	0.004PL 0.025EP 0.10PL 0.63EP	0.005EP 0.016EP 0.12EP 0.41EP
7.8740 200	7.8772 7.8760 200,079 200,050	p6 0.0044T 0.0020T 109T 50T	11.8117 11.8137 300,017 300,069	G7 0.0007L 0.0043L 17L 109L	7.8720 7.8708 199,950 199,921	f6 0.0008L 0.0032L 20L 79L	11.8066 11.8078 299,879 299,911	R6 0.0044T 0.0016T 121T 49T	0.002PL 0.025EP 0.09PL 0.62EP	0.006EP 0.017EP 0.12EP 0.42EP

① These spacer assemblies employ the "Set-Right" automated bearing setting technique. The resulting probable mounted setting range listed in these tables can be expected for 99.73% of the assemblies.

L = Loose   T = Tight   PL = Preload   EP = End Play

TWO-ROW ASSEMBLY - DOUBLE CONE, SINGLE CUPS

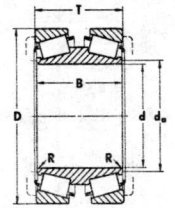

for available cups refer to bearing selection index under series indicated

| | | width | | rating at 500 RPM for 3000 hours L10 | | | factor | part number | | cone max. shaft fillet radius | backing shoulder diameter |
| bore | outside diameter range | over cups | cone | one row radial | thrust | two row radial | | cone | bearing series | | |
d	D	T	B	lb daN	lb daN	lb daN	K			R①	d_a
1.1875 30.162	2.4409 62.000	1.3306 33.797	1.3750 34.925	1620 720	1060 470	3090 1375	1.53	17116D	17000	0.03 0,8	1.40 35.5
1.4375 36.512	2.6875 — 2.8125 68.262 — 71.438	1.4492 36.810	1.5000 38.100	2000 890	1530 680	3810 1695	1.31	19145D	19000	0.03 0,8	1.67 42.5
1.4375 36.512	2.8346 72.000	1.5392 39.096	1.5000 38.100	2000 890	1530 680	3810 1695	1.31	19145D	19000	0.03 0,8	1.67 42.5
2.0000 50.800	3.6718 93.264	②1.9690 50.013	2.0940 53.188	3430 1525	1980 880	6550 2900	1.73	375D	375 (374)③	0.03 0,8	2.24 57,0
2.0000 50.800	3.8125 96.838	②2.0940 53.188	2.0940 53.188	3430 1525	1980 880	6550 2900	1.73	375D	375 (372A)③	0.03 0,8	2.24 57,0
2.0000 50.800	3.9370 100.000	2.3124 58.735	2.0940 53.188	3430 1525	1980 880	6550 2900	1.73	375D	375	0.03 0,8	2.24 57,0
†2.1654 †55.000	5.3750 — 5.5130 136.525 — 140.030	2.6020 66.091	2.5980 65.989	6750 3000	10100 4480	12900 5700	0.67	78216D	78000	0.09 2,3	3.11 78,9
†2.1654 †55.000	5.7080 144.983	②2.5616 65.065	2.5980 65.989	6750 3000	10100 4480	12900 5700	0.67	78216D	78000 (78571)③	0.09 2,3	3.11 78,9
2.4375 61.912	4.3307 — 4.3750 110.000 — 111.125	2.1870 55.550	2.1870 55.550	4000 1790	2770 1235	7650 3400	1.45	399D	395	0.03 0,8	2.76 70,0
2.5000 63.500	4.4375 112.712	2.3750 60.325	2.3750 60.325	7000 3100	4050 1800	13300 5900	1.72	39585D	39500	0.03 0,8	2.83 72,0
2.5000 63.500	4.7238 119.985	③2.5788 65.502	2.3750 60.325	7000 3100	4050 1800	13300 5900	1.72	39585D	39500 (39528)①	0.03 0,8	2.83 72,0
2.5000 63.500	5.3750 — 5.5130 136.525 — 140.030	2.6020 66.091	2.5980 65.989	6750 3000	10100 4480	12900 5700	0.67	78251D	78000	0.09 2,3	3.11 78,9
2.5000 63.500	5.7080 144.983	②2.5616 65.065	2.5980 65.989	6750 3000	10100 4480	12900 5700	0.67	78251D	78000 (78571)③	0.09 2,3	3.11 78,9
†2.5591 †65.000	5.3750 — 5.5130 136.525 — 140.030	2.6020 66.091	2.5980 65.989	6750 3000	10100 4480	12900 5700	0.67	78255D	78000	0.06 1,5	3.11 78,9
†2.5591 †65.000	5.7080 144.983	③2.5616 65.065	2.5980 65.989	6750 3000	10100 4480	12900 5700	0.67	78255D	78000 (78571)③	0.06 1,5	3.11 78,9
3.1875 80.962	5.2500 — 5.3750 133.350 — 136.525	2.3750 60.325	2.3440 59.538	6550 2920	5000 2220	12500 5550	1.31	496D	495	0.06 1,5	3.58 91,0
3.1875 80.962	5.5000 — 5.5115 139.700 — 139.992	3.1875 80.962	3.1549 80.134	8800 3920	6100 2700	16800 7500	1.45	581D	575	0.06 1,5	3.62 92,0

①These maximum fillet radii will be cleared by the bearing corners.
†Dimension shown is maximum value—see note at bottom of fitting practice table page 4 in Reference Tables.
③Specific cup part number indicated in ( ) when dimension "T" varies from others in series.

Two-Row Assembly - Double Cone, Single Cups — TDI

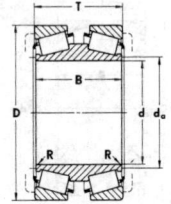

for available cups refer to bearing selection index under series indicated

											cone	
bore	**outside diameter range**	**width**		**rating at 500 RPM for 3000 hours L10**			**factor**	**part number**			**max. shaft fillet radius**	**backing shoulder diameter**
		over cups	cone	one row radial	thrust	two row radial		cone	bearing series			
d	**D**	**T**	**B**	**lb daN**	**lb daN**	**lb daN**	**K**	cone	bearing series		**R①**	**dₐ**
3.5000 88,900	6.3750 — 6.6250 161,925 — 168,275	3.9980 101,549	4.2500 107,950	13800 6100	8050 3580	26200 11650	1.71	767D	755		0.06 1,5	3.99 101,3
3.6250 92,075	5.8437 148,430	② 2.2500 57,150	2.2812 57,942	7100 3160	6000 2660	13600 6050	1.19	42362D	42000 (42584)④		0.06 1,5	4.06 103,0
3.6250 92,075	5.8750 149,225	② 2.5000 63,500	2.2812 57,942	7100 3160	6000 2660	13600 6050	1.19	42362D	42000 (42587)④		0.06 1,5	4.06 103,0
4.0000 101,600	7.5000 190,500	4.6250 117,475	5.0000 127,000	19300 8600	11100 4950	36900 16400	1.74	868D	855		0.06 1,5	4.57 116,0
4.2500 107,950	7.5000 190,500	3.8750 98,425	4.0000 101,600	15900 7050	11300 5050	30200 13450	1.40	71426D	71000		0.06 1,5	4.80 122,0
4.2500 107,950	8.3750 212,725	5.6250 142,875	6.0000 152,400	24300 10800	13600 6050	46500 20600	1.79	946D	935		0.13 3,3	5.04 128,0
4.5000 114,300	7.5000 190,500	3.8750 98,425	4.0000 101,600	15900 7050	11300 5050	30200 13450	1.40	71450D	71000		0.06 1,5	5.04 128,0
4.7500 120,650	6.8750 174,625	2.6251 66,678	2.6875 68,262	11300 5000	6400 2840	21400 9550	1.76	M224749D	M224700		0.03 0,8	5.08 129,0
5.0000 127,000	7.1875 182,562	3.0000 76,200	3.0000 76,200	12900 5750	6750 3000	24600 10950	1.91	48290D	48200		0.06 1,5	5.39 137,0
5.1183 130,005	8.4646 — 8.5000 215,000 — 215,900	4.8750 123,825	4.8750 123,825	17200 7650	14300 6400	32800 14600	1.20	74510D	74000		0.06 1,5	5.75 146,0
5.2500 133,350	7.7500 — 8.0000 196,850 — 203,200	3.6250 92,075	3.6250 92,075	16900 7500	9950 4420	32200 14350	1.70	67390D	67300		0.06 1,5	5.71 145,0
5.3750 136,525	7.5000 190,500	3.0625 77,788	3.0625 77,788	13700 6100	7500 3340	26100 11600	1.82	48393D	48300		0.06 1,5	5.67 144,0
5.3750 136,525	8.8750 225,425	4.7500 120,650	4.7500 120,650	29200 13000	16600 7400	55500 24800	1.76	H228649D	H228600		0.06 1,5	5.98 152,0
5.5000 139,700	7.8750 200,025	3.0625 77,788	2.9688 75,408	13900 6200	8000 3560	26600 11800	1.74	48680D	48600		0.03 0,8	5.91 150,0
6.5000 165,100	8.8750 225,425	3.1250 79,375	3.0000 76,200	15100 6750	9950 4420	28800 12800	1.52	46790D	46700		0.03 0,8	6.89 175,0
7.0000 177,800	9.7500 247,650	3.5625 90,488	3.5625 90,488	19500 8650	14700 6500	37100 16500	1.33	67790D	67700		0.06 1,5	7.48 190,0
7.0000 177,800	11.3750 — 11.7500 288,925 — 298,450	4.8750 123,825	4.8750 123,825	30000 13350	24000 10650	57000 25400	1.25	94706D	94000		0.06 1,5	7.68 195,0

①These maximum fillet radii will be cleared by the bearing corners.
②Specific cup part number indicated in ( ) when dimension "T" varies from others in series.

TWO-ROW ASSEMBLY - DOUBLE CONE, SINGLE CUPS

TDI

for available cups refer to bearing selection index under series indicated

| bore | outside diameter range | width | | rating at 500 RPM for 3000 hours L10 | | | factor | part number | | cone max. shaft fillet radius | backing shoulder diameter |
| | | over cups | cone | one row radial | thrust | two row radial | | cone | bearing series | | |
d	D	T	B	lb daN	lt daN	lb daN	K			R[1]	d_a
7.0000 177.800	11.3750 288.925	4.8750 123.825	4.8750 123.825	35500 15800	19400 8600	67500 30000	1.83	HM237546D	HM237500	0.06 1,5	7.64 194,0
7.0000 177.800	12.0000 304.800	4.3086 109.438	4.5000 114.300	24500 10900	15100 6750	49000 21800	1.62	EE280700D	280000	0.13 3.3	7.87 200,0
7.3750 187.325	10.6250 269.875	4.0000 101.600	4.0000 101.600	24200 10750	13700 6100	48400 21500	1.76	M238849D	M238800	0.06 1,5	7.87 199.9
7.3750 187.325	12.5970 — 12.6250 319.964 — 320.675	6.6250 168.275	6.3750 161.925	44500 19800	24300 10800	89000 39600	1.83	H239649D	H238600	0.13 3.3	8.23 209,0
7.5000 190.500	14.1732 — 14.5000 360.000 — 368.300	6.2500 158.750	6.0000 152.400	48500 21600	33500 14900	97000 43200	1.45	EE420750D	420000	0.13 3.3	8.70 221,0
8.0000 203.200	12.5000 317.500	⊘5.2500 133.350	5.2500 133.350	32900 14650	29400 13050	65800 29300	1.12	93801D	93000 (93125)⊘	0.25 6,4	8.93 226.9
8.0000 203.200	12.5000 317.500	⊘5.6250 142.875	5.2500 133.350	32900 14650	29400 13050	65800 29300	1.12	93801D	93000 (93126)⊘	0.25 6,4	8.93 226.9
8.0000 203.200	14.1732 — 14.5000 360.000 — 368.300	6.2500 158.750	6.0000 152.400	48500 21600	33500 14900	97000 43200	1.45	EE420800D	420000	0.13 3.3	9.06 230,0
8.1250 206.375	13.2500 336.550	7.1250 180.975	7.2500 184.150	61000 27200	34800 15500	122000 54400	1.76	H242649D	H242600	0.06 1,5	8.94 227,0
8.6250 219.075	14.1250 358.775	7.7500 196.850	7.8750 200.025	69500 31000	39600 17600	139000 62000	1.76	H244849D	H244800	0.06 1,5	9.53 242,0
9.0000 228.600	12.2500 311.150	3.7500 95.250	3.7500 95.250	24900 11100	14200 6300	49800 22200	1.76	LM245149D	LM245100	0.06 1,5	9.53 242,0
9.0000 228.600	15.7500 400.050	5.5000 139.700	5.5000 139.700	48000 21200	25300 11250	96000 42400	1.89	EE529091D	529000	0.13 3.3	10.08 256,0
9.2500 234.950	12.8750 327.025	3.6875 93.662	3.6875 93.662	24900 11100	17300 7700	49800 22200	1.44	8576D	8500	0.06 1,5	9.84 250,0
9.4970 241.224	13.7460 — 13.9960 349.148 — 355.498	4.2500 107.950	4.2500 107.950	30800 13700	18700 8300	61600 27400	1.65	EE127094D	127000	0.06 1,5	10.12 257,0
9.5000 241.300	16.5000 419.100	7.0000 177.800	6.8750 174.625	64500 28600	46000 20400	129000 57200	1.40	EE821096D	821000	0.13 3.3	10.55 268,0
9.5070 241.478	13.7460 — 13.9960 349.148 — 355.498	4.2500 107.950	4.2500 107.950	30800 13700	18700 8300	61600 27400	1.65	EE127097D	127000	0.06 1,5	10.16 258,0
9.6250 244.475	12.8750 327.025	3.6250 92.075	3.6250 92.075	27000 12000	14800 6600	54000 24000	1.82	LM247748D	LM247700	0.06 1,5	10.12 257,0
9.6250 244.475	15.0000 381.000	5.7500 146.050	5.7500 146.050	43000 19200	38200 17000	86000 38400	1.13	EE126096D	126000	0.13 3.3	10.59 269,0
9.7500 247.650	16.0000 406.400	8.5000 215.900	8.6250 219.075	96500 43000	55000 24400	193000 86000	1.76	HH249949D	HH249900	0.13 3.3	10.94 278,0
10.0000 254.000	14.1250 358.775	5.1250 130.175	5.1250 130.175	45000 20200	25700 11450	90000 40400	1.76	M249748D	M249700	0.13 3.3	10.73 272,5
10.0000 254.000	14.3720 — 14.5000 365.049 — 368.300	3.6500 92.710	3.6560 92.862	25500 11350	15800 7050	51000 22700	1.61	EE171000D	170000	0.06 1,5	10.59 269,0
10.0000 254.000	17.5000 444.500	5.2500 133.350	5.2500 133.350	46500 20600	27300 12150	93000 41200	1.71	EE822101D	822000	0.13 3.3	11.10 282,0

⊘These maximum fillet radii will be cleared by the bearing corners.
⊘Specific cup part number indicated in ( ) when dimension "T" varies from others in series.

Two-Row Assembly - Double Cone, Single Cups — TDI

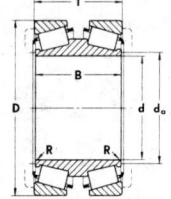

for available cups refer to bearing selection index under series indicated

bore	outside diameter range	width		rating at 500 RPM for 3000 hours L10			factor	part number		cone	
		over cups	cone	one row radial	thrust	two row radial				max. shaft fillet radius	backing shoulder diameter
d	D	T	B	lb daN	lb daN	lb daN	K	cone	bearing series	R①	d_a
10.2500 260.350	15.7500 400,050	4.6874 119,060	4.5000 114,300	37100 16500	25100 11150	74200 33000	1.48	EE221025D	220000	0.25 6,4	11.42 290.0
10.2500 260.350	15.7500 400,050	4.6874 119,060	4.7500 120,650	37100 16500	25100 11150	74200 33000	1.48	EE221028D	220000	0.06 1,5	11.02 280,0
10.2500 260.350	16.0000 406.400	6.1250 155.575	6.0000 152,400	30400 13600	30400 13500	106000 47200	1.75	EE324103D	324000	0.25 6,4	11.31 287,3
10.5000 266,700	14.0000 355,600	4.2500 107,950	4.3125 109,538	34700 15450	21400 9500	69400 30900	1.62	LM451349D	LM451300	0.06 1,5	11.06 281,0
10.5000 266,700	19.2500 488.950	9.0000 228,600	9.3750 238.125	90500 40200	48500 21400	181000 80400	1.87	EE295106D	295000	0.25 6,4	11.97 304.0
10.6250 269,875	15.0000 381,000	5.3750 136,525	5.3750 136.525	50000 22200	28300 12600	100000 44400	1.76	M252349D	M252300	0.13 3,3	11.42 290,0
10.8750 276,225	15.5000 393,700	5.1250 130,175	5.1250 130,175	40000 17800	27600 12300	80000 35600	1.45	EE275109D	275000	0.06 1,5	11.56 293,6
11.0000 279,400	18.0000 457,200	9.6250 244,475	9.6250 244,475	123000 54500	70000 31200	246000 109000	1.76	HH255149D	HH255100	0.06 1,5	12.17 309,0
11.0070 279,578	14.9610 — 14.9960 380,009 — 380,898	4.6250 117,475	4.6250 117,475	38800 17300	28800 12800	77600 34600	1.35	LM654644D	LM654600	0.06 1,5	11.69 297,0
11.2500 285,750	14.9610 — 14.9960 380,009 — 380,898	4.6250 117,475	4.6250 117,475	38800 17300	28800 12800	77600 34600	1.35	LM654648D	LM654600	0.06 1,5	11.89 302,0
11.3750 288,925	16.0000 406,400	5.6875 144,462	5.6875 144,462	59500 26600	34500 15350	119000 53200	1.73	M255449D	M255400	0.13 3,3	12.20 310,0
11.8125 300,038	16.6250 422,275	5.9375 150,812	5.9375 150,812	65000 29000	37600 16750	130000 58000	1.73	HM256849D	HM256800	0.13 3,3	12.68 322,0
11.9940 304,647	17.2460 438,048	5.1875 131,762	5.1875 131,762	50000 22400	28500 12700	100000 44800	1.76	EE329119D	329000	0.13 3,3	12.87 327,0
11.9940 304,647	17.2460 438,048	5.4375 138,112	5.0625 128,588	50500 22400	40500 18000	101000 44800	1.24	M757447D	M757400	0.13 3,3	12.91 328,0
12.0000 304,800	16.5000 419,100	5.1250 130,175	5.1250 130,175	50500 22400	28700 12750	101000 44800	1.76	M257149D	M257100	0.06 1,5	12.68 322,0
12.0000 304,800	17.5000 444,500	4.3750 111,125	4.2500 107,950	35200 15650	22700 10100	70400 31300	1.55	EE291200D	290000	0.31 8,0	13.27 337,0
12.0040 304.901	16.2460 412,648	5.0625 128,588	5.0625 128,588	50000 22200	27200 12100	100000 44400	1.83	M257248D	M257200	0.13 3,3	12.80 325,0

①These maximum fillet radii will be cleared by the bearing corners.

for available cups refer to bearing selection index under series indicated

| bore | outside diameter range | width | | rating at 500 RPM for 3000 hours L10 | | | factor | part number | | cone max. shaft fillet radius | backing shoulder diameter |
| | | over cups | cone | one row radial | thrust | two row radial | | cone | bearing series | | |
d	D	T	B	lb daN	lb daN	lb daN	K			R①	d_a
13.0040 330,301	17.2450 438,023	4.7500 120,650	4.5000 114,300	36800 16400	29000 12900	73600 32800	1.27	EE138131D	138000	0.06 1,5	13.66 347,0
13.1250 333,375	18.5000 469,900	6.5625 166,688	6.5625 166,688	81000 36000	46500 20600	162000 72000	1.74	HM261049D	HM261000	0.13 3,3	14.06 357,0
13.5060 343,052	17.9960 457,098	4.8125 122,238	4.8125 122,238	45000 20200	36400 16200	90000 40400	1.24	LM761649D	LM761600	0.06 1,5	14.21 361,0
13.6250 346,075	17.9960 457,098	4.7500 120,650	4.7500 120,650	36200 16100	29700 13200	72400 32200	1.22	EE133137D	133000	0.06 1,5	14.29 363,0
13.6250 346,075	19.2500 488,950	6.8750 174,625	6.8750 174,625	88000 39200	50500 22600	176000 78400	1.74	HM262749D	HM262700	0.13 3,3	14.61 371,0
14.0000 355,600	17.5000 444,500	4.4375 112,712	4.5000 114,300	42000 18600	22000 9800	84000 37200	1.90	L163149D	L163100	0.06 1,5	14.57 370,0
14.0000 355,600	19.0000 482,600	5.2500 133,350	5.0625 128,588	53000 23400	42500 19000	106000 46800	1.24	LM763449D	LM763400	0.06 1,5	14.76 375,0
14.0000 355,600	19.7500 — 20.2500 501,650 — 514,350	5.0000 127,000	4.3750 111,125	43500 19400	32700 14550	87000 38800	1.33	EE231401D	230000	0.13 3,3	15.04 382,0
14.5000 368.300	20.6250 523,875	7.3125 185,738	7.3125 185,738	102000 45000	57500 25600	204000 90000	1.76	HM265049D	HM265000	0.13 3,3	15.50 393,7
14.5000 368.300	20.6250 523,875	7.3125 185,738	7.3125 185,738	102000 45000	57500 25600	204000 90000	1.76	HM265049XD	HM265000	0.13 3,3	15.50 393,7
15.1250 384,175	21.5000 546,100	7.6250 193,675	7.6250 193,675	110000 49000	63000 28000	220000 98000	1.76	HM266449D	HM266400	0.13 3,3	16.18 411,0
15.5000 393,700	21.5000 546,100	5.4375 138,112	5.4375 138,112	66000 29400	53500 23800	132000 58800	1.23	LM767745D	LM767700	0.06 1,5	16.46 418,0
16.0000 406,400	21.5000 546,100	5.4375 138,112	5.4375 138,112	66000 29400	53500 23800	132000 58800	1.23	LM767749D	LM767700	0.06 1,5	16.81 427,0
16.0000 406,400	21.5000 546,100	5.4375 138,112	5.4375 138,112	71000 31400	57500 25600	142000 62800	1.23	LM767748D	LM767700	0.06 1,5	16.81 427,0
16.0000 406,400	23.2500 590,550	7.6250 193,675	7.6250 193,675	114000 50500	63500 28200	228000 101000	1.80	EE833161XD	833000	0.13 3,3	17.13 435,0
16.1250 409,575	21.5000 546,100	6.3750 161,925	6.3750 161,925	79000 35000	56500 25000	158000 70000	1.40	M667947D	M667900	0.06 1,5	16.97 431,0
16.3750 415,925	23.2500 590,550	8.2500 209,550	8.2500 209,550	130000 58000	73500 32600	260000 116000	1.76	M268749D	M268700	0.13 3,3	17.48 444,0
17.0000 431,800	22.5000 571,500	5.2500 133,350	5.1250 130,175	61500 27400	40500 18000	123000 54800	1.52	EE239171D	239000	0.06 1,5	17.68 449,0
17.0040 431,901	26.9960 685,698	10.0000 254,000	9.9950 253,873	151000 67000	104000 46000	302000 134000	1.45	EE328172D	328000	0.25 6,4	18.66 474,0
17.6250 447,675	25.0000 635,000	8.8125 223,838	8.8125 223,838	150000 66500	85000 37800	300000 133000	1.76	M270748D	M270700	0.13 3,3	18.82 478,0
17.6250 447,675	25.0000 635,000	8.8125 223,838	8.8125 223,838	150000 66500	85000 37800	300000 133000	1.76	M270749D	M270700	0.13 3,3	18.82 478,0
18.0000 457,200	23.5000 596,900	5.3750 136,525	5.2500 133,350	64500 28800	52000 23200	129000 57600	1.24	L770849D	L770800	0.06 1,5	18.82 478,0
18.0000 457,200	33.9960 863,498	14.5000 368,300	14.5000 368,300	235000 104500	145000 64500	470000 209000	1.62	EE480181D	480000	0.25 6,4	20.31 516,0

① These maximum fillet radii will be cleared by the bearing corners.

Two-Row Assembly - Double Cone, Single Cups — TDI

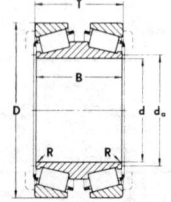

for available cups refer to bearing selection index under series indicated

										cone	
bore	outside diameter range	width		rating at 500 RPM for 3000 hours L10			factor	part number		max. shaft fillet radius	backing shoulder diameter
		over cups	cone	one row radial	thrust	two row radial		cone	bearing series		
d	D	T	B	lb daN	lb daN	lb daN	K			R①	d_a
18.8750 479.425	26.7500 679.450	9.3750 238.125	9.3750 238.125	172000 76500	98000 43600	344000 153000	1.76	M272749D	M272700	0.13 3,3	20.08 510,0
19.0000 482,600	25.5500 647,700	7.9375 201,612	7.9375 201,612	133000 59500	75500 33600	266000 119000	1.76	M272647D	M272600	0.13 3,3	20.08 510,0
19.2530 489,026	24.9950 634,873	6.0000 152,400	6.0000 152,400	79500 35400	47000 21000	159000 70800	1.70	EE243193D	243000	0.13 3,3	20.31 516,0
19.2530 489,026	24.9950 634,873	6.0625 153,988	6.0625 153,988	86500 38400	69500 31000	173000 76800	1.24	LM772749D	LM772700	0.13 3,3	20.31 516,0
20.4375 519,112	29.0000 736,600	10.1875 258,762	10.1875 258,762	202000 89500	115000 51000	404000 179000	1.76	M275349D	M275300	0.13 3,3	21.73 552,0
21.0000 533,400	38.0000 965,200	19.5000 495,300	19.5000 495,300	450000 200000	243000 108000	900000 400000	1.85	EE715210XD	715000	0.25 6,4	23.50 597,0
21.1250 536,575	29.9950 761,873	10.6250 269,875	10.6250 269,875	216000 96000	122000 54500	432000 192000	1.76	M276448D	M276400	0.13 3,3	22.20 564,0
21.5000 546,100	38.0000 965,200	19.5000 495,300	19.5000 495,300	450000 200000	243000 108000	900000 400000	1.85	EE715215XD	715000	0.25 6,4	23.50 597,0
21.9950 558,673	35.4950 901,573	18.0000 457,199	17.4375 442,912	410000 184000	257000 114500	820000 368000	1.60	EE546220D	546000	0.25 6,4	24.45 621,0
22.0000 558,800	26.0000 660,400	3.7500 95,250	3.6250 92,075	41500 18600	38900 17300	83000 37200	1.07	LL876449D	LL876400	0.06 1,5	22.68 576,0
22.5000 571,500	32.0000 812,800	11.2500 285,750	11.2500 285,750	246000 109500	140000 62500	492000 219000	1.76	M278749D	M278700	0.13 3,3	23.98 609,0
23.4375 595,312	33.2500 844,550	11.6875 296,862	11.6875 296,862	265000 118000	151000 67000	530000 236000	1.76	M280049D	M280000	0.13 3,3	24.92 633,0
24.0000 609,600	31.0000 787,400	6.7500 171,450	6.7500 171,450	121000 54000	76500 34000	242000 108000	1.58	EE649241D	649000	0.13 3,3	25.04 636,0
25.0000 635,000	35.5000 901,700	12.5000 317,500	12.5000 317,500	302000 134000	171000 76500	604000 268000	1.76	M281049D	M281000	0.13 3,3	26.57 675,0
25.8010 655,345	36.7500 — 39.4410 933,450 — 1001,801	12.9375 328,612	12.9375 328,612	324000 144000	184000 82000	648000 288000	1.76	M281647D	M281600	0.13 3,3	27.40 696,0
25.8750 657,225	36.7500 — 39.4410 933,450 — 1001,801	12.9375 328,612	12.9375 328,612	324000 144000	184000 82000	648000 288000	1.76	M281649D	M281600	0.13 3,3	27.52 699,0
27.0000 685,800	34.5000 876,300	6.7500 171,450	6.6250 168,275	131000 58000	94000 41800	262000 116000	1.40	EE655271D	655000	0.13 3,3	28.23 717,0

①These maximum fillet radii will be cleared by the bearing corners.

TWO-ROW ASSEMBLY - DOUBLE CONE, SINGLE CUPS

for available cups refer to bearing selection index under series indicated

cone

| bore | outside diameter range | width | | rating at 500 RPM for 3000 hours L10 | | | factor | part number | | max. shaft fillet radius | backing shoulder diameter |
| | | over cups | cone | one row radial | thrust | two row radial | | cone | bearing series | | |
d	D	T	B	lb daN	lb daN	lb daN	K			R①	d_a
†27.9528 †710,000	†35.4331 †900,000	7.8740 200,000	7.8740 200,000	158000 70500	143000 63500	316000 141000	1.11	L882449D	L882400	0.13 3.3	29.17 741.0
28.0000 711,200	36.0000 914,400	5.8750 149,225	5.8750 149,225	108000 48000	70500 31400	216000 96000	1.54	EE755281D	755000	0.13 3.3	29.29 744.0
30.0000 762,000	42.5000 1079,500	15.0000 381,000	15.0000 381,000	430000 192000	246000 109500	860000 384000	1.76	M284249D	M284200	0.19 4,8	31.89 810.0
30.0000 762,000	51.0000 1295,400	12.2500 311,150	12.2500 311,150	362000 161000	238000 106000	724000 322000	1.52	EE433301D	433000	0.25 6,4	33.54 852.0
30.5000 774,700	48.0000 1219,200	③16.0000 406,400	16.0108 406,674	465000 208000	313000 139000	930000 416000	1.49	EE631305D	631000 (631480)③	0.25 6,4	33.19 843.0
30.5000 774,700	†48.0315 †1220,000	③16.0108 406,674	16.0108 406,674	465000 208000	313000 139000	930000 416000	1.49	EE631305D	631000 (631484)④	0.25 6,4	33.19 843.0
†30.7087 †780,000	48.0000 1219,200	③16.0000 406,400	16.0108 406,674	465000 208000	313000 139000	930000 416000	1.49	EE631307D	631000 (631480)③	0.25 6,4	33.43 849.0
†30.7087 †780,000	†48.0315 †1220,000	③16.0108 406,674	16.0108 406,674	465000 208000	313000 139000	930000 416000	1.49	EE631307D	631000 (631484)③	0.25 6,4	33.43 849.0
34.0000 863,600	48.0000 1219,200	17.2500 438,149	16.7500 425,450	555000 246000	314000 140000	1110000 492000	1.76	EE547341D	547000	0.19 4,8	36.14 918.0
34.5625 877,888	†48.0315 †1220,000	15.6250 396,875	15.6250 396,875	510000 228000	290000 129000	1020000 456000	1.76	LM286749D	LM286700	0.19 4,8	36.61 930.0
35.5000 901,700	51.0000 1295,400	17.7500 450,849	17.2500 438,150	620000 276000	356000 158500	1240000 552000	1.74	EE634356D	634000	0.19 4,8	37.80 960.0
36.9375 938,212	50.0000 1270,000	15.7500 400,050	15.7500 400,050	535000 238000	303000 135000	1070000 476000	1.76	LM287649D	LM287600	0.19 4,8	38.98 990.0
37.0000 939,800	52.5000 1333,500	18.2500 463,550	18.2500 463,550	665000 296000	377000 167500	1330000 592000	1.76	LM287849D	LM287800	0.19 4,8	39.33 999.0
39.6250 1006,475	51.0000 1295,400	14.5275 369,000	14.5275 369,000	500000 222000	283000 126000	1000000 444000	1.76	LM288249D	LM288200	0.19 4,8	41.54 1055.0
47.2500 1200,150	62.7500 1593,850	19.0000 482,600	19.0000 482,600	820000 364000	465000 208000	1640000 728000	1.76	LM288949D	LM288900	0.19 4,8	49.61 1260.0

①These maximum fillet radii will be cleared by the bearing corners.
†Dimension shown is maximum value—see note at bottom of fitting practice table page 4 in Reference Tables.
③Specific cup part number indicated in ( ) when dimension "T" varies from others in series.

TWO-ROW ASSEMBLY - TAPERED BORE, DOUBLE CONE, SINGLE CUPS

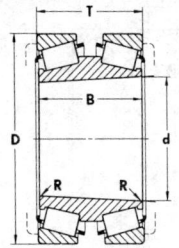

'or available cups refer to bearing selection index under series indicated

cone

bore	taper	outside diameter range	width		rating at 500 RPM for 3000 hours L10			factor	part numbers		max. shaft fillet radius
			over cups	cone	one row radial	thrust	two row radial		cone	bearing series	
d	D	D	T	B	lb daN	lb daN	lb daN	K			R①
1.1866 30,140	1:19.2	2.4409 62,000	1.3306 33,797	1.3750 34,925	1620 720	1060 470	3090 1375	1.53	17117TD	17000	0.03 0,8
1.4581 37,036	1:19.2	2.6875 — 2.8125 68,262 — 71,438	1.4492 36,810	1.5000 38,100	2000 890	1530 680	3810 1695	1.31	19146TD	19000	0.03 0,8
1.4581 37,036	1:19.2	2.8346 72,000	①1.5392 39,096	1.5000 38,100	2000 890	1530 680	3810 1695	1.31	19146TD	19000 (19283-19283X)②	0.03 0,8
1.8024 45,781	1:19.2	3.3465 85,000	1.9790 50,267	2.0620 52,375	3140 1395	1640 730	6000 2660	1.91	359TD	355	0.03 0,8
1.8024 45,781	1:19.2	3.5480 90,119	②2.1650 54,991	2.0620 52,375	3140 1395	1640 730	6000 2660	1.91	359TD	355(352)②	0.03 0,8
2.0541 52,174	1:19.2	3.6718 93,264	①1.9690 50,013	2.0940 53,188	3430 1525	1980 880	6550 2900	1.73	377TD	375(374)②	0.03 0,8
2.0541 52,174	1:19.2	3.8125 96,838	②2.0940 53,188	2.0940 53,188	3430 1525	1980 880	6550 2900	1.73	377TD	375(372A)②	0.03 0,8
2.0541 52,174	1:19.2	3.9370 100,000	2.3124 58,735	2.0940 53,188	3430 1525	1980 880	6550 2900	1.73	377TD	375	0.03 0,8
2.2651 57,534	1:19.2	3.8125 — 3.9370 96,838 — 100,000	2.0196 51,298	2.0940 53,188	3590 1595	2180 970	6850 3040	1.65	388TD	385	0.03 0,8
2.2651 57,534	1:19.2	3.8125 96,838	②2.3660 60,096	2.0940 53,188	3590 1595	2180 970	6850 3040	1.65	388TD	385 (382S)②	0.03 0,8
2.5579 64,971	1:19.2	4.3307 — 4.3750 110,000 — 111,125	2.1870 55,550	2.1870 55,550	4000 1790	2770 1235	7650 3400	1.45	395TD	395	0.03 0,8
2.8375 72,072	1:19.2	4.7244 120,000	2.6557 67,455	2.6590 67,539	5900 2640	3900 1735	11300 5000	1.52	487TD	475	0.03 0,8
2.8375 72,072	1:19.2	4.7244 120,000	②2.7181 69,040	2.6590 67,539	5900 2640	3900 1735	11300 5000	1.52	487TD	475 (472)②	0.03 0,8
3.3518 85,136	1:19.2	5.5000 — 5.5115 139,700 — 139,992	3.1875 80,962	3.1549 80,134	8800 3920	6100 2700	16800 7500	1.45	579TD	575	0.03 0,8
3.9453 100,211	1:19.2	6.1875 — 6.3750 157,162 — 161,925	3.7812 96,042	3.7500 95,250	9900 4400	8050 3580	18800 8400	1.23	52394TD	52000	0.03 0,8
3.9453 100,211	1:19.2	6.6250 — 6.6929 168,275 — 170,000	3.7500 95,250	3.7500 95,250	11500 5100	9250 4120	21900 9700	1.24	688TD	675	0.03 0,8
4.0000 101,600	1:12	7.5000 190,500	4.6250 117,475	5.0000 127,000	22000 9750	12600 5600	42000 18600	1.74	HH221449TD	HH221400	0.03 0,8
4.5625 115,888	1:19.2	7.5000 190,500	4.2500 107,950	4.3750 111,125	15900 7050	11300 5050	30200 13450	1.40	71457TD	71000	0.06 1,5

①These maximum fillet radii will be cleared by the bearing corners
②Specific cup part number indicated in ( ) when dimension "T" varies from others in series.

Two-Row Assembly - Tapered Bore, Double Cone, Single Cups — TDIT

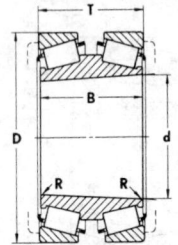

for available cups refer to bearing selection index under series indicated

cone

bore d	taper	outside diameter range D	width		rating at 500 RPM for 3000 hours L10			factor	part numbers		max. shaft fillet radius
			over cups T	cone B	one row radial lb daN	thrust lb daN	two row radial lb daN	K	cone	bearing series	R①
5.0000 127,000	1:12	7.1875 182,562	3.0000 76,200	3.0000 76,200	12900 5750	6750 3000	24600 10950	1.91	48290TD	48200	0.06 1,5
5.2500 133,350	1:12	7.7500 — 8.0000 196,850 — 203,200	3.6250 92,075	3.6250 92,075	16900 7500	9950 4420	32200 14350	1.70	67390TD	67300	0.06 1,5
5.3750 136,525	1:12	8.4646 — 8.5000 215,000 — 215,900	4.8750 123,825	4.8750 123,825	17200 7650	14300 6400	32800 14600	1.20	74539TD	74000	0.06 1,5
5.6250 142,875	1:12	7.8750 200,025	3.0625 77,788	2.9375 74,612	13900 6200	8000 3560	26600 11800	1.74	48685TD	48600	0.03 0,8
5.8125 147,638	1:12	9.3125 — 9.5000 236,538 — 241,300	5.2500 133,350	5.2100 132,334	23000 10200	17400 7750	44000 19400	1.32	82581TD	82000	0.06 1,5
6.0000 152,400	1:12	9.8425 — 10.0000 250,000 — 254,000	4.7500 120,650	4.7500 120,650	29200 12950	20400 9050	55500 24800	1.43	99600TD	99000	0.06 1,5
6.2500 158,750	1:12	8.8750 225,425	3.1250 79,375	3.0000 76,200	15100 6750	9950 4420	28800 12800	1.52	46780TD	46700	0.03 0,8
6.5000 165,100	1:12	10.6250 269,875	5.7500 146,050	5.7500 146,050	41500 18400	23600 10500	79000 35200	1.76	H234649TD	H234600	0.06 1,5
7.1250 180,975	1:12	11.3750 — 11.7500 288,925 — 298,450	6.2500 158,750	6.2500 158,750	30000 13350	24000 10650	57000 25400	1.25	94713TD	94000	0.06 1,5
7.1250 180,975	1:12	11.3750 288,925	6.2500 158,750	6.2500 158,750	35500 15800	19400 8600	67500 30000	1.83	HM237549TD	HM237500	0.06 1,5
7.4896 190,236	1:12	11.3750 288,925	4.3750 111,125	4.3750 111,125	26600 11850	16300 7250	53200 23700	1.63	82785TD	82700	0.06 1,5
7.5000 190,500	1:12	14.1732 — 14.5000 360,000 — 368,300	6.2500 158,750	6.0000 152,400	48500 21600	33500 14900	97000 43200	1.45	EE420750TD	420000	0.13 3,3
7.8125 198,438	1:12	11.1250 282,575	3.4375 87,312	3.4375 87,312	19900 8850	17300 7700	39800 17700	1.15	67980TD	67900	0.03 0,8
8.2500 209,550	1:12	12.5000 317,500	⑦7.2500 184,150	7.2500 184,150	32900 14650	29400 13050	65800 29300	1.12	93826TD	93000 (93125)②	0.06 1,5
8.2500 209,550	1:12	12.5000 317,500	⑦7.6250 193,675	7.2500 184,150	32900 14650	29400 13050	65800 29300	1.12	93826TD	93000 (93126)②	0.06 1,5
9.0000 228,600	1:12	12.8750 327,025	3.6875 93,662	3.6875 93,662	24900 11100	17300 7700	49800 22200	1.44	8573TD	8500	0.06 1,5
9.9375 252,412	1:12	14.1250 358,775	5.1250 130,175	5.5000 139,700	45000 20200	25700 11450	90000 40400	1.76	M249746TD	M249700	0.06 1,5
10.5000 266,700	1:12	14.0000 355,600	4.2500 107,950	4.3125 109,538	34700 15450	21400 9500	69400 30900	1.62	LM451349TD	LM451300	0.06 1,5

①These maximum fillet radii will be cleared by the bearing corners
②Specific cup part number indicated in ( ) when dimension "T" varies from others in series.

TWO-ROW ASSEMBLY · TAPERED BORE, DOUBLE CONE, SINGLE CUPS

for available cups refer to bearing selection index under series indicated

cone

bore	taper	outside diameter range	width		rating at 500 RPM for 3000 hours L10			factor	part numbers		max. shaft fillet radius
			over cups	cone	one row radial	thrust	two row radial		cone	bearing series	
d		D	T	B	lb daN	lb daN	lb daN	K			R ①
11.0236 280,000	1:12	16.0000 406,400	8.1250 206,375	8.1250 206,375	41000 18200	27200 12100	82000 36400	1.51	EE128113TD	128000	0.13 3,3
11.3750 288,925	1:12	16.0000 406,400	5.6875 144,462	5.6875 144,462	59500 26600	34500 15350	119000 53200	1.73	M255449TD	M255400	0.13 3,3
11.6250 295,275	1:12	16.0000 406,400	8.0000 203,200	8.0000 203,200	40500 18000	30700 13650	81000 36000	1.32	LM757043TD	LM757000	0.06 1,5
11.9375 303,212	1:12	19.5000 495,300	10.3750 263,525	10.3750 263,525	144000 64000	82000 36400	288000 128000	1.76	HH258249TD	HH258200	0.13 3,3
13.1250 333,375	1:12	18.5000 469,900	6.5625 166,688	6.5625 166,688	81000 36000	46500 20600	162000 72000	1.74	HM261049TD	HM261000	0.13 3,3
13.1250 333,375	1:12	20.6250 523,875	7.3125 185,738	7.3125 185,738	102000 45000	57500 25600	204000 90000	1.76	HM265032TD	HM265000	0.13 3,3
13.6250 346,075	1:12	19.2500 488,950	6.8750 174,625	6.8750 174,625	88000 39200	50500 22600	176000 78400	1.74	HM262749TD	HM262700	0.13 3,3
13.7500 349,250	1:12	18.0000 457,200	4.7500 120,650	4.7500 120,650	49500 22000	27100 12050	99000 44000	1.83	LM263145TD	LM263100	0.06 1,5
14.5000 368,300	1:12	20.6250 523,875	7.3125 185,738	7.3125 185,738	102000 45000	57500 25600	204000 90000	1.76	HM265049TD	HM265000	0.13 3,3
15.1250 384,175	1:12	21.5000 546,100	7.6250 193,675	7.6250 193,675	110000 49000	63000 28000	220000 98000	1.76	HM266449TD	HM266400	0.13 3,3
16.3750 415,925	1:12	23.2500 590,550	8.2500 209,550	8.2500 209,550	130000 58000	73500 32600	260000 116000	1.76	M268749TD	M268700	0.13 3,3
17.6250 447,675	1:12	25.0000 635,000	8.8125 223,838	8.8125 223,838	150000 66500	85000 37800	300000 133000	1.76	M270749TD	M270700	0.13 3,3
18.8750 479,425	1:12	26.7500 679,450	9.3750 238,125	9.3750 238,125	172000 76500	98000 43600	344000 153000	1.76	M272749TD	M272700	0.13 3,3
19.7500 501,650	1:12	28.0000 711,200	9.8750 250,825	9.8750 250,825	188000 83500	107000 47500	376000 167000	1.76	M274149TD	M274100	0.13 3,3
20.4375 519,112	1:12	29.0000 736,600	10.1875 258,762	10.1875 258,762	202000 89500	115000 51000	404000 179000	1.76	M275349TD	M275300	0.13 3,3
22.5000 571,500	1:12	32.0000 812,800	11.2500 285,750	11.6875 296,862	246000 109500	140000 62500	492000 219000	1.76	M278748TD	M278700	0.13 3,3

①These maximum fillet radii will be cleared by the bearing corners

TWO-ROW ASSEMBLY - DOUBLE CUP, SINGLE CONES

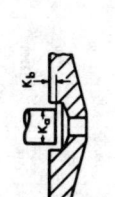

figure 1 — double cup with lubricant holes and groove.

figure 2 — double cup with ONE hole in o.d. for locking pin and lubricant.

for available cones refer to bearing selection index under series indicated

Rating columns below are headed: **rating at 500 RPM for 3000 hours L10**

bore range d (in / mm)	outside diameter D (in / mm)	width through cones T (in / mm)	width cup C (in / mm)	one row radial (lb / daN)	thrust (lb / daN)	two row radial (lb / daN)	factor K	bearing series	cup fig. 1	cup fig. 2	max hsg fillet radius r① (in / mm)	backing shoulder diameter Da (in / mm)	pin max diam Ka (in / mm)	pin max depth into cup Kb (in / mm)
0.3750 — 0.4724 / 9,525 — 12,000	1.2000 / 30,480	1.0000 / 25,400	0.8370 / 21,260	435 / 192	301 / 134	825 / 366	1.44	A2000	A2120D		Spec	1.10 / 28.0		
0.4992 — 0.5906 / 12,680 — 15,000	1.3775 / 34,988	0.9911 / 25,174	0.8125 / 20,638	500 / 222	387 / 172	950 / 422	1.29	A4000	A4138D		0.03 / 0.8	1.24 / 31.5		
0.6250 — 0.7874 / 15,875 — 20,000	1.8504 / 47,000	1.2500 / 31,750	0.9926 / 25,212	1020 / 450	620 / 276	1940 / 860	1.64	05000	05185D		0.03 / 0.8	1.67 / 42.5		
0.7874 — 1.0000 / 20,000 — 25,400	1.9687 / 50,005	1.3126 / 33,340	1.0000 / 25,400	1130 / 500	780 / 346	2150 / 955	1.45	07000	07196D	07196DC	0.03 / 0.8	1.83 / 46.5	0.12 / 3.0	.06 / 1.5
0.9600 — 1.3125 / 24,384 — 33,338	3.1875 / 80,962	2.1875 / 55,562	1.5625 / 39,688	2880 / 1285	3320 / 1475	5500 / 2440	0.87	43000	43319D	43319DC	0.06 / 1.5	2.91 / 74.0	.25 / 6,4	.15 / 3.8
0.9835 — 1.1875 / 24,981 — 30,162	2.4409 / 62,000	1.5625 / 39,688	1.4275 / 36,258	1620 / 720	1060 / 470	3090 / 1375	1.53	17000	17245D		0.03 / 0.8	2.24 / 57.0		
1.0000 — 1.2500 / 25,400 — 31,750	2.5000 / 63,500	1.8125 / 46,038	1.4375 / 36,512	1990 / 885	1190 / 530	3790 / 1685	1.67	15000	15251D		0.03 / 0.8	2.32 / 59.0		
1.0000 — 1.2500 / 25,400 — 31,750	2.5000 / 63,500	⑥1.7425 / 44,260	1.4375 / 36,512	1990 / 885	1190 / 530	3790 / 1685	1.67	15000 (15100SR & 15123①)	15251D		0.03 / 0.8	2.32 / 59.0		
1.0000 — 1.3125 / 25,400 — 33,338	2.8125 / 71,438	1.6875 / 42,862	1.4375 / 36,512	2210 / 985	1370 / 605	4200 / 1880	1.62	26000	26282D		0.02 / 0.5	2.56 / 65.0		
1.0000 — 1.3125 / 25,400 — 33,338	2.8338 / 71,979	1.6835 / 42,761	1.4375 / 36,512	2210 / 985	1370 / 605	4200 / 1880	1.62	26000	26284D		0.03 / 0.8	2.56 / 65.0		

① These maximum fillet radii will be cleared by the bearing corners.
⑥ Specific cone part number indicated in ( ) when dimension "T" varies from others in series.
† Dimension shown is maximum value—See note at bottom of fitting practice table page 4 in Reference Tables.

TWO-ROW ASSEMBLY - DOUBLE CUP, SINGLE CONES

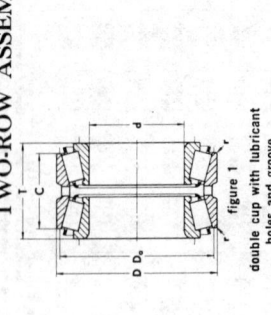

figure 1
double cup with lubricant holes and groove.

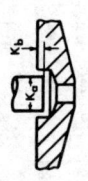

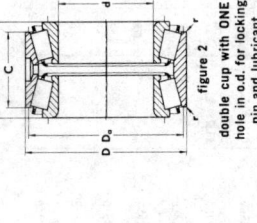

figure 2
double cup with ONE hole in o.d. for locking pin and lubricant.

for available cones refer to bearing selection index under series indicated

| bore range | outside diameter | width | | rating at 500 RPM for 3000 hours L10 | | | factor | bearing series | part numbers | | cup | | pin | |
d	D	through cones T	cup C	one row radial lb / daN	thrust lb / daN	two row radial lb / daN	K		cup fig. 1	cup fig. 2	max. hsg. fillet radius r	backing shoulder diameter D_a	max. diam. K_a	max. depth into cup K_b
1.2500 – 1.3125 / 28.575 – 33.338	2.7500 / 69.850	2.6250 / 66.675	2.5000 / 57.150	3280 / 1460	1530 / 685	6250 / 2780	2.14	2500	2523D	2523DC	.03 / 0.8	2.52 / 64.0	.31 / 7.9	.12 / 3.0
1.2500 – 1.3750 / 28.575 – 34.925	3.0000 / 76.200	1.8750 / 47.625	1.5000 / 38.100	2620 / 1165	2030 / 900	5000 / 2220	1.29	02800	02823D		.03 / 0.8	2.76 / 70.0		
1.811 – 1.3770 / 30.000 – 34.976	2.7170 / 69.012	1.8126 / 46.040	1.5000 / 38.100	2180 / 970	1420 / 635	4150 / 1840	1.53	14000	14276D		.03 / 0.8	2.48 / 63.0		.06 / 1.5
1.1875 – 1.2500 / 30.162 – 31.750	2.3125 / 58.738	1.2812 / 32.542	0.9688 / 24.608	1280 / 570	1040 / 465	2440 / 1085	1.23	08000	08231D	08231DC	.02 / 0.5	2.17 / 55.0	.12 / 3.0	
1.1875 – 1.5748 / 30.162 – 40.000	3.1510 / 80.035	1.8126 / 46.040	1.3750 / 34.925	2440 / 1085	1680 / 750	4650 / 2060	1.45	28000	28318D		.03 / 0.8	2.87 / 73.0		
1.2500 – 1.8125 / 31.750 – 46.038	3.7500 / 95.250	2.4376 / 61.915	2.0000 / 50.800	4950 / 2200	2410 / 1070	9400 / 4180	2.05	435	4320	4320C	.03 / 0.8	3.43 / 87.0	.43 / 10.9	.15 / 3.8
1.3125 – 1.6250 / 33.338 – 41.275	3.6250 / 92.075	2.2875 / 55.562	1.5625 / 39.688	3180 / 1410	4250 / 1880	6050 / 2700	0.75	44000	44363D		.06 / 1.5	3.35 / 85.0		
1.3750 – 1.5000 / 34.925 – 38.100	3.1510 / 80.035	2.2500 / 57.150	1.7700 / 44.958	3080 / 1370	2960 / 1315	5850 / 2600	1.04	27800	27820D		.03 / 0.8	2.95 / 75.0		
1.4375 – 1.5000 / 36.512 – 38.100	2.7170 / 69.012	1.8124 / 46.035	1.5000 / 38.100	2230 / 990	1540 / 685	4250 / 1880	1.45	13600	13621D	13621DC	.03 / 0.8	2.56 / 65.0	.25 / 6.4	.09 / 2.3
1.4375 – 1.7960 / 36.512 – 45.618	3.2650 / 82.931	2.2500 / 57.150	1.8750 / 47.625	3680 / 1635	2110 / 940	7000 / 3120	1.74	25500	25520D	25520DC	.03 / 0.8	3.03 / 77.0	.37 / 9.4	.09 / 2.3

① These maximum fillet radii will be cleared by the bearing corners.

TWO-ROW ASSEMBLY - DOUBLE CUP, SINGLE CONES — TDO-TDODC

for available cones refer to bearing selection index under series indicated

bore range d	outside diameter D	width through cones T	width cup C	rating at 500 RPM for 3000 hours L10 — one row radial lb/daN	thrust lb/daN	two row radial lb/daN	factor K	bearing series	part numbers cup fig. 1	cup fig. 2	cup max. hsg. fillet radius r ①	backing shoulder diameter Da	pin max. diam. Ka	max. depth into cup Kb
1.5000 — 2.1250 / 38,100 — 53,975	3.7500 / 95,250	2.5000 / 63,500	2.0624 / 52,385	5250 / 2320	2960 / 1315	9950 / 4440	1.77	33800	33821D	33821DC	0.03 / 0.8	3.54 / 90,0	.43 / 10,9	.09 / 2,3
1.5000 — 1.7500 / 38,100 — 44,450	3.7500 / 95,250	2.5626 / 65,090	1.7500 / 44,450	3850 / 1715	4900 / 2160	7350 / 3260	0.79	53000	53376D		0.03 / 0.8	3.50 / 89,0	.31 / 7,9	.15 / 3,8
1.5748 — 1.8125 / 40,000 — 46,038	3.5480 / 90,119	2.0000 / 50,800	1.7500 / 44,450	3140 / 1395	1640 / 730	6000 / 2660	1.91	355	353D	353DC	0.03 / 0.8	3.23 / 82,0	.31 / 7,9	.15 / 3,8
1.5748 / 40,000	3.6250 / 92,075	⊕ 2.1375 / 54,292	1.5625 / 39,688	3180 / 1410	4250 / 1880	6050 / 2700	0.75	44000 (44150X) ②	44363D		0.06 / 1,5	3.35 / 85,0	.56 / 14,2	
1.5748 — 2.1250 / 40,000 — 53,975	4.3750 / 111,125	3.1250 / 79,375	2.5000 / 63,500	6900 / 3060	3500 / 1560	13100 / 5850	1.97	535	533D	533DC	0.06 / 1,5	3.94 / 100,0	.31 / 7,9	.09 / 2,3
1.6250 / 41,275	3.0000 / 76,200	1.9375 / 49,212	1.5625 / 39,688	3040 / 1355	2040 / 910	5800 / 2800	1.49	24700	24720D	24720DC	0.03 / 0.8	2.83 / 72,0	.31 / 7,9	.09 / 2,3
1.6250 — 2.0312 / 41,275 — 51,592	3.5433 / 90,000	1.9689 / 50,010	1.6563 / 42,070	3310 / 1475	1810 / 805	6300 / 2800	1.83	365	363D	363DC	0.03 / 0.8	3.31 / 84,0	.31 / 7,9	.09 / 2,3
1.6250 — 2.2500 / 41,275 — 57,150	4.2500 / 107,950	2.5626 / 65,090	2.1250 / 53,975	5400 / 2400	3090 / 1375	10200 / 4550	1.74	455	452D	452DC	0.03 / 0.8	3.94 / 100,0	.43 / 10,9	.15 / 3,8
1.7500 — 1.8125 / 44,450 — 46,038	3.1250 / 79,375	1.6249 / 41,272	1.3125 / 33,338	2090 / 930	1340 / 595	3990 / 1775	1.56	18600	18620D	18620DC	0.03 / 0.8	2.91 / 74,0	.18 / 4,6	.09 / 2,3
1.7500 — 2.0625 / 44,450 — 52,388	3.8718 / 93,264	2.5625 / 65,088	2.0625 / 52,388	5000 / 2220	2890 / 1285	9500 / 4240	1.73	3700	37290	37290DC	0.03 / 0.8	3.46 / 88,0	.37 / 9,4	.09 / 2,3
1.7500 — 2.0625 / 44,450 — 52,388	4.4375 / 112,712	2.5625 / 65,088	1.8125 / 46,038	4150 / 1840	6300 / 2800	7900 / 3520	0.66	55000	55444D		0.06 / 1,5	4.13 / 105,0		
1.8750 — 2.2500 / 47,625 — 57,531	3.9370 / 100,000	1.9370 / 49,200	1.5620 / 39,675	3590 / 1595	2180 / 970	6850 / 3040	1.65	385	384ED	384EDC	0.03 / 0.8	3.66 / 93,0	.31 / 7,9	.12 / 3,0
1.8750 — 2.2650 / 47,625 — 57,531	3.9370 / 100,000	2.0625 / 52,388	1.6875 / 42,862	3590 / 1595	2180 / 970	6850 / 3040	1.65	385	384D	384DC	0.03 / 0.8	3.66 / 93,0	.31 / 7,9	.12 / 3,0
1.8750 — 1.875 / 47,625 — 55,562	4.8750 / 123,825	3.0625 / 77,788	2.1875 / 55,562	6250 / 2780	7900 / 3520	11900 / 5300	0.79	72000	72488D		0.06 / 1,5	4.53 / 115,0		
1.9685 — 2.6875 / 50,000 — 68,262	4.3307 / 110,000	2.0625 / 52,388	1.8125 / 46,038	4000 / 1790	2770 / 1235	7650 / 3400	1.45	395	394D	394DC	0.03 / 0.8	4.11 / 104,5	.37 / 9,4	.09 / 2,3
2.0000 — 2.2500 / 50,800 — 57,150	4.6250 / 117,475	2.8750 / 73,025	2.1250 / 53,975	5750 / 2560	6200 / 2760	11000 / 4900	0.93	66000	66462D	66462DC	0.03 / 0.8	4.37 / 111,0	.43 / 10,9	.21 / 5,3
2.0000 — 2.6875 / 50,800 — 68,262	4.8750 / 123,825	3.1250 / 79,375	2.5000 / 63,500	7900 / 3520	4700 / 2080	15100 / 6700	1.69	555	552D	552DC	0.06 / 1,5	4.53 / 115,0	.56 / 14,2	.18 / 4,6
2.1250 — 2.3622 / 53,975 — 60,000	5.1174 / 129,982	2.7500 / 69,850	1.8750 / 47,625	6000 / 2680	6850 / 3040	11400 / 5100	0.88	66500	66522D		0.03 / 0.8	4.65 / 118,0		

① These maximum fillet radii will be cleared by the bearing corners.

② Specific cone part number indicated in ( ) when dimension "T" varies from others in series.

TWO-ROW ASSEMBLY · DOUBLE CUP, SINGLE CONES

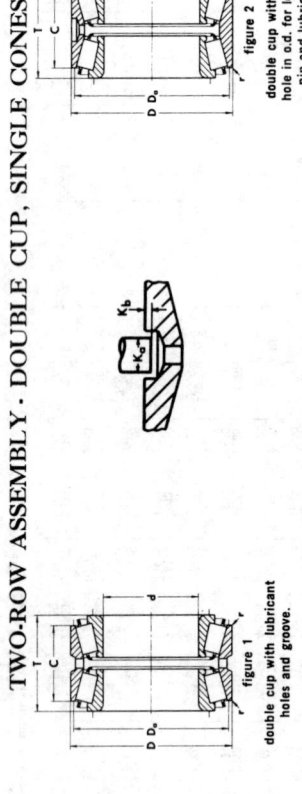

figure 1
double cup with lubricant holes and groove.

figure 2
double cup with ONE hole in o.d. for locking pin and lubricant.

for available cones refer to bearing selection index under series indicated

| bore range | outside diameter | width | | rating at 500 RPM for 3000 hours L10 | | | factor | | part numbers | | cup | | pin | |
d	D	through cones T	cup C	one row radial	thrust	two row radial	K	bearing series	cup fig. 1	cup fig. 2	max. hous. fillet radius r①	backing shoulder diameter Da	max. diam. Ka	Max. depth into cup Kb
2.1250 — 2.8125 53.975 — 71.438	5.3750 136.525	3.7500 95.250	3.0000 76.200	9600 4260	5950 2640	18300 8150	1.61	635	6320	6320C	0.06 1.5	4.92 125.0	.62 15.7	.21 5.3
2.1250 — †2.5591 53.975 — †65.000	5.5000 139.700	3.0625 77.788	2.0395 51.803	6750 3000	10100 4480	12900 5700	0.67	78000	78549D		0.06 1.5	5.16 131.0		
2.1664 — 2.7559 55.000 — 70.000	4.7244 120.000	2.5626 65.090	2.1250 53.975	5900 2640	3900 1735	11300 5000	1.52	475	4720	4720C	0.03 0.8	4.49 114.0	.56 14.2	.12 3.0
2.2500 — 2.8750 57.150 — 73.025	4.6250 117.475	2.6250 66.675	2.1250 53.975	5950 2660	4450 1980	11400 5050	1.34	33000	33462D	33462DC	0.03 0.8	4.41 112.0	.43 10.9	.15 3.8
2.2500 — 2.8750 57.150 — 73.025	4.7244 120.000	3.1460 79.908	2.6490 67.285	5950 2660	4450 1980	11400 5050	1.34	33000	33472D	33472DC	0.03 0.8	4.45 113.0	.43 10.9	.15 3.8
2.3750 — 2.4700 60.325 — 62.738	3.9370 100.000	2.1874 55.560	1.7500 44.450	4550 2020	3310 1470	8650 3840	1.37	28900	28921D	28921DC	0.03 0.8	3.78 96.0	.31 7.9	.09 2.3
2.3750 60.325	6.3750 161.925	4.0310 102.387	2.7810 70.637	11500 5100	14000 6200	21800 9700	0.82	9200	9220D		0.03 0.8	6.03 153.0		
2.4400 61.976	3.9370 100.000	②2.1250 53.975	1.7500 44.450	8250 3660	5100 2280	15700 6950	1.37	28900 (28990)②	28921D	28921DC	0.06 1.5	3.78 96.0	.31 7.9	.09 2.3
2.5000 — 2.9062 63.500 — 73.817	5.0000 127.000	3.1875 80.962	2.5625 65.088	5500 2020	3310 1470	8650 3840	1.61	565	563D	563DC	0.06 1.5	4.69 119.0	.56 14.2	.15 3.8
2.5000 — 3.3475 63.500 — 85.026	6.1250 155.575	4.0000 101.600	3.3750 85.725	13200 5850	7350 3260	25100 11200	1.80	745	742D	742DC	0.06 1.5	5.63 143.0	.75 19.1	.21 5.3

① These maximum fillet radii will be cleared by the bearing corners.

TWO-ROW ASSEMBLY - DOUBLE CUP, SINGLE CONES — TDO-TDODC

for available cones refer to bearing selection index under series indicated

d (bore range) in / mm	D (outside diameter) in / mm	T (through cones) in / mm	C (cup width) in / mm	one row radial lb / daN	two row radial lb / daN	thrust lb / daN	K (factor)	bearing series	cup fig. 1	cup fig. 2	r (cup max. housing fillet radius) ① in / mm	Da (backing shoulder diameter) in / mm	Ka (pin max. diam.) in / mm	Kb (max. depth into cup) in / mm
2.7500 — 2.9062 / 69,850 — 73,817	4.4995 / 114,287	2.3125 / 58,738	1.8125 / 46,038	4900 / 2180	9350 / 4160	4100 / 1820	1.20	29600	29620	29622DC	.03 / 0,8	4.29 / 109,0	.31 / 7,9	.09 / 2,3
2.7500 — 2.8125 / 69,850 — 71,438	4.7244 / 120,000	2.8125 / 71,438	2.3125 / 58,738	7600 / 3380	14500 / 6450	4700 / 2080	1.62	47400	474200	47420DC	.03 / 0,8	4.49 / 114,0	.56 / 14,2	.12 / 3,0
2.7500 — 3.3750 / 69,850 — 85,725	6.0000 / 152,400	3.7500 / 95,250	3.0000 / 76,200	10300 / 4600	19500 / 8650	7150 / 3180	1.43	655	6540	654DC	.06 / 1,5	5.55 / 141,0	.62 / 15,7	.21 / 5,3
2.7540 — 3.0625 / 69,952 — 77,788	4.7812 / 121,442	2.0626 / 52,390	1.5000 / 38,100	4250 / 1900	8100 / 3600	3270 / 1455	1.30	34000	34478D	34478DC	.03 / 0,8	4.57 / 116,0	.25 / 6,4	.09 / 2,3
2.8125 — 3.3750 / 71,438 — 85,725	5.3750 / 136,525	2.7500 / 69,850	2.1250 / 53,975	6550 / 2920	12500 / 5550	5000 / 2220	1.31	495	4930	493DC	.03 / 0,8	5.12 / 130,0	.50 / 12,7	.18 / 4,6
2.8750 — 3.2500 / 73,025 — 82,550	5.5115 / 139,992	3.2500 / 82,550	2.6250 / 66,675	8800 / 3920	16800 / 7500	6100 / 2700	1.45	575	5720	572DC	.03 / 0,8	5.24 / 133,0	.62 / 15,7	.18 / 4,6
2.8750 — 3.5625 / 73,025 — 90,488	6.3750 / 161,925	4.1250 / 104,775	3.3750 / 85,725	13800 / 6100	26200 / 11650	8050 / 3580	1.71	755	7520	752DC	.06 / 1,5	5.91 / 150,0	.75 / 19,1	.21 / 5,3
3.0000 — 3.7500 / 76,200 — 95,250	6.0000 / 152,400	3.2500 / 82,550	2.5000 / 63,500	9350 / 4160	17900 / 7950	7100 / 3160	1.32	595	5920	592DC	.03 / 0,8	5.67 / 144,0	.56 / 14,2	.21 / 5,3
3.0000 / 76,200	6.3750 / 161,925	② 4.1560 / 105,562	2.7810 / 70,637	11500 / 5100	21800 / 9700	14000 / 6200	0.82	9200 (9285) ②	92200		.03 / 0,8	6.03 / 153,0		
3.0000 — 3.1250 / 76,200 — 84,138	7.0000 / 177,800	4.3125 / 109,538	2.9375 / 74,612	12000 / 5350	22800 / 10150	15800 / 7000	0.76	9300	93200		.09 / 2,3	6.46 / 164,0		
3.0000 / 76,200	7.0000 / 177,800	② 4.5625 / 115,888	2.9375 / 74,612	12000 / 5350	22800 / 10150	15800 / 7000	0.76	9300 (9378) ②	93200		.09 / 2,3	6.46 / 164,0		
3.0000 — 4.0000 / 76,200 — 101,600	7.5000 / 190,500	5.0000 / 127,000	4.1250 / 104,775	22000 / 9750	42000 / 18600	12600 / 5600	1.74	HH221400	HH221410D	HH221410DC	.06 / 1,5	7.05 / 179,0	.87 / 22,1	.21 / 5,3
3.1496 — 4.0000 / 80,000 — 101,600	7.8750 / 200,025	4.5625 / 115,888	3.1581 / 80,216	16500 / 7350	31500 / 14000	17900 / 8000	0.92	98000	98789D	98789DC	.09 / 2,3	7.40 / 188,0	.68 / 17,3	.31 / 7,9
3.3750 — 4.0000 / 85,725 — 101,600	6.6250 / 168,275	3.6250 / 92,075	2.7500 / 69,850	11500 / 5100	21900 / 9700	9250 / 4120	1.24	675	6720	6720DC	.03 / 0,8	6.30 / 160,0	.62 / 15,7	.18 / 4,6
3.4375 — 4.0000 / 87,312 — 101,600	7.5000 / 190,500	5.0000 / 127,000	4.0000 / 101,600	19300 / 8600	36900 / 16400	11100 / 4950	1.74	855	8540	8540DC	.06 / 1,5	6.85 / 174,0	.75 / 19,1	.21 / 5,3
3.4630 — 3.8125 / 87,960 — 96,838	5.8750 / 149,225	2.6249 / 66,672	2.0625 / 52,388	7100 / 3160	13600 / 6050	6000 / 2660	1.19	42000	425870	42587DC	.03 / 0,8	5.63 / 143,0	.43 / 10,9	.15 / 3,8
3.5000 / 88,900	4.8750 / 123,825	1.9999 / 50,797	1.6875 / 42,862	4300 / 1920	8200 / 3640	2430 / 1080	1.77	L217800	L217810D	L217810DC	.03 / 0,8	4.69 / 119,0	.31 / 7,9	.09 / 2,3
3.5400 / 89,916	7.4790 / 189,967	3.3800 / 85,852	2.1300 / 54,102	11200 / 5000	21400 / 9500	16800 / 7450	0.67	HM921300	HM921310D	HM921310DC	.06 / 1,5	7.13 / 181,0	.43 / 10,9	.25 / 6,4

① These maximum fillet radii will be cleared by the bearing corners.
② Specific cone part number indicated in ( ) when dimension "T" varies from others in series.

TWO-ROW ASSEMBLY · DOUBLE CUP, SINGLE CONES

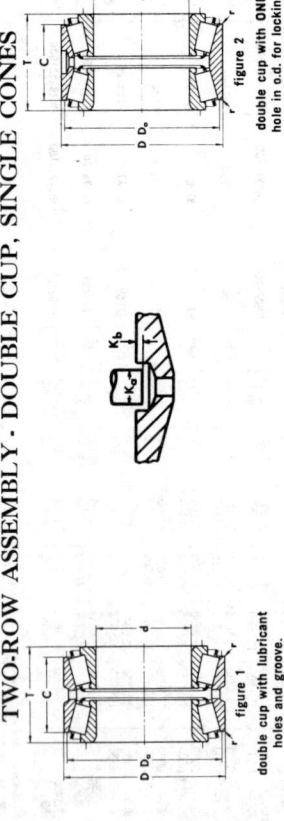

figure 1
double cup with lubricant holes and groove.

figure 2
double cup with ONE hole in o.d. for locking pin and lubricant.

for available cones refer to bearing selection index under series indicated

bore range d	outside diameter D	width through cones T	width cup C	rating at 500 RPM for 3000 hours L10 one row radial lb/daN	thrust lb/daN	two row radial lb/daN	factor K	bearing series	part numbers cup fig. 1	cup fig. 2	cup max. hsg. fillet radius r ①	cup backing shoulder diameter Da	pin max. diam. Ka	pin Max. depth into cup Kb
3.5425 / 89.980	6.3740 / 161.900	2.7500 / 69.850	1.7500 / 44.450	7900 / 3500	9850 / 4380	15000 / 6700	0.80	M919000	M919010D		0.06 / 1.5	6.06 / 154.0		.21 / 5,3
3.6250 — 4.1250 / 92.075 — 104.775	7.0866 / 180.000	4.1250 / 104.775	2.3750 / 85.725	14900 / 6600	9850 / 4380	28300 / 12600	1.51	775	773D	7730C	0.03 / 0.8	6.61 / 168.0	.75 / 19.1	.21 / 5,3
3.6250 — 4.1250 / 92.075 — 104.775	7.1250 / 180.975	4.1250 / 104.775	3.3750 / 85.725	14900 / 6600	9850 / 4380	28300 / 12600	1.51	775	774D	7740C	0.06 / 1.5	6.61 / 168.0	.75 / 19.1	.21 / 5,3
3.7500 / 95.250	5.1250 / 130.175	1.8749 / 47.622	1.5625 / 39.688	4450 / 1980	2670 / 1190	8500 / 3780	1.67	L319200	L319210D		0.03 / 0.8	4.92 / 125.0	.56 / 14.2	.21 / 5,3
3.7500 — 4.0000 / 95.250 — 101.600	6.3750 / 161.925	3.2499 / 82.547	2.4375 / 61.912	9900 / 4400	8050 / 3580	18800 / 8400	1.23	52000	52637D	52637DC	0.03 / 0.8	6.06 / 154.0		
3.9362 / 99.979	7.7500 / 196.850	4.0700 / 103.378	2.9300 / 74.422	14600 / 6500	15200 / 6750	27800 / 12350	0.96	HM821500	HM821511D		0.06 / 1.5	7.36 / 187.0		
4.0000 — 4.2500 / 101.600 — 107.950	5.7500 / 146.050	1.9375 / 49.212	1.5625 / 39.688	4700 / 2080	3140 / 1400	8900 / 3960	1.49	L521900	L521910D	L521910DC	0.03 / 0.8	5.55 / 141.0	.31 / 7.9	.12 / 3.0
4.0000 — 4.5000 / 101.600 — 114.300	8.3750 / 212.725	5.6250 / 142.875	4.6250 / 117.475	24300 / 10800	13600 / 6050	46500 / 20600	1.79	935	9320	9320C	0.06 / 1.5	7.60 / 193.1	.87 / 22.1	.31 / 7.9
4.0000 — 4.5000 / 101.600 — 114.300	8.3750 / 212.725	5.6250 / 142.875	4.6250 / 117.475	28300 / 12600	15800 / 7050	54000 / 24000	1.79	HH224300	HH224310D	HH224310DC	0.06 / 1.5	7.94 / 201.7	1.00 / 25.4	.21 / 5,3
4.0000 — 4.3750 / 101.500 — 111.125	8.4375 / 214.312	4.5625 / 115.888	3.3125 / 84.138	19200 / 8550	22100 / 9800	36600 / 16250	0.87	H924000	H924010D		0.06 / 1.5	8.07 / 205.0		

① These maximum fillet radii will be cleared by the bearing corners.

TWO-ROW ASSEMBLY - DOUBLE CUP, SINGLE CONES — TDO-TDODC

for available cones refer to bearing selection index under series indicated

bore range d	outside diameter D	width through cones T	width cup C	rating at 500 RPM for 3000 hours L10				factor K	bearing series	part numbers cup fig. 1	cup fig. 2	cup max hsng fillet radius r⊕	backing shoulder diameter Da	pin max diam Ka	max depth into cup Kb
				one row radial (lb/daN)	two row radial (lb/daN)	thrust (lb/daN)	two row radial (lb/daN)								
4.1250 — 4.4310 / 104.775 — 115.087	7.5000 / 190.500	4.1875 / 106.362	3.1875 / 80.962	15900 / 7050	30200 / 13450	11300 / 5050	30200 / 13450	1.40	71000	71751D	71751DC	0.06 / 1.5	7.13 / 181.0	.68 / 17.3	.21 / 5.3
4.1875 — 4.2500 / 106.362 — 107.950	6.5000 / 165.100	3.2500 / 82.550	2.5000 / 63.500	10100 / 4500	19300 / 8600	8600 / 3820	19300 / 8600	1.18	56000	56500	56650DC	0.03 / 0.8	6.26 / 159.0	.56 / 14.2	.18 / 4.6
4.2500 — 4.3125 / 107.950 — 109.538	6.2500 / 158.750	2.1251 / 53.978	1.5625 / 39.688	5050 / 2240	9600 / 4280	5250 / 2340	9600 / 4280	0.96	37000	376260	37626DC	0.03 / 0.8	5.98 / 152.0	.31 / 7.9	.15 / 3.8
4.2500 — 4.3302 / 107.950 — 109.987	6.2987 / 159.987	2.9375 / 74.612	2.3125 / 58.738	9350 / 4160	17800 / 7900	6450 / 2860	17800 / 7900	1.45	LM522500	LM522510	LM522510DC	0.03 / 0.8	6.06 / 154.0	.56 / 14.2	.12 / 3.0
4.3304 — 14.5276 / 109.992 — 115.000	7.0000 / 177.800	3.6250 / 92.075	2.7500 / 69.850	12100 / 5400	23100 / 10250	10700 / 4750	23100 / 10250	1.13	64000	647000	647000DC	0.03 / 0.8	6.77 / 172.0	.62 / 15.7	.21 / 5.3
4.3750 / 111.125	9.5000 / 241.300	6.2500 / 158.750	4.2500 / 107.950	27600 / 12250	52500 / 23400	34500 / 15350	52500 / 23400	0.80	HH924300	HH924310	HH924310DC	0.06 / 1.5	8.90 / 226.0	.87 / 22.1	.31 / 7.9
4.5000 — 5.0312 / 114.300 — 127.792	9.0000 / 228.600	4.5625 / 115.888	3.3125 / 84.138	20500 / 9100	39000 / 17350	25900 / 11550	39000 / 17350	0.79	HH926700	HH926710D	HH926710DC	0.09 / 2.3	8.63 / 219.3	.75 / 19.1	.31 / 7.9
4.7230 — 5.5118 / 119.964 — 140.000	8.5000 / 215.900	4.1875 / 106.362	3.1875 / 80.962	17200 / 7650	32800 / 14600	14300 / 6400	32800 / 14600	1.20	74000	74851D	74851DC	0.06 / 1.5	8.19 / 208.0	.75 / 19.1	.21 / 5.3
4.7500 / 120.650	6.3750 / 161.925	2.5000 / 63.500	2.1250 / 53.975	5150 / 2280	9750 / 4340	3830 / 1700	9750 / 4340	1.34	L624500	L624514D		0.03 / 0.8	6.14 / 156.0		.15 / 3.8
4.7500 / 120.650	6.8750 / 174.625	3.0625 / 77.788	2.4375 / 61.912	11300 / 5000	21400 / 9550	6400 / 2840	21400 / 9550	1.76	M224700	M224700D	M224710DC	0.03 / 0.8	6.61 / 168.0	.56 / 14.2	.15 / 3.8
4.7500 — 5.0000 / 120.650 — 127.000	7.1875 / 182.562	3.3750 / 85.725	2.8750 / 73.025	12900 / 5750	24600 / 10950	6750 / 3000	24600 / 10950	1.91	48200	482200	48220DC	0.03 / 0.8	6.93 / 176.0	.62 / 15.7	.15 / 3.8
4.7500 — 5.1250 / 120.650 — 130.175	8.1250 / 206.375	4.2500 / 107.950	3.2500 / 82.550	16800 / 7450	32000 / 14200	13200 / 5900	32000 / 14200	1.27	795	792D	792DC	0.03 / 0.8	7.80 / 198.0	.75 / 19.1	.25 / 6.4
4.7500 — 5.2500 / 120.650 — 133.350	9.2500 / 234.950	5.6250 / 142.875	4.5000 / 114.300	27300 / 12150	52000 / 23200	17300 / 7700	52000 / 23200	1.58	95000	95927D	95927DC	0.06 / 1.5	8.54 / 217.0	.87 / 22.1	.31 / 7.9
5.0000 — 5.2500 / 127.000 — 133.350	7.7500 / 196.850	4.0000 / 101.600	3.3750 / 85.725	16900 / 7500	32200 / 14350	9950 / 4420	32200 / 14350	1.70	67300	673220	673220C	0.03 / 0.8	7.48 / 190.0	.75 / 19.1	.18 / 4.6
5.0000 — 5.2500 / 127.000 — 133.350	7.7500 / 196.850	4.2500 / 107.950	3.6250 / 92.075	16900 / 7500	32200 / 14350	9950 / 4420	32200 / 14350	1.70	67300	673230		0.03 / 0.8	7.48 / 190.0		
5.0000 — 5.2500 / 127.000 — 133.350	7.8750 / 200.025	4.0000 / 101.600	3.3750 / 85.725	16900 / 7500	32200 / 14350	9950 / 4420	32200 / 14350	1.70	67300	673250		0.03 / 0.8	7.52 / 191.0		
5.2500 / 133.350	6.9688 / 177.008	2.2500 / 57.150	1.8750 / 47.625	7250 / 3220	13800 / 6150	4300 / 1920	13800 / 6150	1.68	L327200	L327210D	L327210DC	0.03 / 0.8	6.73 / 171.0	.37 / 9.4	.09 / 2.3
5.2500 — 5.3750 / 133.350 — 136.525	7.5000 / 190.500	3.3750 / 85.725	2.8750 / 73.025	13700 / 6100	26100 / 11600	7500 / 3340	26100 / 11600	1.82	48300	483200	48320DC	0.03 / 0.8	7.24 / 184.0	.62 / 15.7	.15 / 3.8

⊕These maximum fillet radii will be cleared by the bearing corners.
†Dimension shown is maximum value—See note at bottom of fitting practice table page 4 in Reference Tables.

TWO-ROW ASSEMBLY - DOUBLE CUP, SINGLE CONES

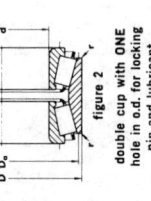

figure 1

double cup with lubricant holes and groove.

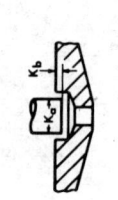

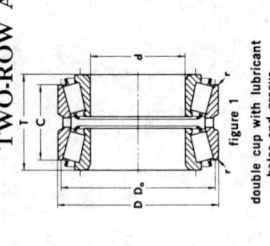

figure 2

double cup with ONE hole in o.d. for locking pin and lubricant.

for available cones refer to bearing selection index under series indicated

| bore range | outside diameter | width | | rating at 500 RPM for 3000 hours L10 | | | factor | bearing series | part numbers | | cup | | pin | | |
d	D	through cones T	cup C	one row radial lb daN	thrust lb daN	two row radial lb daN	K		cup fig. 1	cup fig. 2	max hsng fillet radius r	backing shoulder diameter Da	max. diam. Ka	max depth into cup Kb
5.3750 — 5.5000 136.525 — 139.700	9.0000 228.600	4.8750 123.825	3.8750 98.425	23000 10250	16500 7350	44000 19400	1.39	895	892D	892DC	0.06 1.5	8.50 216.0	.87 22.1	.21 5.3
5.5000 139.700	8.7500 222.250	2.9800 75.692	2.1250 53.975	10200 4550	7600 3380	19400 8600	1.34	73000	73876D	73876DC	0.09 2.3	8.15 207.0	.43 10.9	.15 3.8
5.5000 — 5.7500 139.700 — 146.050	9.5000 241.300	5.1875 131.762	4.1875 106.362	23000 10200	17400 7750	44000 19400	1.32	82000	82951D	82951DC	0.06 1.5	8.90 226.0	.87 22.1	.31 7.9
5.5000 — 6.0000 139.700 — 152.400	10.0000 254.000	5.8750 149.225	4.3750 111.125	29200 12950	20400 9050	55500 24800	1.43	99000	99102D	99102DC	0.06 1.5	9.37 238.0	.87 22.1	.25 6.4
5.5000 — 6.0000 139.700 — 152.400	10.0000 254.000	6.0000 152.400	4.5000 114.300	29200 12950	20400 9050	55500 24800	1.43	99000	99101D	99101DC	0.06 1.5	9.37 238.0	.87 22.1	.25 6.4
5.5000 — 6.0000 139.700 — 152.400	12.1250 307.975	7.8750 200.025	6.1250 155.575	49500 22200	27800 12350	94500 42200	1.79	HH234000	HH234011D	HH234011DC	0.09 2.3	11.24 285.4	1.12 28.4	.31 7.9
5.6250 — 5.7500 142.875 — 146.050	7.6250 193.675	2.5624 65.085	2.1250 53.975	9700 4320	6100 2720	18500 8200	1.59	36600	366200	366200DC	0.03 0.8	7.40 188.0	.43 10.9	.15 3.8
5.6250 142.875	7.8750 200.025	3.4376 87.315	2.8750 73.025	13900 6200	8000 3560	26600 11800	1.74	48600	48620D	48620DC	0.03 0.8	7.60 193.0	.62 15.7	.18 4.6
5.7500 — 5.8750 146.050 — 149.225	9.3125 236.538	5.1875 131.762	4.1875 106.362	26300 11700	14400 6400	50000 22400	1.83	HM231100	HM231111D	HM231111DC	0.06 1.5	8.82 224.0	.87 22.1	.21 5.3
5.7500 — 5.8750 146.050 — 149.225	9.5000 241.300	5.1875 131.762	4.1875 106.362	26300 11700	14400 6400	50000 22400	1.83	HM231100	HM231116D	HM231116DC	0.06 1.5	8.82 224.0	.87 22.1	.21 5.3

(¹) These maximum fillet radii will be cleared by the bearing corners.

TWO-ROW ASSEMBLY - DOUBLE CUP, SINGLE CUP, SINGLE CONES — TDO-TDODC

for available cones refer to bearing selection index under series indicated

bore range d	outside diameter D	width through cones T	width cup C	rating one row radial lb/daN	rating thrust lb/daN	rating two row radial lb/daN	factor K	bearing series	part numbers cup fig. 1	part numbers cup fig. 2	cup max hsg fillet radius r①	backing shoulder diameter Da	pin max diam Ka	pin max depth into cup Kb
5.7500 — 6.0000 / 146.050 — 152.400	10.5625 / 268.288	6.3125 / 160.338	4.9375 / 125.412	34400 / 15300	22800 / 10150	65500 / 29200	1.51	107000	1071050	1071050C	0.06 / 1.5	9.82 / 249.4	1.12 / 28.4	.37 / 9.4
6.0000 / 152.400	8.7500 / 222.250	3.9374 / 100.010	3.0000 / 76.200	17400 / 7750	9900 / 4400	33200 / 14750	1.76	M231600	M2316100	M2316100C	0.03 / 0.8	8.39 / 213.0	.75 / 19.1	.18 / 4.6
6.0000 / 152.400	12.1250 / 307.975	7.8750 / 200.025	5.7500 / 146.050	44000 / 19600	24600 / 10950	84000 / 37400	1.79	450000	4512150	451215DC	0.09 / 2.3	10.82 / 274.8	1.12 / 28.4	.43 / 10.9
6.2500 — 6.5000 / 158.750 — 165.100	8.8750 / 225.425	3.3750 / 85.725	2.7500 / 69.850	15100 / 6750	9950 / 4420	28800 / 12800	1.52	46700	467200	46720DC	0.03 / 0.8	8.58 / 218.0	.62 / 15.7	.18 / 4.6
6.3120 — 7.0000 / 160.325 — 177.800	11.3750 / 288.925	5.6250 / 142.875	4.3750 / 111.125	35500 / 15800	19400 / 8600	67500 / 30000	1.83	HM237500	HM2375100	HM237510DC	0.06 / 1.5	10.68 / 271.3	.87 / 22.1	.31 / 7.9
6.5000 — 7.0000 / 165.100 — 177.800	9.7500 / 247.650	4.0625 / 103.188	3.3125 / 84.138	19500 / 8650	14700 / 6500	37100 / 16500	1.33	67700	67720D	67720DC	0.03 / 0.8	9.45 / 240.0	.75 / 19.1	.21 / 5.3
6.5000 / 165.100	10.0000 / 254.000	4.0000 / 101.600	3.0000 / 76.200	20700 / 9200	11300 / 5050	39400 / 17550	1.83	M235100	M235113D	M235113DC	0.06 / 1.5	9.45 / 240.0	.75 / 19.1	.21 / 5.3
6.5000 — 7.0000 / 165.100 — 177.800	11.7500 / 298.450	5.6250 / 142.875	4.3750 / 111.125	30000 / 13350	24000 / 10650	57000 / 25400	1.25	94000	941140	94114DC	0.06 / 1.5	10.71 / 272.0	.87 / 22.1	.37 / 9.4
6.5000 — 7.0000 / 165.150 — 177.800	11.7500 / 298.450	5.6250 / 142.875	4.3750 / 111.125	30000 / 13350	24000 / 10650	57000 / 25400	1.25	94000	941180		0.06 / 1.5	10.71 / 272.0		
6.5000 — 8.1250 / 165.100 — 206.375	14.5000 / 368.300	7.6250 / 193.675	5.3750 / 136.525	48500 / 21600	33500 / 14900	97000 / 43200	1.45	420000	4214510	421451DC	0.06 / 1.5	13.16 / 334.4	1.00 / 25.4	.43 / 10.9
6.5000 — 8.1250 / 165.100 — 206.375	14.6250 / 371.475	7.6250 / 193.675	5.3750 / 136.525	48500 / 21600	33500 / 14900	97000 / 43200	1.45	420000	421462XD		0.06 / 1.5	13.16 / 334.4		
7.0000 — 7.3750 / 177.800 — 187.325	10.6250 / 269.875	4.6875 / 119.062	3.6875 / 93.662	24200 / 10750	13700 / 6100	48400 / 21500	1.76	M238800	M2388100	M238810DC	0.06 / 1.5	10.08 / 256.0	.75 / 19.1	.21 / 5.3
7.0000 — 7.3750 / 177.800 — 187.325	12.6250 / 320.675	7.3125 / 185.738	5.4375 / 138.112	44500 / 19800	24300 / 10800	89000 / 39600	1.83	H239600	H239612D	H239612DC	0.06 / 1.5	11.73 / 298.0	1.12 / 28.4	.37 / 9.4
7.0866 — 7.4830 / 180.000 — 190.068	10.5000 / 266.700	4.0211 / 102.136②	3.3125 / 84.138	19200 / 8550	15800 / 7000	38400 / 17100	1.22	67800 (67875 - 67886)	678200	67820DC	0.03 / 0.8	10.20 / 259.0	.75 / 19.1	.21 / 5.3
†7.0866 — 8.2500 / †180.000 — 209.550	12.5000 / 317.500	5.7500 / 146.050	4.3750 / 111.125	32900 / 14650	29400 / 13050	65800 / 29300	1.12	93000	931270	93127DC	0.06 / 1.5	11.81 / 300.0	.87 / 22.1	.37 / 9.4
7.2500 — 7.5625 / 184.150 — 192.088	10.5000 / 266.700	4.0625 / 103.188	3.3125 / 84.138	19200 / 8550	15800 / 7000	38400 / 17100	1.22	67800	678200	67820DC	0.03 / 0.8	10.20 / 259.0	.75 / 19.1	.21 / 5.3
7.3750 — 7.6250 / 187.325 — 193.675	11.1250 / 282.575	4.2500 / 107.950	3.1250 / 79.375	17200 / 7650	12200 / 5400	34400 / 15300	1.41	87000	871120	87112DC	0.06 / 1.5	10.50 / 266.6	.68 / 17.3	.21 / 5.3
7.7500 / 196.850	10.0000 / 254.000	2.4374 / 61.910	1.8750 / 47.625	8900 / 3960	6050 / 2700	17800 / 7920	1.47	L540000	L5400010	L540010DC	0.03 / 0.8	9.72 / 247.0	.37 / 9.4	.12 / 3.0

① These maximum fillet radii will be cleared by the bearing corners.
② Specific cone part number indicated in ( ) when dimension "T" varies from others in series.
† Dimension shown is maximum value—See note at bottom of fitting practice table page 4 in Reference Table.

TWO-ROW ASSEMBLY - DOUBLE CUP, SINGLE CONES

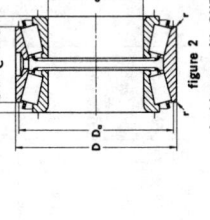

figure 1
double cup with lubricant holes and groove.

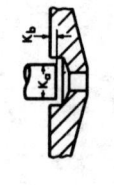

figure 2
double cup with ONE hole in o.d. for locking pin and lubricant.

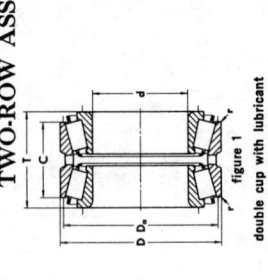

for available cones refer to bearing selection index under series indicated

bore range	outside diameter	width		rating at 500 RPM for 3000 hours L10			factor	bearing series	part numbers		cup		pin	
d	D	through cones T	cup C	one row radial	thrust	two row radial	K		cup fig. 1	cup fig. 2	max. hsg. fillet radius r⊕	backing shoulder diameter Da	max. diam. Ka	Max. depth into cup Kb
				lb / daN	lb / daN	lb / daN								
7.7500 / 196,850	10.1250 / 257,175	3.3750 / 85,725	2.6250 / 66,675	15600 / 6950	11900 / 5300	31200 / 13900	1.31	LM739700	LM739710D	LM739710DC	.03 / 0,8	9.88 / 251,0	.56 / 14,2	.15 / 3,8
7.8750 — 8.2500 / 200,025 — 209,550	13.1250 / 333,375	5.8750 / 149,225	4.5000 / 114,300	41000 / 18200	30700 / 13650	82000 / 36400	1.33	HM743300	HM743310D	HM743310DC	.06 / 1,5	12.48 / 317,1	1.00 / 25,4	.31 / 7,9
7.8750 — 9.2500 / 200,025 — 234,950	15.1250 / 384,175	9.3750 / 238,125	7.6250 / 193,675	81500 / 36200	46500 / 20600	163000 / 72400	1.76	H247500	H247510D	H247510DC	.06 / 1,5	14.26 / 362,1	1.12 / 28,4	.43 / 10,9
8.0000 / 203,200	10.8750 / 276,225	3.5624 / 90,485	2.8750 / 73,025	19100 / 8450	10400 / 4650	38200 / 16900	1.83	LM241100	LM241110D	LM241110DC	.03 / 0,8	10.51 / 267,0	.62 / 15,7	.15 / 3,8
8.0000 — 8.1250 / 203,200 — 206,375	11.1250 / 282,575	4.0000 / 101,600	3.2500 / 82,550	19900 / 8850	17300 / 7700	39800 / 17700	1.15	67900	67920D	67920DC	.03 / 0,8	10.83 / 275,0	.75 / 19,1	.25 / 6,4
8.0000 — 8.0625 / 203,200 — 204,788	11.5000 / 292,100	4.9376 / 125,415	4.0000 / 101,600	28500 / 12700	16200 / 7200	57000 / 25400	1.76	M241500	M241510D	M241510DC	.06 / 1,5	10.98 / 279,0	.75 / 19,1	.21 / 5,3
8.0000 / 203,200	16.0000 / 406,400	7.7500 / 196,850	5.0000 / 127,000	42500 / 18800	58000 / 25800	85000 / 37600	0.73	114000	114161D	114161DC	.13 / 3,3	14.71 / 373,7	1.12 / 28,4	.43 / 10,9
8.2500 — 9.2500 / 209,550 — 234,950	14.0000 / 355,600	6.0000 / 152,400	4.3750 / 111,125	35300 / 15700	35600 / 15850	70600 / 31400	0.99	96000	96140D	96140DC	.06 / 1,5	13.15 / 334,0	1.00 / 25,4	.31 / 7,9
8.3750 — 8.5000 / 212,725 — 215,900	11.2500 / 285,750	3.8750 / 98,425	3.0000 / 76,200	20100 / 8950	16600 / 7400	40200 / 17900	1.21	LM742700	LM742710D	LM742710DC	.03 / 0,8	10.98 / 279,0	.68 / 17,3	.18 / 4,6
8.5000 — 9.0000 / 215,900 — 228,600	14.0000 / 355,600	6.0000 / 152,400	4.3750 / 111,125	36100 / 16050	20400 / 9050	72200 / 32100	1.77	130000	131401D	131401DC	.06 / 1,5	13.01 / 330,4	.87 / 22,1	.31 / 7,9

⊕These maximum fillet radii will be cleared by the bearing corners.

TWO-ROW ASSEMBLY · DOUBLE CUP, SINGLE CONES — TDO·TDODC

for available cones refer to bearing selection index under series indicated

bore range d	outside diameter D	width through cones T	width cup C	rating one row radial	rating thrust	rating two row radial	factor K	bearing series	part numbers cup fig. 1	part numbers cup fig. 2	cup max. hsng. fillet radius r①	cup backing shoulder diameter Da	pin max. diam. Ka	pin Kb max. depth into cup
8.5000 / 215.900	14.5000 / 368.300	②6.8750 / 174.625	5.3750 / 136.525	48500 / 21600	33500 / 14900	97000 / 43200	1.45	420000 (EE420850)①	421451D	421451DC	0.06 / 1.5	13.16 / 334.4	1.00 / 25.4	.43 / 10.9
8.5000 / 215.900	14.6250 / 371.475	②6.8750 / 174.625	5.3750 / 136.525	48500 / 21600	33500 / 14900	97000 / 43200	1.45	420000 (EE420850)①	421462X0		0.06 / 1.5	13.16 / 334.4	1.12 / 28.4	.43 / 10.9
8.5000 / 215.900	16.0000 / 406.400	7.6875 / 195.262	5.8125 / 147.638	61500 / 27200	41500 / 18400	123000 / 54400	1.48	820000	820161D	820161DC	0.06 / 1.5	14.64 / 372.0	1.12 / 28.4	.43 / 10.9
8.6875 / 220.662	12.3750 / 314.325	5.1875 / 131.762	4.1875 / 106.362	33700 / 15000	19100 / 8500	67400 / 30000	1.76	M244200	M244210D	M244210DC	0.06 / 1.5	11.81 / 300.0	.87 / 22.1	.25 / 6.4
8.8750 — 9.0000 / 225.425 — 228.600	15.7500 / 400.050	7.3750 / 187.325	5.3750 / 136.525	50500 / 22400	38000 / 16900	101000 / 44800	1.33	430000	431576D	431576DC	0.06 / 1.5	14.34 / 364.2	1.12 / 28.4	.43 / 10.9
8.9920 — 8.9945 / 228.397 — 228.460	17.0000 / 431.800	7.7500 / 196.850	4.3750 / 111.125	45500 / 20200	69000 / 30800	91000 / 40400	0.66	113000	113171D		0.13 / 3.3	15.64 / 397.2	1.12 / 28.4	.43 / 10.9
9.0000 — 9.5000 / 228.600 — 241.300	12.8750 / 327.025	4.5000 / 114.300	3.2500 / 82.550	24500 / 11100	17300 / 7700	49800 / 22200	1.44	8500	85200	85200DC	0.06 / 1.5	12.32 / 313.0	.75 / 19.1	.28 / 7.1
9.0000 / 228.600	14.0000 / 355.600	6.0000 / 152.400	4.5000 / 114.300	43500 / 19200	34900 / 15550	87000 / 38400	1.24	HM746600	HM746610D	HM746610DC	0.06 / 1.5	13.34 / 338.7	1.00 / 25.4	.31 / 7.9
9.0000 — 10.0000 / 228.600 — 254.000	14.1250 / 358.775	6.0000 / 152.400	4.6250 / 117.475	45000 / 20200	25700 / 11450	90000 / 40400	1.76	M249700	M249710D	M249710DC	0.06 / 1.5	13.50 / 343.0	1.00 / 25.4	.25 / 6.4
9.0000 / 228.600	19.2500 / 488.950	10.0000 / 254.000	6.0000 / 152.400	74000 / 33000	119000 / 53000	148000 / 66000	0.62	HH949500	HH949510D	HH949510DC	0.06 / 1.5	17.94 / 455.7	1.12 / 28.4	.43 / 10.9
9.2500 / 234.950	12.2500 / 311.150	3.8750 / 98.425	2.8750 / 73.025	20900 / 9300	13000 / 5750	41800 / 18600	1.61	LM446300	LM446310D		0.03 / 0.8	11.85 / 301.0	1.12 / 28.4	.43 / 10.9
9.5000 — 9.7500 / 241.300 — 247.650	14.5000 / 368.300	4.7500 / 120.650	3.3750 / 85.775	25500 / 11350	15800 / 7050	51000 / 22700	1.61	170000	171451D	171451DC	0.06 / 1.5	13.27 / 337.0	.75 / 19.1	.31 / 7.9
9.5000 — 10.7500 / 241.300 — 273.050	15.5000 / 393.700	6.1875 / 157.162	4.3125 / 109.538	40000 / 17800	27600 / 12300	80000 / 35600	1.45	275000	275156D	275156DC	0.06 / 1.5	14.89 / 378.1	1.00 / 25.4	.25 / 6.4
9.5000 / 241.300	16.0000 / 406.400	8.5000 / 215.900	7.2500 / 184.150	72500 / 32200	41000 / 18400	145000 / 64400	1.76	H249100	H249111D	H249111DC	0.06 / 1.5	15.16 / 385.0	1.12 / 28.4	.43 / 10.9
9.9000 / 241.300	17.5000 / 444.500	8.2500 / 209.550	6.2500 / 158.750	66500 / 29600	38500 / 17100	133000 / 59200	1.73	923000	923176D	923176DC	0.06 / 1.5	16.02 / 407.0	1.12 / 28.4	.43 / 10.9
9.6250 — 9.8130 / 244.475 — 249.250	15.0000 / 381.000	6.7500 / 171.450	5.0000 / 127.000	43000 / 19200	38200 / 17000	86000 / 38400	1.13	126000	126151D	126151DC	0.06 / 1.5	14.09 / 358.0	1.12 / 28.4	.43 / 10.9
10.0000 — 10.5000 / 254.000 — 266.700	12.7500 / 323.850	2.5000 / 63.500	2.0000 / 50.800	7900 / 3500	4650 / 2080	15800 / 7000	1.69	29800	298200	298200DC	0.03 / 0.8	12.28 / 312.0	.43 / 10.9	.21 / 5.3
10.0000 / 254.000	13.6875 / 347.662	3.7500 / 95.250	2.7500 / 69.850	23600 / 10500	13400 / 5950	47200 / 21000	1.76	LM249700	LM249710D	LM249710DC	0.06 / 1.5	13.11 / 333.0	.62 / 15.7	.18 / 4.6

① These maximum fillet radii will be cleared by the bearing corners.
② Specific cone part number indicated in ( ) when dimension "T" varies from others in series.

TWO-ROW ASSEMBLY - DOUBLE CUP, SINGLE CONES

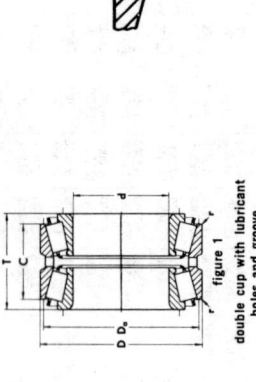

figure 1
double cup with lubricant holes and groove.

figure 2
double cup with ONE hole in o.d. for locking pin and lubricant.

for available cones refer to bearing selection index under series indicated

bore range d	outside diameter D	width through cones T	width cup C	rating one row radial (lb / daN)	rating thrust (lb / daN)	rating two row radial (lb / daN)	factor K	bearing series	part numbers cup fig. 1	part numbers cup fig. 2	cup max hsg fillet radius r [1]	cup backing shoulder diameter Da	pin max diam Ka	pin max depth into cup Kb
10.0000—10.2500 / 254.000—260.350	14.3750 / 365.125	5.1250 / 130.175	3.8750 / 98.425	32200 / 14350	20700 / 9200	64400 / 28700	1.56	134000	134144D	134144DC	0.06 / 1.5	13.66 / 347.0	.75 / 19.1	.28 / 7.1
10.0000—10.2500 / 254.000—260.350	16.6250 / 422.275	6.8125 / 173.038	5.0625 / 128.588	54000 / 24000	30700 / 13650	108000 / 48000	1.76	HM252300	HM252311D		0.06 / 1.5	15.66 / 397.7		
10.0000—10.2500 / 254.000—260.350	16.6250 / 422.275	7.0312 / 178.592	5.5000 / 139.700	54000 / 24000	30700 / 13650	108000 / 48000	1.76	HM252300	HM252310D	HM252310DC	0.06 / 1.5	15.73 / 399.5	1.12 / 28.4	.31 / 7.9
10.0000—10.2500 / 254.000—260.350	16.9970 / 431.723	6.8125 / 173.038	5.0625 / 128.588	54000 / 24000	30700 / 13650	108000 / 48000	1.76	HM252300	HM252315D	HM252315DC	0.06 / 1.5	15.68 / 398.2	1.00 / 25.4	.43 / 10.9
10.0000 / 254.000	17.5000 / 444.500	6.5000 / 165.100	4.5000 / 114.300	46500 / 20600	27300 / 12150	93000 / 41200	1.71	822000	8221760		0.06 / 1.5	19.96 / 405.3		
10.0000 / 254.000	21.0000 / 533.400	10.8750 / 276.225	6.5000 / 165.100	90000 / 40000	145000 / 64500	180000 / 80000	0.62	HH953700	HH953710D	HH953710DC	0.06 / 1.5	19.51 / 495.6	1.12 / 28.4	.43 / 10.9
10.2500 / 260.350	15.7500 / 400.050	6.1250 / 155.575	4.2500 / 107.950	37100 / 16500	25100 / 11150	74200 / 33000	1.48	220000	2215760	2215760DC	0.06 / 1.5	14.63 / 371.5	.87 / 22.1	.37 / 9.4
10.2500 / 260.350	16.6250 / 422.275	[2] 6.8125 / 173.038	5.0625 / 128.588	56000 / 24800	31700 / 14100	112000 / 49600	1.76	HM252300 (HM252349) [2]	HM252311D		0.06 / 1.5	15.66 / 397.7		
10.2500 / 260.350	16.6250 / 422.275	[2] 7.0312 / 178.592	5.5000 / 139.700	56000 / 24800	31700 / 14100	112000 / 49600	1.76	HM252300 (HM252349) [2]	HM252310D	HM252310DC	0.06 / 1.5	15.73 / 399.5	1.12 / 28.4	.31 / 7.9
10.2500 / 260.350	16.9970 / 431.723	[2] 6.8125 / 173.038	5.0625 / 128.588	56000 / 24800	31700 / 14100	112000 / 49600	1.76	HM252300 (HM252349) [2]	HM252315D	HM252315DC	0.06 / 1.5	15.68 / 398.2	1.00 / 25.4	.43 / 10.9

[1] These maximum fillet radii will be cleared by the bearing corners.
[2] Specific cone part number indicated in ( ) when dimension "T" varies from others in series.

TWO-ROW ASSEMBLY - DOUBLE CUP, SINGLE CONES — TDO-TDODC

for available cones refer to bearing selection index under series indicated

bore range d	outside diameter D	width through cones T	width cup C	one row radial	two row radial	thrust	factor K	bearing series	part numbers cup fig. 1	cup fig. 2	cup max hsg fillet radius r ①	backing shoulder diameter Da	pin max diam Ka	pin max depth into cup Kb
10.3750 — 10.5000 / 263.525 — 266.700	14.0000 / 355.600	5.0000 / 127.000	4.0000 / 101.600	34700 / 15450	69400 / 30900	21400 / 9500	1.62	LM451300	LM451310D	LM451310DC	0.06 / 1.5	13.50 / 343.0	.87 / 22.1	.21 / 5.3
11.0000 — 11.5000 / 279.400 — 292.100	18.5000 / 469.900	7.8750 / 200.025	5.8750 / 149.225	62500 / 27800	125000 / 55600	40000 / 17800	1.55	722000	72218D	72218DC	0.06 / 1.5	17.04 / 432.9	1.12 / 28.4	.43 / 10.9
11.0229 — 11.2500 / 279.981 — 285.750	14.9960 / 380.898	5.5000 / 139.700	4.2500 / 107.950	38800 / 17300	77600 / 34600	28800 / 12800	1.35	LM654600	LM654610D	LM654610DC	0.06 / 1.5	14.49 / 368.0	.87 / 22.1	.25 / 6.4
11.0312 / 280.192	16.0000 / 406.400	4.7500 / 120.650	3.3750 / 85.725	28300 / 12600	56600 / 25200	19800 / 8800	1.43	100000	101601D	101601DC	0.06 / 1.5	14.80 / 376.0	.75 / 19.1	.31 / 7.9
11.0312 / 280.192	16.0000 / 406.400	5.8750 / 149.225	4.6250 / 117.475	41000 / 18200	82000 / 36400	27200 / 12100	1.51	128000	128160D	128160DC	0.06 / 1.5	15.12 / 384.0	1.00 / 25.4	.31 / 7.9
11.2500 / 285.750	19.7500 / 501.650	8.0000 / 203.200	4.7500 / 120.650	57500 / 25400	115000 / 50800	82000 / 36400	0.70	147000	147198D	147198DC	0.13 / 3.3	18.43 / 468.1	1.12 / 28.4	.43 / 10.9
11.3750 / 288.925	16.0000 / 406.400	6.5000 / 165.100	5.1250 / 130.175	59500 / 26600	119000 / 53200	34500 / 15350	1.73	M255400	M255410D	M255410DC	0.06 / 1.5	15.27 / 387.9	1.12 / 28.4	.31 / 7.9
11.7500 — 12.5000 / 298.450 — 317.500	17.5000 / 444.500	5.7500 / 146.050	3.8750 / 98.425	35200 / 15650	70400 / 31300	22700 / 10100	1.55	290000	291751D	291751DC	0.06 / 1.5	16.30 / 413.9	.87 / 22.1	.37 / 9.4
11.8125 / 300.038	16.6250 / 422.275	6.8750 / 174.625	5.3750 / 136.525	65000 / 29000	130000 / 58000	37600 / 16750	1.73	HM256800	HM256810D	HM256810DC	0.06 / 1.5	15.88 / 403.3	1.12 / 28.4	.28 / 7.1
12.0000 / 304.800	15.5000 / 393.700	4.2500 / 107.950	3.2500 / 82.550	29200 / 13000	58400 / 26000	17900 / 7950	1.63	L357000	L357010D	L357010DC	0.06 / 1.5	14.96 / 380.0	.75 / 19.1	.21 / 5.3
12.0000 / 304.800	16.2500 / 412.750	4.8750 / 123.825	3.6250 / 92.075	29400 / 13050	58800 / 26100	21400 / 9550	1.37	109000	109163D		0.06 / 1.5	15.53 / 394.4		
12.0000 / 304.800	19.5000 / 495.300	6.6376 / 168.595	5.0000 / 127.000	54000 / 24200	108000 / 48400	37400 / 16650	1.45	940000	9419530		0.06 / 1.5	18.25 / 463.4		
13.0000 / 330.200	19.0000 / 482.600	7.0000 / 177.800	5.0000 / 127.000	57000 / 25400	114000 / 50800	38400 / 17100	1.49	526000	526191D	526191DC	0.06 / 1.5	17.87 / 454.0	1.12 / 28.4	.31 / 7.9
13.1250 / 333.375	18.5000 / 469.900	7.5000 / 190.500	6.0000 / 152.400	81000 / 36000	162000 / 72000	46500 / 20600	1.74	HM261000	HM261010D	HM261010DC	0.06 / 1.5	17.69 / 449.2	1.12 / 28.4	.43 / 10.9
13.6250 / 346.075	19.2500 / 488.950	7.8750 / 200.025	6.2500 / 158.750	88000 / 39200	176000 / 78400	50500 / 22600	1.74	HM262700	HM262710D	HM262710DC	0.06 / 1.5	18.39 / 467.0	1.12 / 28.4	.37 / 9.4
13.7500 — 14.0000 / 349.250 — 355.600	20.5000 / 514.350	7.6250 / 193.675	6.0000 / 152.400	66500 / 29600	133000 / 59200	42000 / 18600	1.59	333000	333203D	333203DC	0.06 / 1.5	18.83 / 478.2	1.12 / 28.4	.43 / 10.9
14.0000 / 355.600	17.5000 / 444.500	5.3750 / 136.525	4.3750 / 111.125	42000 / 18600	84000 / 37200	22000 / 9800	1.90	L163100	L163110D	L163110DC	0.06 / 1.5	16.93 / 430.0	.87 / 22.1	.21 / 5.3
14.4980 / 368.249	20.6250 / 523.875	8.4375 / 214.312	6.6875 / 169.862	102000 / 45000	204000 / 90000	57500 / 25600	1.76	HM265000	HM265010D		0.06 / 1.5	19.63 / 498.7		

① These maximum fillet radii will be cleared by the bearing corners.

TWO-ROW ASSEMBLY · DOUBLE CUP, SINGLE CONES

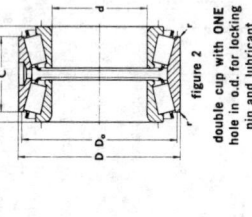

figure 1
double cup with lubricant holes and groove.

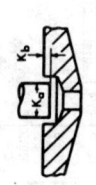

figure 2
double cup with ONE hole in o.d. for locking pin and lubricant.

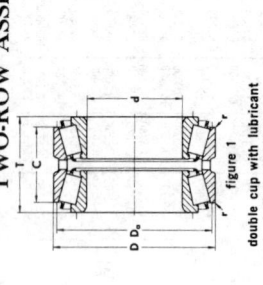

for available cones refer to bearing selection index under series indicated

bore range d	outside diameter D	width T (through cones)	width C (cup)	one row radial lb / daN	thrust lb / daN	two row radial lb / daN	factor K	bearing series	cup fig. 1	cup fig. 2	cup max. hsg. fillet radius r ①	backing shoulder diameter Da	pin max. diam. Ka	Max. depth into cup Kb
15.0000 / 381.000	20.0000 / 508.000	5.5000 / 139.700	3.5000 / 88.900	33300 / 14800	30300 / 13450	66600 / 29600	1.10	192000	192201D	192201DC	0.06 / 1.5	18.98 / 482.0	.75 / 19.1	.31 / 7,9
15.0000 — 15.1250 / 381.000 — 384.175	21.5000 / 546.100	8.5000 / 222.250	7.0000 / 177.800	110000 / 49000	63000 / 28000	220000 / 98000	1.76	HM266400	HM266410D	HM266410DC	0.06 / 1.5	20.47 / 520.0	1.12 / 28,4	.43 / 10,9
15.0000 — 16.3750 / 381.000 — 415.925	23.2500 / 590.550	9.6250 / 244.475	7.6250 / 193.675	130000 / 58000	73500 / 32600	260000 / 116000	1.76	M268700	M268710D	M268710DC	0.06 / 1.5	22.14 / 562.4	1.12 / 28,4	.43 / 10,9
15.6250 — 16.0000 / 396.875 — 406.400	21.2500 / 539.750	5.6250 / 142.875	4.0000 / 101.600	46000 / 20400	37300 / 16600	92000 / 40800	1.23	234000	234213D	234213DC	0.06 / 1.5	20.30 / 515.6	.75 / 19,1	.31 / 7,9
16.0000 / 406.400	23.2500 / 590.550	9.0000 / 228.600	6.8750 / 174.625	114000 / 50500	63500 / 28200	228000 / 101000	1.80	833000	833233D		0.06 / 1.5	22.07 / 560.5		
16.0000 / 406.400	30.0000 / 762.000	14.5000 / 368.300	8.7500 / 222.250	189000 / 84000	304000 / 135500	378000 / 168000	0.62	H969200	H969210D		0.13 / 3.3	28.32 / 719.3		
17.0000 — 431.800	22.5000 / 571.500	6.1250 / 155.575	4.3750 / 111.125	63000 / 28000	59000 / 26200	126000 / 56000	1.07	LM869400	LM869410D	LM869410DC	0.06 / 1.5	21.61 / 549.0	.87 / 22.1	.37 / 9,4
17.6250 / 447.675	25.0000 / 635.000	10.1250 / 257.175	8.1250 / 206.375	150000 / 66500	85000 / 37800	300000 / 133000	1.76	M270700	M270710D	M270710DC	0.06 / 1.5	23.82 / 605.1	1.12 / 28,4	.43 / 10,9
18.0000 / 457.200	23.5000 / 596.900	6.5000 / 165.100	4.7500 / 120.650	63500 / 28200	44000 / 19600	127000 / 56400	1.44	244000	244236D	244236DC	0.06 / 1.5	22.47 / 570.7	1.12 / 28,4	.31 / 7,9
18.0000 / 457.200	26.0000 / 660.400	9.0000 / 228.600	6.7500 / 171.450	116000 / 51500	63500 / 28200	232000 / 103000	1.83	M271600	M271610D		0.06 / 1.5	24.77 / 629.1		

① These maximum fillet radii will be cleared by the bearing corners.

TWO-ROW ASSEMBLY · DOUBLE CUP, SINGLE CONES — TDO-TDODC

for available cones refer to bearing selection index under series indicated

In each cell the values are given as imperial (top) / metric (bottom); ratings as lb / daN.

bore range d	outside diameter D	width through cones T	cup C	rating one row radial	two row radial	thrust	factor K	bearing series	cup fig. 1	cup fig. 2	cup max hsng fillet radius r ①	backing shoulder diameter Da	pin max diam Ka	max depth into cup Kb
18.8750 / 479,425	26.7500 / 679,450	10.8750 / 276,225	8.5000 / 222,250	172000 / 76500	344000 / 153000	98000 / 43600	1.76	M272700	M272710D	M272710DC	0.06 / 1,5	25.52 / 648,2	1.12 / 28,4	.43 / 10,9
19.0000 / 482,600	24.2500 / 615,950	7.2500 / 184,150	5.7500 / 146,050	91000 / 40400	182000 / 80800	51500 / 23000	1.76	LM272200	LM272210D	LM272210DC	0.06 / 1,5	23.48 / 596,4	1.12 / 28,4	.31 / 7,9
19.2500 / 488,950	24.9950 / 634,873	7.1250 / 180,975	5.3750 / 136,525	86500 / 38400	173000 / 76800	69500 / 31000	1.24	LM772700	LM772710D	LM772710DC	0.06 / 1,5	24.15 / 613,3	1.12 / 28,4	.43 / 10,9
19.2500 / 488,950	26.0000 / 660,400	8.1250 / 206,375	6.2500 / 158,750	104000 / 46000	208000 / 92000	55000 / 24400	1.90	640000	640281D	640261DC	0.06 / 1,5	24.82 / 630,5	1.12 / 28,4	.37 / 9,4
21.1250 / 536,575	29.9950 / 761,873	12.2500 / 311,150	9.7500 / 247,650	216000 / 96000	432000 / 192000	122000 / 54500	1.76	M276400	M276410D	M276410DC	0.06 / 1,5	28.57 / 725,6	1.12 / 28,4	.43 / 10,9
22.0000 / 558,800	29.0000 / 736,600	6.5000 / 165,100	4.5000 / 114,300	71000 / 31600	142000 / 63200	62000 / 27600	1.15	542000	542291D	542291DC	0.13 / 3,3	27.76 / 705,1	1.00 / 25,4	.31 / 7,9
22.0000 / 558,800	29.0000 / 736,600	7.3751 / 187,328	5.4375 / 138,112	103000 / 45500	206000 / 91000	60500 / 26800	1.70	843000	843291D	843291DC	0.06 / 1,5	27.84 / 707,1	1.12 / 28,4	.31 / 7,9
22.0000 / 558,800	29.0000 / 736,600	8.8750 / 225,425	7.0000 / 177,800	140000 / 62500	280000 / 125000	82500 / 36600	1.69	LM377400	LM377410D	LM377410DC	0.06 / 1,5	27.84 / 707,1	1.12 / 28,4	.43 / 10,9
24.0000 / 609,600	31.0000 / 787,400	8.1250 / 206,375	6.2500 / 158,750	121000 / 54000	242000 / 108000	76500 / 34000	1.58	649000	649311D	649311DC	0.06 / 1,5	29.74 / 755,3	1.12 / 28,4	.43 / 10,9
24.0000 / 609,600	32.0000 / 812,800	7.5000 / 190,500	5.7500 / 146,050	91000 / 40400	182000 / 80800	51500 / 23000	1.77	743000	743321D	743321DC	0.13 / 3,3	30.12 / 765,0	1.12 / 28,4	.43 / 10,9
27.0000 / 685,800	34.5000 / 876,300	7.8750 / 200,025	6.0000 / 152,400	131000 / 58000	262000 / 116000	94000 / 41800	1.40	655000	655346D	655346DC	0.06 / 1,5	33.13 / 841,4	1.12 / 28,4	.43 / 10,9
28.0000 / 711,200	36.0000 / 914,400	7.5000 / 190,500	5.5000 / 139,700	108000 / 48000	216000 / 96000	70500 / 31400	1.54	755000	753361D	753361DC	0.06 / 1,5	34.53 / 877,0	1.12 / 28,4	.43 / 10,9
28.5000 / 723,900	36.0000 / 914,400	7.3750 / 187,325	5.5000 / 139,700	108000 / 48000	216000 / 96000	70500 / 31400	1.54	755000	753361D	753361DC	0.06 / 1,5	34.53 / 877,0	1.12 / 28,4	.43 / 10,9
36.0000 / 914,400	42.0000 / 1066,800	5.5000 / 139,700	4.0000 / 101,600	93000 / 41400	186000 / 82800	65000 / 29000	1.43	L686900	L686910D		0.13 / 3,3	40.83 / 1037,2		
50.0000 / 1270,000	56.5000 / 1435,100	5.7500 / 146,050	4.0000 / 101,600	113000 / 50500	226000 / 101000	111000 / 49500	1.02	L889000	L889010D		0.13 / 3,3	55.12 / 1400,0		
54.9450 — 55.0000 / 1395,602 — 1397,000	66.8125 / 1697,038	10.2500 / 260,350	7.5000 / 190,500	274000 / 121500	548000 / 243000	203000 / 90000	1.35	292000	2926680		0.13 / 3,3	63.76 / 1619,6	.68 / 17,3	.31 / 7,9
56.3750 / 1431,925	62.3750 / 1584,324	5.1250 / 130,175	3.1250 / 79,375	98500 / 43800	197000 / 87600	105000 / 46500	0.94	L989300	L989310XD	L989310DC	0.13 / 3,3	61.17 / 1553,7		
56.3750 / 1431,925	62.3750 / 1584,324	5.1250 / 130,175	3.1250 / 79,375	98500 / 43800	197000 / 87600	105000 / 46500	0.94	L989300	L989310XD		0.13 / 3,3	61.17 / 1553,7		
72.0000 / 1828,800	79.0000 / 2006,599	7.0000 / 177,800	4.8750 / 123,825	195000 / 86500	390000 / 173000	158000 / 70500	1.23	L789900	L789910XD		0.13 / 3,3	77.56 / 1970,0		
†82.0866 / †2085,000	†96.8504 / †2460,000	16.5355 / 420,002	11.4173 / 290,000	715000 / 318000	1430000 / 636000	1070000 / 475000	0.67	L990300	L990310XD		0.13 / 3,3	94.91 / 2410,7		

① These maximum fillet radii will be cleared by the bearing corners.
† Dimension shown is maximum value—See note at bottom of fitting practice table page 4 in Reference Tables.

TWO-ROW ASSEMBLY - PRE-SET, DOUBLE CUP, SINGLE CONES

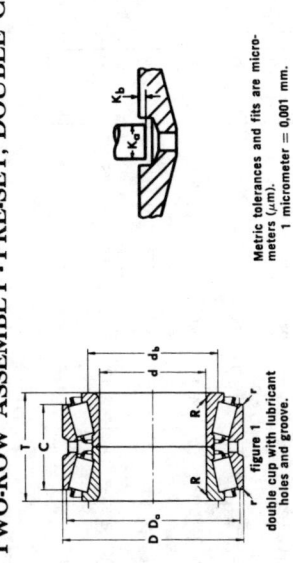

figure 1
double cup with lubricant holes and groove.

K_b

K_a

Metric tolerances and fits are in micrometers (μm).
1 micrometer = 0.001 mm.

figure 2
double cup with ONE hole in o.d. for locking pin and lubricant.

①These maximum fillet radii will be cleared by the bearing corners
(T)—tight   (L)—loose

bore d	outside diam. D	width through cones T	width cup C	factor K	rating one row radial lb daN	rating two row radial lb daN	thrust lb daN	two row radial lb daN	part numbers cone	part numbers cup fig. 1	part numbers cup fig. 2	cone max. shaft fillet radius R① db	cup back- ing shoul- der diam. db	cup max. back- ing shoul- der radius r①	cup back- ing shoul- der diam. Da	pin max. diam. Ka	pin max. depth into cup Kb	live shaft diam. limits	live shaft fit (tight)	dead shaft diam. limits	dead shaft fit	live shaft bore limits	live shaft fit (L)	dead shaft bore limits	dead shaft fit (T)
1.4375 36.512	3.6250 92.075	2.1875 55.562	1.5625 39.688	0.75	3180 1410	6050 2700	4250 1880	6950 2700	NA44143	443630		0.03 0.8	2.01 51.0	0.06 1.5	3.35 85.0			1.4390 36.985 36.539	0.0015 0.0005 38 13	1.4380 36.525 36.513	0.0005T 0.0005L 13	3.6280 92.150 92.125	0.003 0.001 76 25	3.6240 92.050 92.024	0.001 0.003 25 76
1.6250 41.275	3.6250 92.075	2.1875 55.562	1.5625 39.688	0.75	3180 1410	6050 2700	4250 1880	6950 2700	NA44163	443630		0.03 0.8	2.13 54.0	0.06 1.5	3.35 85.0			1.6265 41.313 41.301	0.0015 0.0005 38 13	1.6255 41.288 41.275	0.0005T 0.0005L 13	3.6280 92.150 92.125	0.003 0.001 76 25	3.6240 92.050 92.024	0.001 0.003 25 76
1.9685 50.000	3.5433 90.000	1.9689 50.010	1.6563 42.070	1.83	3310 1475	6300 2800	1810 805	12250 5450	MA366	363D	363DC	0.14 3.5	2.40 61.0	0.03 0.8	3.31 84.0	0.31 7.9	0.09 2.3	1.9700 50.036 50.026	0.0015 0.0005 38 13	1.9690 50.013 50.000	0.0005T 0.0005L 13	3.5463 90.076 90.050	0.003 0.001 76 25	3.5423 89.975 89.949	0.001 0.003 25 76
2.0000 50.800	4.3500 107.950	2.5636 65.030	2.1259 53.999	1.74	5400 2400	10250 4550	3095 1375	13200 5850	NA455	452D	452DC	0.14 3.5	2.56 65.0	0.03 0.8	3.94 100.0	0.43 10.9	0.15 3.8	2.0020 50.851 50.826	0.0020 0.0005 51 13	2.0005 50.813 50.800	0.0005T 0.0005L 13	4.2530 108.026 108.000	0.003 0.001 76 25	4.2490 107.925 107.899	0.001 0.003 25 76
2.1250 53.975	4.3750 111.125	3.1250 79.375	2.5000 63.500	1.97	6900 3060	13100 5850	3900 1560	13100 5850	NA539	533D	533DC	0.14 3.5	2.68 68.0	0.06 1.5	3.94 100.0	0.56 14.2	0.15 3.8	2.1270 54.051 54.001	0.0020 0.0005 51 13	2.1255 53.988 53.975	0.0005T 0.0005L 13	4.3780 111.201 111.175	0.003 0.001 76 25	4.3740 111.100 111.074	0.001 0.003 25 76
2.1250 53.975	4.8750 123.825	3.0625 77.788	2.1875 55.562	0.79	6250 2780	11900 5300	7900 3520	11900 5300	NA72212	724880		0.09 2.3	2.91 74.0	0.06 1.5	4.53 115.0			2.1270 54.051 54.001	0.0020 0.0005 51 13	2.1255 53.988 53.975	0.0005T 0.0005L 13	4.8780 123.901 123.875	0.003 0.001 76 25	4.8740 123.800 123.774	0.001 0.003 25 76
2.1654 55.000	3.9370 100.000	2.0625 52.388	1.6875 42.862	1.65	3990 1595	6850 3040	2180 970	6850 3040	MA385	384D	384DC	0.14 3.5	2.64 67.0	0.03 0.8	3.66 93.0	0.31 7.9	0.12 3.0	2.1674 55.051 55.027	0.0020 0.0005 51 13	2.1659 55.024 55.000	0.0005T 0.0005L 13	3.9400 100.076 100.050	0.003 0.001 76 25	3.9360 99.975 99.949	0.001 0.003 25 76

TWO-ROW ASSEMBLY - PRE-SET, DOUBLE CUP, SINGLE CONES

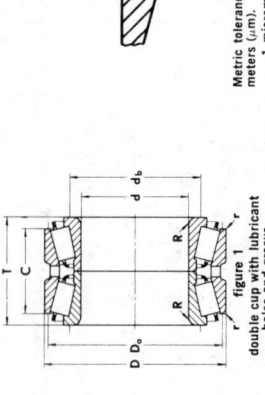

figure 1
double cup with lubricant holes and groove.

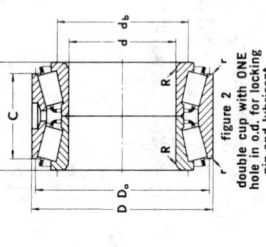

Metric tolerances and fits are micrometers (μm).
1 micrometer = 0.001 mm.

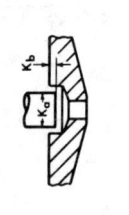

figure 2
double cup with ONE hole in o.d. for locking pin and lubricant.

bearings manufactured with correct running clearance for these fits

bore d	outside diam. D	width through cones T	width cup C	rating — one row radial lb/daN	thrust lb/daN	two row radial lb/daN	factor K	cone	cup fig.1	cup fig.2	cone max shaft fillet radius R	cone backing shoulder diam. db	cup max housing fillet radius r	cup backing shoulder diam. Da	pin max diam. Ka	pin max depth into cup Kb	live shaft diam. limits	live shaft fit (tight)	dead shaft diam. limits	dead shaft fit	housing live shaft bore limits	housing live shaft fit (L)	housing dead shaft bore limits	housing dead shaft fit (T)
2.7500 / 69.850	4.7244 / 120.000	2.5626 / 65.090	2.1250 / 53.975	5900 / 2640	3900 / 1735	11300 / 5000	1.52	NA482	4720	4720DC	0.14 / 3.5	3.27 / 83.0	0.03 / 0.8	4.49 / 114.0	.56 / 14.2	.12 / 3.0	2.7525 2.7515 / 69.888	0.0025T 0.0010 / 65 25	2.7505 2.7500 / 69.850	0.0005T 0.0005L / 13 13	4.7274 4.7264 / 120.050	0.003 0.001 / 76 25	4.7234 4.7224 / 119.949	0.001 0.003 / 25 76
2.7559 / 70.000	4.7244 / 120.000	2.5626 / 65.090	2.1250 / 53.975	5900 / 2640	3900 / 1735	11300 / 5000	1.52	NA484	4720	4720DC	0.14 / 3.5	3.27 / 83.0	0.03 / 0.8	4.49 / 114.0	.56 / 14.2	.12 / 3.0	2.7584 2.7574 / 70.064	0.0025T 0.0010 / 65 25	2.7564 2.7559 / 70.013	0.0005T 0.0005L / 13 13	4.7284 4.7274 / 120.076	0.003 0.001 / 76 25	4.7244 4.7224 / 119.975	0.001 0.003 / 25 76
2.8750 / 73.025	5.0000 / 127.000	3.1875 / 80.962	2.5625 / 65.088	8250 / 3660	5100 / 2280	15700 / 6950	1.61	NA567	5630	5630DC	0.14 / 3.5	3.70 / 94.0	0.06 / 1.5	4.69 / 119.0	.56 / 14.2	.15 / 3.8	2.8775 2.8765 / 73.089 73.063	0.0025T 0.0010 / 64 25	2.8755 2.8750 / 73.038 73.025	0.0005T 0.0005L / 13 13	5.0020 5.0010 / 127.076 127.050	0.003 0.001 / 76 25	4.9990 4.9980 / 126.975 126.949	0.001 0.003 / 25 76
3.0000 / 76.200	6.0000 / 152.400	3.7500 / 95.250	3.0000 / 76.200	10300 / 4600	7150 / 3180	19500 / 8650	1.43	NA659	6540	6540DC	0.27 / 6.8	3.66 / 93.0	0.06 / 1.5	5.55 / 141.0	.62 / 15.7	.21 / 5.3	3.0025 3.0013 / 76.264 76.238	0.0025T 0.0010 / 64 25	3.0005 3.0000 / 76.213	0.0005T 0.0005L / 13 13	6.0030 6.0020 / 152.476 152.450	0.003 0.001 / 76 25	5.9990 5.9980 / 152.375 152.349	0.001 0.003 / 25 76
3.0000 / 76.200	7.0000 / 177.800	4.3065 / 109.385	2.9375 / 74.612	12000 / 5350	15800 / 7000	22800 / 10150	0.76	NA9378	93200		0.14 / 3.5	4.13 / 105.0	0.09 / 2.3	6.46 / 164.0	.62 / 15.7	.21 / 5.3	3.0025 3.0013 / 76.264 76.238	0.0025 0.0010 / 64 25	3.0005 3.0000 / 76.213 76.200	0.0005T 0.0005L / 13 13	7.0030 7.0020 / 177.876 177.850	0.003 0.001 / 76 25	6.9990 6.9980 / 177.775 177.749	0.001 0.003 / 25 76
3.5000 / 88.900	6.3750 / 161.925	4.1250 / 104.775	3.3750 / 85.725	13800 / 6100	8050 / 3580	26200 / 11650	1.71	NA759	7520	7520DC	0.14 / 3.5	4.17 / 106.0	0.06 / 1.5	5.91 / 150.0	.75 / 19.1	.21 / 5.3	3.5030 3.5020 / 88.950	0.0030 0.0010 / 76 25	3.5010 3.5000 / 88.900	0.0010L 0.0010L / 25 25	6.3780 6.3770 / 162.001 161.975	0.003 0.001 / 76 25	6.3740 6.3730 / 161.900 161.874	0.001 0.003 / 25 76
3.7500 / 95.250	6.3750 / 161.925	3.2499 / 82.547	2.4375 / 61.912	9900 / 4400	8050 / 3580	18800 / 8400	1.23	NA52375	526370	526370DC	0.14 / 3.5	4.41 / 112.0	0.03 / 0.8	6.06 / 154.0	.56 / 14.2	.21 / 5.3	3.7530 3.7520 / 95.300 95.275	0.0030 0.0010 / 76 25	3.7510 3.7500 / 95.250	0.0010L 0.0010L / 25 25	6.3780 6.3770 / 162.001 161.975	0.003 0.001 / 76 25	6.3740 6.3730 / 161.900 161.874	0.001 0.003 / 25 76

① These maximum fillet radii will be cleared by the bearing corners
(T)—tight
(L)—loose

Two-Row Assembly · Pre-set, Double Cup, Single Cones — TNA-TNADC

bearings manufactured with correct running clearance for these fits

bore d	outside diam. D	width through cones T	cup C	rating at 500 RPM for 3000 hours L10 — one row radial lb/daN	two row radial lb/daN	thrust lb/daN	factor K	part numbers cone	cup fig. 1	cup fig. 2	cone max shaft fillet radius R	back. shoul. diam. d_b	cup max housing fillet radius r	back. shoul. diam. D_a	pin max diam. K_a	max depth into cup K_b	live shaft diam. limits	live shaft fit (tight)	dead shaft diam. limits	dead shaft fit	housing live shaft bore limits	housing live shaft fit (L)	housing dead shaft bore limits	housing dead shaft fit (T)
3.7500 95.250	7.0866 180.000	4.1250 104.775	3.3750 85,725	14900 6600	28300 12600	9850 4380	1.51	NA776	773D	773DC	0.14 3.5	4.49 114.0	0.03 0.8	6.61 168.0	.75 19.1	.21 5.3	3.7530 3.7520 95.326 95.300	0.0030 0.0010 76 25	3.7510 3.7500 95.275 95.250	0.0010T 0.0010L 25 25	7.0896 7.0886 180.075 180.050	0.003 0.001 76 25	7.0856 7.0975 179.975 179.949	0.001 0.003 25 76
3.7500 95.250	7.1250 180.975	4.1250 104.775	3.3750 85,725	14900 6600	28300 12600	9850 4380	1.51	NA776	774D	774DC	0.14 3.5	4.49 114.0	0.06 1.5	6.61 168.0	.75 19.1	.21 5.3	3.7530 3.7520 95.326 95.300	0.0030 0.0010 76 25	3.7510 3.7500 95.275 95.250	0.0010T 0.0010L 25 25	7.1280 7.1270 181.095 181.025	0.003 0.001 76 25	7.1240 7.1230 180.975 180.924	0.001 0.003 25 76
4.0000 101.600	6.6250 168.275	3.6250 92.075	2.7500 69,850	11500 5100	21900 9700	9250 4120	1.24	NA691	6720	6720C	0.14 3.5	4.65 118.0	0.03 0.8	6.30 160.0	.62 15.7	.18 4.6	4.0030 4.0020 101.676 101.650	0.0030 0.0010 76 25	4.0000 101.625 101.600	0.0010T 0.0010L 25 25	6.6280 6.6270 168.351 168.325	0.003 0.001 76 25	6.6240 6.6230 168.250 168.224	0.001 0.003 25 76
4.0000 101.600	7.0866 180.000	4.1250 104.775	3.3750 85,725	14900 6600	28300 12600	9850 4380	1.51	NA780	773D	773DC	0.14 3.5	4.69 119.0	0.03 0.8	6.61 168.0	.75 19.1	.21 5.3	4.0030 4.0020 101.676 101.650	0.0030 0.0010 76 25	4.0010 4.0000 101.625 101.600	0.0010T 0.0010L 25 25	7.0896 7.0886 180.075 180.050	0.003 0.001 76 25	7.0856 7.0846 179.975 179.949	0.001 0.003 25 76
4.0000 101.600	7.1250 180.975	4.1250 104.775	3.3750 85,725	14900 6600	28300 12600	9850 4380	1.51	NA780	774D	774DC	0.14 3.5	4.69 119.0	0.06 1.5	6.61 168.0	.75 19.1	.21 5.3	4.0030 4.0020 101.676 101.650	0.0030 0.0010 76 25	4.0010 4.0000 101.625 101.600	0.0010T 0.0010L 25 25	7.1280 7.1270 181.095 181.025	0.003 0.001 76 25	7.1240 7.1230 180.975 180.924	0.001 0.003 25 76
4.1250 104.775	7.0866 180.000	4.1250 104.775	3.3750 85,725	14900 6600	28300 12600	9850 4380	1.51	NA782	773D	773DC	0.14 3.5	4.80 122.0	0.03 0.8	6.61 168.0	.75 19.1	.21 5.3	4.1280 4.1270 104.851 104.825	0.0030 0.0010 76 25	4.1260 4.1250 104.800 104.775	0.0010T 0.0010L 25 25	7.0896 7.0886 180.076 180.050	0.003 0.001 76 25	7.0856 7.0846 179.975 179.949	0.001 0.003 25 76
4.1250 104.775	7.1250 180.975	4.1250 104.775	3.3750 85,725	14900 6600	28300 12600	9850 4380	1.51	NA782	774D	774DC	0.14 3.5	4.80 122.0	0.06 1.5	6.61 168.0	.75 19.1	.21 5.3	4.1280 4.1270 104.851 104.825	0.0030 0.0010 76 25	4.1260 4.1250 104.800 104.775	0.0010T 0.0010L 25 25	7.1280 7.1270 181.025 181.025	0.003 0.001 76 25	7.1240 7.1230 180.980 180.924	0.001 0.003 25 76
4.5000 114.300	7.5000 190.500	4.1875 106.362	3.1875 80,962	15900 7050	30200 13450	11300 5050	1.40	NA71450	717510	717510C	0.14 3.5	5.20 132.0	0.06 1.5	7.13 181.0	.68 17.3	.21 5.3	4.5035 4.5025 114.389 114.363	0.0035 0.0015 89 38	4.5010 4.5000 114.325 114.300	0.0010T 0.0010L 25 25	7.5030 7.5020 190.576 190.550	0.003 0.001 76 25	7.4990 7.4980 190.475 190.449	0.001 0.003 25 76
4.5000 114.300	8.3750 212.725	5.6250 142.875	4.6250 117.475	24300 10800	46500 20600	13600 6050	1.79	NA938	9320	9320C	0.14 3.5	5.28 134.0	0.06 1.5	7.60 193.1	.87 22.1	.31 7.9	4.5035 4.5025 114.389 114.363	0.0035 0.0015 89 38	4.5010 4.5000 114.325 114.300	0.0010T 0.0010L 25 25	8.3780 8.3770 212.801 212.775	0.003 0.001 76 25	8.3740 8.3730 212.725 212.674	0.003 25 76
5.0000 127.000	7.1875 182.562	3.3750 85,725	2.8750 73,025	12900 5750	24600 10950	6750 3000	1.91	NA48291	482200	482200C	0.14 3.5	5.55 141.0	0.03 0.8	6.93 176.0	.62 15.7	.19 5.0	5.0035 5.0025 127.089 127.063	0.0035 0.0015 89 38	5.0010 5.0000 127.025 127.000	0.0010T 0.0010L 25 25	7.1905 7.1895 182.639 182.613	0.003 0.001 76 25	7.1865 7.1855 182.538 182.512	0.001 0.003 25 76
5.6250 142.875	7.8750 200.025	3.6876 93,665	2.8750 73,025	13900 6200	26600 11800	8000 3560	1.74	NA48686	486200	486200C	0.14 3.5	6.22 158.0	0.03 0.8	7.60 193.0	.62 15.7	.18 4.6	5.6290 5.6280 142.992 142.951	0.0040 0.0020 102 51	5.6260 5.6250 142.906 142.875	0.0040 0.0020 102 51	7.8780 7.8770 200.103 200.075	0.003 0.001 76 25	7.8740 7.8730 200.025 199.974	0.001 0.003 25 76
5.7500 146.050	5.1875 131.762	5.1875 131.762	4.1875 106.362	23000 10200	44000 19400	17400 7750	1.32	NA82576	829510	829510C	0.14 3.5	6.54 166.0	0.06 1.5	7.60 193.0	.87 22.1	.31 7.9	5.7540 5.7530 146.152 146.132	0.0040 0.0020 102 51	5.7510 5.7500 146.075 146.050	0.0040 0.0020 102 51	9.5030 9.5020 241.376 241.350	0.003 0.001 76 25	9.4990 9.4980 241.300 241.249	0.001 0.003 25 76
6.0000 152.400	10.0000 254.000	5.6250 142.875	4.3750 111,125	29200 12950	55500 24800	20400 9050	1.43	NA99600	991020	991020C	0.14 3.5	6.85 174.0	0.06 1.5	9.37 238.0	.87 22.1	.25 6.4	6.0040 6.0030 152.502 152.476	0.0040 0.0020 102 51	6.0040 6.0030 152.502 152.476	0.0040 0.0020 102 51	10.0030 10.0020 254.076 254.050	0.003 0.001 76 25	10.0030 10.0020 254.076 254.050	0.003 0.001 76 25

① These maximum fillet radii will be cleared by the bearing corners
(T)—tight   (L)—loose

TWO-ROW ASSEMBLY - PRE-SET, DOUBLE CUP, SINGLE CONES

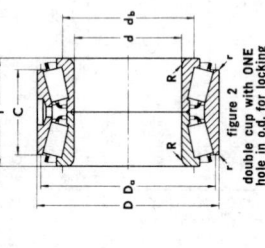

figure 1
double cup with lubricant holes and groove.

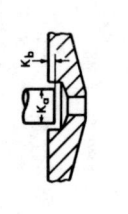

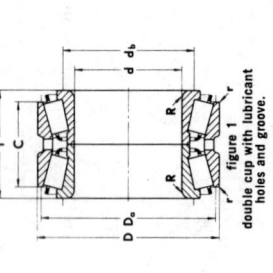

figure 2
double cup with ONE hole in o.d. for locking pin and lubricant.

Metric tolerances and fits are in micrometers (μm).
1 micrometer = 0,001 mm.

bore d	outside diam. D	width through cones T	width cup C	cup cup	rating at 500 RPM for 3000 hours L10 — one row radial lb daN	rating two row radial lb daN	thrust lb daN	two row radial lb daN	factor K	part numbers cone fig. 1	part numbers cup fig. 1	part numbers cup fig. 2	cone max. shaft fillet radius R	cone back-ing should-er diam. db	cup max. hous-ing fillet radius r	cup back-ing shoul-der Da	pin max. diam. Ka	pin max. depth into cup Kb	live shaft diam. limits	live shaft fit (tight)	housing live shaft bore limits	housing live shaft fit (L)
6,8750 174,625	9,7500 247,650	4,0625 103,188	3,3125 84,138	3,1250 79,375	19500 8650	37100 16500	14700 6500	—	1.33	NA67787	677200	67720DC	0,14 3,5	7,56 192,0	0,03 0,8	9,45 240,0	.75 19,1	.21 5,3	6,8795 6,8785 174,739 174,714	0,0045 0,0025 114 64	9,7530 9,7520 247,726 247,700	0,003 0,001 76 25
7,0000 177,800	11,1250 282,575	4,2500 107,950	3,1250 79,375	1,7680	17200 7650	34400 15300	12200 5400	—	1.41	NA87700	871120	87112DC	0,14 3,5	7,87 200,0	0,06 1,5	10,50 266,6	.68 17,3	.21 5,3	7,0045 7,0035 177,914 177,889	0,0045 0,0025 114 64	11,1280 11,1270 282,651 282,625	0,003 0,001 76 25
7,0000 177,800	11,3750 298,925	5,6250 142,875	4,3750 111,125	4,3750 111,125	30000 13350	57000 25400	24000 10650	—	1.25	NA94700	941140	94114DC	0,22 5,5	7,99 203,0	0,06 1,5	10,71 272,0	.87 22,1	.37 9,4	7,0045 7,0035 177,914 177,889	0,0045 0,0025 114 64	11,3780 11,3770 289,001 288,975	0,003 0,001 76 25
7,0000 177,800	11,3750 288,925	5,6250 142,875	4,3750 111,125	4,3750 111,125	35500 15800	67500 30000	19400 8600	—	1.83	HM237545NA	HM237510D	HM237510DC	0,22 5,5	7,95 202,0	0,06 1,5	10,68 271,3	.87 22,1	.31 7,9	7,0035 7,0025 177,889 177,864	0,0045 0,0025 114 64	11,3780 11,3770 289,001 288,975	0,003 0,001 76 25
7,0000 177,800	11,7500 298,450	5,6250 142,875	4,3750 111,125	5,4375 138,112	30000 13350	57000 25400	24000 10650	—	1.25	NA94700	941180	94118DC	0,22 5,5	7,99 203,0	0,06 1,5	10,71 272,0	.87 22,1	.37 9,4	7,0045 7,0035 177,914 177,889	0,0045 0,0025 114 64	11,7530 11,7520 298,526 298,500	0,003 0,001 76 25
7,3750 187,325	12,6250 320,675	7,3125 185,738	5,4375 138,112	—	44500 19800	89000 39600	24300 10800	—	1.83	H239649NA	H239612D	H239612DC	0,22 5,5	8,43 214,0	0,06 1,5	11,73 298,0	1.12 28,4	.37 9,4	7,3795 7,3785 187,439 187,414	0,0045 0,0025 114 64	12,6310 12,6290 320,827 320,777	0,006 0,002 152 51
8,0000 203,200	12,5000 317,500	5,7500 146,050	4,3750 111,125	—	32900 14650	65800 29300	29400 13050	—	1.12	NA93800	931270	93127DC	0,22 5,5	9,06 230,0	0,06 1,5	11,81 300,0	.87 22,1	.37 9,4	8,0050 8,0030 203,327 203,301	0,0050 0,0030 127 76	12,5060 12,5040 317,652 317,602	0,006 0,002 152 51

① These maximum fillet radii will be cleared by the bearing corners

(T)—tight   (L)—loose

bearings manufactured with correct running clearance for these fits

Two-Row Assembly - Pre-set, Double Cup, Single Cones — TNA-TNADC

bearings manufactured with correct running clearance for these fits

bore d	outside diam. D	width through cones T	width cup C	one row radial (lb/daN)	thrust (lb/daN)	two row radial (lb/daN)	factor K	cone	cup fig. 1	cup fig. 2	cone max shaft fillet radius R①	cone backing shoulder diam. d_b	cup max housing fillet radius r①	cup backing shoulder diam. D_a	pin max diam. K_a	pin max depth into cup K_b	live shaft diam. limits	live shaft fit (tight)	housing live shaft bore limits	housing fit (L)	housing fit (T)
9.5000 / 241,300	14.5000 / 368,300	4.7500 / 120,650	3.3750 / 85,725	25500 / 11350	15800 / 7050	51000 / 22700	1.61	NA170950	171451D	171451DC	0.25 / 6,4	10.59 / 269,0	0.06 / 1,5	13.27 / 337,0	.75 / 19,1	.31 / 7,9	9.5060 / 9.5050 / 241,452 / 241,427	0.0060 / 0.0040 / 152 / 102	14.5060 / 14.5040 / 368,452 / 368,402	0.006 / 152	0.002 / 51
10.0000 / 254,000	16.6250 / 422,275	6.8125 / 173,038	5.0625 / 128,588	56000 / 24800	31700 / 14100	112000 / 49600	1.76	HM252344NA	HM252311D		0.25 / 6,4	11.26 / 286,0	0.06 / 1,5	15.66 / 397,7			10.0050 / 10.0050 / 254,152 / 254,127	0.0060 / 0.0040 / 152 / 102	16.6310 / 16.6290 / 422,427 / 422,377	0.006 / 152	0.002 / 51
10.0000 / 254,000	16.9970 / 431,724	6.8125 / 173,038	5.0625 / 128,588	56000 / 24800	31700 / 14100	112000 / 49600	1.76	HM252344NA	HM252315D	HM252315DC	0.25 / 6,4	11.26 / 286,0	0.06 / 1,5	15.68 / 398,2	1.00 / 25,4	.43 / 10,9	10.0060 / 10.0050 / 254,152 / 254,127	0.0060 / 0.0040 / 152 / 102	17.0030 / 17.0010 / 431,876 / 431,826	0.006 / 152	0.002 / 51
10.2500 / 260,350	15.7500 / 400,050	5.7500 / 146,050	4.2500 / 107,950	37100 / 16500	25100 / 11150	74200 / 33000	1.48	NA221026	221978D	221978DC	0.25 / 6,4	11.42 / 290,0	0.06 / 1,5	14.63 / 371,5	.87 / 22,1	.37 / 9,4	10.2560 / 10.2550 / 260,592 / 260,477	0.0060 / 0.0040 / 152 / 102	15.7560 / 15.7540 / 400,202 / 400,152	0.006 / 152	0.002 / 51
10.2500 / 260,350	16.6250 / 422,275	6.8125 / 173,038	5.0625 / 128,588	56000 / 24800	31700 / 14100	112000 / 49600	1.76	HM252349NA	HM252311D		0.25 / 6,4	11.46 / 291,0	0.06 / 1,5	15.66 / 397,7			10.2550 / 10.2550 / 260,592 / 260,477	0.0060 / 0.0040 / 152 / 102	16.6310 / 16.6290 / 422,427 / 422,377	0.006 / 152	0.002 / 51
10.2500 / 260,350	16.9970 / 431,723	6.8125 / 173,038	5.0625 / 128,588	56000 / 24800	31700 / 14100	112000 / 49600	1.76	HM252349NA	HM252315D	HM252315DC	0.25 / 6,4	11.46 / 291,0	0.06 / 1,5	15.68 / 398,2	1.00 / 25,4	.43 / 10,9	10.2560 / 10.2550 / 260,592 / 260,477	0.0060 / 0.0040 / 152 / 102	17.0010 / 17.0010 / 431,876 / 431,826	0.006 / 152	0.002 / 51
12.0000 / 304,800	17.2460 / 438,048	6.3750 / 161,925	4.8750 / 123,825	50000 / 22400	28500 / 12700	100000 / 44800	1.76	NA329120	329173D	329173DC	0.25 / 6,4	13.11 / 333,0	0.06 / 1,5	16.30 / 414,1	.87 / 22,1	.37 / 9,4	12.0070 / 12.0060 / 304,978 / 304,952	0.0070 / 0.0050 / 178 / 127	17.2520 / 17.2500 / 438,200 / 438,150	0.006 / 152	0.002 / 51
16.0000 / 406,400	22.6250 / 574,675	6.1875 / 157,162	4.1875 / 106,362	47500 / 21000	40500 / 18000	95000 / 42000	1.17	NA285160	285228D	285228DC	0.25 / 6,4	17.36 / 441,0	0.06 / 1,5	21.02 / 534,0	.87 / 22,1	.37 / 9,4	16.0100 / 16.0080 / 406,654 / 406,603	0.0100 / 0.0060 / 254 / 152	22.6310 / 22.6290 / 574,827 / 574,777	0.006 / 152	0.002 / 51

①These maximum fillet radii will be cleared by the bearing corners

(T)—tight (L)—loose

The cones in these bearings are slotted and chamfered to provide lubricant passage in applications where the bearings are lubricated through the shaft. The double cup has lubricant holes and groove.

The large cone rib outside diameter (d₁) on the TNASWE type is ground for sealing purposes.

Metric tolerances and fits are micrometers (μm)
1 micrometer = 0,001 mm.

TNASWE figure 2

TNASW figure 1

bore		width			rating at 500 RPM for 3000 hours L10				part numbers		fig. no.	cone				cup								bearings manufactured with correct running clearance for these fits									
																								these fits for stationary shaft applications only						unclamped cup design in sheaves only		fit (tight)
		through cones	cup	factor K	one row radial lb daN	thrust lb daN	two row radial lb daN	cone	cup		rib out-side diam. d₁*	max. shaft fillet radius R⊙	back-ing shoul-der diam. d_b	max. back-ing fillet radius r⊙	back-ing shoul-der diam. D_a		shaft diam. limits	fit (loose)	clamped cup design		housing bore limits		
d	D	T	C					cone	cup								housing bore limits			housing bore limits	fit (tight)		
0.7500 19,050	1.8504 47,000	1.3750 34,925	0.9926 25,212	1.64	1020 450	620 276	1940 860	NA05078SW	05185D	2	1.2741 32,362	0.03 0,8	0.94 24,0	0.03 0,8	1.67 42,5		0.7500 0.7495 19,050 19,038	0 0,001 0 25	1.8494 1.8484 46,975 46,949	0.001 25 76	1.8494 1.8484 46,975 46,949	1.8484 1.8474 46,949 46,923	0.002 0.004 51 102
1.1811 30,000	2.8125 71,438	1.6875 42,862	1.4375 36,512	1.62	2210 985	1370 605	4200 1880	NA28118SW	28282D	1	... ...	0.06 1,5	1.50 38,0	0.02 0,5	2.56 65,0		1.1806 1.1801 29,987 29,975	0 0,001 0 25	2.8115 2.8105 71,413 71,387	0.001 25 76	2.8115 2.8105 71,413 71,387	2.8105 2.8095 71,387 71,361	0.002 0.004 51 102
1.1811 30,000	2.8338 71,979	1.6835 42,761	1.4375 36,512	1.62	2210 985	1370 605	4200 1880	NA28118SW	28284D	1	... ...	0.06 1,5	1.50 38,0	0.03 0,8	2.56 65,0		1.1806 1.1801 29,987 29,975	0 0,001 0 25	2.8328 2.8318 71,954 71,928	0.001 25 76	2.8328 2.8318 71,954 71,928	2.8318 2.8308 71,928 71,902	0.002 0.004 51 102
1.1813 30,005	2.5000 63,500	2.0001 50,803	1.4375 36,512	1.67	1990 885	1190 530	3790 1685	NA15117SW	15251D	2	1.8017 45,763	0.03 0,8	1.40 35,5	0.03 0,8	2.32 59,0		1.1808 1.1808 29,993 29,993	0 0,001 0 25	2.4990 2.4980 63,475 63,449	0.001 25 76	2.4990 2.4980 63,475 63,449	2.4980 2.4970 63,449 62,423	0.002 0.004 51 102
1.5000 38,100	3.0000 76,200	2.3125 58,738	1.5625 39,688	1.49	3040 1355	2040 910	5800 2580	NA24778ESW	24720D	2	2.2933 58,250	0.03 0,8	1.77 45,0	0.03 0,8	2.83 72,0		1.5000 1.4995 38,100 38,088	0 0,001 0 25	2.9990 2.9980 76,175 76,149	0.001 25 76	2.9990 2.9980 76,175 76,149	2.9980 2.9970 76,149 76,123	0.002 0.004 51 102
1.7500 44,450	3.7500 95,250	2.8126 71,440	2.0000 50,800	2.05	4950 2200	2410 1070	9400 4180	NA4435SW	432D	2	2.5598 65,019	0.14 3,5	2.24 57,0	0.03 0,8	3.43 87,0		1.7500 1.7495 44,450 44,438	0 0,001 0 25	3.7490 3.7480 95,225 95,199	0.001 25 76	3.7490 3.7480 95,225 95,199	3.7480 3.7470 95,199 95,173	0.002 0.004 51 102
2.0000 50,800	3.6718 93,264	2.5625 65,088	2.0625 52,388	1.73	5000 2220	2890 1285	9500 4240	NA3780SW	3729D	1	... ...	0.14 3,5	2.52 64,0	0.03 0,8	3.46 88,0		2.0000 1.9995 50,800 50,788	0 0,001 0 25	3.6708 3.6698 93,239 93,213	0.001 25 76	3.6708 3.6698 93,239 93,213	3.6698 3.6688 93,213 93,187	0.002 0.004 51 102
2.0000 50,800	4.2500 107,950	2.9376 74,615	2.1250 53,975	1.74	5400 2400	3090 1375	10200 4550	NA4565SW	452D	2	3.1141 79,098	0.14 3,5	2.56 65,0	0.03 0,8	3.94 100,0		2.0000 1.9995 50,800 50,788	0 0,001 0 25	4.2490 4.2480 107,925 107,899	0.001 25 76	4.2490 4.2480 107,925 107,899	4.2480 4.2470 107,899 107,873	0.002 0.004 51 102
2.3750 60,325	4.8750 123,825	3.1250 79,375	2.5000 63,500	1.69	7900 3520	4700 2080	15100 6700	NA5585W	552D	1	... ...	0.14 3,5	2.99 76,0	0.06 1,5	4.53 115,0		2.3750 2.3745 60,325 60,313	0 0,001 0 25	4.8740 4.8730 123,800 123,774	0.001 25 76	4.8740 4.8730 123,800 123,774	4.8730 4.8720 123,774 123,748	0.002 0.004 51 102

*Tolerance = +0.005″ or +127 μm
−0 −0
⊙These maximum fillet radii will be cleared by the bearing corners.
†Dimension shown is maximum value having minus tolerance.

TWO-ROW ASSEMBLY · PRE-SET, DOUBLE CUP, SLOTTED CONES

The cones in these bearings are slotted and chamfered to provide lubricant passage in applications where the bearings are lubricated through the shaft. The double cup has lubricant holes and groove.

The large cone rib outside diameter (d_1) on the TNASWE type is ground for sealing purposes.

Metric tolerances and fits are micrometers (μm)
1 micrometer = 0,001 mm.

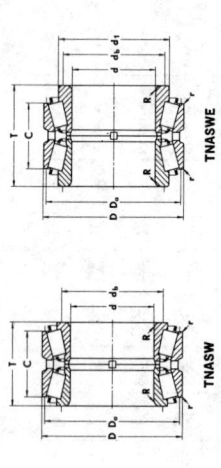

TNASW figure 1 · TNASWE figure 2

Dimensions, ratings, part numbers and cone/cup geometry

bore d (in / mm)	outside diam D (in / mm)	width T (in / mm)	width C (in / mm)	one row radial (lb / daN)	two row radial (lb / daN)	thrust (lb / daN)	factor K	cone	cup	fig. no.	rib outside diam d₁* (in / mm)	max shaft fillet radius R (in / mm)	backing shoulder diam db (in / mm)	max housing fillet radius r (in / mm)	backing shoulder diam Da (in / mm)
2.7500 / 69,850	5.3750 / 136,525	3.7500 / 95,250	3.0000 / 76,200	9600 / 4260	18300 / 8150	5950 / 2640	1.61	NA643SW	632D	1	…	0.14 / 3,5	3.39 / 86,0	0.06 / 1,5	4.92 / 125,0
2.7559 / 70,000	4.7244 / 120,000	2.9376 / 74,615	2.1250 / 53,975	5900 / 2640	11300 / 5000	3900 / 1735	1.52	NA483SW	472D	2	3.6540 / 92,812	0.14 / 3,5	3.27 / 83,0	0.03 / 0,8	4.49 / 114,0
3.2500 / 82,550	5.5115 / 139,992	3.6250 / 92,075	2.6250 / 66,675	8800 / 3920	16800 / 7500	6100 / 2700	1.45	NA3805W	572D	2	4.3229 / 109,802	0.14 / 3,5	3.86 / 98,0	0.03 / 0,8	5.24 / 133,0
3.3750 / 85,725	5.3750 / 136,525	2.8750 / 73,025	2.1250 / 53,975	6550 / 2920	12500 / 5550	5000 / 2220	1.31	NA4975W	493D	2	4.2828 / 108,783	0.14 / 3,5	3.90 / 99,0	0.03 / 0,8	5.12 / 130,0
3.5000 / 88,900	6.0000 / 152,400	3.6250 / 92,075	2.5000 / 63,500	9350 / 4160	17900 / 7950	7100 / 3160	1.32	NA5945W	592D	2	4.7725 / 121,222	0.14 / 3,5	4.09 / 104,0	0.03 / 0,8	5.67 / 144,0
3.5000 / 88,900	6.3750 / 161,925	4.1250 / 104,775	3.3750 / 85,725	13800 / 6100	26200 / 11650	8050 / 3580	1.71	NA759SW	752D	1	…	0.14 / 3,5	4.17 / 106,0	0.06 / 1,5	5.91 / 150,0
4.0000 / 101,600	6.6250 / 168,275	3.6250 / 92,075	2.7500 / 69,850	11500 / 5100	21900 / 9700	9250 / 4120	1.24	NA691SW	672D	1	…	0.14 / 3,5	4.65 / 118,0	0.03 / 0,8	6.30 / 160,0
4.2500 / 107,950	6.5000 / 165,100	3.5000 / 88,900	2.5000 / 63,500	10100 / 4500	19300 / 8600	8600 / 3820	1.18	NA56425SW	56850D	2	5.4249 / 137,792	0.14 / 3,5	4.84 / 123,0	0.03 / 0,8	6.26 / 159,0
5.0000 / 127,000	7.1875 / 182,562	3.6874 / 93,660	2.8750 / 73,025	12900 / 5750	24600 / 10950	6750 / 3000	1.91	NA48290SW	48220D	2	6.1075 / 155,130	0.14 / 3,5	5.55 / 141,0	0.03 / 0,8	6.93 / 176,0

Fits for stationary shaft applications / bearings manufactured with correct running clearance for these fits

bore d	shaft diam. limits (in / mm)	fit (loose) (in / μm)	clamped cup — housing bore limits (in / mm)	fit (tight) (in / μm)	stationary — housing bore limits (in / mm)	fit (tight) (in / μm)	undamped cup (sheaves only) — housing bore limits (in / mm)	fit (tight) (in / μm)
2.7500	2.7500 / 2.7490 • 69,850 / 69,824	0 / 0.001 • 0 / 25	5.3740 / 5.3730 • 136,500 / 136,474	0.001 / 0.003 • 25 / 76	5.3740 / 5.3730 • 136,500 / 136,474	0.001 / 0.003 • 25 / 76	5.3730 / 5.3720 • 136,474 / 136,448	0.002 / 0.004 • 51 / 102
2.7559	2.7559 / 2.7549 • 70,000 / 69,974	0 / 0.001 • 0 / 25	4.7234 / 4.7224 • 119,975 / 119,949	0.001 / 0.003 • 25 / 76	4.7234 / 4.7224 • 119,975 / 119,949	0.001 / 0.003 • 25 / 76	4.7224 / 4.7214 • 119,949 / 119,923	0.002 / 0.004 • 51 / 102
3.2500	3.2500 / 3.2490 • 82,550 / 82,524	0 / 0.001 • 0 / 25	5.5105 / 5.5095 • 139,967 / 139,941	0.001 / 0.003 • 25 / 76	5.5105 / 5.5095 • 139,967 / 139,941	0.001 / 0.003 • 25 / 76	5.5095 / 5.5085 • 139,941 / 139,915	0.002 / 0.004 • 51 / 102
3.3750	3.3750 / 3.3740 • 85,725 / 85,699	0 / 0.001 • 0 / 25	5.3740 / 5.3730 • 136,500 / 136,474	0.001 / 0.003 • 25 / 76	5.3740 / 5.3730 • 136,500 / 136,474	0.001 / 0.003 • 25 / 76	5.3730 / 5.3720 • 136,474 / 136,448	0.002 / 0.004 • 51 / 102
3.5000	3.5000 / 3.4990 • 88,900 / 88,874	0 / 0.001 • 0 / 25	5.9990 / 5.9980 • 152,375 / 152,349	0.001 / 0.003 • 25 / 76	5.9990 / 5.9980 • 152,375 / 152,349	0.001 / 0.003 • 25 / 76	5.9980 / 5.9970 • 152,349 / 152,323	0.002 / 0.004 • 51 / 102
3.5000	3.5000 / 3.4990 • 88,900 / 88,874	0 / 0.001 • 0 / 25	6.3740 / 6.3730 • 161,900 / 161,874	0.001 / 0.003 • 25 / 76	6.3740 / 6.3730 • 161,900 / 161,874	0.001 / 0.003 • 25 / 76	6.3730 / 6.3720 • 161,874 / 161,848	0.002 / 0.004 • 51 / 102
4.0000	4.0000 / 3.9990 • 101,600 / 101,574	0 / 0.001 • 0 / 25	6.6240 / 6.6230 • 168,250 / 168,224	0.001 / 0.003 • 25 / 76	6.6240 / 6.6230 • 168,250 / 168,224	0.001 / 0.003 • 25 / 76	6.6230 / 6.6220 • 168,224 / 168,198	0.002 / 0.004 • 51 / 102
4.2500	4.2500 / 4.2490 • 107,950 / 107,924	0 / 0.001 • 0 / 25	6.4990 / 6.4980 • 165,075 / 165,049	0.001 / 0.003 • 25 / 76	6.4990 / 6.4980 • 165,075 / 165,049	0.001 / 0.003 • 25 / 76	6.4980 / 6.4970 • 165,049 / 165,023	0.002 / 0.004 • 51 / 102
5.0000	5.0000 / 4.9990 • 127,000 / 126,974	0 / 0.001 • 0 / 25	7.1865 / 7.1855 • 182,537 / 182,511	0.001 / 0.003 • 25 / 76	7.1865 / 7.1855 • 182,537 / 182,511	0.001 / 0.003 • 25 / 76	7.1855 / 7.1845 • 182,511 / 182,485	0.002 / 0.004 • 51 / 102

*Tolerance = +0.005″ or +127 μm / −0.000″ −0 μm

⊙These maximum fillet radii will be cleared by the bearing corners.

44

Column legend — dimensions given as **inch / mm**. Ratings given as two values (lb / daN). Right‑hand fit data: **bearings manufactured with correct running clearance for these fits — these fits for stationary shaft applications only.**

bore d	O.D. D	width T	cup width C	rating one‑row radial	rating thrust	rating two‑row radial	factor K	cup	cone	fig	rib o.s. diam d₁s	max shaft fillet R⊙	back shoulder db	max hous fillet r⊕	back shoulder Da	back shoulder diam Da	shaft diam limits	fit (loose)	clamped cup: housing bore limits	clamped fit (tight)	unclamped cup (sheaves only): housing bore limits	unclamped fit (tight)
5.6250 / 142,875	7.8750 / 200,025	3.6876 / 93,665	2.8750 / 73,025	13900 / 6200	8000 / 3560	26500 / 11800	1.74	48620D	NA48685SW	2	6.7717 / 172,000	0.14 / 3,5	6.22 / 158,0	0.03 / 0,8	7.60 / 193,0		5.6250 5.6240 / 142,875 142,849	0 / 0.002 / 51	7.8740 7.8730 / 200,000 199,974	0.001 / 0.003 / 76	7.8730 7.8720 / 199,974 199,948	0.002 / 0.004 / 51 102
6.5000 / 165,100	8.8750 / 225,425	3.7500 / 95,250	2.7500 / 69,850	15100 / 6750	9950 / 4420	28800 / 12800	1.52	46720D	NA46790SW	2	7.7600 / 197,104	0.14 / 3,5	7.13 / 181,0	0.03 / 0,8	8.58 / 218,0		6.5000 6.4990 / 165,100 165,074	0 / 0.002 / 51	8.8740 8.8730 / 225,400 225,374	0.001 / 0.003 / 76	8.8730 8.8720 / 225,374 225,348	0.002 / 0.004 / 51 102
7.0000 / 177,800	9.7500 / 247,650	4.0625 / 103,188	3.3125 / 84,138	19500 / 8650	14700 / 6500	37100 / 16500	1.33	67720D	NA67791SW	1	…	0.14 / 3,5	7.64 / 194,0	0.03 / 0,8	9.45 / 240,0		7.0000 6.9990 / 177,800 177,774	0 / 0.002 / 51	9.7490 9.7480 / 247,625 247,599	0.001 / 0.003 / 76	9.7480 9.7470 / 247,599 247,573	0.002 / 0.004 / 51 102
7.0000 / 177,800	11.1250 / 282,575	4.2500 / 107,950	3.1250 / 79,375	17200 / 7650	12200 / 5400	34400 / 15300	1.41	87112D	NA87700SW	2	9.1816 / 233,213	0.14 / 3,5	7.87 / 200,0	0.06 / 1,5	10.50 / 266,6		7.0000 6.9990 / 177,800 177,774	0 / 0.002 / 51	11.1240 11.1230 / 282,550 282,524	0.001 / 0.003 / 76	11.1230 11.1220 / 282,524 282,498	0.002 / 0.004 / 51 102
7.2500 / 184,150	9.5625 / 242,888	3.7500 / 95,250	2.7500 / 69,850	15800 / 7000	11300 / 5050	30000 / 13350	1.39	LM637310D	LM637349NW	2	8.4803 / 215,400	0.14 / 3,5	7.83 / 199,0	0.03 / 0,8	9.29 / 236,0		7.2500 7.2490 / 184,150 184,124	0 / 0.002 / 51	9.5615 9.5605 / 242,863 242,837	0.001 / 0.003 / 76	9.5605 9.5595 / 242,837 242,811	0.002 / 0.004 / 51 102
7.5000 / 190,500	10.8750 / 276,225	4.3125 / 109,538	3.3125 / 84,138	19200 / 8550	15800 / 7000	38400 / 17100	1.22	67820D	NA67885SW	2	9.1444 / 232,268	0.14 / 3,5	8.23 / 209,0	0.03 / 0,8	10.20 / 259,0		7.5000 7.4990 / 190,500 190,474	0 / 0.002 / 51	10.8740 10.8730 / 276,200 276,174	0.001 / 0.003 / 76	10.8730 10.8720 / 276,174 276,148	0.002 / 0.004 / 51 102
8.0000 / 203,200	10.7500 / 273,050	4.0000 / 101,600	2.8750 / 73,025	20900 / 9300	13000 / 5750	41800 / 18600	1.83	LM241110D	LM241149NW	2	9.4659 / 240,434	0.14 / 3,5	8.66 / 220,0	0.03 / 0,8	10.51 / 267,0		8.0000 7.9990 / 203,200 203,174	0 / 0.002 / 51	10.7490 10.7480 / 273,025 272,999	0.001 / 0.003 / 76	10.7480 10.7470 / 272,999 272,973	0.002 / 0.004 / 51 102
9.2500 / 234,950	12.2500 / 311,150	4.6250 / 117,475	2.8750 / 73,025	24900 / 11100	17300 / 7700	49800 / 22200	1.61	LM446310D	LM446349NW	2	10.8156 / 274,716	0.14 / 3,5	9.92 / 252,0	0.06 / 1,5	11.85 / 301,0		9.2500 9.2490 / 234,950 234,924	0 / 0.002 / 51	12.2490 12.2480 / 311,125 311,099	0.001 / 0.005 / 127	12.2480 12.2470 / 311,099 311,073	0.002 / 0.006 / 51 152
9.2500 / 234,950	12.8750 / 327,025	4.0000 / 101,600	3.2500 / 82,550	23600 / 10500	13400 / 5950	47200 / 21000	1.44	8520D	NA8575SW	2	11.0065 / 279,565	0.25 / 6,4	10.20 / 259,0	0.06 / 1,5	12.32 / 313,0		9.2500 9.2490 / 234,950 234,924	0 / 0.002 / 51	12.8740 12.8730 / 327,000 326,974	0.001 / 0.005 / 127	12.8730 12.8720 / 326,974 326,948	0.002 / 0.006 / 51 152
†10.0000 / †254,000	13.6875 / 347,662	4.0000 / 101,600	2.7500 / 69,850	27400 / 12150	15000 / 6650	54800 / 24300	1.76	LM249710D	LM249747NW	2	11.5860 / 294,284	0.14 / 3,5	10.71 / 272,0	0.06 / 1,5	13.11 / 333,0		9.9990 9.9980 / 253,975 253,949	0 / 0.002 / 51	13.6865 13.6855 / 347,638 347,612	0.001 / 0.005 / 127	13.6855 13.6845 / 347,612 347,587	0.002 / 0.006 / 51 152
10.5000 / 266,700	13.8750 / 352,425	4.2500 / 107,950	3.2500 / 82,550	27400 / 12150	15000 / 6650	54800 / 24300	1.83	LM251610D	LM251649NW	2	12.1994 / 309,865	0.25 / 6,4	11.46 / 291,0	0.06 / 1,5	13.39 / 340,0		10.5000 10.4990 / 266,700 266,674	0 / 0.002 / 51	13.8740 13.8730 / 352,400 352,374	0.001 / 0.005 / 127	13.8730 13.8720 / 352,374 352,349	0.002 / 0.006 / 51 152
12.0000 / 304,800	15.5000 / 393,700	4.2500 / 107,950	3.2500 / 82,550	29200 / 13000	17900 / 7950	58400 / 26000	1.63	L357010D	L357049NW	2	13.7971 / 350,446	0.25 / 6,4	12.95 / 329,0	0.06 / 1,5	14.96 / 380,0		12.0000 11.9990 / 304,800 304,774	0 / 0.002 / 51	15.4990 15.4980 / 393,675 393,649	0.001 / 0.005 / 127	15.4980 15.4970 / 393,649 393,624	0.002 / 0.006 / 51 152

*Tolerance = +0.005″ / −0.000″   or   +127 μm / −0 μm

⊕These maximum fillet radii will be cleared by the bearing corners.

†Dimension shown is maximum value having minus tolerance.

AUXILIARY PARTS

Auxiliary parts are available from The Timken Company for use with Timken bearing applications. These parts are made to specific standards of precision to comply with the requirements for which the parts and bearing application were designed. The parts available appear on the following pages.

PAGE

Cup Shims 1

Cone Shims 2

Keyed (Tongued) Washers 3-5

Keyway Dimensions 6

Locknuts 3-5

Lockwashers 3-5

Shaft Thread Dimensions 6

Cup Shims

Standard Metal Shims for Cup Adjusted Bearings

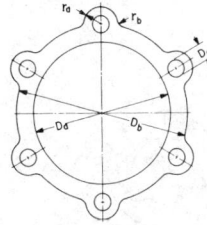

SHIMS .005", .007", & .020" THICK

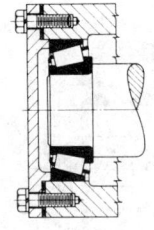

WITHOUT CARRIER

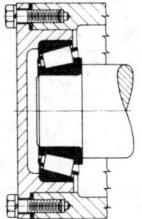

WITH CARRIER
CARRIER SECTION SHOULD BE EQUAL TO AVERAGE CUP WALL SECTION

Suggested shim set consists of three .005", three .007" and one .020" thick. In ordering, specify the exact quantity for each part number. Shims shown in this table are made from aluminum alloy shim stock.

cup shims
part number identifies the following:

shim	size	thickness
K2	00	00

for example

K2	06	05	covers number 6 shim .005" thick
K2	06	07	covers number 6 shim .007" thick
K2	06	20	covers number 6 shim .020" thick

.005" thick	.007" thick	.020" thick	no.	size	D_a	D_b	D_c	r_a	r_b
K20605	K20607	K20620	4	1/4	1 13/32	1 7/8	5/32	1/4	1/8
K20705	K20707	K20720	4	1/4	1.783	2 1/4	5/32	1/4	1/8
K20805	K20807	K20820	4	3/8	2 1/2	2 3/4	13/32	3/8	3/16
K20905	K20907	K20920	4	3/8	2 11/32	3	13/32	3/8	3/16
K21005	K21007	K21020	4	3/8	2 9/32	3 1/4	13/32	3/8	3/16
K21105	K21107	K21120	4	3/8	2 25/32	3 1/2	13/32	3/8	3/16
K21205	K21207	K21220	4	3/8	3 1/2	3 3/4	13/32	3/8	3/16
K21405	K21407	K21420	4	3/8	3 17/32	4 1/4	13/32	3/8	3/16
K21505	K21507	K21520	4	3/8	3 25/32	4 1/2	13/32	3/8	3/16
K21605	K21607	K21620	4	1/2	4 1/32	5	17/32	1/2	1/4
K21705	K21707	K21720	4	1/2	4 9/32	5 1/4	17/32	1/2	1/4
K21805	K21807	K21820	4	1/2	4 17/32	5 1/2	17/32	1/2	1/4
K21905	K21907	K21920	6	1/2	4 25/32	5 3/4	17/32	1/2	1/4
K22005	K22007	K22020	6	1/2	5 1/32	6	17/32	1/2	1/4
K22205	K22207	K22220	6	1/2	5 17/32	6 1/2	17/32	1/2	1/4
K22405	K22407	K22420	6	1/2	6 1/32	7	17/32	1/2	1/4
K22505	K22507	K22520	6	5/8	6 9/32	7 1/2	21/32	5/8	5/16

.005" thick	.007" thick	.020" thick	no.	size	D_a	D_b	D_c	r_a	r_b
K22605	K22607	K22620	6	5/8	6 17/32	7 3/4	21/32	5/8	5/16
K22705	K22707	K22720	6	5/8	6 25/32	8	21/32	5/8	5/16
K22905	K22907	K22920	6	5/8	7 5/32	8 1/2	21/32	5/8	5/16
K23005	K23007	K23020	6	5/8	7 11/32	8 3/4	21/32	5/8	5/16
K23205	K23207	K23220	6	5/8	8 1/32	9 1/4	21/32	5/8	5/16
K23405	K23407	K23420	6	5/8	8 17/32	9 3/4	21/32	5/8	5/16
K23605	K23607	K23620	6	5/8	9 1/32	10 1/4	21/32	5/8	5/16
K23805	K23807	K23820	6	5/8	9 17/32	10 3/4	21/32	5/8	5/16
K24005	K24007	K24020	6	3/4	10 1/2	11 1/2	25/32	3/4	3/8
K24105	K24107	K24120	8	3/4	10 17/32	12	25/32	3/4	3/8
K24205	K24207	K24220	8	3/4	11 21/32	13 1/8	25/32	3/4	3/8
K24405	K24407	K24420	8	3/4	12 17/32	14	25/32	3/4	3/8
K24605	K24607	K24620	8	7/8	13 11/32	15 1/4	15/16	7/8	7/16
K24805	K24807	K24820	8	7/8	14 17/32	16 1/4	15/16	7/8	7/16
K25005	K25007	K25020	8	1	15 17/32	17 1/2	1 1/16	1	1/2
K25205	K25207	K25220	8	1	16 17/32	18 1/2	1 1/16	1	1/2

these parts have been designed and developed for use with Timken bearings only.

Standard Metal Shims for Cone Adjusted Bearings

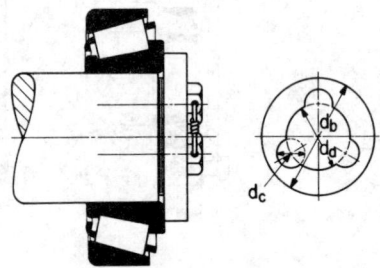

Suggested shim set consists of three .005", three .007" and one .020" thick.
In ordering specify the exact quantity for each part number.

Shims shown in this table are made from aluminum alloy shim stock.

shims		shaft	cap screws		d_a	d_b	d_c	shims		shaft	cap screws		d_a	d_b	d_c
part no.	thickness	size	no.	size				part no.	thickness	size	no.	size			
T50605	.005	2½						T50614	.005	5					
T50606	.007	to	3	½	1⅜	2⅜	⁷⁄₁₆	T50615	.007	to	4	¾	3½	4⅞	¹³⁄₁₆
T50607	.020	2⅞						T50616	.020	5⅜					
T50608	.005	3						T50617	.005	5½					
T50609	.007	to	3	½	1¾	2⅞	⁹⁄₁₆	T50618	.007	to	4	¾	3½	5⅜	¹³⁄₁₆
T50610	.020	3⅜						T50619	.020	5⅞					
T50611	.005	3½						T50620	.005	6					
T50612	.007	to	3	½	2¼	3⅜	⁹⁄₁₆	T50621	.007	to	6	¾	4	5⅞	¹³⁄₁₆
T50613	.020	4⅛						T50622	.020	6⅞					
T45882	.005	4¼						T50623	.005	7					
T50633	.007	to	3	⅝	3	4¹⁄₁₆	¹¹⁄₁₆	T50624	.007	to	6	1	5	6⅞	1¹⁄₁₆
T45884	.020	4⅝						T50625	.020	7⅞					
T45885	.005	4¾						T50626	.005						
T50634	.007	to	3	⅝	3½	4⅝	¹¹⁄₁₆	T50627	.007	8	6	1¼	6	7⅞	1⁵⁄₁₆
T45887	.020	4⅞						T50628	.020						

these parts have been designed and developed for use with Timken bearings only.

Locknuts and Lockwashers

Standard Locknut and Lockwasher Assemblies

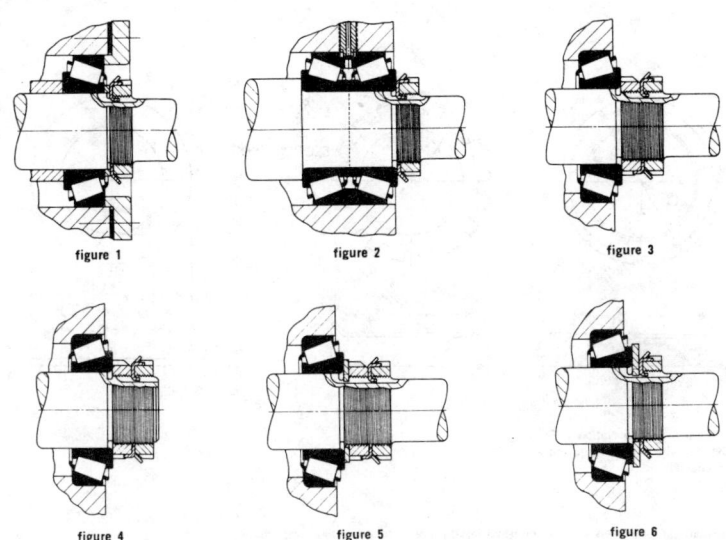

figure 1

figure 2

figure 3

figure 4

figure 5

figure 6

The designs shown in figures 1 to 6 inclusive show various methods of using standard locknuts and lockwashers indicated in the tables on pages 4 and 5. A single nut and washer can be used to clamp the cone against a sleeve shown in figure 1 or directly against a shaft shoulder. A narrow spacer is applied between the front face of the cone and the tongued lockwasher so that the lockwasher will clear the bearing cage by a minimum of ⅛". The spacer outside diameter should be made a minimum of ¼" smaller than the cage inside diameter but must still provide the recommended cone backing diameter indicated as dimension "d_a" shown in the single-row, type TS, Bearing Tables. Figure 2 shows another clamped design using a single nut and washer with a two-row bearing of either type TDODC with cone spacer or type TNADC. Since no cage clearance problem is present, the narrow spacer shown in figure 1 is unnecessary.

Figures 3, 4 and 5 indicate an adjustable bearing arrangement using two nuts and a separating lock washer. These may be used with either single or two-row bearings of the types permitting a cone ad-

justed arrangement. The design in figure 3 allows the maximum shaft extension diameter which can be used with a shaft thread outside diameter which will still clear the cone bore during assembly. Figure 4 shows an alternate design using a smaller nut and washer. The nut outside diameter minus 2 times "r" (pages 4 and 5) must not be less than the recommended cone backing diameter indicated as dimension "d_b" shown in the Bearing Tables. Figure 5 indicates the use of a hardened tongued washer located between the inner nut and cone. This is intended for applications where the cones are applied with light press fits on hardened shafts as found in many automotive applications.

When space does not permit the use of two locknuts and a lockwasher in an adjustable arrangement and a single locknut and a lockwasher is used, then a keyed (tongued) washer must be placed between the cone and lockwasher as illustrated in figure 6. This is necessary to provide adequate backing for the cone and to prevent damage to the lockwasher if the cone should creep on the shaft.

Standard Locknuts, Lockwashers and Keyed (Tongued) Washers for Tapered Roller Bearings

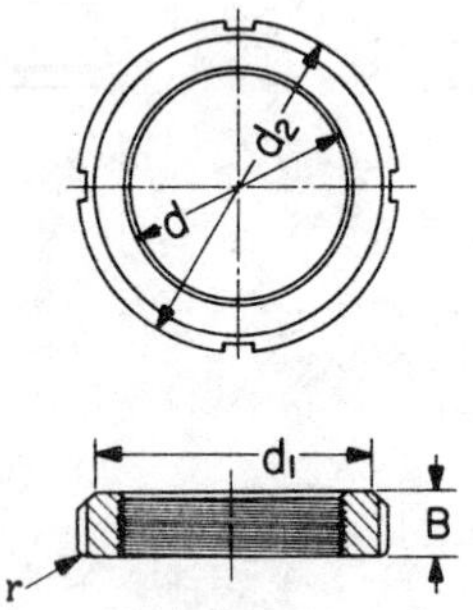

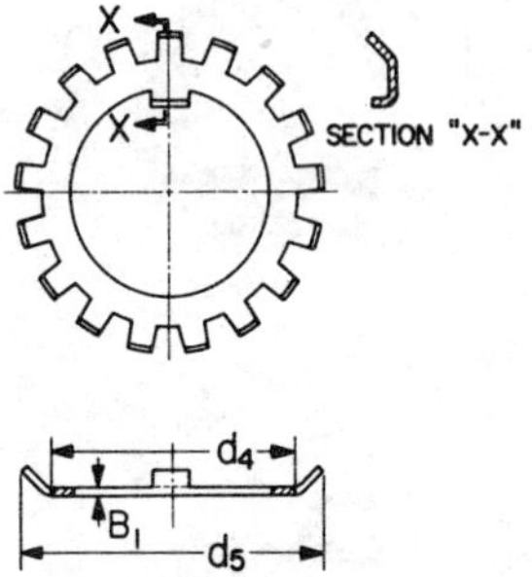

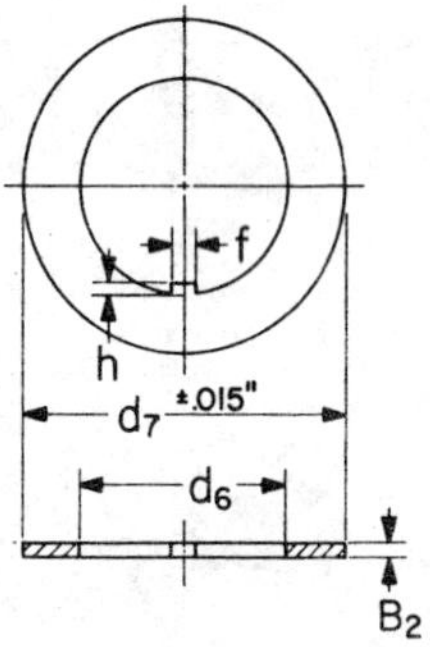

Threads are American National, Form NS, Class 3, with thread length based on 45° chamfer.

These locknuts and lockwashers are standard AFBMA tapered roller bearing mounting accessories.

locknut dimensions							lockwasher dimensions					keyed (tongued) washer dimensions						
	threads												bore d_6				maximum	
AFBMA locknut number	minimum value of major diameter d	number per inch	outside diameter d_2	thickness B	face outside diameter d_1	r	AFBMA lockwasher number	maximum diameter over tangs d_5	face diameter d_4	thickness B_1	number of tangs	Timken Company keyed (tongued) washer number	min.	max.	outside diameter d_7	thickness B_2	tang depth h	tang width f
T N00	.391	32	3/4	7/32	39/64	3/64	T W100	57/64	5/8	.042	9	..	..	..	..	..	..	..
T N01	.469	32	7/8	5/16	45/64	3/64	T W101	1 1/32	23/32	.042	9	K91501	.484	.499	15/16	.109	.072	.120
T N02	.586	32	1	5/16	51/64	3/64	T W102	1 5/32	13/16	.058	11	K91502	.601	.616	1 3/16	.125	.088	.120
T N03	.664	32	1 1/8	11/32	59/64	3/64	T W103	1 11/32	15/16	.058	11	K91503	.679	.694	1 3/16	.125	.088	.120
T N04	.781	32	1 3/8	3/8	1 7/64	3/64	T W104	1 9/16	1 1/8	.058	11	K91504	.801	.816	1 7/16	.125	.088	.176
T N05	.969	32	1 9/16	13/32	1 17/64	3/64	T W105	1 45/64	1 9/32	.062	13	K91505	.989	1.009	1 7/8	.125	.092	.176
T N06	1.173	18	1 3/4	13/32	1 31/64	3/64	T W106	1 61/64	1 1/2	.062	13	K91506	1.193	1.213	1 7/8	.125	.112	.176
T N065	1.3125	18	2 1/16	7/16	1 51/64	1/16	T W065	2 15/64	1 13/16	.062	15	K915065	1.333	1.353	2 3/16	.125	.112	.176

AFBMA locknut number	threads min. value of major diameter d	number per inch	outside diameter d2	thickness B	face outside diameter d1	r	AFBMA lockwasher number	maximum diameter over tangs d5	face diameter d4	thickness B1	number of tongs	Timken Company keyed (tongued) washer number	bore d6 min.	bore d6 max.	outside diameter d7	thickness B2	maximum tang depth h	maximum tang width f
T N07	1.376	18	2 1/16	7/16	1 51/64	1/16	T W107	2 1/4	1 13/16	.062	15	K91507	1.396	1.416	2 3/16	.125	.112	.176
T N08	1.563	18	2 1/4	7/16	1 43/64	1/16	T W108	2 31/64	2	.072	15	K91508	1.583	1.603	2 3/4	.156	.122	.290
T N09	1.767	18	2 17/32	7/16	2 7/16	1/16	T W109	2 23/32	2 5/32	.072	17	K91509	1.792	1.817	2 3/4	.156	.122	.290
T N10	1.967	18	2 11/16	1/2	2 27/64	1/16	T W110	2 49/64	2 7/16	.072	17	K91510	1.992	2.017	3 1/4	.156	.122	.290
T N11	2.157	18	2 21/32	1/2	2 41/64	1/16	T W111	3 5/32	2 21/32	.072	17	K91511	2.182	2.207	3 1/4	.156	.122	.290
T N12	2.360	18	3 5/32	17/32	2 53/64	1/16	T W112	3 35/64	2 27/32	.082	17	K91512	2.400	2.425	3 3/4	.187	.152	.290
T N13	2.548	18	3 3/8	9/16	3 3/64	3/32	T W113	3 9/16	3 1/16	.082	19	K91513	2.588	2.613	3 3/4	.187	.152	.290
T N14	2.751	18	3 5/8	9/16	3 19/64	3/32	T W114	3 13/16	3 1/4	.082	19	K91514	2.791	2.816	3 3/4	.187	.152	.290
T AN15	2.933	12	3 7/8	19/32	3 25/64	3/32	T W115	4 3/64	3 9/16	.095	19	K91515	2.973	3.003	4 3/16	.218	.165	.290
T AN16	3.137	12	4 5/32	19/32	3 43/64	3/32	T W116	4 25/64	3 27/32	.095	19	K91516	3.177	3.207	4 3/16	.218	.165	.353
T AN17	3.340	12	4 13/32	5/8	4 1/64	3/32	T W117	4 5/8	4 1/32	.095	19	K91517	3.395	3.425	4 5/8	.218	.165	.353
T AN18	3.527	12	4 21/32	11/16	4 17/64	3/32	T W118	4 61/64	4 9/32	.125	19	K91518	3.582	3.612	5 1/8	.250	.195	.353
T AN19	3.730	12	4 15/16	23/32	4 25/64	1/8	T W119	5 15/64	4 7/16	.125	19	K91519	3.800	3.830	5 1/8	.250	.195	.353
T AN20	3.918	12	5 3/16	3/4	4 45/64	1/8	T W120	5 23/64	4 13/16	.125	19	K91520	3.988	4.018	5 5/8	.250	.210	.353
T AN21	4.122	12	5 7/16	3/4	4 45/64	1/8	T W121	5 45/64	5	.125	19	K91521	4.192	4.222	5 5/8	.250	.210	.353
T AN22	4.325	12	5 23/32	25/32	5 17/64	1/8	T W122	6	5 9/32	.140	19	K91522	4.395	4.425	6 1/8	.281	.225	.353
T AN24	4.716	12	6 1/8	13/16	5 49/64	1/8	T W124	6 17/32	5 11/16	.165	19	K91524	4.801	4.831	6 3/4	.375	.250	.353
T AN26	5.106	12	6 3/4	7/8	6 11/64	1/8	T W126	7 3/64	6 3/16	.165	19	K91526	5.191	5.226	7 1/2	.375	.270	.435
T AN128	5.497	12	7 3/32	1 3/16	6 35/64	1/8	T W128	7 7/16	6 17/32	.165	19	K91528	5.582	5.617	7 1/2	.375	.270	.590
T AN130	5.888	12	7 11/16	1 1/4	7 3/64	1/8	T W130	8 1/8	7 1/16	.203	19	. .	. .	. .	. .	. .	. .
T AN132	6.284	8	8 1/16	1 5/32	7 13/32	5/32	T W132	8 35/64	7 3/4	.203	19	K91532	6.389	6.424	8 1/2	.375	.308	.590
T AN134	6.659	8	8 21/32	1 11/32	8	5/32	T W134	9 5/64	8 1/32	.203	19	. .	. .	. .	. .	. .	. .
T AN136	7.066	8	9 1/16	1 13/32	8 1/32	5/32	T W136	9 7/16	8 3/8	.203	19	. .	. .	. .	. .	. .	. .
T AN138	7.472	8	9 15/16	1 13/32	8 3/4	5/32	T W138	9 45/64	8 25/32	.203	19	. .	. .	. .	. .	. .	. .
T AN140	7.847	8	9 27/32	1 1/2	9 1/8	5/32	T W140	10 13/32	9 5/32	.203	19	K91540	7.982	8.017	10 1/8	.375	.308	.840

Shaft Thread and Keyway Dimensions for Standard Locknuts and Lockwashers

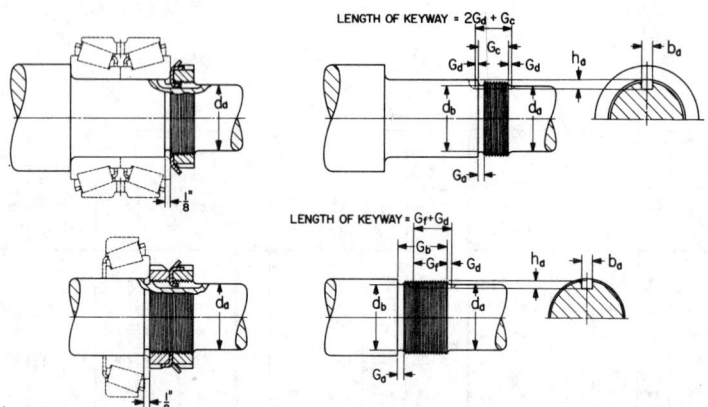

LENGTH OF KEYWAY = 2G$_d$ + G$_c$

LENGTH OF KEYWAY = G$_f$+G$_d$

These dimensions are AFBMA standards.

AFBMA locknut number	no. per inch	threads major diameter max.	tol.	min.	pitch diameter (1) max.	tol.	min.	minor diam. max.	relief diameter d$_b$	relief width G$_a$ +1/64 -0	shaft extension diam. d$_a$ +1/64 -0 max.	thread length G$_b$ +1/64 -0	G$_c$ +1/64 -0	keyway depth h$_a$ +1/64 -0	width b$_a$ +1/64 -0	G$_d$ +1/64 -0	G$_f$ +1/64 -0
T N00	32	0.391	.0054	0.3856	0.3707	.0026	0.3681	0.3527	0.3371 ± .005	1/16	5/16	19/32	3/8	3/32	1/8	3/32	15/32
T N01	32	0.469	.0054	0.4636	0.4487	.0026	0.4461	0.4307	0.4151 ± .005	1/16	13/32	25/32	15/32	3/32	1/8	3/32	9/16
T N02	32	0.586	.0054	0.5806	0.5657	.0030	0.5627	0.5477	0.5321 ± .005	1/16	1/2	13/16	1/2	3/32	1/8	3/32	19/32
T N03	32	0.664	.0054	0.6586	0.6437	.0030	0.6407	0.6257	0.6101 ± .005	1/16	9/16	7/8	17/32	3/32	1/8	3/32	5/8
T N04	32	0.781	.0054	0.7756	0.7607	.0034	0.7573	0.7427	0.7271 ± .005	1/16	45/64	29/32	17/32	3/32	3/16	3/32	5/8
T N05	32	0.969	.0054	0.9636	0.9487	.0034	0.9453	0.9307	0.9151 ± .005	1/16	7/8	1	19/32	1/8	3/16	1/8	23/32
T N06	18	1.173	.0082	1.1648	1.1369	.0040	1.1329	1.1048	1.0892 ± .005	3/32	1- 1/16	1	19/32	1/8	3/16	1/8	23/32
T N065	18	1.3125	.0082	1.3043	1.2764	.0040	1.2724	1.2443	1.2287 ± .005	3/32	1- 3/16	1- 1/16	5/8	1/8	3/16	1/8	3/4
T N07	18	1.376	.0082	1.3678	1.3399	.0040	1.3359	1.3078	1.2922 ± .005	3/32	1- 1/4	1- 1/16	5/8	1/8	3/16	1/8	3/4
T N08	18	1.563	.0082	1.5548	1.5269	.0045	1.5224	1.4948	1.4792 ± .005	3/32	1- 7/16	1- 1/16	5/8	1/8	5/16	1/8	3/4
T N09	18	1.767	.0082	1.7588	1.7309	.0045	1.7264	1.6988	1.6832 ± .005	1/8	1-21/32	1- 1/16	5/8	1/8	5/16	5/32	25/32
T N10	18	1.967	.0082	1.9588	1.9309	.0045	1.9264	1.8988	1.8832 ± .005	1/8	1-55/64	1- 3/16	11/16	1/8	5/16	5/32	27/32
T N11	18	2.157	.0082	2.1488	2.1209	.0051	2.1158	2.0888	2.0732 ± .005	1/8	2- 3/64	1- 3/16	11/16	1/8	5/16	5/32	27/32
T N12	18	2.360	.0082	2.3518	2.3239	.0051	2.3188	2.2918	2.2762 ± .005	1/8	2- 1/4	1- 9/32	3/4	5/32	5/16	5/32	29/32
T N13	18	2.548	.0082	2.5398	2.5119	.0051	2.5068	2.4798	2.4642 ± .005	1/8	2-27/64	1-11/32	25/32	5/32	5/16	5/32	15/16
T N14	18	2.751	.0082	2.7428	2.7149	.0051	2.7098	2.6828	2.6672 ± .005	1/8	2- 5/8	1-11/32	25/32	5/32	5/16	1/4	1
T AN15	12	2.933	.0112	2.9218	2.8789	.0054	2.8735	2.8308	2.7995 ± .010	5/32	2-25/32	1-13/32	13/16	3/16	5/16	1/4	1- 3/16
T AN16	12	3.137	.0112	3.1258	3.0829	.0059	3.0770	3.0348	3.0035 ± .010	5/32	3	1-13/32	13/16	3/16	3/8	1/4	1- 1/32
T AN17	12	3.340	.0112	3.3288	3.2859	.0059	3.2800	3.2378	3.2065 ± .010	5/32	3- 3/16	1-15/32	27/32	3/16	3/8	1/4	1- 1/16
T AN18	12	3.527	.0112	3.5158	3.4729	.0074	3.4655	3.4248	3.3935 ± .010	5/32	3- 3/8	1- 5/8	15/16	7/32	3/8	1/4	1- 5/32
T AN19	12	3.730	.0112	3.7188	3.6759	.0074	3.6685	3.6278	3.5965 ± .010	5/32	3- 9/16	1-11/16	31/32	7/32	3/8	1/4	1- 3/16
T AN20	12	3.918	.0112	3.9068	3.8639	.0074	3.8565	3.8158	3.7845 ± .010	5/32	3-49/64	1- 3/4	1	7/32	3/8	5/16	1- 9/32
T AN21	12	4.122	.0112	4.1108	4.0679	.0083	4.0596	4.0198	3.9885 ± .010	5/32	3-15/16	1- 3/4	1	7/32	3/8	5/16	1- 9/32
T AN22	12	4.325	.0112	4.3138	4.2709	.0083	4.2626	4.2228	4.1915 ± .010	5/32	4- 5/32	1-13/16	1- 1/32	7/32	3/8	5/16	1- 5/16
T AN24	12	4.716	.0112	4.7048	4.6619	.0083	4.6536	4.6138	4.5825 ± .010	5/32	4-17/32	1-29/32	1- 3/32	1/4	3/8	5/16	1- 3/8
T AN26	12	5.106	.0112	5.0948	5.0519	.0083	5.0436	5.0038	4.9725 ± .010	5/32	4-29/32	2- 1/32	1- 5/32	1/4	1/2	5/16	1- 7/16
T AN128	12	5.497	.0112	5.4858	5.4429	.0083	5.4346	5.3948	5.3635 ± .010	5/32	5-19/64	2-21/32	1-15/32	1/4	5/8	3/8	1- 3/4
T AN130	12	5.888	.0112	5.8768	5.8339	.0083	5.8256	5.7858	5.7545 ± .010	5/32	5-21/32	2-13/16	1- 9/16	9/32	5/8	3/8	1-29/32
T AN132	8	6.284	.0152	6.2688	6.2028	.0091	6.1937	6.1306	6.0993 ± .010	1/4	6- 1/16	2- 7/8	1-19/32	5/16	5/8	3/8	1-15/16
T AN134	8	6.659	.0152	6.6438	6.5778	.0091	6.5687	6.5056	6.4743 ± .010	1/4	6- 7/16	3	1-21/32	5/16	3/4	3/8	2
T AN136	8	7.066	.0152	7.0508	6.9848	.0091	6.9757	6.9126	6.8813 ± .010	1/4	6-27/32	3- 1/8	1-23/32	5/16	3/4	3/8	2- 1/16
T AN138	8	7.472	.0152	7.4568	7.3908	.0091	7.3817	7.3186	7.2873 ± .010	1/4	7- 1/4	3- 1/8	1-23/32	5/16	3/4	3/8	2- 1/16
T AN140	8	7.847	.0152	7.8318	7.7658	.0114	7.7544	7.6936	7.6623 ± .010	1/4	7- 5/8	3- 5/16	1-13/16	5/16	7/8	3/8	2- 1/8

(1) This standard is applicable to steel nuts. When either the nut or the shaft is made of stainless steel, aluminum or other material having a tendency to seize, it is recommended that the max. thread diameter of the shaft, both major and pitch, be reduced by 20% of the listed pitch diameter tolerance.